ADULT ARTICULAR CARTILAGE

The Contributors

M. A. R. Freeman BA MB BCh MD FRCS
Consultant Orthopaedic Surgeon to the London Hospital
Senior Lecturer in Orthopaedic Surgery at The London Hospital
Medical College
Research Fellow and Director of the Biomechanics Unit, Imperial
College, London

G. E. Kempson PhD BSc(Eng) DIC ACGI
Lecturer in Medical Engineering, Southampton University, South-
ampton General Hospital

B. McKibbin MS MD FRCS
Professor of Traumatic and Orthopaedic Surgery, Welsh National
School of Medicine, Cardiff

A. Maroudas PhD DIC Dip-Sup-es-Sc-Phys BSc(Eng)
Head of Physical Biochemistry, Bone and Joint Research Unit, The
London Hospital Medical College

G. Meachim MA MD FRCPath
Reader in Pathology, University of Liverpool
Consultant Pathologist, Liverpool Area Health Authority (Teach-
ing) and Mersey Regional Health Authority

I. H. M. Muir MA DPhil DSc FRS
Director and Head of Division of Biochemistry, The Kennedy
Institute, London

R. A. Stockwell BSc MB BS DCC PhD
Reader in Anatomy, University of Edinburgh

S. A. V. Swanson DSc(Eng) PhD DIC ACGI MIMechE
Professor of Biomechanics and Director of the Biomechanics Unit,
Imperial College, London

B. Weightman BSc(Eng) PhD
Lecturer in Mechanical Engineering, Imperial College, London

ADULT ARTICULAR CARTILAGE

Second Edition

Edited by

M.A.R. Freeman, BA MB BCh MD FRCS

Consultant Orthopaedic Surgeon to The London Hospital
Senior Lecturer in Orthopaedic Surgery at The London
Hospital Medical College
Research Fellow and Director of the Biomechanics Unit
Imperial College, London

 **PITMAN MEDICAL**

First published 1973
Second edition 1979

Catalogue Number 21 1000 81

Pitman Medical Publishing Co Ltd
P O Box 7, Tunbridge Wells,
Kent, TN1 1XH, England

Associated Companies
UNITED KINGDOM
Pitman Publishing Ltd, London
Focal Press Ltd, London

AUSTRALIA
Pitman Publishing Pty Ltd, Carlton

NEW ZEALAND
Pitman Publishing NZ Ltd, Wellington

British Library Cataloguing in Publication Data
Adult articular cartilage. – 2nd ed
   1. Cartilage
   I. Freeman, Michael Alexander Reykers
   611'.0183   QM567

   ISBN 0–272–79430–9

Set in 10 on 11 pt VIP Times
Printed by offset-lithography and bound
in Great Britain at The Pitman Press, Bath

Contents

Preface

Articular cartilage is crucial to the normal function of synovial joints since its presence enables the articulating bones to transmit high loads whilst maintaining contact stresses at an acceptably low level, and to move on each other with little frictional resistance. Cartilage demands study 'because it is there' and because, in the applied field, the clinical and pathological evolution of many forms of arthritis can be attributed to its destruction. Thus the purpose of this book is to provide a description of the biology of cartilage which it is hoped will be useful both for those pursuing basic investigations in the field and for those practising in related clinical disciplines.

The physiological, mechanical properties of cartilage depend upon the physical properties of its matrix (Chapter 1), and the matrix in turn is dependent for its existence and composition upon the chondrocytes (Chapter 2). Thus the structure of the matrix and of the chondrocytes forms the subject of the first two chapters of this volume. A description of the biochemistry and physical chemistry of the matrix follows. The latter is of importance since fluid flow through the tissue is crucial to its ability to carry load and possibly to the low friction between cartilage surfaces. Further chapters deal with the two mechanical, or strictly physiological, properties of articular cartilage: load carriage and lubrication. Since the nutrition of articular cartilage is a subject of long-standing controversy, this subject is dealt with in a separate chapter. Finally, an attempt, to a large extent necessarily speculative, is made to explain the breakdown of cartilage that occurs with ageing and the onset of osteoarthrosis in terms of the conclusions reached in the preceding chapters.

The discussion is confined to adult cartilage and therefore the subjects of ossification and growth are not discussed. Wherever possible, observations are drawn from human material and from articular rather than from other forms of cartilage. The subjects of the immune response to cartilage and of its fate in diseases such as rheumatoid and septic arthritis have not been considered since the primary objective of this volume has been to deal with the tissue in its normal environment.

The chapters in this book do not purport to provide an exhaustive historical review of the subject-matter with which they are concerned. They do, however, seek to deploy data and ideas based upon fifteen years of work by the authors and others, with reference to earlier work only in so far as it is material to current knowledge.

Throughout the book it will be obvious to the reader that there are still considerable gaps in our understanding of the biology of cartilage and it is hoped that the realization of this fact may stimulate the further work which will be necessary to close them.

1. The Matrix

G. Meachim and R. A. Stockwell

1. INTRODUCTION

The basic 'purpose' of adult articular cartilage is to provide a suitable covering material for the articular ends of bones at synovial joints. In large human joints such as the hip and knee, the thickness of this covering material is some 2–4 mm. Thickness tends to vary (Figure 1.1) from area to area within the joint, from joint to joint in the same species, and from species to species (W. Simon 1970). Provided that the surface remains locally intact, the thickness of human articular cartilage often remains unchanged during adult life (Meachim 1971). Thus the material does not thin simply as a result of physiological joint activity. However, localized destructive lesions, due mainly to a process of cartilage splitting termed 'fibrillation', are extremely common amongst the general population, and such lesions can lead to thinning of the cartilage and sometimes even to exposure of the underlying bone. Examination of cartilage structure can suggest an explanation for its mechanical properties in the intact state and for the failure of these properties in severe fibrillation.

Articular cartilage is devoid of nerves and is generally considered to be avascular, although a few blood-vessels may be found in its deepest parts adjacent to the bone. The tissue consists of a relatively small number of cells and an abundant extracellular matrix (Figure 1.2). Although the cells and the matrix are structurally separate, they are functionally interdependent: chondrocyte activity is necessary for the synthesis of matrix and probably also for its physiological degradation (Mankin and Lippiello 1969); in turn the matrix plays an important part in maintaining the homeostasis of the cells' environment (Gersh and Catchpole 1960). The matrix contains a large amount of water, a meshwork of collagen fibres, and a non-fibrous 'filler' substance. Together these form a stiff gel ('gristle'). The filler substance is principally composed of carbohydrate and non-collagenous proteins; if it is removed by experimental procedures or through pathological

1

Figure 1.1 Variation in the thickness of adult articular cartilage, as seen in sections cut perpendicular to the articular surface.
(a) Human femoral condylar cartilage ×56.
(b) Rabbit femoral condylar cartilage ×56.
(c) Mouse femoral condylar cartilage ×350.
(d) Human auditory ossicular cartilage (malleus) ×350.
Note that (c) and (d) are photographed at approximately six times the magnification of (a) and (b).
S = articular surface; O = osseochondral junction.
Haematoxylin and eosin.

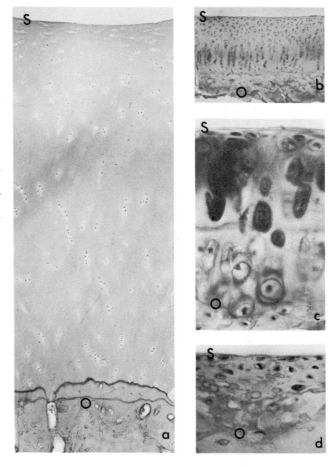

causes, cartilage loses its rigidity although it may retain its form. The matrix also contains a small amount of lipid and inorganic chemicals; adult tissue becomes pigmented.

Biological variation is observed not only in the thickness of articular cartilage, but also in its cellularity and in other morphological, chemical and physical properties. Variation occurs between different sites in the same subject, and between different subjects at the same site. Some variation must be determined genetically, and is presumably mediated by factors controlling tissue organization during skeletal development. Other factors include physiological variation in local biomechanical requirements. In addition to these causes of variation in completely healthy tissue, quasi-pathological phenomena collectively termed 'regressive change' can alter the local texture of the cartilage

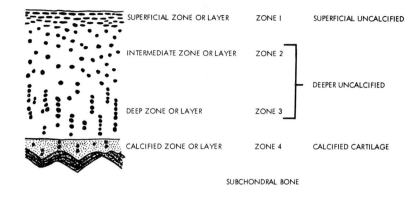

Figure 1.2 The zones of adult articular cartilage.
Uncalcified matrix white; cells black.

(Section 8). In all cases, the suitability of adult articular cartilage as a covering for the load-bearing, moving surfaces of synovial joints depends primarily on the mechanical and other properties of its extracellular matrix. The main role of the cells is to manufacture and maintain this matrix.

2. MATRIX MORPHOLOGY

A wide range of methods is used to study the morphology of the cartilage matrix and of the articular surface: the methods include naked-eye examination, light, interference and phase contrast microscopy, stereomicroscopy and electron microscopy.* Electron microscopy employs two complementary techniques. In transmission electron microscopy the electron beam is directed through an ultrathin section of cartilage to give what is virtually a two-dimensional image of cells and extracellular tissue; cartilage sections for transmission electron microscopy are cut in a plane at right angles or tangential to the articular surface. Scanning electron microscopy, in contrast, enables examination of the three-dimensional contour of the matrix as shown on a cut surface orientated at right angles or tangentially to the joint surface. In studies of the contour of the natural face of the articular surface, either transmission or scanning electron microscopy is employed, in conjunction with stylus tracing and other techniques such as reflected-light interference microscopy.

* Units of length commonly used in microscopy include: millimetre (mm) = 10^{-3} metre (m); micrometre (μm) = 10^{-6} m; nanometre (nm) = 10^{-9} m; ångström (Å) = 10^{-10} m.

2.1. Zonal Classification

The distribution of the cells and of matrix constituents varies throughout the thickness of the cartilage. Hence, it is convenient for descriptive purposes to subdivide the tissue into zones or strata aligned parallel to the articular surface (Figure 1.2). The following classification is based on Collins (1949), but is consistent with more recent work (McCall 1969a).

Zone 1. Superficial or tangential, adjacent to the joint cavity; where the fibres are arranged tangentially to the surface. The cells are discoidal with their long axes parallel to the surface. The most superficial part of this zone is sometimes termed the 'surface lamina'.

Zone 2. Intermediate or transitional; where the coiled fibres form an interlacing meshwork. The cells are spheroidal and equally spaced.

Zone 3. Deep or radiate; where the fibres form a tighter meshwork and are predominantly radial to the articular surface. Spheroidal cells are arranged in columnar groups of four to eight cells.

Zone 4. Calcified; adjacent to the subchondral bone; where there are few cells and the matrix is heavily impregnated with crystals of calcium salts.

In human femoral condylar cartilage, zone 1 occupies about 5–10%, zone 4 about 5–10% and zones 2 and 3 each about 40–45% of the total thickness. These values should be taken only as an approximate guide, considerable differences being found in smaller joints. Zones 1, 2 and 3 merge imperceptibly, while zones 3 and 4 meet at a weakly basophilic line designated the 'tide mark' by Fawns and Landells (1953). Only zone 4 is calcified (Figure 1.2). The periphery of the articular area of a synovial joint, where articular cartilage, synovial membrane, joint capsule and periosteum merge, is termed the 'marginal transitional zone' (Figure 1.3).

The extracellular cartilage matrix comprises (1) specialized regions immediately surrounding the chondrocytes, termed 'pericellular matrix', and (2) the general matrix, termed 'intercellular matrix' (Figure 1.4).

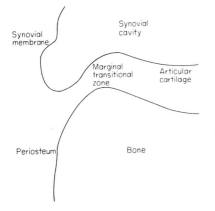

Figure 1.3 Topographical relations of articular cartilage and marginal transitional zone.

* Fibrocartilage is found covering the bone ends in the temporomandibular joint, in the joints of the clavicle, and sometimes in the apophyseal joints of the spine.

2.2. Fibrous Component of the Matrix

In most joints,* adult human articular cartilage is of the hyaline type, and its matrix has a homogeneous, 'ground glass' appearance in routine histological preparations. Special techniques are required to demonstrate a fibrous texture in the matrix (Maximow and Bloom 1948, pp. 118–19). The fibres are not easily visualized with the usual histological methods, probably because the cationic staining sites on them are masked by amorphous polysaccharide

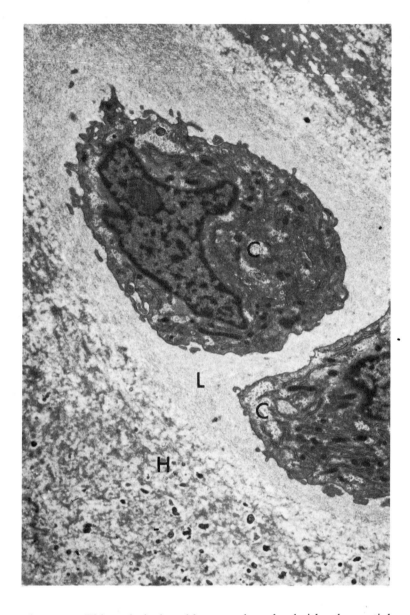

Figure 1.4 A pair of chondrocytes (C) surrounded by pericellular matrix (L) which contrasts in texture with that of the intercellular matrix (H).

This and all subsequent illustrations are from adult human articular cartilage unless indicated otherwise.

Transmission electron micrograph ×7500.

substances. This technical problem may be solved either by partial elution of the amorphous substances (for example with dilute alkali) or by the use of polarized light or phase contrast microscopy. Electron microscopy confirms the presence of numerous fibres: many of them have the characteristic morphology of collagen, and this protein accounts for more than half the dry weight of human articular cartilage (Anderson, Ludowieg, Harper and Engleman 1964). The collagen fibres show electron-dense bands aligned transversely to the long axis of the fibres (Figure 1.5), and the pattern formed by a consecutive sequence of bands

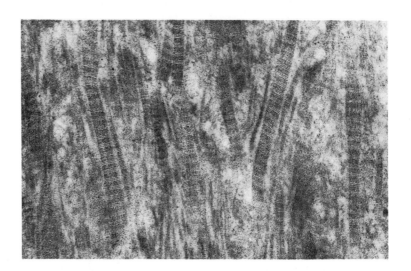

Figure 1.5 Striated collagen fibres in the intercellular matrix. Compare with Figure 1.6.

Transmission electron micrograph ×37 500.

repeats itself at regular intervals with a 'periodicity' averaging 64 nm (640 Å) along the length of the fibre (Boni and Monteleone 1957). In articular cartilage from the knee joint of young adults, collagen fibres range from approximately 30 to 80 nm in diameter (Weiss, Rosenberg and Helfet 1968), figures which are in keeping with results originally published by Boni and Monteleone (1957). In addition to the usual type of banded collagen fibre, adult human articular cartilage occasionally contains localized collections of unusually wide collagen fibres, up to 150 nm or more in diameter, with very prominent periodic banding; coarse fibres of this type are sometimes seen at the site of a necrotic chondrocyte which has disintegrated (Meachim 1969a, pp. 76, 83).

By no means all of the fibres show the typical morphology of banded collagen. Smaller fibres and slender filaments which lack the characteristic periodicity of collagen also occur: the nature of these smaller fibres and slender filaments cannot be determined solely by morphological studies, and it is uncertain whether or not they too are collagen (Weiss *et al.* 1968). Slender filaments are the only type of fibrillar component found in a variable width of finely textured matrix immediately surrounding a chondrocyte (pericellular matrix). This specialized pericellular matrix is devoid of typical collagen fibres, and contrasts in texture with the more coarsely fibrous intercellular matrix which forms the bulk of the cartilage (Figure 1.4).

The type of collagen obtained from articular cartilage differs chemically from that found, for example, in skin, tendon and bone.

6

Type II collagen is characteristic of human articular cartilage while type I is characteristic of skin, tendon, bone and fibrocartilage.

2.3. Ground Substance

The ground substance forms the 'filler' material between the fibrous component of the matrix; it contains a wide variety of chemical constituents (Gersh and Catchpole 1960), but is principally composed of protein–polysaccharide complexes. Ground substance does not bind sufficient osmium to become readily visible in electron micrographs of tissue prepared by conventional methods (Hancox and Boothroyd 1964), and it is difficult to determine whether it is structurally organized or an amorphous material. At high magnification a faint but definite pattern can be detected within it after fixation of the tissue by routine techniques: the appearance of a fine meshwork is seen in adult human articular cartilage in the specialized regions of pericellular matrix (Figure 1.6) surrounding the chondrocytes (Meachim and Roy 1967), and

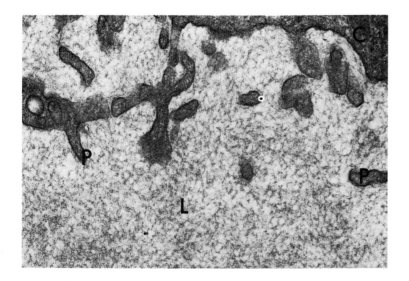

Figure 1.6 'Fine meshwork' appearance of the pericellular matrix (L) after tissue fixation in glutaraldehyde. Compare with Figure 1.5. Part of a chondrocyte (C); cell processes (P).

Transmission electron micrograph ×37 500.

(Reproduced from Meachim *et al.* (1974) by courtesy of the Editor, *Journal of Anatomy*.)

between the typical banded collagen fibres of the general intercellular matrix (Weiss *et al.* 1968). The meshwork consists of fine filaments showing sharply angled junctions one with another.

A rather less filamentous appearance has been described in the matrix of epiphyseal and nasal cartilage. Here electron-dense polygonal matrix granules (Matukas, Panner and Orbison 1967; Anderson and Sajdera 1971) about 40 nm in diameter are often linked to each other and to collagen fibrils by projecting filaments 3 nm in diameter. Minute densely stained particles are found within the matrix granules after treatment with bismuth nitrate (Smith, Peters and Serafini-Fracassini 1967; Smith 1970) and other cationic reagents. This indicates the presence of proteoglycan in the granules. It is postulated that the granules represent proteoglycan chains which have become clumped during tissue preparation (Matukas *et al.* 1967), with non-collagenous protein precipitated around the proteoglycan (Smith 1970). The granules are present in articular cartilage and are much less numerous in osteoarthrosic cartilage than in the immature tissue (Ali and Bayliss 1974).

The filamentous component often shows beading or striation but it is uncertain whether the filaments represent collagen, proteoglycan or non-collagenous glycoproteins (Smith *et al.* 1967; Thyberg, Lohmander and Friberg 1973); thus it is arguable whether they should be regarded as an intrinsic component of the ground substance or as part of the fibrous component of the matrix or, perhaps, as evidence of the interaction between the two. Even so, it is of interest that the shape and size of the 'meshwork' pattern resembles that seen in electron micrographs of monolayer preparations of protein–polysaccharide (Rosenberg, Hellmann and Kleinschmidt 1970). Electron micrographs of proteoglycan aggregates from bovine articular cartilage have recently been published by Rosenberg, Hellmann and Kleinschmidt (1975), who discuss the appearances in terms of the central hyaluronate 'threads' of the 'super-complex' (Section 4.1.1).

The patterns formed by the filaments suggest netted 'open' structures, perhaps joined one with another to form a three-dimensional continuum, and do not suggest the system of closed chambers or vacuoles (approximately 50–200 nm in size) which Gersh and Catchpole (1960) postulated was present in ground substance. The findings are of interest in view of electron micrographs published by Durning (1958) illustrating what he believed to be an organized structure amongst cartilage ground substance in the epiphyseal growth plate. However, protein precipitation during tissue fixation can in itself give rise to artefactual 'network' patterns containing angled, polyhedral shapes (Meachim 1972a): for this reason the existence of similar patterns amongst living ground substance cannot be accepted as fully proven.

2.4. Pericellular Matrix and Cell Lacunae

When routine histological preparations of cartilage are viewed with the light microscope, many of the chondrocytes apparently lie within holes in the tissue. Although the 'holes', termed 'lacunae', are not truly cavities in the tissue, the spheroidal zones of pericellular matrix often have a distinct rim, and shrinkage artefacts, combined with the possible leaching out of ground substance during tissue processing, can give the observer the understandable though erroneous impression of a cavity. If correctly fixed and stained, the ground substance nearest to the cell stains intensely, the staining intensity decreasing as the distance from the cell increases. Since each lacuna may contain one or more cells or deposits of debris from necrotic cells which have disintegrated (Meachim and Roy 1967), the overall pattern on light microscopy is of intensely stained 'chondrin balls' lying within a background of more lightly stained matrix.

Ultrastructural observations show that the specialized pericellular matrix is devoid of typical banded collagen fibres; it contains fine fibres and slender filaments lacking the morphology and characteristic periodicity of collagen (Meachim and Roy 1967; Weiss et al. 1968). As already noted, these filaments in fixed tissue form a delicate meshwork amongst the pericellular ground substance; matrix granules are abundant here in certain cartilages. This corona of finely textured matrix surrounding the cell (Figure 1.4) is of variable width; in a few places, the limiting plasma membrane of the chondrocyte may abut onto the intercellular matrix of typically banded collagen. In mature adult articular cartilage there is usually a sharply defined boundary between the pericellular and the intercellular matrix. In immature and young adult cartilage, the pericellular finely textured matrix tends to be of narrower width, and the distinction between pericellular and intercellular matrix is less clear-cut than in older subjects.

Certain observations made by light microscopy of the central layer of aged horse nasal cartilage may be relevant when considering the structure of articular cartilage, particularly that of its deeper layers (zones 2 and 3), which show histological similarities to the nasal tissue. In nasal cartilage, a narrow rim of matrix peripheral to the intensely stained pericellular region shows certain special characteristics. First, its staining properties with cationic dyes and with the periodic acid–Schiff technique suggest that it contains a high concentration of protein and glycoprotein. Second, interferometric studies indicate that the dry mass is maximal (0.44 g/cm^3) in this zone compared with adjacent matrix (Galjaard 1962; Szirmai 1963). This 'border zone' or 'perilacunar rim' seen with the light microscope (Szirmai 1963) corresponds to the abrupt transition between finely and coarsely textured matrix seen with the electron microscope (Figure 1.4) or to a region peripheral to this. Experiments indicate that it has considerable mechanical strength, many 'chondrin balls' being morphologically intact after homogenization of the tissue (Szirmai 1969).

Electron probe analyses of articular cartilage matrix show no evidence of a higher density in the pericellular region (Chapter 4, Section 2). However, as noted below (Section 2.5.2), transmission electron microscopy suggests that collagen fibres in the vicinity of cell lacunae are orientated to form enclosures around them, in the deeper layers of articular cartilage (Weiss *et al.* 1968). The results of scanning microscopy of articular cartilage are not in agreement on this point. Clarke (1974) believes that there is no surrounding pericellular basket of collagen fibrils significant enough to be termed a protective envelope. On the other hand, Mulholland (1974) refers to strong enclosures around the lacunae, although it should be noted that his tissue had received prior mild treatment with papain. Thus while results from horse nasal cartilage cannot be applied, without considerable modification, to articular cartilage, it is possible that a similar kind of 'cell protecting' mechanism may occur.

In conclusion, the finely textured pericellular matrix forms a micro-environment for the chondrocytes (within the general environment of cartilage tissue) which has some resemblance to fetal cartilage in its morphology. If the chondrocytes are free to move in the tissue, their movements are probably restricted to within this part of the matrix, except perhaps during active remodelling.

2.5. Zonal Variation in Fibrous Component

2.5.1. Superficial Layer. In zone 1 of adult human articular cartilage with an intact surface, the intercellular matrix contains closely packed collagen fibres with only a small amount of intervening ground substance. The fibres are approximately 30 nm in diameter and show the typical periodicity of banded collagen. In the young adult the collagen fibres of the superficial layer are sometimes arranged in bundles consisting of up to thirty individual fibres (Weiss *et al.* 1968), but 'large' surface bundles of the size (1–3 μm diameter) postulated by Walker, Sikorski, Dowson, Longfield, Wright and Buckley (1969) have not been seen.

Because the collagen framework of articular cartilage is three-dimensional, the orientation of its fibres can be described in relation to (a) planes vertical to the articular surface and (b) *en face* planes approximately parallel to the surface. Thus the terms 'fibre orientation' and 'fibre alignment' can be used in either of these two different senses.

Studies of orientation within the vertical plane have shown that the superficial collagen fibres of human articular cartilage are mostly aligned parallel to the synovial cavity interface (Weiss *et al.* 1968; Meachim and Roy 1969).

Orientation *en face* is more complex. Meachim, Denham, Emery and Wilkinson (1974) have studied this by transmission electron microscopy of tissue blocks cut tangentially in the same plane as that of the articular surface. In 33 of 47 blocks, an estimated 60–80% of the superficial collagen fibres showed an *en*

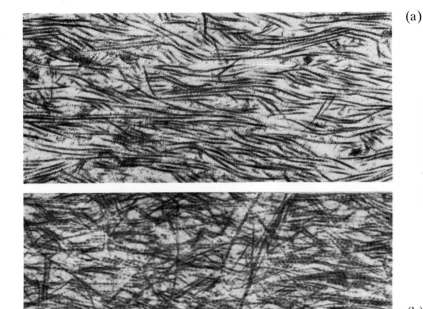

(a)

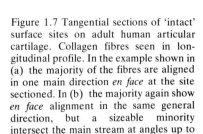

Figure 1.7 Tangential sections of 'intact' surface sites on adult human articular cartilage. Collagen fibres seen in longitudinal profile. In the example shown in (a) the majority of the fibres are aligned in one main direction *en face* at the site sectioned. In (b) the majority again show *en face* alignment in the same general direction, but a sizeable minority intersect the main stream at angles up to 90 degrees.

Transmission electron micrographs ×20 000.

(b)

face alignment in the same general direction (Figure 1.7). However, in the other 14 blocks a dominant alignment was very slight or absent. Thus at the ultrastructural level a tendency to dominant orientation is not equally apparent at all sites sectioned. Moreover, where a dominant *en face* orientation is demonstrable by transmission electron microscopy there is often a substantial minority of fibres intersecting the main stream. Intersections can be at any angle up to 90 degrees. This arrangement may help to bond the fabric of the superficial layer, perhaps aided by a hypothetical 'cementing' property of the ground substance.

It should be noted here that the above findings refer particularly to sites where the cartilage surface is locally 'intact'. At sites where they are minor ultrastructural aberrations, indicative of an 'imperfect' surface, collagen orientation can be disturbed (Figure 1.8). This disturbance may affect vertical plane or *en face* or both sorts of orientation.

Figure 1.8 An example of an 'imperfect' site on the surface, with ultrastructural aberrations. Tangential section cut at a slight angle so that the synovial cavity interface is slightly nearer the left than the right of the field. Note the abnormally wide separation of the collagen fibres. In this example they mostly present a longitudinal profile, but *en face* alignment is random; in other examples of 'imperfect' sites, dominant *en face* alignment is retained.

Transmission electron micrograph ×20 000.

(Reproduced from Meachim *et al.* (1974) by courtesy of the Editor, *Journal of Anatomy*.)

Artificial splits can be made by inserting the point of a pin vertically into articular cartilage from above the surface. The splits thus produced by a round object are nearly always elongated when examined *en face* (Figures 1.9 and 1.10). They are typically straight and unbranched; a minority have a curved, sharply angled, forked, stellate or other non-typical appearance. The *en face*

Figure 1.9 (a–c) Diagrams of articular cartilage *en face*, showing orientation of (d–f) tissue blocks used for transmission electron micrographs of the superficial layer. The black lines represent typical elongated artificial splits. That face of the block used for sectioning is stippled.

(a) and (d) Tangential section in a plane approximately parallel to the surface.
(b) and (e) Vertical section cut at right angles to the *en face* direction of nearby artificial splits.
(c) and (f) Vertical section cut parallel to the *en face* direction of nearby artifical splits.

Note that the cartilage/synovial cavity interface has not been included in the electron micrographs of the vertical sections. ×20 000.
(Reproduced from Meachim *et al.* (1974) by courtesy of the Editor, *Journal of Anatomy*.)

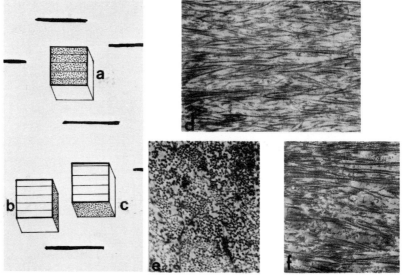

Figure 1.10 Photograph of the artificial splits on a proximal tibial surface, seen as dark linear marks filled with Indian ink. The other stippled or confluent markings represent stained sites of naturally occurring change on the cartilage surface; para-articular soft tissue is also stained black.
(Reproduced from Meachim *et al.* (1974) by courtesy of the Editor, *Journal of Anatomy*.)

direction taken by a typical elongated split tends to follow (Figure 1.9) the dominant orientation *en face* of nearby surface collagen

 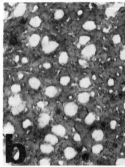

Figure 1.11 (a) Tangential section through the intermediate layer (zone 2) of articular cartilage, showing random orientation of collagen fibres. (b) Tangential section through the deep uncalcified layer (zone 3). Collagen fibres ('empty' appearance) seen in transverse section, indicative of alignment radial to the surface.
  Transmission electron micrographs ×25 000.

(Benninghoff 1925; Bullough and Goodfellow 1968; Meachim, Denham, Emery and Wilkinson 1974). This does not necessarily mean that elongation of artificial splits is simply a consequence of the 'weave' of the surface fabric. An alternative or additional possibility might be that the act of pricking releases built-in tensile stresses acting transversely to the line of the split.

Elongated splits are created by a round pin on intact surfaces and on surfaces showing minimal fibrillation, but are not obtained where overt fibrillation has caused major damage to the superficial layer.

On *in vitro* testing, the tensile strength and stiffness of isolated superficial cartilage slices are greater in a direction parallel to than at right angles to the direction taken by nearby artificial splits (Chapter 6, Section 4.3). Thus the patterns formed by producing multiple artificial splits on whole articular surfaces (Figure 1.10) can in general be used as an approximate guide to the *en face* alignment both of the surface collagen and of surface tensile properties. This pattern varies from joint to joint, but, with few exceptions, is relatively constant for the same anatomical site in different individuals (Benninghoff 1925; Meachim, Denham, Emery and Wilkinson 1974).

MacConaill (1951) noted a bright narrow band immediately below the articular surface on examination of cartilage sections by phase contrast microscopy: he named this appearance the 'lamina splendens'. By analogy with corneal structure and function, it now seems possible that the appearance is due to the brilliant transmission of light by the superficial layer of the cartilage matrix as a consequence of the orderly orientation of its collagen fibres.

At the marginal transitional zone (Figure 1.3) the fibrous matrix of the surface layer of adult articular cartilage appears to merge into the fibrous periosteum of the adjacent bone. Weiss *et al.* (1968) point out that the intercellular matrix of the superficial layer (zone 1) of adult human articular cartilage resembles that of fibrous tissue, and that the cells, particularly as seen in vertical sections of this layer, differ in shape from those in the deeper uncalcified layers (zones 2 and 3). This observation would be in keeping with a hypothesis that the type of matrix in a non-osseous connective tissue is influenced locally by biomechanical and other factors. This hypothesis also suggests that the same basic cell can alter its morphology in accordance with these local factors.

2.5.2. Deeper Layers. In the intermediate and deep layers of uncalcified cartilage the intercellular matrix differs from that in the superficial layer. Banded fibres showing the typical periodicity of collagen are again present, but they appear to be more widely spaced in electron micrographs. However, chemical analysis of young adult bovine articular cartilage has shown that its collagen content, if expressed as percentage per dry weight of tissue, is similar in the deeper and in the superficial layers, except for a higher content in a surface band only 25 μm in vertical thickness (Lipshitz, Etheredge and Glimcher 1975). In contrast, stereological analysis of electron micrographs of rat femoral condylar cartilage indicates that the volume fraction of collagen is highest in the middle zone (Palfrey 1975). In electron micrographs of zones 2 and 3 the fibres are more variable in diameter and often broader than in the superficial layer. In adults their width usually ranges from approximately 30 nm to 80 nm (Weiss *et al.* 1968), and fibres up to 100 nm or more in diameter have been observed (Muir, Bullough and Maroudas 1970). In transmission electron micrographs from the intermediate layer, the collagen fibres are mostly randomly orientated in relation to the vertical plane and *en face* and show little tendency to form bundles. In the vicinity of cells they tend to run parallel to the cell surface, forming a protective basket-like enclosure around a cell or group of cells (Weiss *et al.* 1968). Using scanning electron microscopy McCall (1969b) has observed that, in the intermediate layer (zone 2) of human articular cartilage, collagen fibre bundles form a 'tangled open meshwork' when the tissue is not under load; deep to this layer (zone 3) the fibres are more tightly packed and show an orientation radial to the articular surface (Figure 1.11). (This 'tangled open meshwork' formed by the collagen fibre bundles is, of course, a separate entity from the much finer 'meshwork' already described when discussing the ground substance in Section 2.3.) These observations confirm a previous report by Little, Pimm and

Trueta (1958). McCall (1969a, b) has further observed that, when the cartilage is subjected to a physiological compressive load for a period of about 12 hours' duration, the open fibrous meshwork of the intermediate zone becomes obliterated, the fibres becoming orientated at right angles to the direction of loading (Figure 1.12). The radial fibres in the deep layer show little change when under load.

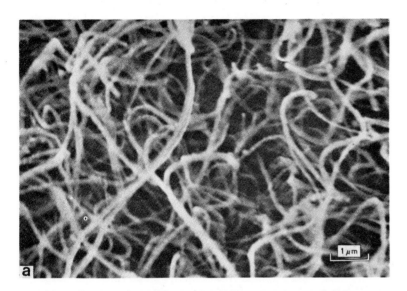

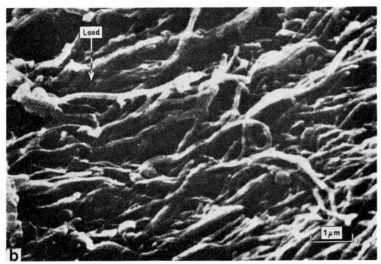

Figure 1.12 (a) Scanning electron micrograph (McCall 1969b) from the 'mid-zone' (zone 2) of adult human articular cartilage, showing the fibres as a 'tangled open meshwork'. (b) Effect of a physiological compressive load: note that the fibres have become orientated at right angles to the direction of loading.

(Reproduced by permission of Dr J. G. McCall and the Editor, *Journal of Anatomy*.)

Lothe, Spycher and Rüttner (1973) report the presence of 'matrix streaks' in sections from the deep uncalcified layer (zone 3) of upper femoral articular cartilage from middle-aged and older subjects. This feature can occur on the superolateral aspect of the femoral head, but is not apparent in samples taken inferomedial to the fovea. On light microscopy of histological sections the 'streaks' are seen as linear markings extending from lacunar rims out into the interterritorial matrix. The histochemical staining reactions of a linear marking differ from those of the surrounding matrix. Transmission electron microscopy shows that the general radial orientation of the zone 3 collagen fibres is locally interrupted at the site of a 'streak', due to the presence of one or more undulations in fibre direction. It is not known whether these undulations are a feature of living cartilage *in situ* on the bone, or whether they result from an artefactual distortion in the tissue samples.

2.6. Contour of Articular Surface

Is the surface of healthy articular cartilage smooth or not smooth? Several comments, some theoretical and some technical, are pertinent before discussing this question. The term 'articular surface' denotes the interface between cartilage and synovial fluid. It cannot be assumed that this interface is sharply demarcated at the ultrastructural level. Instead it is theoretically possible that synovial-derived products may intermingle with or adhere to cartilage-derived matrix at the interface, thus perhaps promoting slipperiness and wear-resistance of the articular surface (Chapter 7, Section 6.6). The term 'healthy' cartilage also needs clarification. There is now much evidence that adult human synovial joints almost invariably contain sites at which there is local fraying of the articular surface. Such sites are, of course, usually interspersed with large or small areas where the surface is still locally intact. The following discussion refers specifically to intact sites.

The articular surface contour may sometimes be altered artefactually, thus affecting the results from *in vitro* studies. For example, loss of fluid from the cartilage sample can potentially distort its appearance. This drying effect may occur during collection of specimens and their transport to the laboratory, and during subsequent handling in the laboratory. It can be avoided by keeping the articular surface in contact with physiological saline solution during collection, transport and subsequent examination of samples (Meachim 1972b). Cutting out blocks from a cartilage sheet, without prior fixation in formalin or glutaraldehyde while still *in situ* on the bone, is another potential source of contour artefact. This is because blocks cut out from unfixed material may subsequently curl or otherwise distort (Gibson and Davis 1958), probably because of release of 'interlocked tensile stresses' in the tissue (Fry and Robertson 1967). This difficulty with unfixed material can be avoided by examining whole cartilage sheets still attached to their underlying bone (Meachim 1972b) or, alternatively, by thorough fixation before cutting out the surface blocks. However, it should be noted here that fixation may in itself cause tissue volume changes, with the theoretical possibility of contour artefacts.

Methods used to examine the surface are another potential source of contour disturbance. This comment applies especially to scanning electron microscopy, since specimen preparation for this technique can inherently cause a drying effect, with the possibility of shrinkage and other artefacts at the articular surface.

The above theoretical and technical comments may help partly to explain why different investigators have given differing accounts of the cartilage surface contour. Recent studies of the surface *en face* have suggested that it is not smooth (Gardner and McGillivray 1971; Longmore and Gardner 1975) but has 'tertiary irregularities'. This appearance may be attributable to the presence of multiple bowl-shaped surface depressions of microscopic size, overlying cell lacunae (Clarke 1971a). However, the results from studies *en face* appear to be inconsistent with those from transmission electron microscopy of vertical sections through the surface (Davies, Barnett, Cochrane and Palfrey 1962). Any hypothesis about the articular contour ought to explain satisfactorily the results both from *en face* techniques and from transmission light or electron microscopy of vertically cut sections.

McCall (1968) has used scanning electron microscopy to study adult human articular cartilage. He states that normal samples have an articular surface on which 'the fibre pattern is coarse and shows a parallel orientation'. Walker *et al.* (1969), who have employed scanning electron microscopy in conjunction with stylus tracing techniques, state that the surface of human cartilage is 'gently undulating, the peak to valley height of the roughness being about 2.5 μm and the pitch 25 μm'. They suggest that these surface ridges contain large bundles of collagen fibres ranging from 1 to 3 μm in diameter. Walker *et al.* (1969) also suggest that 'trapped pools' of synovial fluid are formed in the 'valleys' on the surface when cartilage is compressed. Redler and Zimny (1970) have similarly reported that the surface of normal cartilage is undulating, with mound-like elevations as an additional feature in some areas.

On the other hand, Clarke (1971b) has obtained evidence that the ridges observed in scanning electron micrographs of the articular surface are probably artefacts created by preparation techniques (Figure 1.13). In his material he observes that ridges occur more frequently adjacent to fractured edges of the specimen; the periodicity of the ridges is locally regular, but varies between sites and specimens. Away from the fractured edges the surface of adult human cartilage is not ridged: however, it does show bowl-shaped depressions, many of which are of a figure-of-eight pattern (Figure 1.14). He estimated that their depth is 1–6 μm and

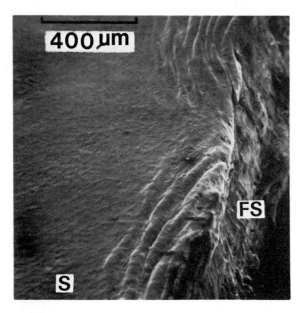

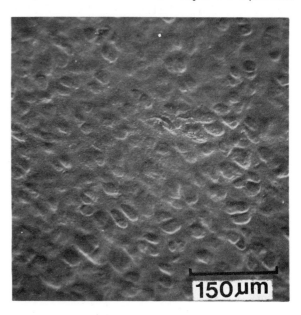

Figure 1.13 Scanning electron micrograph (Clarke 1971b) demonstrating that the surface of adult human articular cartilage shows depressions (Figure 1.14) but is not ridged (S) except alongside and parallel to fractured edges (FS). Note that this artefactual ridging has a locally regular periodicity.

(Reproduced by courtesy of Dr I. C. Clarke and the Editor, *Journal of Anatomy*.)

Figure 1.14 Scanning electron micrograph of the articular surface, showing bowl-shaped depressions, many of which are of a figure-of-eight pattern. Compare with Figure 1.39.
(Reproduced by courtesy of Dr I. C. Clarke.)

that their diameter varies from 15 to 30 μm: it is of interest to note the similarity of these measurements to those of the 'surface undulations' reported by Walker *et al.* (1969) in human material. An observation made by Gardner and Woodward (1969) is also relevant: they comment that the articular surface of the guinea-pig femur displays 'many randomly arranged round and ovoid hollows and prominences of 20–40 μm diameter'.

Clarke (1971b) has further noted that the bowl-shaped depressions (Figure 1.14), observed on scanning electron micrographs of the articular surface of adult human cartilage, are very similar in size and pattern to cell lacunae as shown in specimens from which a thin strip of surface cartilage has been artificially removed. He concludes that the bowl-shaped depressions seen on the surface are attributable to the presence of underlying lacunae (Figure 1.15); the frequency of the depressions is of a similar order to that

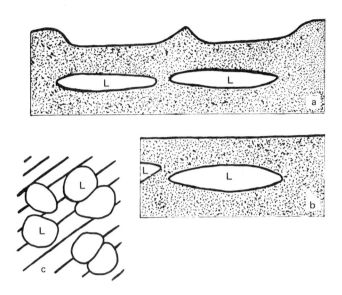

Figure 1.15 (a) Model for a vertical section through the adult human articular surface as interpreted from scanning electron micrographs by Clarke (1971b). The white shapes (L) represent the 'lacunae'. (b) Diagram traced from a transmission electron micrograph by Davies *et al.* (1962) of a vertical section through young rabbit articular cartilage. L = lacunae. Compare with Figure a. (c) Diagram of the 'lacunar markings' seen when a thin tangential slice of the surface of adult human articular cartilage is viewed *en face* by transmission light microscopy.

of cell counts obtained from light microscopy of histological sections cut tangentially to the immediate joint surface (Clarke 1971a).

Are the bowl-shaped depressions found in scanning electron micrographs present on the articular surface during life, or are they due to an artefactual collapse of overlying tissue into the matrix lacunae during specimen preparation? The answer to this question is of more than academic interest, since initial experiments by Gardner (1972) suggest that the depressions are not obliterated under load. If present *in vivo*, one might expect the undulations and depressions to be demonstrable also in transmission electron micrographs of sections cut at right angles to the articular surface, but the evidence from such sections is inconclusive. Davies *et al.* (1962) used transmission electron microscopy to study transverse sections of articular cartilage from young adult rabbits: they found that in their material the articular surface is 'remarkably smooth' (Figure 1.15) and that any irregularities which do occur are usually less than $0.025\,\mu$m in depth over a length of $0.5\,\mu$m; but that there are occasional, deeper irregularities as well. Weiss *et al.* (1968) studied young adult human articular cartilage by transmission electron microscopy; they reported that 'the surface is characterised by the presence of depressions usually less than $0.3\,\mu$m but occasionally up to $1.5\,\mu$m in depth'. Meachim and Roy (1969) merely state that intact areas of the articular surface in mature adults are 'smooth or gently undulating'.

'Surface markings' of similar shape and size to those observed by Clarke with the scanning electron microscope can also be demonstrated by light microscopy (Clarke 1971a). They are seen when the surface of adult human articular cartilage is examined in incident light, and when transmitted light is directed through a thin tangential slice cut from the surface (Figure 1.15). Such markings represent the site of the cells in the superficial matrix (Clarke 1971a; Meachim 1972b). The question then arises whether they are simply a consequence of the differing optical properties of the lacunae and intercellular matrix, or whether actual depressions of the surface are present over the cells. Gardner and McGillivray (1971) have seen what appear to be very shallow undulations, approximately 20–$30\,\mu$m diameter, on the surface of living cartilage examined by special techniques of light microscopy. Although these might be due to differences between the optical properties of underlying lacunae and intercellular matrix, or perhaps to some rapid change occurring between exposure of the joint surface and its microscopic examination, the results provide evidence that the articular surface is irregular in life.

Subsequently, Longmore and Gardner (1975) have used reflected light interference microscopy to study the human articular surface *in vitro*. This technique was originally developed to examine metallic surfaces for roughness. Its application to cartilage assumes that the interference patterns obtained are due solely to reflections from the surface, and are not influenced by the optical non-homogeneity known to be present in the underlying semitranslucent matrix. The results suggest that the articular surface has 'tertiary irregularities', due to the presence of multiple hollows which in adults are approximately 30–$45\,\mu$m in diameter and 1–$2\,\mu$m in depth. Hollows with similar dimensions were also described in rabbit and canine cartilage surfaces by Clarke, Schurman and Amstutz (1975) using replication, SEM and light microscopy. It will be noted that the maximum depth now proposed is less than that previously estimated by Clarke (1971b), but that the estimated diameter is similar. Using the data published by Longmore and Gardner (1975) on the size and frequency of the hollows, it is possible to construct diagrams of vertical cuts through cartilage, drawn so as to show hypothetical surface contours consistent with their findings (Figure 1.16). Such diag-

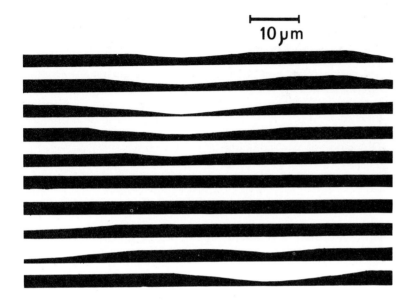

Figure 1.16 Diagram showing a series of vertical cuts through articular cartilage, and drawn to a hypothetical surface contour which might be present if there were 'tertiary hollows' of the diameter, depth and frequency postulated by Longmore and Gardner (1975). Note that segments between the hollows would appear virtually smooth in transmission light or electron micrographs. The scale marker gives a guide to the degree of 'roughness' which might be imparted by the hollows themselves. Mean diameter and mean depth of hollows increase during maturation and adult ageing: the hypothetical drawings were made using the combined range of data from children and adults.

rams demonstrate, between hollows, surface segments which would appear virtually smooth in transmission electron micrographs. Thus the apparently inconsistent findings from transmission electron microscopy of vertical sections might in theory be due to sampling effects.

Gardner and McGillivray (1971) comment that it was often difficult to tell whether the surface irregularities observed are of hollows or of prominences. The superficial cells might be associated either with surface depressions or with surface prominences (Clarke 1971a). Hence the surface contour might be in a constant state of change, the undulatory character being dependent on physiological factors affecting the shape of the superficial chondrocytes. Future investigations of these cells may shed light on this possibility.

3. WATER CONTENT

Some of the water in cartilage is intracellular, but the rest forms an important constituent of the extracellular matrix. The water content of adult human patellar cartilage is about 75–78% of the wet weight (Lindahl 1948; Linn and Sokoloff 1965), and similar values are found for articular cartilage from a number of other human joints (Miles and Eichelberger 1964). The water content does not change with ageing and is higher in patellar articular cartilage than in costal cartilage, which contains only 61% of water (Linn and Sokoloff 1965). A temporary swelling of the cartilage, attributed to the absorption of water from the joint space, has been described after exercise (Ingelmark and Ekholm 1948; Ekholm and Ingelmark 1952) (but see Chapter 8, Section 3.3). Extracellular water is also said to increase after long periods of disuse caused by experimental denervation or immobilization (Akeson, Eichelberger and Roma 1958; Eichelberger, Roma and Moulder 1959). Makowsky (1948) states that regions of the joint subject to what he terms 'sliding friction' have more fluid than the 'load-bearing areas'.

Discussion of extracellular fluid is relevant when considering the physical properties of cartilage (Chapter 4, Section 6; Chapter 5, Section 3; Chapter 6, Section 3.8 and Chapter 9, Section 5.1).

3.1. Zonal Variation

The water content is generally highest next to the articular surface (Muir *et al.* 1970), although its variation in successively deeper slices (cut tangential to the surface) is apparently small (Maroudas, Muir and Wingham 1969). X-ray microprobe analyses reveal no differences in density of the matrix with respect to distance from the cell or groups of cells (Chapter 4, Section 2), although such variation has been described in other forms of cartilage (Galjaard 1962).

4. GROUND SUBSTANCE HISTOCHEMISTRY

4.1. Introduction

A knowledge of the nature, amount and distribution of the components of the ground substance of articular cartilage is important since, apart from its role in the anatomy, physiology and biomechanics of the tissue, it is generally believed that loss of ground substance is associated with early degenerative change in articular cartilage. The organization of the material is more complicated than might be suspected from an inspection of the routine histological preparation, and this complexity influences its staining properties and their interpretation.

4.1.1. Proteoglycan Organization. The 'filler' substance which endows cartilage with its elasticity in compression is made up of large molecules of carbohydrates and protein. Cartilage and other connective tissues contain polysaccharide molecules which have a considerable negative charge and a molecular weight up to 50 000. These are termed acid mucopolysaccharides or, more precisely, glycosaminoglycans; chondroitin sulphate, keratan sulphate and a very small amount of hyaluronic acid are found in cartilage. Chondroitin sulphate and keratan sulphate chains are covalently bound as side-chains to a central core of protein which forms about 6–8% of the whole molecule. These protein–polysaccharides (known as 'proteoglycans') have a molecular weight of about $1–4 \times 10^6$ and vary considerably in their precise chemical content. Some, though not all, proteoglycan molecules can aggregate to form very large complexes; the basis of this aggregation depends upon a highly specific interaction of proteoglycans with hyaluronic acid and certain glycoproteins. Thus electron micrographs might be expected to show hyaluronate 'threads' in the 'super-complex' (Rosenberg *et al.* 1975). Closely associated with the protein–polysaccharide complexes are neutral glycoprotein molecules containing a large proportion of protein and only a small carbohydrate moiety; they carry little or no negative charge.

4.1.2. Interaction of collagen and proteoglycan. There is almost certainly an interaction between the proteoglycan of the ground substance and the collagen fibril in addition to that of mechanical entanglement. Specific interactions are suggested from the results of investigations concerned with collagen fibrillogenesis and with fibre stability in different tissues (see Chapter 3, Section 5). Neither the precise mechanism of the interaction nor the level of organization of the interacting macromolecules is fully elucidated. Factors influencing the formation of fibrils from monomeric collagen in the presence of proteoglycan include electrostatic interactions, the molecular weight of the polysaccharide and the native state of the macromolecules (Mathews 1970). Thus Toole and Lowther (1968) found that proteoglycans enhanced fibre formation but that the free glycosaminoglycans had no effect. However, there is evidence from other studies (Öbrink 1973; Scott 1975) that isolated glycosaminoglycans such as chondroitin and dermatan sulphates do interact with collagen although hyaluronic acid and keratan sulphate do not.

In the tissues there appear to be two general possibilities as to the method of association of proteoglycan and collagen. The first is that there is some form of direct binding. It was early postulated that the proteoglycan core protein lay parallel to the long axis of the collagen fibrils which were linked by the glycosaminoglycan side-chains (Mathews 1968). Serafini-Fracassini and Smith (1966) investigated the interaction of collagen and ground substance using the electron microscope and bismuth staining. A fraction extracted from nasal cartilage, consisting in part of a combination of collagen and proteoglycan, shows particulate staining across the collagen fibres at the a and b_1 bands of each repeating 64 nm period. As a result of this and other observations, the authors conclude that some proteoglycan molecules are coiled transversely around the collagen fibres at these positions and that other molecules lie free in the matrix between the fibres. Similar evidence has been obtained by Ruggeri, dell'Orbo and Quacci (1975). Using Alcian blue in 0.3 mol/litre (0.3 M) $MgCl_2$ solution (a technique thought to demonstrate chondroitin sulphate) they find stained 'filaments' 4–12 nm thick partially surrounding single collagen fibrils at 64 nm intervals and often connecting two or more neighbouring fibrils.

The second possibility is that proteoglycan is bound to collagen through the agency of a non-collagenous protein or glycoprotein. The ultrastructural appearance of 3 nm filaments interconnecting matrix granules with collagen fibrils would be compatible with this idea, although there is as yet no conclusive evidence as to the chemical nature of the filaments. However, non-collagenous glycoprotein extracted from cartilage (Shipp and Bowness 1975), when viewed in the electron microscope, forms filaments which have the same dimensions and staining characteristics with lead, ruthenium red and Alcian blue–phosphotungstic acid as do the filaments arrayed along the collagen fibrils in the native tissue. It has also been shown that material thought to be glycoprotein, extracted from fibrous tissue, becomes attached to newly forming fibrils at regular intervals when introduced during fibrillogenesis (Reynolds 1975). The nature of the association between extracted glycoprotein and collagen fibril is not known, although there is a strong binding of the glycoprotein to proteoglycan (Shipp and Bowness 1975). It is of some interest that Hopwood and Robinson (1974) recently proposed a structure for keratan sulphate which suggests that the second, alkali-stable, bond between the glycosaminoglycan and glutamic acid might provide sites for linkage between proteoglycans and glycoproteins.

The biochemistry of the matrix is fully discussed in Chapter 3.

4.2. Histochemical Procedures for Glycosaminoglycans

The carbohydrate components of the proteoglycans have been those most extensively investigated. Glycosaminoglycans have characteristic ion-binding properties which facilitate their histochemical demonstration using cationic dyes, often staining metachromatically. Before the results of histochemical studies can be considered, it must be recognized that there are pitfalls in glycosaminoglycan histochemistry, some of which are noted below.

There is evidence that fixation with aqueous formalin alone may not be an adequate procedure (Szirmai 1963). Unfortunately there appears to be no infallible method of fixation. Experiments using tissue containing glycosaminoglycans labelled with ^{35}S-sulphate show that fresh-frozen sections lose 30% of their radioactivity after fixation in formalin (Engfeldt and Hjertquist 1967; 1968), the loss being somewhat smaller after fixation in glutaral-dehyde. While immersion of the fresh-frozen sections in azure A (a cationic dye) preserves the labelled glycosaminoglycan satisfac-torily, it has been recommended that cetylpyridinium chloride (CPC) should be added to formalin or glutaraldehyde to ensure adequate fixation. However, although CPC–formalin may be the best method of fixation where autoradiography is involved, CPC is not completely effective and may adversely affect subsequent staining with cationic dyes (Figure 1.17), since by binding to the

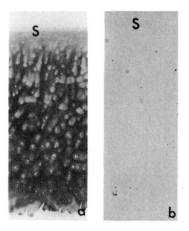

Figure 1.17 Blockage of cationic dye-binding following tissue fixation with cetyl-pyridinium chloride (CPC). Fresh-frozen vertical sections of femoral condylar cartilage, fixed in (a) 10% formalin, (b) 10% formalin containing 0.5% CPC. S = articular surface.

Both sections with 0.05% Alcian blue containing 0.9 mol/litre (0.9M) $MgCl_2$ in 0.05 mol/litre (0.05M) acetate buffer, pH 5.8   ×28.

glycosaminoglycan and so fixing it, CPC blocks cationic dye-binding (Kelly, Bloom and Scott 1963; Engfeldt and Hjertquist 1967; Gustafson and Pihl 1967). Although such CPC blocking may be reversed (Kelly *et al.* 1963), at least partially, by long periods of staining, discrepancies are found in the results (Quintarelli and Dellovo 1965; Stockwell, unpublished). It may there-fore be preferable to work with fresh-frozen material stained immediately after sectioning although it is probable that some matrix material becomes detached as the knife passes through the tissue due to either the momentary thawing or the local disruption of the collagen mesh. Fixation of tissue-blocks with alcohol–forma-lin mixtures at low temperature (Stockwell and Scott 1965; Scott and Dorling 1965) is probably adequate as an alternative, pro-vided that the tissue does not come into contact with water prior to staining.

The routine preparative procedure for electron microscopy also results in a considerable loss of glycosaminoglycan, particularly during the post-osmication stage (Engfeldt and Hjertquist 1968). It appears that preservation of polyanionic material is not greatly enhanced by adding either CPC or ruthenium red to the fixative (Thyberg *et al.* 1973).

Staining of the glycosaminoglycans may be modified by factors other than poor fixation, a fact which is not suprising in view of the complex nature of the molecules and aggregates which they form. Many of the classical methods employ cationic dyes which give regions of basophilia and metachromasia where polyanions are localized. The degree of polymerization of glycosaminogly-can–protein complexes affects the degree of metachromasia; the lower the molecular weight, the more orthochromatic the reaction. When immunofluorescent methods are used, the more highly polymerized the polysaccharide, the more effective is the exclusion of the antibody protein from the site of the antigen. This causes reduction or loss of immunofluorescence (Loewi 1965; Barland, Janis and Sandson 1966). With staining methods employing cationic dyes, the pH of the dye-bath is a well known factor which may lead to false negative results. At low pH, this is due to competition between the dye-ions and cationic groups of protein moieties in the vicinity of the glycosaminoglycan (Szirmai 1963).

Apart from selective digestion by enzymes such as hyaluronidase, localization of different glycosaminoglycans can be obtained by histochemical methods employing the 'critical electrolyte concentration' (CEC) principle. With this technique, Alcian blue is commonly used in the presence of various concentrations of magnesium chloride at pH 5.8 to differentiate between the various polyanions (Scott and Dorling 1965). Cationic dyes other than Alcian blue (such as azure A, toluidine blue or safranin) may be used provided that the dye selected does not have specific staining affinities for particular substances (Scott and Willett 1966). Alcian blue appears to be superior to most other cationic dyes, in that it is a better precipitant of carbohydrate polyanions and behaves as though bound only by electrostatic forces; in some situations, however, Alcian blue may fail to stain glycosaminoglycan unless the tissue receives prior treatment with hyaluronidase (Mason 1971). Methods involving applications of the CEC principle (Scott 1955) are also affected by the degree of polymerization of a given type of glycosaminoglycan. This is particularly noticeable after decalcification, even after ethylene diamine tetra-acetic acid (EDTA), when the CEC of the polyanion is reduced (Quintarelli and Dellovo 1965); extraction of the polyanion from the tissue may also occur. However, the Alcian blue–CEC method does not appear to suffer from the false negative results associated with protein competition mentioned above: this is prevented by the salt ($MgCl_2$) in the dye-bath and because a relatively high pH is used (Scott, Dorling and Stockwell 1968).

Alcian blue has a further advantage in that it can be used for the visualization of polyanions at the ultrastructural level, due to the presence of a copper atom in the dye-ion, although post-osmication is needed to intensify the electron density (Behnke and Zelander 1970). Although it is not as electron dense as ruthenium red, colloidal iron, bismuth, lanthanum or other cations containing elements of high atomic number, Alcian blue is more amenable to the application of the CEC principle.

A number of ultrastructural studies of cartilage have used these cationic reagents. They all stain the matrix granules well (Thyberg *et al.* 1973), indicating the polyanionic nature of these particles. Alcian blue–CEC procedures have also been applied. Using

26

epiphyseal cartilage, matrix granules (Schofield, Williams and Doty 1975) or 'rods' (Ruggeri *et al.* 1975) are stained well at a low CEC (0.05 mol/litre (0.05 M) MgCl$_2$). At a medium CEC (0.5 mol/litre (0.5 M) MgCl$_2$) the granules become more ribbon-like and less electron dense, while at high CEC (1.0–1.2 mol/litre (1.0–1.2 M) MgCl$_2$) staining is absent. These results indicate the presence of chondroitin sulphate in the matrix granules of epiphyseal cartilage, confirming earlier studies, but give little further information concerning molecular structure. Alcian blue–CEC procedures at 0.4 and 0.9 mol/litre (0.4 and 0.9 M) MgCl$_2$ in unfixed bovine nasal septal cartilage (Scott 1973) demonstrate electron-dense filamentous and network-like structures which have a similar distribution in general to the alcianophilia seen in light microscope studies. Structures closely resembling the proteoglycans extracted from bovine nasal septum and photographed in monolayer preparations by Rosenberg *et al.* (1970) have been demonstrated *in situ* in ultrathin sections by Scott (1974) using 'cinchomeronic phthalocyanine' (a low molecular weight analogue of Alcian blue) at 0.3 mol/litre (0.3 M) MgCl$_2$. However, there are many problems in the ultrastructural demonstration of the proteoglycan molecules and aggregates *in situ* and a satisfactory method is still needed. In the following account of glycosaminoglycan distribution in articular cartilage the results of the histochemical methods cited were mostly obtained with the light microscope.

4.3. Glycosaminoglycan Distribution

In human cartilage, chondroitin and keratan sulphate are the two principal types of acid glycosaminoglycan so far identified (Kaplan and Meyer 1959; Rosenberg, Johnson and Schubert 1965); hyaluronic acid forms a small fraction (about 0.7% of the total uronic acid) which is highly significant in proteoglycan aggregation (Hardingham and Muir 1974). Chemical analyses of adult human cartilage show that the amount of these substances is extremely variable (Rosenberg *et al.* 1965; Bollet and Nance 1966), but that a minimum of 1% of the wet weight of the tissue consists of chondroitin sulphate, with, in addition, a rather smaller amount of keratan sulphate. The amount of glycosaminoglycan in cartilage of different parts of the joint surface shows variation. Thus cartilage on the superior surface of the femoral head has a higher fixed charge density (proportional to glycosaminoglycan concentration) than that on the inferior aspect (Maroudas, Evans and Almeida 1973). Within the knee joint, similar variations have been recorded: the patella has a lower fixed charge density than the femoral condyle (Maroudas 1975). On the femoral condyle itself, cartilage on the posterior part has a lower hexosamine content than the intermediate part (summit) of the articular area (Bjelle 1975). In addition, histochemical investigation has shown that, even at a single spot on the articular area, the glycosaminoglycans are not distributed uniformly throughout the depth of the cartilage.

4.3.1. Zonal Variation.

In agreement with the earlier descriptions of Schaffer (1930) and Hirsch (1944), Collins and McElligott (1960) found that basophilia and metachromasia are less intense in the superficial (zone 1) than in the intermediate and deep zones (zones 2 and 3) of normal adult human articular cartilage. The matrix of the intermediate zone is diffusely stained but, in the deep zone, pools of colour are found around the cell groups. In immature cartilage, the matrix stains evenly throughout the whole thickness of the tissue.

In adult human articular cartilage, Alcian blue staining at a low CEC, due to keratan sulphate and chondroitin sulphate together, is most intense (Figure 1.18) in the deep and intermediate zones of

Figure 1.18 Vertical sections of young adult articular cartilage of capitulum of humerus, stained for glycosaminoglycan content. (a) Alcian blue: 0.4 mol/litre (0.4м) $MgCl_2$, pH 5.8 showing distribution of chondroitin sulphate and keratan sulphate. (b) Alcian blue: 0.9 mol/litre (0.9м) $MgCl_2$, pH 5.8 showing distribution of high molecular weight keratan sulphate.

Note the diminution of stain intensity toward the articular surface particularly in (b) ×35.

Figure 1.19 Variation of glycosaminoglycan components with distance from the articular surface of young adult femoral condylar cartilage determined by chemical analysis. The proportion of hexose (representing keratan sulphate) rises in the deeper half of the tissue. Compare with histochemical distribution in Figure 1.18.

(Data from Stockwell and Scott 1967.)

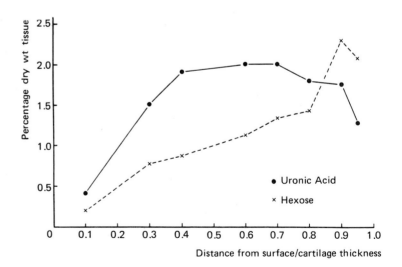

uncalcified cartilage (zones 2 and 3), and decreases towards the joint surface (Stockwell and Scott 1965). Staining intensity at high CEC, attributable to high molecular weight keratan sulphate, is diminished compared with the intensity at a low CEC. It is maximal in the deep zone (zone 3) and decreases towards the joint surface, where very little staining can be detected (Figure 1.18). The same distribution is found when fresh-frozen sections are used, and control sections previously treated with testicular hyaluronidase to remove chondroitin sulphate confirm this localization of keratan sulphate (Scott and Stockwell 1967).

The results of chemical analysis (Figure 1.19) of successive tangential slices cut from the surface of adult human femoral condylar cartilage are in agreement with the histochemical findings (Stockwell and Scott 1967). Uronic acid (indicating chondroitin sulphate) concentration rises from about 0.4–0.8% of the dry weight of tissue in the superficial zone to about 2% dry weight in the intermediate zone. Hexose (a component of keratan sulphate) is least in the superficial zone and is greatest in the deep zone adjacent to the calcified layer, where it may exceed the concentration of uronic acid. These findings have been confirmed by other workers (Maroudas *et al.* 1969). The zonal variations in the concentrations of uronic acid and hexose are compatible with values based on the analysis of the full thickness of the tissue (Bollet and Nance 1966).

4.3.2. Pericellular Variation.

Results with the Alcian blue–CEC technique suggest that the distribution of chondroitin sulphate in the uncalcified cartilage varies with distance from the cell or cell group as well as with the distance from the articular surface (Stockwell and Scott 1965). Chondroitin sulphate is present throughout the whole matrix but appears to be more concentrated in the vicinity of the cell or cell groups, particularly in the deeper parts (zone 3) of the tissue (Figure 1.20). In young adult cartilage (zones 2 and 3), staining due to keratan sulphate is more intense in matrix lying remote from, rather than adjacent to, chondrocytes (Figure 1.21). This heterogeneous distribution does not seem to be due to the inhibitory effects of protein interaction, since the CEC method with Alcian blue is largely free of this artefact. The distribution of chondroitin sulphate, both zonally and with respect to the cells, may be confirmed using the two-stage periodic acid–Schiff technique (Scott and Dorling 1969; Stockwell 1970): in this method the slowly oxidized polyuronides are rendered Schiff-positive, and hence chondroitin sulphate is probably the only substance stained in human cartilage (Figure 1.22) X-ray microprobe analysis provides further evidence of the distribution, particularly in the deep uncalcified cartilage (zone 3) described above. Sulphur content and fixed charge density (a measure of the

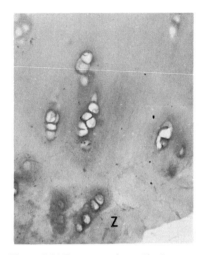

Figure 1.20 Deep zone (zone 3) of young adult articular cartilage. Staining (attributed to chondroitin sulphate and keratan sulphate) is most intense in the pericellular regions. Z = calcified zone.
Alcian blue: 0.4 mol/litre (0.4M) $MgCl_2$, pH 5.8 ×180.

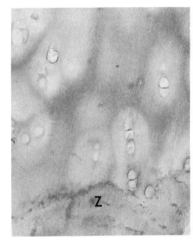

Figure 1.21 As Figure 1.20, but showing stain distribution attributed to high molecular weight keratan sulphate only. This is most intense in the general matrix at a distance from the cells. Z = calcified zone.
Alcian blue: 0.4 mol/litre (0.4M) $MgCl_2$, pH 5.8 ×180.

glycosaminoglycan content) are higher near the lacunar rim than more distant from the cells (Chapter 4, Section 2). Using this method, only small variations with distance from the cell can be found in zone 2; with staining methods also, it is found that the pericellular localization is much more prominent in zone 3 than zone 2.

Figure 1.22 (*left*) Zones 2 and 3 of articular cartilage stained using the two-stage periodic acid–Schiff (PAS) technique for chondroitin sulphate. Staining intensity is increased slightly in the pericellular regions ×50.

Figure 1.23 (*right*) Zones 2 and 3 of articular cartilage stained using the routine (short oxidation) PAS technique. Stain intensity (attributed to glycoprotein) is reduced in the pericellular regions. Compare with Figure 1.22 ×50.

The zonal variation in chondroitin sulphate and keratan sulphate must depend on physiological factors as well as presumably being associated with mechanical requirements. For example, it has been suggested that a determining factor for an increase in the keratan sulphate/chondroitin sulphate ratio could be an increasing distance from an oxygen supply (Stockwell and Scott 1965): the zonal distribution of keratan sulphate in adult human articular cartilage is compatible with this suggestion if it is assumed that the principal source of nutrition is the synovial fluid (Chapter 8, Section 2).

4.4. Proteoglycan Distribution

As described in Chapter 3, Section 3.1, the proteoglycans of articular cartilage exhibit a spectrum of molecular size. At any one stage of development of the tissue, it appears that the larger molecules contain more protein and more keratan sulphate. At different stages of development, proteoglycan molecules of the same hydrodynamic size also differ in their chemical composition, the more mature cartilage containing molecules with a higher proportion of protein and keratan sulphate. It would be of great interest to know if this chemical heterogeneity is associated with a topographical heterogeneity in the tissue. Comparatively little work has been done to investigate this possibility, although something might be inferred from the results of glycosaminoglycan localization. Since it appears that large proteoglycan molecules contain a higher proportion of keratan sulphate than small molecules, keratan sulphate might be more abundant in sites where there was a preponderance of large molecules, assuming an equivalent volume of proteoglycan in the sites compared.

4.4.1. Immunofluorescent Studies of Matrix Proteoglycan. The results obtained by these methods may be relevant. Reactive sites closely associated with the protein component of the proteoglycan can be 'stained' by use of an immunofluorescent technique. This technique is carried out in two stages. First, an antiserum to the proteoglycan is layered on a histological section of cartilage. After incubation, this antiserum is washed off, and a second type of serum (anti-gammaglobulin), conjugated with fluorescein *iso*thiocyanate, is layered on the slide. Sites at which the first antiserum has reacted with proteoglycan can then be detected by use of a fluorescence microscope (Loewi 1965; Barland *et al.* 1966).

Barland *et al.* (1966) have used this technique to study adult human articular cartilage. They find that in non-fibrillated specimens fluorescent staining of the matrix is localized to pericellular areas. In vertical sections it shows as spindle-shaped patterns around the cells of the superficial zone (zone 1) and as small haloes of granular fluorescence immediately surrounding the chondrocytes of the middle and deep zones (zones 2 and 3), but the proteoglycan of the intercellular matrix fails to react with the antibody. Barland *et al.* suggest that this result is due to an increasing polymerization and entanglement of proteoglycan in matrix more distant from the chondrocytes. Similar results have been obtained in pig articular cartilage (Loewi 1965).

4.4.2. Studies of Extracted Tissue. A different approach involves the use of 'dissociative extraction' of cartilage with guanidinium chloride; this removes much of the proteoglycan material. Anderson and Sajdera (1971) have studied bovine nasal cartilage histochemically and with the electron microscope, before and after extraction. It appears that the procedure results in considerable damage to collagen fibres, which become split into very fine fibrils. The greater part of the extracted tissue fails to react with cationic dyes, residual staining being found only in pericellular matrix close to the cell; subsequent treatment with trypsin renders the pericellular matrix negative also. Anderson and Sajdera suggest that the 15% of the total proteoglycan, which cannot be extracted with guanidinium, must therefore be located close to the chondrocytes.

Hence, unless a protective collagen 'basket' (Section 2.4) around the cell lacuna prevents extraction, the pericellular proteoglycan must differ in some way from that of the intercellular matrix. It cannot be assumed necessarily that these results using nasal cartilage apply also to articular cartilage, in which guanidinium fails to extract a higher proportion of the proteoglycan, the unextractable material being released only after collagenase treatment. However, it is of interest that Anderson and Sajdera's residual staining site would correspond to the location of immunofluorescent staining demonstrated by Barland *et al.* (1966) in articular cartilage.

4.5. Glycoprotein Distribution

In addition to proteoglycans, cartilage contains macromolecules in which protein is covalently bound to carbohydrate but with the protein moiety forming the bulk of the molecule. In cartilage these glycoproteins are the most likely compounds to react to the standard periodic acid–Schiff technique (using a short oxidation time), provided that the presence of glycogen can be excluded. Schiff-positive material is less abundant in the superficial zone (zone 1) than in the deeper tissue; whilst in the deep zone (zone 3) the most intense PAS staining is in the intercellular matrix, forming 'collars' (Figure 1.23; see p. 30) around the cell groups (Collins and McElligott 1960).

4.6. Ageing

Despite earlier work which perhaps suggested that the glycosaminoglycan content of articular cartilage diminished with age (Kuhn and Leppelmann 1958), it now appears that most if not all of the reduction in ground substance occurs during the growth period of the two decades. Little change, particularly in chondroitin sulphate, can be detected after this period if analyses are made of the full thickness of the uncalcified cartilage (Anderson *et al.* 1964; Bollet and Nance 1966). However, in deep tissue (zone 3) adjacent to the basal calcified layer, analyses indicate a rather abrupt increase in the ratio of keratan sulphate to chondroitin sulphate. This occurs during the third and fourth decades, a low 'plateau' value during the growth period rising to a high 'plateau' after the fourth decade (Stockwell 1970). Histochemically, a change is also found in the microscopic localization of keratan sulphate in the deep zone adjacent to the calcified layer (Section 4.3.2). After the third decade, keratan sulphate is distributed close to the cells (Figure 1.24) as opposed to remote from them (Stockwell 1970), thus closely resembling the localization of this substance in the central regions of mature human costal cartilage (Stockwell and Scott 1965; Quintarelli and Dellovo 1966).

The territorial distribution of keratan sulphate in normal mature articular cartilage is restricted to the deepest 10–15% of the thickness of the uncalcified cartilage in the femoral condyle but may be more extensive in the thinner cartilage of smaller joints (Stockwell 1975). The heterogeneous distribution of the glycosaminoglycans, and of keratan sulphate in particular, with respect to the cells may be associated with differences in their

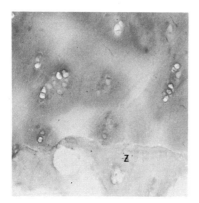

Figure 1.24 Deep zone (zone 3) of aged articular cartilage showing stain distribution attributed to high molecular weight keratan sulphate. Stain intensity is maximal in the pericellular regions. Z = calcified zone. Compare with Figure 1.21.

Alcian blue: 0.9 mol/litre (0.9M) MgCl₂, pH 5.8 ×120.

32

turnover rates; in rabbit cartilage, turnover of keratan sulphate is very much slower than that of chondroitin sulphate (Davidson, Woodhall and Baxley 1962). It has been suggested that initially the relatively slow turnover of keratan sulphate proteoglycans permits them to diffuse away from the cell, until the diffusion gradient (e.g. between two cells) becomes reversed; i.e. keratan sulphate first concentrates in the interterritorial matrix (Mason 1971). Subsequently during ageing when the interterritorial matrix becomes impenetrable, perhaps due to extensive cross-linking, the keratan sulphate perforce becomes restricted to the cell territory.

The changes concerning keratan sulphate occur on completion of skeletal growth. It is possible that they are related to changing nutritional conditions in the deep cartilage at this time, since the nutritional supply from the marrow spaces in the subchondral bone is reduced in the adult as compared with the immature (Chapter 8, Section 2.1).

4.7. Relation of Matrix Structure and Function

It is tempting to speculate that the zonal variation in the intercellular matrix of adult cartilage reflects a functional adaptation to two different but closely related roles. In terms of this concept, the tightly packed orientated collagen fibres of the superficial layer (zone 1) might form a 'protective armour coat' and 'tension-resisting diaphragm' designed to resist wear and apparently requiring only a small amount of intervening glycosaminoglycan for this purpose. In contrast, the underlying deeper part of the uncalcified cartilage (zones 2 and 3) is perhaps designed mainly to respond to physiological compression. This requires a different arrangement of the collagen fibres and a more abundant glycosaminoglycan content. The specialized pericellular matrix may act as a 'shock-absorber' for the cell or cell groups (Stockwell and Scott 1965), which are afforded additional protection by the enclosing coarse collagen fibres. Taken together, the 'chrondrin balls' and the 'tangled open meshwork' of intercellular fibre bundles with their interstitial proteoglycan ground substance will tend to cushion ('dampen') and distribute the load (Thompson and Bassett 1970), not only within the cartilage but also over the articular ends of the bones. Although slight ageing changes occur next to the basal calcified layer, it appears that the bulk of the collagen and ground substance of articular cartilage may remain remarkably unchanged during adult life provided that the surface remains intact.

The disease osteoarthrosis is characterized by destructive thinning of articular cartilage, potentially to expose bone at a site where the bone is then subjected to abrasive and other damage. It represents a functional failure of articular cartilage. Studies of the changes which occur in this disease suggest that articular cartilage has at least three functions in healthy joints: it provides a covering material which protects the underlying bone from abrasive and other damage (Meachim 1975); it helps to dampen and distribute the load on the subarticular bone; and it facilitates movement between articular surfaces.

These subjects are fully discussed in Chapters 5, 6 and 7.

4.8. 'Interlocked Stresses'

Fry and Robertson (1967) believe that 'specifically aligned tensile stresses' ('interlocked stresses') are present within human costal and nasal septal cartilage; they believe that the outer layers of the tissue are maintained in tension, so that the intact cartilage has a balanced system of forces, the resultant of which is zero. Cartilage may become distorted in shape if this balance of forces is altered *in vivo* or *in vitro* (Gibson and Davis 1958): if, for example, a series of cuts is made along one side of nasal cartilage, it will tend to curl towards the intact side. Fry and Robertson (1967) have suggested that the tensile stresses are set up against a hypothetical 'swelling pressure', this 'swelling pressure' being due to the ability of cartilage matrix to imbibe fluid, and they have shown that the proteoglycan of cartilage matrix is intimately involved in establishing the stresses.

Similar 'interlocked stresses' may be present in human articular cartilage. Cartilage removed from the subchondral bone tends to curl, the deformation occurring much more quickly (1 minute) in thin than in thick cartilage (Fry 1974). The convex articular surface usually becomes concave on curling. Thus, the superficial layer (zone 1) may be both tension-resisting and also itself in a state of tension even at rest. This topic is discussed further in Chapter 5, Section 3.

4.9. Electromechanical Potentials

Lotke, Black and Richardson (1974) have measured electro-mechanical potentials from within the matrix of human articular cartilage. The origin of the potential is complex, and artefacts must also be carefully excluded. The potential is increased with increasing load, increasing load rate and increasing strain concentration.

5. EXTRACELLULAR LIPID

5.1. Distribution

Lipid forms about 1% of the wet weight of human adult articular cartilage (Stockwell 1967) and is found both in the cells and the matrix. As revealed by quantitative analysis and by the Sudan colourants, the amount of lipid varies considerably from one subject to another. Extracellular lipid is found in two types of location (Figure 1.25). In all zones, it is found in a pericellular site, though in reduced amounts in the deeper parts of the tissue; in the superficial zone (Figure 1.26) it is also seen spread more diffusely throughout the matrix (Putschar 1931; Schallock 1942). The superficial diffuse lipid is commonly present by the third decade, although it is infrequent and minimal in childhood and adolescence (Schallock 1942; Stockwell 1965; Ghadially, Meachim and Collins 1965). Stockwell (1967) was unable to find an age-related increase in the lipid content in full thickness samples of femoral condylar cartilage, but it is possible that the amount of diffuse extracellular lipid in a limited portion of the tissue—the superficial zone—was insufficient to affect the analyses of full-thickness aged specimens. Bonner, Jonsson, Malanos and Bryant (1975) have shown that this explanation may have been correct. They find that in the superficial 0.5–1.00 mm of the cartilage, the total lipid content increases with age over the range 15–66 years; a much smaller increase occurs in the deeper cartilage where also the lipid content is much less. However, inspection of their results shows that little change can be detected in either the superficial or the deep zones once growth has ceased (e.g. after the age of 25–30 years), although analysis of more specimens may clarify the situation.

Extracellular lipid in both sites reacts histochemically for phospholipid and neutral lipid (Zbinden 1953; Stockwell 1965) and is extractable with hot pyridine or chloroform/methanol. Bonner *et al.* (1975) find that cholesterol is present also. Their results suggest that triglyceride is present in the extracellular lipid of all zones but that cholesterol and phospholipid are much more prominent, particularly deep to the superficial zone. Quantitative analysis shows that an unknown lipid is present in considerable quantity, since triglyceride, cholesterol, phospholipid and glycolipid do not account for the total quantity of extractable lipid (Bonner *et al.* 1975).

Electron microscopy reveals electron-dense granules and membranous bodies in the matrix of mature rabbit (Barnett, Cochrane and Palfrey 1963) and human (Ghadially *et al.* 1965) articular cartilage (Figure 1.27). At least part of this material is thought to

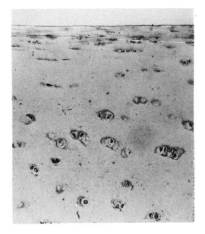

Figure 1.25 Superficial part (zones 1 and 2) of femoral condylar cartilage showing distribution of extracellular lipid. This occurs as 'haloes' surrounding the cell lacunae; in addition, this specimen contains a rather small amount of diffuse lipid near the articular surface.

Sudan black B, frozen section ×110.

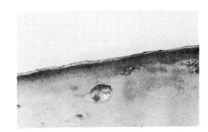

Figure 1.26 Superficial layer (zone 1) showing a darkly staining continuous band of lipidic material in the matrix. A narrow 'lipid-free lamina' is seen between the lipidic band and the articular surface.

Oil red 0, frozen section ×200.

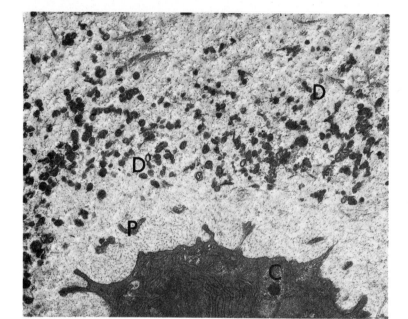

Figure 1.27 Electron-dense granules and membranous bodies (D) in the extracellular matrix, separated from the chondrocyte (C) by a 'clear band' traversed by cell processes (P).

Transmission electron micrograph ×12 500.

represent the extracellular lipid seen with the light microscope (Ghadially *et al.* 1965). The material consists of rounded bodies varying in size and morphology. Some of these rounded bodies are uniformly electron dense; others show an eccentric or central region which is less dense or electron lucent, and appear similar to the 'extracellular vesicles' concerned in the calcification of growth plate cartilage. The more prominent bodies are seen against a background of smaller granular particles with indistinct outlines. Electron microscopy shows that the debris is patchy in distribution. Some of it is found as accumulations in the matrix near viable chondrocytes, and shows a tendency to be concentrated near one side of the cell; some of it is found in focal aggregates which also contain organelle and cytomembrane remnants marking the site of a necrotic chondrocyte which has disintegrated.

The possible significance of lipid in synovial joint lubrication is discussed in Chapter 7, Section 7.2.2.

5.2. Origin of Extracellular Lipid

Various hypotheses, not mutually exclusive, have been suggested for the origin of the extracellular lipid, or at least for its ease of demonstration in adult cartilage. Barnett *et al.* (1963) suggest that much of it is the debris of cell necrosis. Ghadially *et al.* (1965) consider that the origin is also from intact cells and is thus more physiological. They suggest that the tips of chondrocyte processes can be shed into the surrounding matrix, the lipid of the detached cell membranes accumulating in a pericellular position. The hypothesis of cellular origin receives support from the demonstration of proteolytic activity in the pericellular osmiophilic vesicles (Chrisman, Semonsky and Bensch 1967), suggesting that the particles may play a part in matrix remodelling in the neighbourhood of the cell ('extracellular vesicles').

In epiphyseal cartilage similar vesicles contain a variety of phosphatases and are involved in the initiation of calcification (Ali, Anderson and Sajdera 1970). However, in articular cartilage, not all vesicles contain phosphatase (Ali and Bayliss 1974). Further data on the enzyme content of the matrix vesicles are required. Schott (1963) also believes that the extracellular lipid is derived from the cell. He suggests that it becomes 'masked' or unstainable beyond the pericellular area, perhaps by being incorporated into the macromolecules of the matrix. Stockwell (1965) suggests that an additional source of the superficial diffuse lipid could be the synovial fluid, which contains significant amounts of phospholipid and cholesterol (Bole 1962). Although on light microscopy a narrow 'lipid-free lamina' (Figure 1.26) is often found separating the diffuse lipid from the articular surface (Ghadially et al. 1965), small lipid globules have been detected less than 1 μm from the surface by use of electron microscopy (Meachim and Roy 1969): these globules could, of course, be moving either into or out of the cartilage. Ghadially, Mehta and Kirkcaldy-Willis (1970) believe that articular cartilage can in fact readily imbibe lipid, since they find a transient increase in the intracellular lipid content of rabbit articular chondrocytes after experimental injection of lipid into the synovial cavity; although no gradient of lipid concentration diminishing from the articular surface could be found, lipid was also detected in the extracellular matrix. Recent autoradiographic studies of labelled triglyceride injected intra-articularly (Sprinz and Stockwell 1976) confirm that the fatty acid moiety, at least, of the injected triglyceride passes through the cartilage to the chondrocytes (see Chapter 2, Section 2.5.2).

There is no evidence that the accumulation of extracellular lipid in the matrix predisposes to cartilage fibrillation (Ghadially et al. 1965). Thus the superficial articular cartilage of the central region of the humeral head can contain lipid throughout adult life and yet remain free from fibrillation. Conversely, fibrillation has no effect on the extracellular lipid pattern, except indirectly by causing flaking away of a lipid-laden superficial layer.

On the other hand, recent studies show that matrix vesicles and alkaline phosphatase activity are increased in the deeper parts of osteoarthrosic cartilage, perhaps partly associated with remodelling (Ali and Wisby 1976).

6. PIGMENTATION

Cartilage becomes yellow with age. Hass (1943) states that this pigmentation is due to neither lipid nor iron compounds. From a more recent chemical investigation, van der Korst, Sokoloff and Miller (1968) find that the pigment is associated with the non-collagenous protein of the tissue, but not with the polysaccharide component as had been suggested previously. They state that costal cartilage is more heavily pigmented than articular cartilage from the knee joint; in articular cartilage the deepest layers are the most discoloured and the superficial zone is free of pigment. However, Ghadially *et al.* (1965) found that the superficial zone of adult articular cartilage is sometimes slightly yellow. It is possible that several types of pigment are involved. Particularly in the case of the superficial zone, the carotenoid content of synovial fluid (Davies 1967) should be considered. It is tempting to speculate on the possible effects of compounds similar to vitamin A, should these diffuse into the superficial matrix. There is no evidence that the yellow pigment investigated by van der Korst *et al.* (1968) renders articular cartilage more prone to fibrillation, unlike the deposition of black pigment in ochronosis (Sharp 1969).

7. CALCIFIED ZONE

The basal calcified layer (zone 4) contains viable chondrocytes, but in adult cartilage they are smaller than those lying outwith the zone. The surface of the calcified layer adjoining the non-calcified cartilage usually appears flat or gently undulating in histological sections cut perpendicular to the surface. The junction stands out as a basophilic line, designated the 'tidemark' by Fawns and Landells (1953). The deep surface of the calcified layer, where it meets the underlying bone, is much more irregular. Hence the thickness of the calcified layer is variable, although it is of the order of 0.1 mm (Figure 1.28). This order of thickness is remarkably constant (Stockwell, unpublished) in specimens of adult cartilage which vary considerably (0.1–3.0 mm) in the thickness of the uncalcified tissue. In very small joints the thickness of the uncalcified zone tends to be less than 0.1 mm, but even so this may account for 50% of the total thickness of the cartilage. The calcified cartilage is more cellular in smaller than in larger joints.

Some authorities consider that the calcified layer should not be classified as part of the articular cartilage but that it should be regarded as a separate entity—metaplastic bone (Haines and Mohuiddin 1968). However, all are agreed that an important function is to provide the non-calcified articular cartilage with a firm attachment to the subchondral lamellar bone.

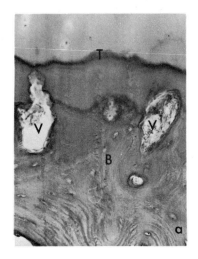 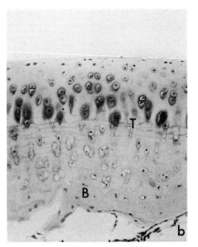

Figure 1.28 (a) Basal part (zones 3 and 4) of adult human femoral condylar cartilage. (b) Full thickness of adult cat metatarsal cartilage. There is a prominent basophilic line, the 'tidemark' (T), at the junction of the uncalcified with the calcified cartilage. In (a) vascular spaces (V) (extensions from the subchondral bone marrow) are seen in the calcified cartilage. Note the similar thicknesses of the calcified zones in man and cat, both photographed at the same magnification. B = subchondral bone.

Haematoxylin and eosin ×180.

7.1. Calcification in Articular Cartilage

In man, the ash content of the whole thickness of articular cartilage accounts for about 4% of the dry weight (Anderson *et al.* 1964; Bollet and Nance 1966). The matrix of zone 4 is normally heavily impregnated with calcium salts. Although there is in general little information about the inorganic material of the tissue, the mineral found in the calcified zone appears to be hydroxy-apatite (Davies *et al.* 1962), as in the calcifying matrix of the cartilaginous growth plate. In epiphyseal cartilage matrix there is evidence that crystals are laid down in clusters in and around small osmiophilic bodies containing large amounts of phosphatidyl-serine (Wuthier 1976), probably derived from cell processes ('extracellular or matrix vesicles'); the clusters eventually coalesce, the matrix becoming totally calcified (Bonucci 1967). Somewhat similar descriptions are given in the case of the calcified zone of rabbit articular cartilage (Davies *et al.* 1962; Barnett *et al.* 1963). Rosettes of crystals are randomly scattered in the matrix without any constant relationship to collagen fibril orientation. Deeper in the zone, where calcification is more complete, the rosettes occupy empty cell lacunae, producing a continuous mass of calcification.

The bulk of tissue in human articular cartilage (zones 1–3) is normally not mineralized to an extent detectable histochemically. However, crystals of calcium salts may impregnate the cartilage matrix in the condition of chondrocalcinosis articularis (pseudo-gout), and urates are found in a similar location in gout.

The earliest deposits in pseudo-gout are found in the midzone of articular cartilage in coarsely fibrous matrix near the margin of the pericellular areas (McCarty 1976) and are said to have no relation to matrix vesicles (Schumacher 1976). It is of interest that the relatively large amounts of extracellular lipid and other electron-dense material found in the superficial zone of articular cartilage are not normally associated with calcium deposits. Conditions must be more favourable for calcification in the epiphyseal cartilage and in costal cartilage (Zbinden 1953; Bonucci and Dearden 1976), where crystals are associated with electron-dense lipidic matrix vesicles. In this context, it is relevant that a particular fraction of protein–polysaccharide inhibits the precipitation of calcium phosphate *in vitro*, and that this fraction has recently been shown to be absent from calcifying cartilage (Chapter 3, Section 3.1).

7.2 The Bone/Cartilage Interface

The junction of the calcified layer with the underlying bone is far from smooth, the irregularities promoting adherence of the cartilage to the bone. It is interrupted at intervals by re-entrants from the bone marrow spaces into the cartilage, occupied by vascular tissue (Figure 1.28). These marrow spaces account for only a small part of the area of the osseo-chondral interface (Holmdahl and Ingelmark 1950) in 10-month-old rabbit joints and rarely penetrate through the full thickness of the calcified layer into the non-calcified tissue. Indeed, in the inferior articular process of the ninth thoracic vertebra in man, subchondral Haversian bone forms a continuous lamina by the age of 20 years (Enneking and Harrington 1969). On the other hand, marrow spaces are found in the articular cartilage of the human femoral head. Here the vessels in many of the spaces become occluded with advancing age, and the spaces filled in with bone (Woods, Greenwald and Haynes 1970). Although there are a smaller number of marrow spaces penetrating the calcified layer in the so-called 'non-contact' than in the 'pressure-bearing' regions of the hip, the same proportion is lost during ageing in both locations. These penetrating vascular spaces may afford an anatomical basis for a nutritional supply to the articular cartilage from the underlying bone. Evidence for this supply route, its extent and importance in relation to other sources of supply, and a discussion of the nutrition of articular cartilage, will be found in Chapter 8.

8. THE SUPERFICIAL ZONE AND REGRESSIVE CHANGES

Much is known of the superficial zone and the articular surface, for this region has been extensively investigated because of its obvious biomechanical importance. The appearances seen in the region, particularly near the surface, are influenced by the site selected for study. Very often the magnification at which this is examined also determines whether or not the surface should be classified as normal. For example, what is normal to the naked eye may show extensive changes with the light microscope. In routine histological sections examined by light microscopy, some specimens of adult cartilage show fraying and splitting of the articular surface, attributable to a process termed fibrillation. In other sections the articular surface appears to be 'intact' on transmission light microscopy; it is locally smooth and flat, and the irregularities described on scanning electron microscopy are not usually apparent with routine methods. Fibrillated areas and 'histologically intact' areas can, of course, both be present on the same cartilage surface.

In the case of obvious disruption of the cartilage (visible to the naked eye) it may be possible to categorize some destructive lesions as 'progressive', leading to clinically overt derangement of a joint, and others as 'non-progressive' (Byers, Contepomi and Farkas 1970). On the other hand, many minor and unobtrusive changes of structure are found during adult life which clearly are often not accompanied by any clinical manifestation. It is very difficult to ascertain whether or not some of these minor differences from 'normal' can lead to further change, and in such instances it is debatable whether they are to be regarded as features of normal ageing or of a localized degenerative process. The most correct statement may be that the normal structure has not been improved by the alterations. The morphological term 'regressive change' carries this implication, although it does not exclude the possibility that the phenomena may cause further local deterioration at the site concerned, or that they can occur as a secondary effect of fibrillation elsewhere on the same surface. Four phenomena, not necessarily interrelated, will be described under this general heading: microscopic foci of loss of glycosaminoglycan and reduced cellularity in the superficial zone; histochemical changes in the surface lamina; quaternary irregularities; and ultrastructural aberrations at the surface. 'Minimal fibrillation', to be described subsequently, might also be considered a regressive change.

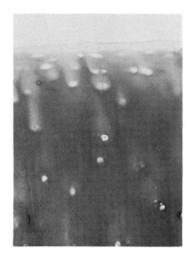

Figure 1.29 Loss of stainable glycosaminoglycan (regressive change) in the superficial zone of human femoral condylar cartilage.

Alcian blue: 0.4 mol/litre (0.4M) $MgCl_2$, pH 5.8 ×140.

8.1. Changes in the Superficial Zone

8.1.1. Loss of Stainable Glycosaminoglycan. Meachim, Ghadially and Collins (1965) have used toluidine blue staining and light microscopy to study the superficial zone (zone 1) in adult human cartilage. In some sections, a band of pronounced pallor of the matrix is observed beneath the surface, although rarely extending right up to the actual synovial interface. A variable proportion of the cells within the band show no pericellular rim of stained material. It is known that basophilia in the superficial zone is weaker in adults than in children (Collins and McElligott 1960), in keeping with the relatively low content of total glycosaminoglycan in the superficial zone of adult cartilage (Stockwell and Scott 1967; Maroudas *et al.* 1969; Maroudas and Thomas 1970; Stockwell 1970). However, the band of pallor described by Meachim *et al.* (1965), attributable to loss of stainable glycosaminoglycan, is superimposed on the normally weaker basophilia in the adult superficial zone (Figure 1.29). Moreover, local variations are observed, in both the degree of pallor and the width of the band. Thus in some sections it is very narrow and occupies microscopic segments interspaced with areas in which it is not apparent. In other sections the band of matrix pallor extends more deeply into the superficial zone. Each individual pale area may be only of microscopic size.

Confirmation of loss of glycosaminoglycan has been obtained using immunofluorescent techniques. Barland *et al.* (1966) find an enhancement of immunofluorescence in the superficial zone of cartilage but showing no gross or microscopic evidence of superficial destructive changes. They attribute the enhanced staining to 'depolymerization' and loss of chondroitin sulphate from this region: they suggest this allows the fluorescein-conjugated antiserum easier access to the site of the proteoglycan antigen in the tissue.

8.1.2. Cell depletion. Within the glycosaminoglycan-depleted matrix there is circumstantial evidence of chondrocyte necrosis, as indicated by a reduction in the number of stained nuclei and the presence of empty lacunae. There is no evidence, however, that cells are shed into the joint cavity from a non-fibrillated articular surface (Barnett *et al.* 1963; Roy and Meachim 1968; Weiss *et al.* 1968; Meachim and Roy 1969).

8.1.3. Effects of Glycosaminoglycan Loss. The above alterations can occur within the superficial zone beneath a surface which appears locally 'intact' on light microscopy and they can occur at sites of 'minimal fibrillation'. It should be emphasized that this regressive change initially develops at the microscopic, or perhaps even the ultrastructural, level. Thus it might perhaps not be detectable by quantitative analysis of cartilage slices 5 mm in diameter and $200\,\mu$m thick (Maroudas, Evans and Almeida 1973). This sort of regressive change is not a uniform process in adult cartilage. Even in the same subject it varies in incidence and severity from joint to joint and from area to area within a single joint. Areas of advanced change, extending deeply into the cartilage, are more common in the knee than in the shoulder, and often the surface adjacent to them shows evidence of overt fibrillation.

It has been suggested that microscopic loss of stainable glycosaminoglycan may be one of several mechanisms that can predispose to fibrillation, or at least accentuate its development and its lateral spread across a joint surface (Meachim *et al.* 1965). This hypothesis does not necessarily imply that the focal depletion of glycosaminoglycans is the primary event which leads to fibrillation in the affected area (Chapter 9, Section 5). Moreover, it must be noted that in some instances fibrillation can develop in the absence of this type of regressive change: this has been seen, for example, in sections of fibrillated cartilage from animals (Meachim and Illman 1967), and in certain types of cartilage fibrillation in man (Meachim, unpublished).

8.2. Changes in the Surface Lamina

A further change in zone 1 has been observed using the Alcian blue–CEC technique. It appears to be confined to the most superficial tissue, within $10-20\,\mu$m of the articular surface (the 'surface lamina').

8.2.1. Histochemical Features. At the articular surface of normal young adult human cartilage, there is little staining with Alcian blue (in 0.9 mol/litre (0.9 M) $MgCl_2$) of the sort due to high molecular weight keratan sulphate (Figure 1.18b). In a large proportion of older individuals, however, marked alcianophilia may be found (Figure 1.30) indicating the presence of significant amounts of keratan sulphate or a similar substance (Stockwell 1970). The stained lamina of matrix abuts on the joint surface, may be up to about $10\,\mu$m in thickness, and lies superficial to any diffuse lipid that may be present. Staining is often patchy rather than continuous along the surface. No enhancement of staining reaction of the sort due to chondroitin sulphate is found, although some additional glycoprotein staining is present. The results of analysis of thin slices of tissue cut tangential to the articular surface indicate changes in the glucosamine/galactosamine ratio which are compatible with the staining properties. The ratio is elevated in the superficial compared with the subjacent $50\,\mu$m of tissue in cartilage exhibiting the stained lamina. It is also higher than in the

Figure 1.30 Aged femoral condylar cartilage showing enhanced staining for polyanionic material in the surface lamina, not seen in young adult tissue (compare Figure 1.18b).
   Alcian blue: 0.9 mol/litre (0.9M) $MgCl_2$, pH 5.8 ×80.

superficial $50\,\mu$m of specimens in which alcianophilia (at 0.9 mol/litre (0.9 M) $MgCl_2$) is absent in the surface lamina (Stockwell 1971). The cell density of the superficial zone is lower in sections exhibiting the Alcian blue-positive material in the surface lamina than in 'negative' sections. Hence, it has been suggested that the phenomenon may be 'regressive' in its nature.

8.2.2. Ultrastructural Features. Electron-dense fibrillary and amorphous material is frequently present on the articular surface (Section 8.4.2). It resembles the electron-dense aggregates found on bovine articular surfaces, thought to contain hyaluronate (Balazs, Bloom and Swann 1966). It seems unlikely that this electron-dense material is the cause of the Alcian blue staining in the surface lamina, since hyaluronate does not stain above a CEC of 0.15 mol/litre (0.15 M) $MgCl_2$ (Scott and Dorling 1965) and microprobe analysis does not reveal the presence of hyaluronate within the surface lamina (Maroudas 1972). Furthermore a thick layer of dense material (Figure 1.31a) may be present where the surface lamina is Alcian blue-negative (Stockwell 1971).

However, within the matrix of the surface lamina, below its synovial interface, closely compacted and entangled fibres may be found which lack the orderly orientation normally present (see Section 8.4.1). Regions containing these unusual arrangements of fibres (Figure 1.31b) correlate well with the sites of staining with Alcian blue at 0.9 mol/litre (0.9 M) $MgCl_2$ (Stockwell 1971).

The compacted Alcian blue-positive matrix could be due either to internal changes resulting in increased stainability, or to the accumulation of stainable material from external sources. In the

Figure 1.31 (a) Electron-dense amorphous and finely fibrillar material (M) on the surface of femoral condylar cartilage not exhibiting staining of the surface lamina with Alcian blue: 0.9 mol/litre (0.9M) $MgCl_2$. (b) Compacted matrix in the surface lamina of femoral condylar cartilage exhibiting positive staining with Alcian blue: 0.9 mol/litre (0.9M) $MgCl_2$. S = articular surface.
 Transmission electron micrographs.
 Glutaraldehyde. (a) ×14 000; (b) ×31 000.

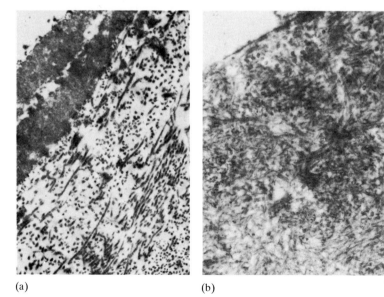

(a)   (b)

first case, some form of collapse of the ground substance might be envisaged, perhaps resulting from a preferential loss of chondroitin sulphate. This would leave behind a keratan-sulphate-rich residuum of the proteoglycan which was originally either closely bound to collagen or in the form of a 'free' complex between the collagen fibres. If this residuum were compressed into a smaller volume, both enhanced staining and a higher glucosamine/galactosamine ratio would ensue. The compacted fibres could be derived either from the delicate meshwork observed after fixation in the ground substance between banded collagen fibres (Meachim 1972a), or from collagen fibres themselves. The collagen fibres might not remain intact, but instead some splitting into finer fibrils could occur.

Alternatively, material might be deposited in the superficial matrix from the synovial fluid (the possibility of an abnormal secretion from chondrocytes could be considered also). Bywaters and Dorling (1970) have described deposits of amyloid in human articular cartilage, particularly near the surface, in cases of primary amyloidosis. The Alcian blue-positive material commonly occurring in adults in the surface lamina has been found to stain with alkaline Congo red (giving apple green birefringence in polarized light) and with thioflavine T (Stockwell 1975). However, although the characteristics of the material are consistent with amyloid in association with keratan sulphate, this cannot be confirmed in the absence of a technique specific for amyloid(s). Possibly the dense meshwork of fine fibrils may be related to the immune complexes seen in the superficial zone of rabbit articular cartilage after experimentally induced arthritis (Jasin, Cooke, Hurd, Smiley and Ziff 1973).

Thus electron-dense and fibrillary material may be found both within the surface lamina and upon the articular surface. Several different types of material probably occur and may coexist, but little is known as yet concerning the origin, chemical composition and possible effects of these substances. In and on the surface lamina, there may be admixture of synovial-derived and cartilage-derived products.

8.3. Quaternary Surface Irregularities

Longmore and Gardner (1975) have studied the appearance *en face* of the articular cartilage surface of the human lateral femoral condyle at various ages. Samples were examined by reflected light interference microscopy and by scanning electron microscopy. With these techniques the surface shows bowl-shaped depressions ('tertiary hollows') as a normal feature (Figure 1.14). Both the mean depth and the mean diameter of the depressions increase during maturation, and continue to do so during adult ageing.

Superimposed on this feature, a further type of surface irregularity ('quaternary irregularities') becomes increasingly apparent with increasing age. It is seen *en face* as irregular surface ridges and undulations, each of microscopic size. It can occur on the surface between the individual bowl-shaped depressions, and also at sites where such depressions have locally become abnormally sparse. The affected cartilage may appear 'macroscopically intact'.

It would be of interest to examine vertically cut histological sections of sites showing the *en face* 'quaternary irregularities' described by Longmore and Gardner, since such irregularities may be related to surface splitting and fraying of the degree termed 'minimal fibrillation' by Meachim (1972b). Undercut ridges and other irregularities of surface contour occur as features of minimal fibrillation, as demonstrated by study of surface profile in photomicrographs of vertical sections through affected sites (Meachim 1972b). Such sections show that tangential surface splitting might appear as a ridge if viewed *en face*; results from transmission electron microscopy (Meachim and Roy 1969) lend some support to this suggestion.

It is not at present known whether the quaternary irregularities studied by Longmore and Gardner represent a multifocal ageing change, with a distribution similar to that of fibrillation, or whether they are generalized and thus affect all adult cartilage sites.

8.4. Ultrastructural Aberrations at the Articular Surface

An area which appears 'intact' on light microscopy can sometimes show ultrastructural disruptions when studied at the higher magnifications obtained by electron microscopy (Meachim and Roy 1969). It is helpful if the findings are considered separately for the two types of surface appearance seen in transmisssion electron micrographs:

(a) areas of the surface which appear intact even at magnifications in the range of ×40 000;
(b) areas which show ultrastructural deviations from this intact pattern.

It should be noted that there is often variation from site to site, so that both patterns can be encountered in the same joint surface. Furthermore, both types of surface occur in areas in which the surface lamina would be Alcian-blue-negative.

8.4.1. Intact Surface. In mature articular cartilage with a surface which appears locally intact in transmission electron micrographs (Figure 1.32a), closely packed tangentially orientated collagen fibres, approximately 30 nm in diameter, occupy the acellular region immediately beneath the articular surface (Meachim and Roy 1969). The fibres appear to be separated by a relatively small amount of intervening ground substance. In vertical section, the outer limit of an ultrastructurally intact surface sometimes shows an osmiophilic line, approximately 8 nm thick. Although the suggestion by Meachim and Roy (1969) that this thin line may represent a specialized surface 'membrane' (possibly lipidic) remains unconfirmed by Maroudas (personal communication), the phenomenon serves as a useful visual marker for this type of surface pattern.

8.4.2. Aberrant Surfaces. In areas showing ultrastructural deviations from the 'intact' pattern (Figure 1.32b and c) one or more of the following features may be seen in transmisssion electron micrographs (Meachim and Roy 1969). The banded collagen fibres immediately beneath the surface can show an abnormally wide separation by intervening material, contrasting with the closer packing considered to be their 'more normal' appearance

Figure 1.32 (a) An example of an 'intact' surface. Collagen fibres approximately 30 nm thick are arranged tangential to the surface with a small amount of amorphous ground substance between them. As seen in this vertical section an osmiophilic line (arrow) (approximately 8 nm thick) delimits the smooth surface. (b) A slightly imperfect surface. The osmiophilic line is present at the surface but a collection of fibrillar material (F) interrupts the orderly arrangement of the collagen fibres. (c) One form of 'aberrant' surface. The smooth outline is lost, and electron-dense material (M) is seen at the margins of an incipient horizontal cleft. This specimen does not exhibit the abnormally wide separation of collagen fibres and cyst formation discussed in the text (Figure 1.8).

Transmission electron micrographs.

Glutaraldehyde. (a) ×24 000; (b) ×31 000; (c) ×13 500.

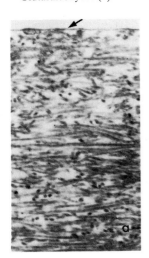 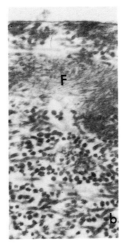 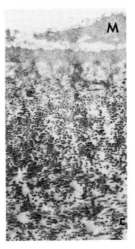

(Figure 1.8); their orientation parallel to the surface may or may not be maintained. In places, collagen fibres appear to be directly exposed to the joint space, and sometimes groups of fragmented fibres are seen in the process of being shed from the surface; for technical reasons it is not possible to determine whether or not there is also fracture of non-exposed fibres lying within the surface layer.

Accompanying these features, patchy areas of electron-dense fibrillary material occur, either on the surface or below it in the superficial matrix; this may account for a report depicting an acellular region of fine fibres and filamentous fibrils immediately below the articular surface (Weiss *et al.* 1968). The surface can also show tuft-like projections containing banded collagen fibres and closely compacted fine unbanded fibrils. Shallow clefts and steeply sloping curves can develop, giving the surface an irregular contour; in such areas the tangentially orientated collagen fibres tend to form curved or wavy patterns. Similar observations have been made in ageing rabbit articular cartilage (Barnett *et al.* 1963).

Can these ultrastructural deviations from the 'intact' pattern be regarded as a physiological phenomenon? Fibrillation may be arbitrarily defined as a state in which the articular surface no longer appears intact in routine histological sections examined by the light microscope. Meachim and Roy (1969) have speculated that the ultrastructural disruptions of the surface may fail to heal and thus could predispose to superficial fibrillation. Hence, these changes are perhaps not 'physiological', but degenerative.

'Blisters' of various shapes and sizes are sometimes seen at the articular surface. They seem to contain only embedding medium, although the occurrence of more deeply placed cystic cavities of similar appearance is inconclusive evidence against the view that they are a surface artefact produced during tissue processing or section cutting (Meachim and Roy 1969).

9. CARTILAGE FIBRILLATION

Specimens of adult articular cartilage frequently show areas where the morphology has been altered by fibrillation. This alteration is often apparent on naked-eye examination, since the cartilage assumes a 'matt' appearance instead of the 'gloss' appearance normally seen (Figure 1.33); fibrillated cartilage is often softer than normal ('chondromalacic').

Fibrillation is a phenomenon in which there is fraying and splitting of the cartilage; it is seen in cartilage which still presents an exposed surface to the synovial cavity, without a covering of new fibrous or bony tissue. During adult life there is an age-related increase in the incidence and severity of this process. Fibrillation is not, however, a uniform or generalized ageing change in adult

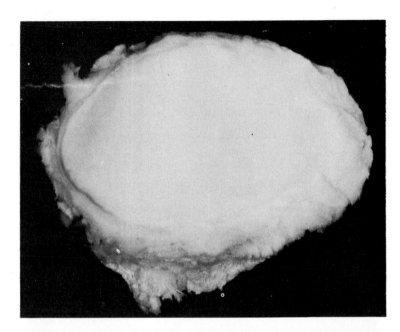

Figure 1.33 Macroscopic appearance of human patellar articular sufaces viewed *en face*. Specimen (a): macroscopically normal. Specimen (b): deep fibrillation. (By courtesy of Dr T. F. McElligott.)

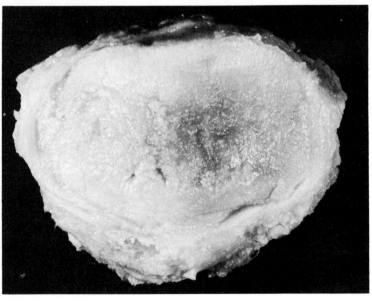

(a)

(b)

human articular cartilage: it is basically a focal change, and in any given subject its incidence and severity vary from joint to joint and from area to area within a joint (Meachim 1969b). As seen in histological sections cut in a plane vertical to the articular surface, the splitting process propagates along the same alignments as that of the collagen framework (Collins 1949).

9.1. Structure of Fibrillated Cartilage

9.1.1. Morphology. In an area of cartilage showing superficial fibrillation, the fraying and splitting is confined to the superficial layer nearest the articular surface (Fig. 1.34). Superficial fibrillation is not always readily apparent to the naked-eye and can

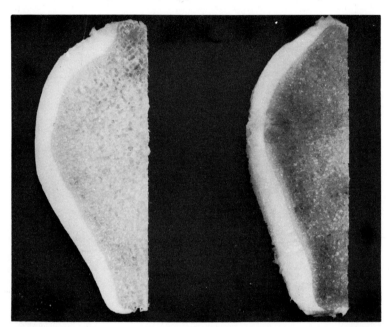

Figure 1.34 Macroscopic appearance of articular surfaces of human patellae viewed in transverse slices: smooth surface (left); fibrillation, mainly superficial (right).

require light microscopy of histological sections for its detection: for this reason biomechanical studies of non-fibrillated cartilage should, where practicable, be accompanied by microscopical verification of the state of the surface in the samples. Stereomicroscopy of Indian ink preparations, examined *en face* at a magnification of ×10, is usually satisfactory for this purpose.

As seen under the light microscope, a superficial fibrillation is characterized by fraying and splitting of the articular surface to form narrow strands and shorter broad-based tufts (Figure 1.35). In more pronounced fibrillation, fraying and splitting can extend

50

more deeply and thus also affect the other layers (Fig. 1.36). The extensive erosion and disintegration of matrix which occurs in deeply fibrillated areas causes thinning of the cartilage and can sometimes lead to its complete loss over part of the joint, with exposure of underlying bone. In some instances the thinned cartilage does not show the splitting typical of fibrillation, but instead presents a smooth or almost smooth surface to the joint cavity.

In keeping with the findings on light microscopy, scanning electron micrographs of fibrillated cartilage show overt disruption of the surface structure (McCall 1968; Walker *et al.* 1969; Redler and Zimny 1970) and transmission electron micrographs demonstrate deep clefts in the tissue (Meachim and Roy 1969). In fibrillated cartilage, chondrocytes sometimes become exposed to the joint cavity, following the loss of their overlying or adjacent matrix (Meachim and Roy 1969). Large quantities of electron-dense material can accumulate at deeply fibrillated surfaces (Figure 1.37).

At present it is not known whether fibrillation of articular cartilage is due to abrasive (apatite granules found in the synovial fluid of some patients with osteoarthrosis (Dieppe, Huskisson, Crocker and Willoughby 1976) may possibly accelerate this process) or adhesive wear, to fatigue failure or overstressing, or to some other process (see Chapter 9); moreover, it cannot be assumed that each instance of surface damage is always initiated, or caused to progress, in the same way. Morphological observations are relevant to this problem, since it is important that any hypothesis eventually put forward to explain fibrillation should be fully consistent with structural changes actually observed in the

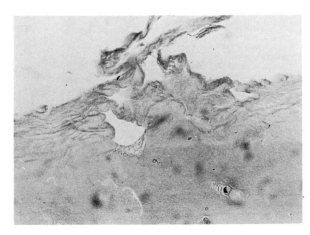

Figure 1.35 The appearance of superficial fibrillation as seen by light microscopy of a vertical section.
Haematoxylin and eosin ×100.

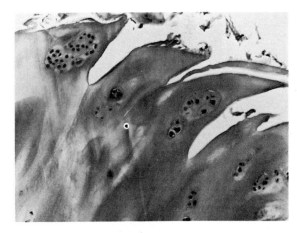

Figure 1.36 Histological section showing deep fibrillation with multicellular cluster formation.
Haematoxylin and eosin ×115.

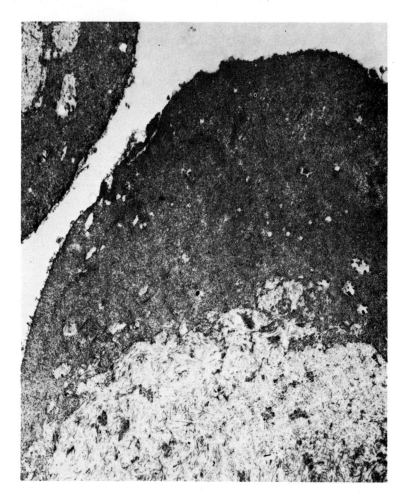

Figure 1.37 Deeply fibrillated cartilage showing part of a deep cleft (upper left). Note the large amount of electron-dense material in the matrix adjacent to the surface.

Transmission electron micrograph ×7500.

tissue. The appearances differ according to which method of examination is used, and it is not possible to present a classification which fully correlates the descriptive terms which various observers have employed. For example, a surface which is 'macroscopically intact' on naked-eye examination may show evidence of 'minimal fibrillation' ('histological fibrillation') when subsequently examined by light microscopy. Use of Indian ink preparations helps to make these minor degrees of fibrillation more readily apparent. The following account is based on a study of Indian ink preparations of fresh unfixed cartilage kept moist in physiological saline (Meachim 1972b). The methods used avoided artefactual distortions from the shrinkage and edge curling which is believed to occur during preparation of specimens for scanning electron microscopy.

For Indian ink studies, the specimen is collected directly into physiological saline and kept in this until required. Indian ink is then applied using an artist's paint brush. The tip of the brush is charged with undiluted ink, which during painting becomes diluted to a variable degree by the layer of physiological saline already present on the cartilage surface. Excess ink is removed by rinsing. Reflected light stereomicroscopy is then used to examine the surface at a magnification of ×10. The cartilage is kept moist during examination, and studied unfixed while still *in situ* on the bone.

The method described avoids artefact from cause such as drying or fixation, and initially avoids the possibility of the shape distortion which can occur in cartilage blocks cut out from their surrounding tissue. The preparations obtained facilitate detection, photography, mapping and quantification of the various patterns of cartilage fibrillation seen *en face* (Figure 1.38). For detailed

Figure 1.38 Indian ink preparation, viewed *en face*, of a random necropsy specimen of patellar articular surface from a woman aged 24 years. Intact cartilage surface is unstained (left and centre). Overt fibrillation is shown as a confluent or semiconfluent blackening (upper right and lower edge). Minimal fibrillation is seen as a 'stippled' appearance, or as dark markings in approximately parallel alignment (upper centre). Note also the transverse 'ravines' (below centre).

study of a particular feature, thin tangential surface slices can be cut free-hand and mounted in saline for examination *en face* by transmitted light microscopy. Also, tissue blocks can be taken for preparation of vertical or tangential sections cut by microtome. If the study requires the use of fixed tissue, the cartilage after painting should be fixed while still *in situ* on the bone, before cutting out tissue blocks or slices.

The appearance of the adult articular surface varies from subject to subject, from joint to joint, and from site to site on the same specimen. Sites with intact cartilage, with minimal fibrillation and with overt fibrillation are often all present on the same surface (Figure 1.38). An initially focal onset of cartilage fibrillation is

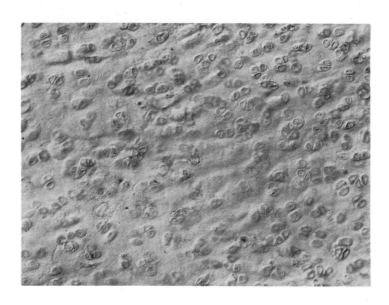

Figure 1.39 An 'intact' surface of articular cartilage, showing the background texture from the underlying cells. Tangential surface slice, viewed *en face*, of Indian ink preparation.

Transmitted light ×150.

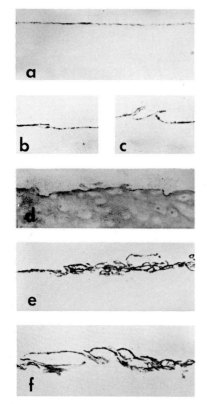

Figure 1.40 (a) Vertical section of an 'intact' surface at ×120. (b–f) Examples of 'minimal fibrillation', as seen in vertical sections at ×120.

apparent on the macroscopic scale, and in some instances also at the microscopic level (Meachim and Fergie 1975). Fibrillated sites are a normal feature of adult human synovial joints, in which they are interspersed with large or small areas where the cartilage surface is still intact. Where fibrillation or other changes are present, two or more different types of change can be intimately admixed at the same site.

(a) At intact sites the adult cartilage surface shows no distinct ink markings when examined *en face* (Figure 1.39). A background texture is seen from the underlying cells. In vertically cut histological sections from such sites (Figure 1.40), the surface presents a line free from sharply angled irregularities when examined at a magnification of ×150 (Meachim 1972b). Such a surface would not necessarily still appear 'intact' if subsequently examined at high magnification by transmission electron microscopy.

'Rounded' cartilage sheets, such as those of the humeral and femoral heads, sometimes show, in adults, occasional localized concentrations of ink particles in positions and sizes corresponding to the lacuna or pericellular matrix of individual cells. The cause of this appearance has not been fully investigated, but in some instances it may be due to localized seepages of ink into subsurface tissue.

In immature articular cartilage, ink markings can occur at intact sites.

(b) At sites of minimal fibrillation in adults, the cartilage surface shows dark ink markings against a pale grey background when examined *en face* by light microscopy (Figures 1.41 and 1.42). In histological sections cut vertically through such sites, a

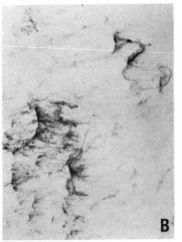

Figure 1.41 Two examples of 'minimal fibrillation' of 'reticular' (A) and 'saw-toothed' (B) patterns. Tangential surface slices, viewed *en face*, of Indian ink preparations of unfixed tissue. Patellofemoral articulation.

Transmitted light   ×120.

very superficial splitting or fraying of the surface (Figure 1.40) is apparent at a magnification of ×150 (Meachim 1972b). The splitting is tangential, so that undercut ridges can occur as a feature of this phenomenon; other irregularities of surface contour may also be seen. Microscopic flaps of partly loosened tissue can form, and may become large enough to be visible to the naked-eye.

The ink markings of minimal fibrillation present a variety of patterns when examined *en face* (Meachim and Fergie 1975). It is not implied that each individual marking necessarily represents an actual split. It is, however, suggested that the presence of minimal markings indicates a localized deterioration of the surface which can be accompanied by minor disintegrations. Moreover, histological and topographical studies have shown that these minor changes can develop into those of overt fibrillation.

Some of the *en face* patterns of minimal fibrillation can occur on any articulation, but the incidence of certain other patterns is influenced by anatomical site and thus presumably by the local biochemical environment and local character of the cartilage (Meachim and Fergie 1975).

Some, although not all, of the *en face* patterns of minimal fibrillation exhibit orientation in the sense either of being predominantly in one alignment (Figure 1.42) or of having two major components aligned one transverse to the other. On surfaces from joints where movement is at least partly multidirectional, *en face* orientation, if present, is very often approximately parallel, or sometimes transverse, to that of the dominant *en face* alignment of the superficial collagen fibres. On surfaces from joints where movement is unidirectional, *en face* orientation, if present, can in some instances be related to the alignment of the superficial collagen and in others to the direction of flexion–extension

55

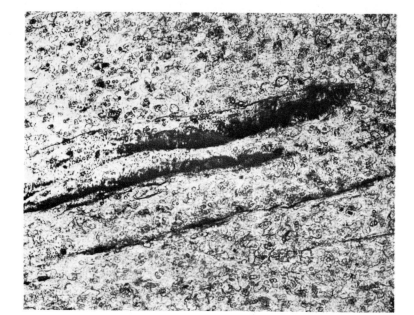

Figure 1.42 An example of 'minimal fibrillation' of the 'parallel linear' pattern. Tangential surface slice, viewed *en face*, of Indian ink preparation of unfixed tissue. Patellofemoral articulation.

Transmitted light ×65.

movement; in the case of the ankle joint, instances of these contrasting relationships are sometimes both macroscopically apparent on the same specimen.

(c) 'Ravines' are sometimes seen (Figures 1.38 and 1.43). Viewed *en face*, they have a tortuous or curvilinear or approximately straight course. When fully developed they show a deeper splitting than that of minimal fibrillation. Their orientation in relation to the dominant *en face* alignment of the superficial cartilage collagen varies, being parallel or acutely angled or at right angles.

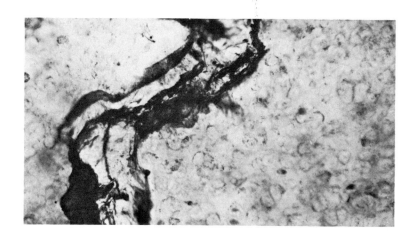

Figure 1.43 Part of a tortuous 'ravine' of overt fibrillation coursing amongst adjacent intact cartilage. Humeral head. Tangential surface slice, viewed *en face*, from Indian ink preparation of unfixed tissue.

Transmitted light ×150.

Figure 1.44 Overt fibrillation, viewed *en face*. Tangential surface slice of Indian ink preparation of unfixed tissue. Transmitted light. ×165.

(d) In a small minority of joints, the articular cartilage shows a localized rounded or elongated defect of sufficient area and depth to be readily apparent to the naked-eye. In the defect the uncalcified cartilage is severely thinned or completely lost.

(e) Sites of overt fibrillation can develop on any articulation. They show a confluent or semiconfluent blackening in Indian ink preparations (Figure 1.38), with frank disintegration of the surface and numerous flaps of partly loosened tissue (Figure 1.44). Usually the flaps are in random alignment; occasionally they show *en face* orientation. It should be noted that, at the edges of a joint, blackening can be due either to overt fibrillation or to an encroachment of a layer of fibrous tissue over the peripheral cartilage surface.

Vertical sections through sites of overt fibrillation (Figure 1.45) show a frank splitting extending down into the superficial (zone 1), intermediate (zone 2) or deep layer (zone 3) of the cartilage.

Sites of overt fibrillation do not necessarily show thinning of the cartilage. Indeed, in occasional instances the affected tissue may appear 'swollen' on macroscopic examination. In certain other instances fibrillation can result in destructive thinning (Figure 1.36), or even in full-thickness loss of the uncalcified cartilage.

(f) Horizontal splitting at the interface between uncalcified cartilage (zone 3) and the calcified layer (zone 4) is observed

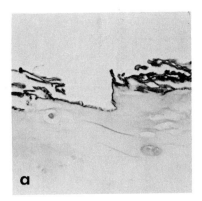

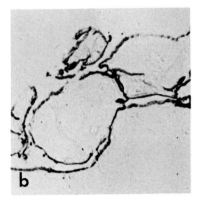

Figure 1.45 Vertical sections through surfaces with 'overt' fibrillation, photographed at the same magnification as that in Figure 1.40. ×120.

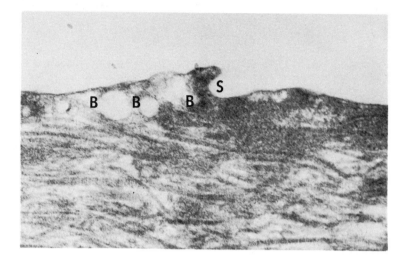

Figure 1.46 Transmission electron micrograph illustrating one hypothetical way in which minimal fibrillation might be initiated at an articular surface. Tangential splitting (S) of the surface with 'blisters' (B) forming clefts in the tissue at the apical side of the split. Vertical section cut with the face of the tissue block orientated in the same direction as the predominant alignment of the superficial zone. ×50 000.

occasionally in histological sections from human articular cartilage. This feature is not, of course, apparent *en face*. When noted, it may or may not be associated with other destructive lesions in the same segment.

(g) Cartilage segments at sites of destructive thinning sometimes do not show the frank splitting typical of overt fibrillation, but instead present a surface which is virtually smooth or shows only shallow indentations. Such cartilage does not give any pronounced blackening with Indian ink.

(h) Areas of full-thickness loss of the uncalcified cartilage are present in some older subjects. They show exposure of the underlying calcified layer (zone 4) or of underlying bone. In joints where movement is unidirectional, 'track markings' indicative of abrasive wear may become macroscopically apparent on the exposed bone surface, and may also extend on to the areas of adjacent cartilage showing smooth-surfaced thinning. Similar 'track markings' are sometimes seen on cartilage from unidirectional joints showing no calcified tissue exposure.

Within areas of bone exposure, the bony surface is often interspersed with gaps plugged by new non-osseous fibrous or chondroid tissue of subarticular origin. These gaps are the source of extrinsic repair tissue which can potentially spread over adjacent exposed bone and thus provide it with a new non-osseous cover. However, this attempt at reparative re-covering is often completely overwhelmed by a destructive mechanism.

9.1.2. Glycosaminoglycan Content. Cartilage fibrillation is basically a focal phenomenon but, since it is also an age-related process, the localized changes with which it is associated must be distinguished from those of generalized ageing in adult articular cartilage (Meachim 1969b). Chemical analysis has shown a deple-tion of glycosaminoglycans in fibrillated areas compared with non-fibrillated cartilage (Matthews 1953; Bollet, Handy and Stur-gill 1963; Bollet and Nance 1966; Mankin and Lippiello 1970). This depletion can also be demonstrated by histochemical staining for glycosaminoglycans. The histochemical findings tend to vary from area to area in the joint, and are also influenced by the depth to which fibrillation extends into the cartilage.

In areas of superficial fibrillation, the deeper uncalcified layers of the tissue can appear normal. The superficial matrix (zone 1) shows diminished staining with toluidine blue or acridine orange, consistent with a reduced amount of acid glycosaminoglycans in this region of the section (Meachim *et al.* 1965; Barland *et al.* 1966). In contrast, immunofluorescent staining for the protein portion of the protein–polysaccharide is more intense and more diffusely distributed than that seen in the superficial matrix of normal cartilage: Barland *et al.* (1966) therefore suggest that the matrix proteoglycan is 'depolymerized' and contains less glycosaminoglycans than are normally present.

In areas where fibrillation extends deeply in the cartilage (Figure 1.36), the intercellular matrix of the deeper uncalcified layers (zones 2 and 3) shows loss of metachromasia, of Alcian blue staining and of basophilia. Abnormal multicellular clusters of chondrocytes can form in deeply fibrillated areas (Figure 1.36), and the matrix within and immediately around some of these cell clusters can show a metachromatic reaction with toluidine blue and intense staining with Alcian blue (Collins and McElligott 1960). The appearance in the vicinity of any clusters which stain in this manner contrasts with the general pallor of the stainable glycosaminoglycan loss in the intervening matrix. The Alcian blue–CEC technique shows that the basophilia around the cell clusters is due to chondroitin sulphate rather than keratan sul-phate. This agrees with the results of chemical analysis of fibril-lated cartilage. In fibrillated cartilage where cell clusters are found, the more superficial tissue (corresponding to the extent of the depth of the fissures) shows a reduction in glycosaminoglycan compared with normal tissue at this depth. However, chondroitin sulphate is reduced to a lesser extent than keratan sulphate. (Stockwell, unpublished). Fibrillated specimens show a decrease in glycosaminoglycan content throughout most of the uncalcified cartilage depth, although where the cartilage is thick there may be relatively small differences from the normal in the deep zone as compared with the differences in the superficial or intermediate zones (Maroudas, Evans and Almeida 1973).

The distribution of stainable glycosaminoglycan in the regions of cartilage *peripheral* to areas of fibrillation is of some interest. Territorial localization of alcianophilia at 0.9 mol/litre (0.9 M) $MgCl_2$ (thought to represent keratan sulphate) is normally restricted to the deepest part of zone 3, adjacent to the tidemark. In regions of cartilage 5–10 mm peripheral to vertically fibrillated areas, the territorial distribution of stain becomes much more extensive, occupying the deeper half the total thickness of the cartilage (Stockwell 1975). This change could be a reaction either to the stresses predisposing to fibrillation or to the stresses set up by loss of cartilage due to fibrillation. However, in regions adjacent to areas of 'smooth-surfaced' destructive thinning of cartilage (Meachim 1975), no such increase in the extent of territorial alcianophilia at 0.9 mol/litre (0.9 M) $MgCl_2$ is observed (Stockwell, unpublished). Since the metabolism and turnover of keratan sulphate is slow, these findings suggest that smooth-surfaced destructive thinning may be a rapid process compared with that usually associated with vertical fibrillation.

9.1.3. Water Content. Samples of deeply fibrillated cartilage have a higher water content than non-fibrillated samples (Lindahl 1948; Bollet and Nance 1966). This result is not attributable to loss of the superficial layer in deeply fibrillated samples: in normal cartilage, water content is generally highest next to the articular surface, although variation from horizontal slice to horizontal slice is small (Muir *et al.* 1970).

9.2. Covering and Replacement of Articular Cartilage by New Tissue

Thinning and loss due to fibrillation occurs in cartilage which still presents an exposed surface to the synovial cavity. As already noted, the thinned cartilage does not always show the splitting and disintegration typical of fibrillation, but instead can show a smooth or virtually smooth exposed surface.

Fibrillation or other destructive lesions of exposed cartilage are not the only cause of the loss of articular cartilage from a joint surface. Another mechanism is also seen, in which the 'old' cartilage becomes submerged under 'new' tissue forming over it and into it at the periphery of the joint; the new tissue can replace the old cartilage in addition to merely covering it. Although the changes usually originate at the edge of cartilage sheets, including the edge around the fovea of the femoral head, they can eventually or initially involve other parts of the articular surface.

The changes to be described are, in general, topographically separate from reactive and reparative responses at sites of destructive thinning of exposed cartilage. Various degrees and various detailed patterns of new tissue formation are seen. They can be osseous or non-osseous, but the phenomena which cause them seem to be histologically interrelated. For descriptive purposes they may therefore be grouped together as 'peripheral remodelling' changes. It will be noted that the word 'remodelling' is in this context being used to denote changes which alter the microanatomy, or even the macroscopic appearance, of a joint. In a different context it may also be used to denote events taking place at the ultrastructural, or even the molecular, level.

Covering of a segment of cartilage surface by a layer of fibrous, or occasionally fibrocartilaginous, tissue is not uncommon, particularly at the periphery of a joint. The covering layer ('pannus') varies in thickness, texture and vascularity. For example, it can be very thin, representing only one or two fibroblasts in vertical section; it can instead be thick, loosely fibrous and richly vascular; it can be thick and densely fibrous; it can be partly or mainly fibrocartilaginous.

New fibrous or chondroid tissue can sometimes replace old cartilage by 'invasion' from the surface, from the edge or through the calcified base. In man it is often difficult to determine whether this is a genuine invasion into healthy cartilage, or just a means of replacing cartilage that is already degenerate. A further possibility would be that chondrocytes originally present might themselves take part in a remodelling process, by modulating into fibroblasts. Covering and 'invasion' of old cartilage by new non-osseous tissue are in some repects reminiscent of phenomena seen in diseased joints affected by rheumatoid disease (Mills 1970), but are now known also to occur in non-rheumatoid subjects, both in 'normal ageing' and in osteoarthrosis.

New bone may form as another feature of peripheral remodelling. Intracartilaginous ossification can take place by osteoblastic invasion into the edge of the old cartilage ('epiarticular osteophytosis'), into its base ('subarticular osteophytosis') and into its surface (from 'pannus'). As a result, new bone is laid down within a plane vertical to the line of the original chondro-osseous junction. Accompanying or preceding this intracartilaginous ossification, bony outgrowths can also form beyond the original edge of the cartilage sheet ('marginal osteophytosis'); this new bone is laid down outside the perimeter of the original articular surface, and results in the development of an osteophytic lip around the articular surface.

Osseous and non-osseous remodelling activity often intermingle at the histological level. One or more of the various fibroblastic, chondroblastic and osteoblastic changes described above can occur at the same articular periphery.

REFERENCES

Akeson W.H., Eichelberger L. and Roma M. (1958) Biochemical studies of articular cartilage, II. Values following the denervation of an extremity. *J. Bone Jt Surg.* **40A,** 153.

Ali S. Y. and Bayliss M. T. (1974) Enzymatic changes in human osteoarthrotic cartilage. *Normal and Osteoarthrotic Articular Cartilage,* Ed. by S. Y. Ali, M. W. Elves and D. H. Leaback, p. 189. Institute of Orthopaedics, London.

Ali S. Y. and Wisby A. (1976) The role of matrix vesicles in human osteoarthrotic cartilage. *Proc. R. Microsc. Soc.* **II,** Suppl., 62.

Ali S. Y., Anderson H. C. and Sajdera S. W. (1970) Isolation and characterization of calcifying matrix vesicles from epiphyseal cartilage. *Proc. Natn. Acad. Sci. U.S.* **67,** 1513.

Anderson C. E., Ludowieg J., Harper H. A. and Engleman E. P. (1964) The composition of the organic component of human articular cartilage. *J. Bone Jt Surg.* **46A,** 1176.

Anderson H. C. and Sajdera S. W. (1971) The fine structure of bovine nasal cartilage—extraction as a technique to study proteoglycans and collagen in the cartilage matrix. *J. Cell Biol.* **49,** 650.

Balazs E. A., Bloom G. D. and Swann D. A. (1966) Fine structure and glycosaminoglycan content of the surface layer of articular cartilage. *Fed. Proc.* **25,** 1813.

Barland P., Janis R. and Sandson J. (1966) Immuno-fluorescent studies of human articular cartilage. *Ann. rheum. Dis.* **25,** 156.

Barnett C. H., Cochrane W. and Palfrey A. J. (1963) Age changes in articular cartilage of rabbits. *Ann. rheum. Dis.* **22,** 389.

Behnke O. and Zelander T. (1970) Preservation of intercellular substance by the cationic dye Alcian blue in preparative procedures for electron microscopy. *J. Ultrastruct. Res.* **31,** 424.

Benninghoff A. (1925) Form und Bau der Gelenk-knorpel in ihren Beziehungen zur Funktion, II. Der Aufbau des Gelenkknorpels in seinen Beziehungen zur Funktion. *Z. Zellforsch. mikr. Anat.* **2,** 783.

Bjelle A. (1975) Content and composition of glycosaminoglycans in human knee joint cartilage. *Conn. Tiss. Res.* **3,** 141.

Bole G. G. (1962) Synovial fluid lipids in normal individuals and patients with rheumatoid arthritis. *Arthritis Rheum.* **5,** 589.

Bollet A. J. and Nance J. L. (1966) Biochemical findings in normal and osteoarthritic articular cartilage. II: Chondroitin sulfate concentration and chain length, water, and ash content. *J. clin. Invest.* **45,** 1170.

Bollet A. J., Handy J. R. and Sturgill B. C. (1963) Chondroitin sulfate concentration and protein-polysaccharide composition of articular cartilage in osteoarthritis. *J. clin. Invest.* **42,** 853.

Boni M. and Monteleone M. (1957) L'Ultrastruttura della cartilagine articolare in condizioni normali e in alcune condizioni patologiche. *Ortopedia Traum.* **25,** 279.

Bonner W. M., Jonsson H., Malanos C. and Bryant M. (1975) Changes in the lipids of human articular cartilage with age. *Arthritis Rheum.* **18,** 461.

Bonucci E. (1967) Fine structure of early cartilage calcification. *J. Ultrastruct. Res.* **20,** 33.

Bonucci E. and Dearden L. C. (1976). Matrix vesicles in ageing cartilage. *Fed. Proc.* **35,** 163.

Bullough P. and Goodfellow J. (1968) The significance of the fine structure of articular cartilage. *J. Bone Jt Surg.* **50B,** 852.

Byers P. D., Contepomi C. A. and Farkas T. A. (1970) A post-mortem study of the hip joint. *Ann. rheum. Dis.* **29,** 15.

Bywaters E. G. L. and Dorling J. (1970) Amyloid deposits in articular cartilage. *Ann. rheum. Dis.* **29,** 294.

Chrisman O. D., Semonsky C. and Bensch K. G. (1967) Cathepsins in articular cartilage. *The Healing of Osseous Tissue,* Ed. by R. A. Robinson, p. 169. National Academy of Science, Washington DC.

Clarke I. C. (1971a) Human articular surface contours and related surface depression frequency studies. *Ann. rheum. Dis.* **30,** 15.

Clarke I. C. (1971b) Surface characteristics of human articular cartilage—a scanning electron microscope study. *J. Anat.* **108,** 23.

Clarke I. C. (1974) Articular cartilage: a review and scanning electron microscope study. II. The territorial fibrillar architecture. *J. Anat. (Lond.)* **118,** 261.

Clarke I. C., Schurman D. J. and Amstutz H. C. (1975) In vivo and in vitro comparative studies of animal articular surfaces. *Ann. Biomed. Engg* **3,** 100.

Collins D. H. (1949) *The Pathology of Articular and Spinal Diseases,* pp. 74–115. Edward Arnold, London.

Collins D. H. and McElligott T. F. (1960) Sulphate ($^{35}SO_4$) uptake by chondrocytes in relation to histological changes in osteo-arthritic human articular cartilage. *Ann. rheum. Dis.* **19,** 318.

Davidson E. A., Woodhall B. and Baxley W. (1962) Age-dependent metabolism of connective tissue polysaccharides. *Biological Aspects of Aging*, Ed. by W. Shock, p. 348. Columbia University Press.

Davies D. V. (1967) Properties of synovial fluid. *Proc. Instn mech. Engrs* **181**, part 3J, p. 25.

Davies D. V., Barnett C. H., Cochrane W. and Palfrey A. J. (1962) Electron microscopy of articular cartilage in the young adult rabbit. *Ann. rheum. Dis.* **21**, 11.

Dieppe P. A., Huskisson E. C., Crocker P. and Willoughby D. A. (1976) Apatite deposition disease. *Lancet* **i**, 266.

Durning W. C. (1958) Submicroscopic structure of frozen-dried epiphyseal plate and adjacent spongiosa of the rat. *J. Ultrastruct. Res.* **2**, 245.

Eichelberger L., Roma M. and Moulder P. V. (1959) Biochemical studies of articular cartilage. III: Values following the immobilization of an extremity. *J. Bone Jt Surg.* **41A**, 1127.

Ekholm R. and Ingelmark B. E. (1952) Functional thickness variations of human articular cartilage. *Upsala Läk-för. Förh.* **57**, 39.

Engfeldt B. and Hjertquist S.-O. (1967) The effect of various fixatives on the preservation of acid glycosaminoglycans in tissues. *Acta path. microbiol. scand.* **71**, 219.

Engfeldt B. and Hjertquist S.-O. (1968) Studies on the epiphysial growth zone. I: The preservation of glycosaminoglycans in tissues in some histotechnical procedures for electron microscopy. *Virchows Arch. Abt B Zellpath.* **1**, 222.

Enneking W. F. and Harrington P. (1969) Pathological changes in scoliosis. *J. Bone Jt Surg.* **51A**, 165.

Fawns H. T. and Landells J. W. (1953) Histochemical studies of rheumatic conditions. I: Observations on the fine structure of the matrix of normal bone and cartilage. *Ann. rheum. Dis.* **12**, 105.

Fry H. (1974) Interlocked stresses in articular cartilage. *Brit. J. plast. Surg.* **27**, 363.

Fry H. and Robertson W. van B. (1967) Interlocked stresses in cartilage. *Nature (Lond.)* **215**, 53.

Galjaard H. (1962) *Histochemisch en interferometrisch onderzoek van hyalien kraakbeen*. Thesis, University of Leyden.

Gardner D. L. (1972) Heberden Oration 1971. The influence of microscopic technology on knowledge of cartilage surface structure. *Ann. rheum. Dis.* **31**, 235.

Gardner D. L. and McGillivray D. C. (1971) Living articular cartilage is not smooth. The structure of mammalian and avian joint surfaces demonstrated *in vivo* by immersion incident light microscopy. *Ann. rheum. Dis.* **30**, 3.

Gardner D. L. and Woodward D. (1969) Scanning electron microscopy and replica studies of articular surfaces of guinea-pig synovial joints. *Ann. rheum. Dis.* **28**, 379.

Gersh I. and Catchpole H. R. (1960) The nature of ground substance of connective tissue. *Perspect. Biol. Med.* **3**, 282.

Ghadially F. N., Meachim G. and Collins D. H. (1965) Extra-cellular lipid in the matrix of human articular cartilage. *Ann. rheum. Dis.* **24**, 136.

Ghadially F. N., Mehta P. N. and Kirkaldy-Willis W. H. (1970) Ultrastructure of articular cartilage in experimentally produced lipoarthrosis. *J. Bone Jt Surg.* **52A**, 1147.

Gibson T. and Davis W. B. (1958) The distortion of autogenous cartilage grafts: its cause and prevention. *Brit. J. plast. Surg.* **10**, 257.

Gustafson G. T. and Pihl E. (1967) Histochemical application of ruthenium red in the study of mast cell ultrastructure. *Acta path. microbiol. scand.* **69**, 393.

Haines R. W. and Mohuiddin A. (1968) Metaplastic bone. *J. Anat. (Lond.)* **103**, 527.

Hancox N. M. and Boothroyd B. (1964) Ultrastructure of bone formation and resorption. *Modern Trends in Orthopaedics*. 4: Science of Fractures, Ed. by J. M. P. Clark, pp. 26–52. Butterworths, London.

Hardingham T. E. and Muir H. (1974) Hyaluronic acid in cartilage and proteoglycan aggregation. *Biochem. J.* **139**, 565.

Hass G. M. (1943) Studies of cartilage: a morphologic and chemical analysis of aging human costal cartilage. *Archs Path.* **35**, 275.

Hirsch C. (1944) A contribution to the pathogenesis of chondromalacia of the patella. *Acta chir. scand.* **90**, Suppl. 83, 1.

Holmdahl D. E. and Ingelmark B. E. (1950) The contact between the articular cartilage and the medullary cavities of the bone. *Acta orthop. scand.* **20**, 156.

Hopwood J. J. and Robinson H. C. (1974) The structure and composition of cartilage keratan sulphate. *Biochem. J.* **141**, 517.

Ingelmark B. E. and Ekholm R. (1948) A study on variations in the thickness of articular cartilage in association with rest and periodic load. *Upsala Läk-för. Förh.* **53**, 61.

Jasin H. E., Cooke T. D., Hurd E. R., Smiley J. D. and Ziff M. (1973) Immunologic models used for the study of rheumatoid arthritis. *Fed. Proc.* **32**, 147.

Kaplan D. and Meyer K. (1959) Ageing of human cartilage. *Nature (Lond.)* **183**, 1267.

Kelly J. W., Bloom G. D. and Scott J. E. (1963) Quaternary ammonium compounds in connective tissue histochemistry. 1: Selective unblocking. *J. Histochem. Cytochem.* **11**, 791.

Korst J. K. van der, Sokoloff L. and Miller E. J. (1968) Senescent pigmentation of cartilage and degenerative joint disease. *Archs Path.* **86**, 40.

Kuhn R. and Leppelmann H. J. (1958) Galaktosamin und Glucosamin im Knorpel in Abhängigkeit vom Lebensalter. *Liebigs Ann. Chem.* **611**, 254.

Lindhal O. (1948) Über den Wassergehalt des Knorpels. *Acta orthop. scand.* **17**, 134.

Linn F. C. and Sokoloff L. (1965) Movement and composition of interstitial fluid of cartilage. *Arthritis Rheum.* **8**, 481.

Lipshitz H., Etheredge R. and Glimcher M. J. (1975) *In vitro* wear of articular cartilage. *J. Bone Jt Surg.* **57A**, 527.

Little K., Pimm L. H. and Trueta J. (1958) Osteoarthritis of the hip: an electron microscope study. *J. Bone Jt Surg.* **40B**, 123.

Loewi G. (1965) Localisation of chondromucoprotein in cartilage. *Ann. rheum. Dis.* **24**, 528.

Longmore R. B. and Gardner D. L. (1975) Development with age of human articular cartilage surface structure. *Ann. rheum. Dis.* **34**, 26.

Lothe K., Spycher M. A. and Ruttner J. R. (1973) 'Matrix-streaks': a peculiar pattern in the cartilage of the femoral head of ageing human subjects. *J. Bone Jt Surg.* **55B**, 581.

Lotke P. A., Black J. and Richardson S. (1974) Electromechanical properties in human articular cartilage. *J. Bone Jt Surg.* **56A**, 1040.

McCall J. G. (1968) Scanning electron microscopy of articular surfaces. *Lancet* **ii**, 1194.

McCall J. G. (1969a) Load deformation response of the micro-structure of articular cartilage. *Lubrication and Wear in Joints,* Ed. by V. Wright, p. 39. Sector, London.

McCall J. G. (1969b) Load-deformation studies of articular cartilage. *J. Anat. (Lond.)* **105**, 212.

McCarty D. J. (1976) Calcium pyrophosphate dihydrate crystal deposition disease. *Arthritis Rheum.* **19**, 275.

MacConaill M. A. (1951) The movements of bones and joints. 4: The mechanical structure of articulating cartilage. *J. Bone Jt Surg.* **33B**, 251.

Makowsky L. (1948) Studien über den Wasserhaushalt des Kniegelenk-knorpels. *Helv. chir. Acta* **15**, 44.

Mankin H. J. and Lippiello L. (1969) The turnover of adult rabbit articular cartilage. *J. Bone Jt Surg.* **51A**, 1591.

Mankin H. J. and Lippiello L. (1970) Biochemical and metabolic abnormalities in articular cartilage from osteoarthritic human hips. *J. Bone Jt Surg.* **52A**, 424.

Maroudas A. (1972) X-ray microprobe analysis of articular cartilage. *Conn. Tiss. Res.* **1**, 153.

Maroudas A. (1975) Glycosaminoglycan turnover in articular cartilage. *Phil. Trans. R. Soc. Lond. B* **271**, 293.

Maroudas A. and Thomas H. (1970) A simple physicochemical micromethod for determining fixed anionic groups in connective tissue. *Biochim. biophys. Acta* **215**, 214.

Maroudas A., Muir H. and Wingham J. (1969) The correlation of fixed negative charge with glycosaminoglycan content of human articular cartilage. *Biochim. biophys. Acta* **177**, 492.

Maroudas A., Evans H. and Almeida L. (1973) Cartilage of the hip joint: topographical variation of glycosaminoglycan content in normal and fibrillated tissue. *Ann. rheum. Dis.* **32**, 1.

Mason R. M. (1971) Observations on the glycosaminoglycans of ageing bronchial cartilage studied with Alcian blue. *Histochem. J.* **3**, 421.

Mathews M. B. (1968) The macromolecular organization of connective tissue. *Chemical Physiology of the Mucopolysaccharides,* Ed. by G. Quintarelli, p. 189. Little, Brown & Co., Boston.

Mathews M. B. (1970) The interaction of proteoglycans and collagen—model systems. *Chemistry and Molecular Biology of the Intercellular Matrix,* Ed. by E. A. Balazs, Vol. 2, p. 1155. Academic Press, New York.

Matthews B. F. (1953) Composition of articular cartilage in osteoarthritis. Changes in collagen/chondroitin sulphate ratio. *Brit. med. J.* **2**, 660.

Matukas V. J., Panner B. J. and Orbison J. L. (1967) Studies on the ultrastructural identification and distribution of protein-polysaccharide in cartilage matrix. *J. Cell Biol.* **32**, 365.

Maximow A. A. and Bloom W. (1948) *A Textbook of Histology,* 5th edn, p. 118. Saunders, Philadelphia.

Meachim G. (1969a) Age and osteoarthritic changes in articular cartilage. *Ultrastructure of Synovial Joints in Health and Disease*, Ed. by F. N. Ghadially and S. Roy, pp. 61–83. Butterworths, London.

Meachim G. (1969b) Age changes in articular cartilage. *Clin. Orthop.* **64**, 33.

Meachim G. (1971) Effect of age on the thickness of adult articular cartilage at the shoulder joint. *Ann. rheum. Dis.* **30**, 43.

Meachim G. (1972a) Meshwork patterns in the ground substance of articular cartilage and nucleus pulposus. *J. Anat. (Lond.)* **111**, 219.

Meachim G. (1972b) Light microscopy of Indian ink preparations of fibrillated cartilage. *Ann. rheum. Dis.* **31**, 457.

Meachim G. (1975) Articular cartilage lesions in the Liverpool population. *Ann. rheum. Dis.* **34**, Suppl. 2, 122.

Meachim G. and Fergie I. A. (1975) Morphological patterns of articular cartilage fibrillation. *J. Path.* **115**, 231.

Meachim G. and Illman O. (1967) Articular cartilage degeneration in hamsters and in pigs. *Z. Versuchstierk.* **9**, 33.

Meachim G. and Roy S. (1969) Surface ultrastructure of mature adult human articular cartilage. *J. Bone Jt Surg.* **51B**, 529.

Meachim G., Ghadially F. N. and Collins D. H. (1965) Regressive changes in the superficial layer of human articular cartilage. *Ann. rheum. Dis.* **24**, 23.

Meachim G., Denham D., Emery I. H. and Wilkinson P. H. (1974) Collagen alignments and artificial splits at the surface of human articular cartilage. *J. Anat. (Lond.)* **118**, 101.

Miles J. S. and Eichelberger L. (1964) Biochemical studies of human cartilage during the ageing process. *J. Amer. Geriat. Soc.* **12**, 1.

Mills K. (1970) Pathology of the knee joint in rheumatoid arthritis. *J. Bone Jt Surg.* **52B**, 746.

Muir H., Bullough P. and Maroudas A. (1970) The distribution of collagen in human articular cartilage with some of its physiological implications. *J. Bone Jt Surg.* **52B**, 554.

Mulholland R. (1974) Lateral hydraulic permeability and morphology of articular cartilage. *Normal and Osteoarthrotic Articular Cartilage,* Ed. by S. Y. Ali, M. W. Elves and D. H. Leaback, p. 85. Institute of Orthopaedics, London.

Öbrink B. (1973) A study of the interactions between monomeric tropocollagen and glycosaminoglycans *Eur. J. Biochem.* **33**, 387.

Palfrey A. J. (1975) Matrix structure in articular cartilage. *Ann. rheum. Dis.* **34**, Suppl. 2, 20.

Putschar W. (1931) Über Fett im Knorpel unter normalen und pathologischen Verhältnissen. *Beitr. path. Anat.* **87**, 526.

Quintarelli G. and Dellovo M. C. (1965) The chemical and histochemical properties of Alcian blue. IV: Further studies on the methods for the identification of acid glycosaminoglycans. *Histochemie* **5**, 196.

Quintarelli G. and Dellovo M. C. (1966) Age changes in the localization and distribution of glycosaminoglycans in human hyaline cartilage. *Histochemie* **7**, 141.

Redler I. and Zimny M. L. (1970) Scanning electron microscopy of normal and abnormal articular cartilage and synovium. *J. Bone Jt Surg.* **52A**, 1395.

Reynolds J. (1975) The structural glycoproteins of elastic ligaments. *J. Anat. (Lond.)* **120**, 623.

Rosenberg L., Johnson B. and Schubert M. (1965) Protein-polysaccharides from human articular and costal cartilage. *J. clin. Invest.* **44**, 1647.

Rosenberg L., Hellman W. and Kleinschmidt A. K. (1970) Macromolecular models of protein-polysaccharides from bovine nasal cartilage based on electron microscopic studies. *J. biol. Chem.* **245**, 4123.

Rosenberg L., Hellman W. and Kleinschmidt A. K. (1975) Electron microscopic studies of proteoglycan aggregates from bovine articular cartilage. *J. biol. Chem.* **250**, 1827.

Roy S. and Meachim G. (1968) Chondrocyte ultrastructure in adult human articular cartilage. *Ann. rheum Dis.* **27**, 544.

Ruggeri A., Dell'Orbo C. and Quacci D. (1975) Electron microscopic visualization of proteoglycans with Alcian blue. *Histochem. J.* **7**, 187.

Schaffer J. (1930) Die Stutzgewebe. *Handbuch der Mikroskopischen Anatomie des Menschen,* Ed. by W. von Möllendorff, Vol. 2, p.l. Springer, Berlin.

Schallock G. (1942) Untersuchungen zur Pathogenese von Aufbrauchveränderungen an den Knorpeligen Anteilen des Kniegelenkes. *Veroff. Konstit. u. Wehrpath.* **49**, 1.

Schofield B. H., Williams B. R. and Doty S. B. (1975) Alcian blue staining of cartilage for electron microscopy. Application of the CEC principle. *Histochem. J.* **7**, 139.

Schott H. J. (1963) Verkommen und Verteilung gebundener Lipide in der Grundsubstanz des hyalinen Knorpels. *Verh. Anat. Ges. (Jena)* **57**, 363.

Schumacher H. R. (1976) Ultrastructural findings in chondrocalcinosis and pseudo-gout. *Arthritis Rheum.* **19**, Suppl., 413.

Scott J. E. (1955) The solubility of cetylpyridinium complexes of biological polyanions in solutions of slats. *Biochim. biophys. Acta* **18**, 428.

Scott J. E. (1973) Distribution of acid mucopolysaccharides in cartilage. *Current Developments in Rheumatology,* Ed. by O. Lövtren, H. Boström, B. Olhagen and R. Sannerstedt, p. 10. Lindgren, Mölndal.

Scott, J. E. (1974) Affinity, competition and specific interactions in the biochemistry and histochemistry of polyelectrolytes. *Biochem. Soc. Trans.* 1, 787.

Scott, J. E. (1975) Physiological function and chemical composition of peri-cellular proteoglycan (an evolutionary view). *Phil. Trans. R. Soc. Lond. B* 271, 235.

Scott J. E. and Dorling J. (1965) Differential staining of acid glycosaminoglycans (mucopolysaccharides) by Alcian blue in salt solutions. *Histochemie* 5, 221.

Scott J. E. and Dorling J. (1969) Periodate oxidation of acid polysaccharides. III: A PAS method for chondroitin sulphates and other glycosaminoglycuronans. *Histochemie* 19, 295.

Scott J. E. and Stockwell R. A. (1967) On the use and abuse of the critical electrolyte concentration approach to the localization of tissue polyanions. *J. Histochem. Cytochem.* 15, 111.

Scott J. E. and Willett I. H. (1966) Binding of cationic dyes to nucleic acids and other biological polyanions. *Nature (Lond.)* 209, 985.

Scott J. E., Dorling J. and Stockwell R. A. (1968) Reversal of protein blocking of basophilia in salt solutions: implications in the localization of polyanions using Alcian blue. *J. Histochem. Cytochem.* 16, 383.

Serafini-Fracassini A. and Smith J. W. (1966) Observations on the morphology of the protein polysaccharide complex of bovine nasal cartilage and its relation to collagen. *Proc. R. Soc. B* 165, 440.

Sharp J. (1969) Osteo-arthrosis. *Textbook of the Rheumatic Diseases,* Ed. by W. S. C. Copeman, 4th edn., p. 385. Livingstone, Edinburgh.

Shipp D. W. and Bowness J. M. (1975) Insoluble non-collagenous cartilage glycoproteins with aggregating sub-units. *Biochim. biophys. Acta* 379, 282.

Simon W. H. (1970) Scale effects in animal joints. 1: Articular cartilage thickness and compressive stress. *Arthritis Rheum.* 13, 244.

Smith J. W. (1970) The disposition of protein-polysaccharide in the epiphyseal plate of the young rabbit. *J. Cell Sci.* 6, 843.

Smith J. W., Peters T. J. and Serafini-Fracassini A. (1967) Observations on the distribution of the proteinpolysaccharide complex and collagen in bovine articular cartilage. *J. Cell Sci.* 2, 129.

Sprinz R. and Stockwell R. A. (1976) Changes in articular cartilage following intra-articular injection of tritiated glyceryl trioleate. *J. Anat. (Lond.)* 122, 91.

Stockwell R. A. (1965) Lipid in the matrix of ageing articular cartilage. *Nature (Lond.)* 207, 427.

Stockwell R. A. (1967) Lipid content of human costal and articular cartilage. *Ann. rheum. Dis.* 26, 481.

Stockwell R. A. (1970) Changes in the acid glycosaminoglycan content of the matrix of ageing human articular cartilage. *Ann. rheum. Dis.* 29, 509.

Stockwell R. A. (1971) The matrix of ageing human articular cartilage. *J. Anat. (Lond.)* 110, 131.

Stockwell R. A. (1975) Stain distribution with Alcian blue in articular cartilage. *Ann. rheum. Dis.* 34, Suppl. 2, 17.

Stockwell R. A. and Scott J. E. (1965) Observations on the acid glycosaminoglycan (mucopolysaccharide) content of the matrix of ageing cartilage. *Ann. rheum. Dis.* 24, 341.

Stockwell R. A. and Scott J. E. (1967) Distribution of acid glycosaminoglycans in human articular cartilage. *Nature (Lond.)* 215, 1376.

Szirmai J. A. (1963) Quantitative approaches in the histochemistry of mucopolysaccharides. *J. Histochem. Cytochem.* 11, 24.

Szirmai J. A. (1969) Structure of cartilage. *Ageing of Connective and Skeletal Tissue,* Ed. by A. Engel and T. Larsson, p. 163. Thule Int. Symp. Nordiska Bokh. Förl., Stockholm.

Thompson R. C. and Bassett C. A. L. (1970) Histological observations in experimentally induced degeneration of articular cartilage. *J. Bone Jt Surg.* 52A, 435.

Thyberg J., Lohmander S. and Friberg U. (1973) Electron microscopic demonstration of proteoglycan in guinea-pig epiphyseal cartilage. *J. Ultrastruct. Res.* 45, 407.

Toole B. P. and Lowther D. A. (1968) The effect of chondroitin sulphate–protein on the formation of collagen fibrils *in vitro*. *Biochem. J.* 109, 857.

Walker P. S., Sikorski J., Dowson D., Longfield M. D., Wright V. and Buckley T. (1969) Behaviour of synovial fluid on surfaces of articular cartilage. A scanning electron microscope study. *Ann. rheum. Dis.* 28, 1.

Weiss C., Rosenberg L. and Helfet A. J. (1968) An ultrastructural study of normal young adult human articular cartilage. *J. Bone Jt Surg.* 50A, 663.

Woods C. G., Greenwald A. S. and Haynes D. W. (1970) Subchondral vascularity in the human femoral head. *Ann. rheum. Dis.* 29, 138.

Wuthier R. E. (1976) Lipids of matrix vesicles. *Fed. Proc.* **35,** 117.

Zbinden G. (1953) Uber Feinstruktur und Alters-veranderungen des hyalinen Knorpels im elektron-mikroskopischen Schnittpraparat und Beitrag zur Verfettung der Knorpelgrundsubstanz. *Schwiez Z. allg. Path. Bakt.* **16,** 165.

2. The Chondrocytes

R. A. Stockwell and G. Meachim

1. INTRODUCTION

The cells of articular cartilage manufacture and maintain the extracellular matrix. This function does not cease after completion of cartilage growth during skeletal development, but persists throughout adult life (Collins and Meachim 1961). Although the number of cells in a unit volume of adult cartilage is small compared with other tissues (Bywaters 1937), the chondrocytes show considerable metabolic activity (Mankin and Lippiello 1969). This activity is associated with a continuous physiological 'turnover' of the extracellular ground substance in adult articular cartilage, involving the synthesis and degradation of ground substance components. Thus adult articular cartilage is not an inert material: the properties of its matrix are continuously influenced by chondrocyte activity. In evaluating the role of the chondrocyte in normal articular cartilage, therefore, the nature both of the individual cell and of the cell population as a whole must be considered.

In addition, more data are needed on the extent to which wear-resistance and other matrix properties might in fact be altered by death of all the chondrocytes in a piece of cartilage. This question is relevant to experimental investigations of the mechanical and physicochemical properties of the matrix, since such investigations are often carried out on tissue in which the cells are dead or moribund. The question is also relevant to the clinical problem of cartilage transplantation: if cell death occurs in the transplant, for how long does the graft still remain functionally adequate as a covering material? No new proteoglycan would be manufactured in the dead tissue, and in theory the resultant depletion of matrix glycosaminoglycans could seriously reduce the stiffness and wear resistance of the cartilage.

2. THE MORPHOLOGY OF THE CHONDROCYTE

Chondrocyte morphology can be studied by light microscopy and by transmission and scanning microscopy. Electron microscopy enables structures within chondrocytes to be identified and studied, and by this means a comprehensive assessment can be made of the overall appearance of individual cartilage cells. A chondrocyte as seen on electron microscopy is always 'dead' in the sense that all the living cells which are present in the cartilage sample are killed during fixation. Moreover, the structure which a chondrocyte has in its living state is almost certainly altered during processing and staining of the specimen for transmission electron microscopy.

Thus an electron micrograph is an artefact, but in the case of transmission electron micrographs it is a useful artefact, since it correlates with data obtained by other techniques to give an approximate representation of the structure of the living cell. In the case of scanning electron micrographs, however, shrinkage and other artefacts may make the procedure less useful.

2.1. General Features

Light microscopy gives morphological data on chondrocytes in histological preparations of cartilage, and data on living chondrocytes as seen in preparations in which the cells have been artificially separated from their surrounding matrix. Observations on the latter preparations have shown that freshly isolated living chondrocytes exhibit amoeboid movement, constantly changing their shape, putting out and withdrawing pseudopodia (Smith 1965; Chesterman and Smith 1968). The living cells contain a granular cytoplasm with relatively few vacuoles. When stained with euchrysine and viewed in the fluorescence microscope the nucleus gives a vivid green fluorescence, the cytoplasmic granules are a brilliant orange-red and intracellular vacuoles are outlined in blue. The cells incorporate ^{35}S-sulphate. The dry mass of isolated chondrocytes determined interferometrically is $2.5 \pm 0.6 \times 10^{-10}$ g per cell (Kawiak, Moskalewski and Darzynkiewicz 1965).

Apart from an abundance of lipid droplets, electron microscopy of cultured articular chondrocytes reveals that they differ little from those *in situ*; however, they and the matrix they synthesize resemble more closely immature than adult tissue (Green and Ferguson 1975). Chondrocytes may be cultured as monolayers, in 'pellets', or in suspension (spinner cultures). Cells in suspension culture are much more active in ground substance synthesis, but much less active in DNA synthesis, than those grown in monolayers (Srivistava, Malemud and Sokoloff 1974). Although there is evidence (see Section 8.2.2.) that cultured chondrocytes (usually derived from embryonic sources) can undergo irreversible dedifferentiation (Holtzer, Chacko, Abbott, Holtzer and Anderson 1970), it appears that this may not always be the case with adult or near-adult articular chondrocytes in culture. Such adult or near-adult cells appear to be protodifferentiated with respect to chondroid expression, since even in monolayer culture, where the cells resemble fibroblasts, quantitative methods show that the glycosaminoglyans which they produce (Srivistava *et al.* 1974) and their mode of respiration (Marcus 1973) are in fact more akin to chondrocytes than to fibroblasts. When resuspended in spinner culture, they form large masses of ground substance of cartilage type. Such 'reversible dedifferentiation' is probably a form of modulation or response to environment.

Articular chondrocytes *in situ* vary in size, shape and distribution according to which horizontal layer (zone) of the tissue is examined. As seen in fixed tissue sectioned perpendicular to the joint surface, they appear to increase in size and become more widely scattered in the matrix with increasing distance from the surface. In vertical section the superficial (zone 1) cells appear to be single and present an elongated oval outline (Figure 2.1a). However, in sections cut tangential to the surface, they are found to be rounded both in calf (Arlet, Mole and Barriuso 1958) and in young adult human articular cartilage (Figure 2.1b); clusters containing two or more cells each of diameter 10–20 μm may be seen. Thus these cells are in fact discoidal, and they present a misleading contour in the vertical plane most often used in the histological investigation of articular cartilage. In the intermediate zone (zone 2) of the uncalcified tissue, the cells are spheroidal (Figure 2.1c and d), 10 μm or more in diameter, at first single and then, more deeply, occurring in groups of two or more. In the deep uncalcified region (zone 3) groups of cells tend to be vertically orientated, with an occasional resemblance to the cell columns of the growth cartilage.

Thus in adult human articular cartilage the structure of individual cells varies according to the zone of cartilage examined (Weiss, Rosenberg and Helfet 1968). It can also be modified locally in a fibrillated area. However, the same basic features are encountered whatever the site and state of the cartilage sample (Roy and Meachim 1968). The following description of cell morphology refers to articular chondrocytes in adult man (Meachim 1967; Roy and Meachim 1968), with reference to findings in other species and other tissues where relevant.

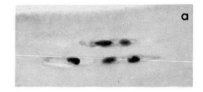

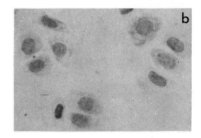

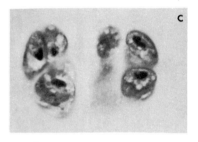

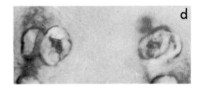

Figure 2.1 The general morphology of adult articular chondrocytes. Superficial cells (zone 1) are flattened and discoidal, while deep cells (zone 2) are ovoid. These and all subsequent illustrations are from adult human articular cartilage unless stated otherwise. (a) Superficial cells in vertical section (i.e. cartilage sectioned perpendicular to the articular surface). (b) Superficial cells in horizontal section (i.e. cartilage sectioned tangential to the articular surface). (c) Deep cells in vertical section. (d) Deep cells in horizontal section. Note artefactual shrinkage of cells in (a), (c) and (d).
Haematoxylin and eosin   ×560

2.2. The Cell Surface

2.2.1. Cell Membrane. At the periphery of the cell, a limiting membrane separates the cytoplasm of the chondrocyte from the surrounding extracellular matrix (Figure 2.2). Small rounded

Figure 2.2 A chondrocyte showing nucleus (N) with nucleolus (S), cytoplasm (C), limiting cell membrane (R), and cell processes (P). Pericellular (L) and intercellular (T) matrix.

Transmission electron micrograph ×10 000.

Glutaraldehyde.

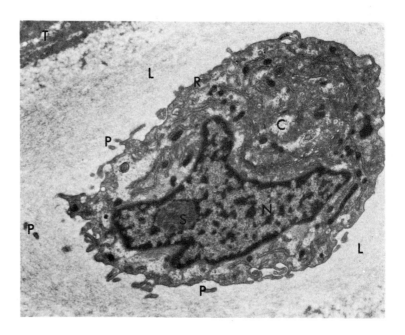

smooth-walled vesicles are often seen in the cytoplasm immediately adjacent to this membrane (Figure 2.3). They are termed micropinocytotic vesicles, implying that they transport material into the cell from the exterior. These small vesicles appear to form by invagination of the cell membrane; a few of them are flask shaped with a narrow external opening.

Large wide indentations of the cell membrane can occur, giving the chondrocyte a scalloped or frankly irregular outline; in certain planes of section a large rounded indentation can simulate a true vacuole by falsely appearing to be completely enclosed by cytoplasm.

2.2.2. Cell Processes. Chondrocytes typically show cytoplasmic processes extending into the adjacent pericellular matrix and sometimes just beyond it. Some processes are short and stumpy; others are long, and occasionally show branching. Cells with cytoplasmic processes (Figure 2.2) are seen in all layers of adult

72

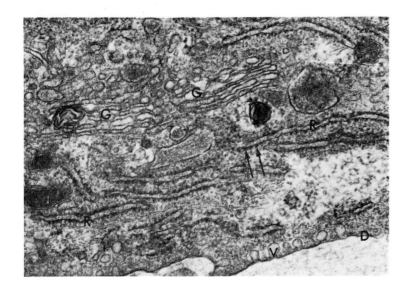

Figure 2.3 Part of a chondrocyte showing paired membranes of rough endoplasmic reticulum (R) with ribosome granules (arrows). The rough endoplasmic reticulum contrasts with the smooth membranes of the Golgi apparatus (G). Micropinocytotic vesicles (V); limiting cell membrane (D).

Transmission electron micrograph ×37 500.

Glutaraldehyde.

human articular cartilage, including the superficial layer (zone 1) nearest the joint surface (Ghadially, Meachim and Collins 1965; Weiss *et al.* 1968). The cytoplasmic processes seen in transmission electron micrographs may represent the pseudopodia seen in preparations of matrix-free living chondrocytes (Chesterman and Smith 1968), and if this is so the processes are probably not static in intact living cartilage. From an analogy with growth-plate cartilage, it is tempting to speculate that extracellular enzyme-containing bodies could arise from the tips of the cytoplasmic processes and play a part in matrix remodelling (Ali 1970, personal communication); this speculation is in line with the hypothesis that the electron-dense bodies found in cartilage matrix are of cellular origin (Ghadially *et al.* 1965).

In mouse (Scherft and Daems 1967) and guinea-pig articular cartilage (Hart 1968), some chondrocytes possess single cilia. They are seen occasionally in young adult human articular chondrocytes (Figure 2.4). The cells of many tissues possess these organelles, which appear to be non-motile; their function is not known. The basal body, found in the cytoplasm at the attachment of the cilium to the cell, is believed to be one of the centrioles of the cell.

In non-fibrillated articular cartilage from adults, each chondrocyte is usually separated from its neighbours by intervening matrix, and the cell membranes do not normally show focal specializations of the types seen when cells are in contiguity, although desmosomes have been demonstrated between adjacent rabbit articular chondrocytes (Palfrey and Davies 1966).

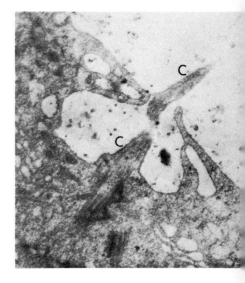

Figure 2.4 Part of a chondrocyte from zone 2 of young adult (21 years) femoral condylar cartilage. A single cilium (C) projects from the cell surface, but is not seen in its full length because of the plane of section.

Transmission electron micrograph ×31 000.

Glutaraldehyde.

2.3. Cell Organelles

2.3.1. The Nucleus. The nucleus (Figure 2.2) is usually oval or elongated, and shows an outline which is smooth or indented. It contains electron-dense granular nucleoplasm, and a nucleolus is seen in favourable sections (Figure 2.2). The nucleus is sur-rounded by two membranes; these form the 'nuclear envelope', in which there are small openings termed 'nucleopores'.

Ultrathin sections of chondrocytes from animals show that there is a band of fine textured material, termed the 'nuclear fibrous lamina', lying between the inner membrane of the nuclear envelope and the marginal condensates of nuclear chromatin. Oryschak, Ghadially and Bhatnagar (1974) find that this lamina is very thin or indiscernible in the articular cartilage of newborn rabbits, and that it thickens as the animals mature. It is similar in thickness (20–40 nm) and texture in adult rabbit, dog, cow and horse cartilage. Its precise nature and function is not known.

The nucleus contains DNA, the genetic material of the cell. Using information stored in this material, it produces messenger chemicals (messenger RNA) by which it transmits instructions to the cytoplasm.

Nucleic acids have been studied in femoral condylar cartilage of a number of species including man (Shaw and Martin 1962). In rabbit femoral condylar cartilage, Mankin and Baron (1965), using an indole technique, estimate a content of 6.5×10^{-12} g DNA per cell, while human articular chondrocytes contain about 7×10^{-12} g DNA (Stockwell 1967a). Both these estimates are equivalent in amount to that in other somatic cells of the species concerned.

2.3.2. Rough Endoplasmic Reticulum. Electron microscopy demonstrates that the cytoplasm contains a variable amount of rough endoplasmic reticulum (Figure 2.3). This forms a complex arrangement of interconnecting channels. In most planes of sec-tion it is seen as paired membranes, on each of which on the cytoplasmic side there is a row of granules termed ribosomes; ribosomes also occur lying free in the cytoplasm. Ribosomes are the sites at which polypeptide chains for new protein molecules are manufactured. Special chemicals (transfer RNA) bring about assembly of amino-acids into the polypeptide chains. It is believed that the ribosomes of the rough endoplasmic reticulum are involved in the production of protein which is ultimately dis-charged from the cell; in contrast, ribosomes lying free in the cytoplasm are thought to synthesize protein which is required for use within the cell. The spaces enclosed between membrane pairs of rough endoplasmic reticulum are termed cisternae; in healthy chondrocytes they can show a variable amount of dilatation.

With the exception of RNA used for special purposes (messenger and transfer RNA), most of the cell's RNA is found in the ribosomal granules of the cytoplasm. In keeping with the presence of these granules as shown by electron microscopy, many of the cells in articular cartilage stain for RNA using the methyl green–pyronin technique; a negative result is obtained with ribonuclease-extracted controls. Unlike the deeper cells, those in the superficial layer (zone 1) contain few is any stained granules (Shaw and Martin 1962). However, in adult rabbit knee joint cartilage, Mankin (1963a) finds that nearly all cells in the tissue, including those of the superficial layer, incorporate ^{3}H-cytidine; this is indicative of active RNA synthesis where DNA synthesis is known to be absent or minimal in the normal tissue.

2.3.3. Golgi Apparatus. In addition to the rough endoplasmic reticulum, the chondrocytes contain smooth membranes. These are seen particularly in the Golgi apparatus (Figure 2.3). This apparatus consists of one or more areas of closely spaced agranular parallel lamellae associated with elongated, bulbous dilatations and small vesicles. Sometimes large multiple vacuoles are also apparent in a Golgi area: the whole complex then forms a prominent cytoplasmic feature in the electron micrograph. In other instances, however, an obvious component of large smooth-walled vacuoles is not included in the plane of section: a closer scrutiny of the cytoplasm may then be needed before the Golgi apparatus is identified. By autoradiographic studies using tracer isotopes in experimental animals, it has been shown that the Golgi apparatus is concerned in the synthesis and transport of chemical substances manufactured in the chondrocytes for secretion into the extracellular matrix (Revel and Hay 1963; Godman and Lane 1964; Neutra and Leblond 1966). Extracellular secretion is probably not the only function of the Golgi apparatus in chondrocytes: other studies, using anterior pituitary cells, suggest that Golgi structures may also contribute small vesicles (termed 'primary lysosomes') to cytoplasmic bodies concerned in intracellular digestive processes (Smith and Farquhar 1966).

2.3.4. Smooth-walled Vacuoles and Vesicles. Smooth-walled large vacuoles and small vesicles occur not only in the Golgi area but also elsewhere in the cytoplasm (Roy and Meachim 1968). Some of the larger vacuoles are lined by a complete or incomplete single membrane and contain mainly electron-lucent material or a small amount of electron-opaque material: thus they have a similar morphology (Figure 2.5) to that of vacuoles found in the Golgi area and are presumably of Golgi origin and secretory in function. The small smooth-walled vesicles usually have an electron-lucent content: they appear to be either of Golgi origin or to be micropinocytotic vesicles (Figure 2.3) which transport material into the cell from the exterior. Occasionally a vacuole lined by a single smooth membrane contains indistinct small rounded structures suggestive of inner vesicles, and may thus represent what is termed in other tissues a multivesicular body (De Duve and Wattiaux 1966; Smith and Farquhar 1966).

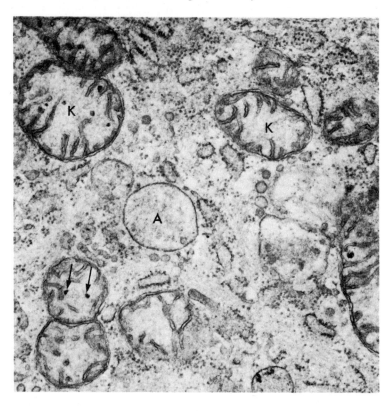

Figure 2.5 Mitochondria (K), with dense granules (arrows), in rabbit articular cartilage. Smooth-walled vacuole (A).

Transmission electron micrograph ×37 500.

Osmium.

2.3.5. Mitochondria. The cytoplasm contains a variable number of mitochondria (Figure 2.6). Mitochondria are elongated or oval bodies with two lining membranes from the inner one of which shelf-like structures termed cristae project into the interior of the organelle (Figure 2.5). Within the interior, one or more small dense granules are sometimes apparent (Figure 2.5). Mitochondria make chemicals which are used as fuel for activities elsewhere in the cell.

In the mitochondria of adult human articular cartilage the cristae are often indistinct (Figure 2.7); unusually 'dark' small mitochondria of high electron density sometimes occur (Figure 2.7); and in some instances an organelle is presumptively identified as a mitochondrion only because it shows the appropriate size and contour and has a double lining membrane.

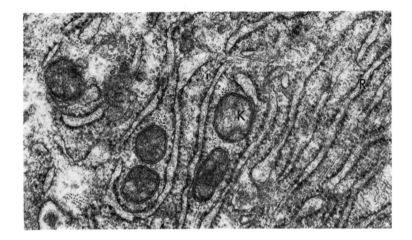

Figure 2.6 Mitochondria (K) and rough endoplasmic reticulum (R).

Transmission electron micrograph ×37 500.

Glutaraldehyde.

2.3.6. Intracytoplasmic Fine Filaments. The chondrocytes frequently contain one or more finely filamentous areas in their cytoplasm (Figure 2.7). Such areas are usually perinuclear in situation; less commonly they are seen in a more peripheral part of the cell (Meachim and Roy 1967). The filaments lie directly within the cytoplasm and are not enclosed in membrane-bound vacuoles. Their diameter is in the range of 7–10 nm (70–100 Å). The filaments do not show the periodic banding of typical collagen. Although Revel and Hay (1963) comment that the fine filaments in chondrocytes are 'not unlike the tonofilaments of epithelial cells', the nature and function of the chondrocyte filaments is in fact unknown. Presumably their function in healthy cells is to

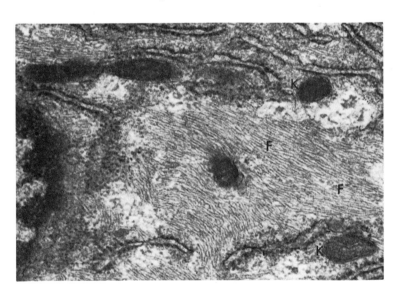

Figure 2.7 Intracytoplasmic fine filaments (F). Note also the unusually 'dark', small mitochondria (K).

Transmission electron micrograph ×37 500.

Glutaraldehyde.

contribute 'structural strength', or, perhaps, contractile properties, to the cytoplasm. This problem of the nature of the filaments is complicated by observations which indicate that more than one type of filament can occur in cartilage cells: chondrogenic cells cultured *in vitro* contain a minimum of two types of filament, one being actin or an actin-like protein, and the other a non-actin material present as 10 nm diameter filaments (Ishikawa, Bischoff and Holtzer 1969).

The presence of a small amount of intracytoplasmic filaments is not a sign that the chondrocyte is degenerate (Meachim and Roy 1967), and intracytoplasmic filaments can be regarded as a normal feature of adult articular cartilage cells. There is, however, evidence that accumulation of filaments in unusually large amounts represents a form of involutionary or degenerative change in the cytoplasm (Meachim and Roy 1967). Further support for this view has come from studies of experimentally produced chronic haemarthrosis and of lipoarthrosis in rabbits: in both conditions an excessive accumulation of intracytoplasmic filaments occurs in cartilage which also shows other degenerative cell changes (Roy 1968; Sprinz and Stockwell 1976).

2.3.7. Microtubules. In additon to the fine filaments already described, long slender structures resembling delicate tubules can also occur in the cytoplasm of the chondrocytes (Weiss *et al.* 1968). The function of these 'microtubules' is unknown, although they may be involved in the intracellular transport and secretion of collagen (Ross 1975). Their chemical relationship to the other types of intracytoplasmic filamentous structures is uncertain (Ishikwa *et al.* 1969).

2.3.8. Centrioles. Although centrioles have been observed in adult human articular chondrocytes, they are seen only rarely (Roy and Meachim 1968). Their functional role in chondrocytes is debatable, but in other tissue cells concerns the process of cell division and of cilia formation.

2.3.9. Electron-dense bodies. Intracytoplasmic spherical and oval structures of a type conveniently described as electron-dense bodies can occur in articular cartilage, although they are an infrequent finding in the cells of a non-fibrillated area (Roy and Meachim 1968). Some of these structures represent unusually 'dark' mitochondria, but in others a single lining membrane and an absence of cristae permit distinction, since in mitochondria the lining membrane is double and cristae are seen. Their copious rather homogeneous content of moderately or intensely electron-dense material distinguishes them from Golgi vacuoles, since in Golgi vacuoles the content is more electron-lucent.

The morphology of the electron-dense bodies suggests that they may be lysosomes. Lysosomes are specialized membrane-bound intracellular structures in which certain enzymes are segregated from the rest of the cytoplasm. When such structures occur in human articular cartilage they could have several possible roles. From studies on other tissues it is known that one function of lysosomes concerns intracellular digestive processes (De Duve and Wattiaux 1966; Smith and Farquhar 1966). Some lysosomes act as enzyme storage sites for this function and are termed primary lysosomes. Their enzymes can subsequently be used in the digestion of exogenous material which has been taken into the cell, and in the digestion of endogenous material such as superfluous effete or damaged cytoplasmic organelles or secretion products which are no longer required: during any of these processes, the primary lysosomes can fuse with other vacuoles, and thus give various morphological forms representing secondary lysosomes or lysosomal derivatives.

Intracellular digestion may not be the only activity of chondrocyte lysosomes. In articular cartilage, a possible role would be to act as a source of degradative enzymes concerned in the normal chemical turnover of the protein–polysaccharide complexes of the cartilage matrix (Mankin and Lippiello 1969). It must be emphasized, however, that firm identification of cytoplasmic bodies as lysosomes requires the use of special histochemical methods suitable for electron microscopy; moreover, further investigation is needed on the morphological aspects of normal 'matrix turnover'. For technical reasons there is some uncertainty about the significance of the histochemical results which have been obtained from adult human articular cartilage, but in rabbit articular cartilage Chrisman (1967) has demonstrated degradative enzymes in membrane-lined bodies whose appearance is consistent with the view that they are lysosomes. Chrisman's results also confirm that there are relatively few lysosomes in the cells of non-fibrillated articular cartilage. It has been suggested that cartilage matrix degradation results from the extracellular release of lysosomal enzymes, at least under abnormal conditions (Dingle 1973), followed by digestion within the cell (see Section 3.).

2.3.10. Complex Bodies. Cytoplasmic structures which have been termed complex bodies (Meachim 1967) are sometimes observed in human articular cartilage. They are characterized by having two or more components of contrasting morphology, these components being contiguous or intermingled (Figure 2.8). Typically they comprise one or more lipid globules which contrast with a region containing a variable mixture of flocculent deposits, fibrillary material, electron-dense granules and electron-lucent areas. They are thus easily distinguished from the usual type of intracytoplasmic lipid globule (Figure 2.9).

Large complex bodies of this description have been encountered both in non-fibrillated and in fibrillated cartilage. However, they are an uncommon finding and it seems unlikely that they are an

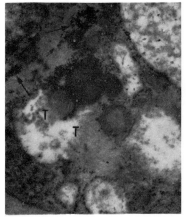

Figure 2.8 A large 'complex body' (T) with components of contrasting morphology. Glycogen particles (arrows).
Transmission electron micrograph ×16 000.
Osmium.

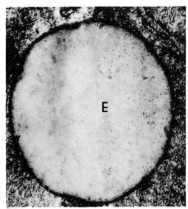

Figure 2.9 Intracytoplasmic lipid globule (E).
Transmission electron micrograph ×37 500.
Glutaraldehyde.

entirely normal phenomenon. It is possible that they are heterophagic or autophagic vacuoles containing either ingested extracellular matrix material or endogenous cytoplasmic material: if so, they may be a form of lysosomal derivative in which material such as lipid has proved relatively resistant to digestion by lysosomal enzymes (Smith and Farquhar 1966). Small complex bodies of similar morphology are occasionally seen: they too may represent lysosomal derivatives.

2.4. Intracellular Fluid

Estimates of the amount of intracellular fluid in articular chondro-cytes have been published by Eichelberger and her associates (Eichelberger, Akeson and Roma 1958; Miles and Eichelberger 1964), but may be based on an unacceptable assumption (Chapter 4, Section 3.2). They state that, in canine and human articular cartilage, intracellular water constitutes over 80% of the total cell substance; in man, this proportion remains fairly constant during the life-span.

Limb denervation in immature animals is said to lead to a loss of intracellular fluid as compared with normal values, but simple immobilization to cause no change (Akeson, Eichelberger and Roma 1958; Eichelberger, Roma and Moulder 1959).

2.5. Cell Inclusions

2.5.1. Glycogen. Deposits of glycogen often occur in articular chondrocytes (Figure 2.8). In electron micrographs the substance is seen as scattered particles, or as small or large aggregates in which the particles are often closely packed (Roy and Meachim 1968).

Data from histochemical studies suggest that the role of glycogen in cartilage may be to provide a store of chemical raw material. Thus glycogen is found in abundance in epiphyseal cartilage (Rouget 1859), where it has been assigned a rather indefinite role in endochondral ossification, possibly as a store of raw material for the synthesis of glycosaminoglycan (Pritchard 1952; Schajowicz and Cabrini 1958). Support for this suggestion comes from the work of Sheldon and Robinson (1960), who observe that glycogen disappears rapidly from ear cartilage cells after intravenous papain administration in experimental animals: this procedure causes matrix dissolution and apparently stimulates glycosaminoglycan synthesis by chondrocytes (McElligott and Potter 1960).

Zonal variations and ageing changes in the localization of glycogen in articular cartilage are compatible with this storage role. Most glycogen is found in the deeper cells of the uncalcified tissue (zones 2 and 3): such cells have the ability to synthesize glycosaminoglycan and show ultrastructural evidence of protein synthesis. In rabbit femoral condyle, little glycogen is found in the cells of the true articular cartilage layer during the early stages of growth, but glycogen increases in amount during the latter period of maturation and remains at a constant level during adult life in the normal tissue (Stockwell 1967b).

2.5.2. Lipid Globules. Lipid globules, first detected in articular chondrocytes by Leidy (1849), have long been considered a normal and constant constituent of these cells (Sacerdotti 1900). The findings from electron microscopy and from recent light microscopy investigations confirm that lipid globules are a normal feature in chondrocytes and that their presence is not evidence of a degenerative change (Collins, Ghadially and Meachim 1965).

On electron microscopy one or more lipid globules (Figure 2.9) are often seen in the plane of section through an articular chondrocyte (Roy and Meachim 1968). The globules are rounded or irregular in outline. They usually have a complete or incomplete rim of electron-dense granules, and usually also show electron-dense granules as an irregular peppering amongst their pale grey to grey-black content. Thus electron-density varies from globule to globule, and varies within each globule. The variable electron-density partly reflects the chemistry of the lipid: the electron-lucent material probably represents non-osmophilic triglycerides and the electron-dense material probably represents phospholipids and unsaturated fatty acids (Ghadially and Roy 1969, page 54).

The distribution of intracytoplasmic lipid globules in adult human articular cartilage has been studied by light microscopy using frozen sections stained with oil red O (Collins *et al.* 1965). Both in fibrillated and in non-fibrillated cartilage most of the chondrocytes in all layers of the tissue show from one to four or more lipid globules. The globules are of various sizes up to half that of the nucleus. In some specimens the intracellular lipid pattern is similar in the superficial and the deeper cells; in other specimens cells with many fine globules are more numerous in the superficial layer. In rabbit femoral condylar cartilage, small lipid droplets only 1–2 μm in diameter are detectable at birth and these react histochemically as phospholipid. During growth and maturity, larger droplets of neutral lipid up to 6 μm in diameter (Figure 2.10) are found in the intermediate zone (zone 2). Intracellular lipid globules increase in size throughout the life-span in this zone of rabbit articular cartilage (Stockwell 1967b), while in non-articular chondrocytes the maximum size is reached in early adult life and subsequently the lipid droplets may even diminish in diameter (Sacerdotti 1900).

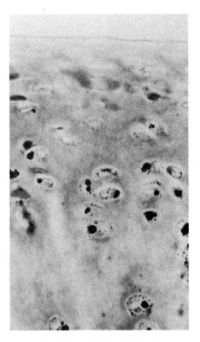

Figure 2.10 Large lipid globules coloured black in zone 2 chondrocytes in aged (6 years) rabbit femoral condylar cartilage. Extracellular lipid is present also.

Sudan black B, frozen section   ×450.

Like the extracellular lipid (see Chapter 1, Section 5.2), the origin of the intracellular lipid is also of interest. As a normal inclusion of the chondrocyte, lipid is presumably formed in the course of normal cell metabolism, but following experimental lipoarthrosis, the rapid increase in the number and size of lipid globules in articular chondrocytes (Ghadially, Mehta and Kirkaldy-Willis 1970) then suggests a more direct imbibition of the lipid injected into the synovial cavity. This is also suggested by observations on the electron-density of the lipid globules accumulating in the cells (Mehta and Ghadially 1973) and is confirmed by radioactive labelling of the cells following intra-articular injection of tritiated fat (Sprinz and Stockwell 1976). It appears that it is the fatty acid rather than the glycerol moiety of the injected triglyceride which is taken up into the intracellular lipid. This suggests that lipolysis occurs either in the synovial cavity or at the chondrocyte surface; evidence of lipase activity in chondrocytes (Montagna 1949) is perhaps compatible with the latter alternative.

While nearly all the workers are agreed on the non-degenerative nature of the usual lipid globules in chondrocytes, it appears that when abnormally large amounts accumulate (as in lipoarthrosis) there is evidence of injurious effects (Ghadially *et al.* 1970; Sprinz and Stockwell 1976). Observations of the chondrocytes affected show an increase in intracytoplasmic filaments, mitochondrial swelling and flattening of the normally projecting cell processes: enzyme activity is affected and there is evidence of a number of cell deaths. The cellular changes occur concomitantly with ground substance depletion in the matrix (Stockwell and Sprinz, unpublished observations) and evidence of roughening of the articular surface (Ghadially *et al.* 1970). It is probable, however, that these deleterious changes in the cartilage as a whole do not inexorably progress to overt fibrillation.

The function of the normal fat content of chondrocytes remains obscure. If regarded as a stored chemical raw material, the amount in the non-articular cartilages seems excessive for the local requirements, yet if it is a subsidiary source of depot fat, then the total quantity in the cartilage seems insignificant. Moreover, although denied by some, intracellular lipids in chondrocytes appear to remain independent of the state of nutrition of the whole organism, both in the rabbit (Sacerdotti 1900) and man (Stockwell 1967c). It might be rewarding to investigate the intracellular lipid under conditions which stimulate the synthesis of matrix material by the cells. In this respect, however, it should be noted that the lipid content of the cell clusters in deeply fibrillated cartilage (believed to be active in the synthesis of glycosaminoglycan) appears to be variable and not significantly different from normal (Collins *et al.* 1965; Chrisman, Semonsky and Bensch 1967).

The globules of intracytoplasmic lipid are not the only lipidic constituent of the cells; they also contain lipidic material as a chemical component of their membranes and organelles. As described in Chapter 1, Section 5, extracellular lipid can occur in the cartilage matrix. The possibility that lipid is involved in the lubrication of articular cartilage is discussed in Chapter 7, Section 7.2.2.

2.6. Zonal Variation in Cell Ultrastructure and its Relation to Function

From electron microscopy of vertical sections of adult human articular cartilage it would seem that the superficial cells generally have less cytoplasm than the underlying deeper cells; often their rough endoplasmic reticulum is poorly developed and their Golgi complex is small (Weiss *et al.* 1968). It has been suggested that the surface cells in non-fibrillated cartilage from young adults represent a dormant or quiescent cell population in which the rate of protein synthesis is reduced (Weiss *et al.* 1968). This suggestion would explain why the surface cells sometimes have low avidity for sulphate, an observation which was previously interpreted as evidence that they are 'effete' (Collins and McElligott 1960; Meachim and Collins 1962), a view no longer acceptable (see Figure 2.15).

On comparison with the superficial cells as seen in vertical sections, the cells in the deeper uncalcified tissue appear to have a more abundant cytoplasm. They show an ovoid, scalloped or frankly irregular outline; they generally contain much rough endoplasmic reticulum, an enlarged Golgi apparatus, and many mitochondria (Weiss *et al.* 1968). From what has already been said about the function of rough endoplasmic reticulum and of Golgi apparatus, it can be concluded that these cells are actively engaged in protein synthesis and particularly in the synthesis of protein destined to be discharged from the cell into the cartilage matrix. The protein which they continually synthesize in the adult is probably for the sulphated proteoglycan in the ground substance rather than protein for collagen fibres (Mankin and Lippiello 1969): thus it is relevant that the deeper cells also have an avidity for sulphate, as shown by radiochemical studies in which cartilage was incubated *in vitro* in medium labelled with tracer isotope (McElligott and Collins 1960; Collins and McElligott 1960; Collins and Meachim 1961; Meachim and Collins 1962).

2.7. Response to Hormones

The endocrine glands influence the structure of normal cartilage, not only in the growth period but also during adult life. Certain hormones are of special interest because of their involvement in human pathological conditions. Thus growth hormone, or somatotrophin, is implicated in the arthritis associated with acromegaly, and has also evoked wider interest because of its role in bone growth and because of certain therapeutic aspects; cortisone (and related pharmacological agents used in medicine) has also undergone investigation because of controversy as to whether it induces arthropathy. In laboratory animals, a number of hormones have been shown to affect articular cartilage, although the results of these studies are often difficult to assess because of variation in the dosage used and in the age and species of the experimental animals.

A series of investigations on the effects of hormones on chondrocyte ultrastructure in mice of varying ages was undertaken by Silberberg, Hasler and Silberberg. Changes in the chondrocyte are much more pronounced in immature than in adult tissue, although they are of similar character (Silberberg and Hasler 1971). There are many variations between the individual hormones but it appears that in general they fall into two groups as regards their effects on ultrastructure. Thus, in a first group, somatotrophin, insulin, thyroxine, testosterone and oestrogen tend to bring about hypertrophy of cells and their organelles, often accompanied by an increase in cell number. An increase in matrix fibre thickness also occurs (Silberberg 1968; Silberberg and Hasler 1971, 1972). These features are specially prominent after somatotrophin administration, the other hormones in this group exhibiting individual differences. Thus, oestrogen does not cause cell hypertrophy although organelles are well developed; insulin has a more marked effect on the Golgi apparatus than on the rough endoplasmic reticulum; while all the hormones can cause signs of cell regression, such as mitochondrial swelling and formation of autophagic vacuoles, cell deaths are most common after thyroxine. In a second group, cortisone and related substances cause a diminution in cell size together with under-development of cytoplasmic organelles, accompanied by cell death (Silberberg, Silberberg and Hasler 1966). Hormones in both groups cause accumulation of glycogen.

Such effects on chondrocytes and their ultrastructure are compatible with the known physiological actions of these hormones and with their macroscopic effects on cartilage. Somatotrophin not only accelerates and accentuates the sequence of growth, development and ageing in young cartilage (Silberberg, Silberberg and Hasler 1964) but also produces similar effects in mature articular chondrocytes (Silberberg and Hasler 1971). The hormone may also assist matrix healing following experimental scarification of a joint surface (Chrisman 1975). However, it appears that somatotrophin does not itself have a direct effect on chondrocytes (since costal chondrocytes in culture do not respond to the hormone) but instead acts through an intermediary substance found in the plasma, originally named 'sulphation factor' (Salmon and Daughaday 1957). There is evidence that this factor, now termed 'somatomedin' (Daughaday, Hall, Raben, Salmon, van den Brande and van Wyk 1972), is produced in the liver (Sledge 1973); several different forms of somatomedin have now been defined. In culture, somatomedin stimulates proteoglycan and collagen synthesis and cell replication in costal cartilage. Recent work suggests that the effects of growth hormone and somatomedin on articular cartilage *in vitro* may not correspond to those observed on rat costal cartilage, the usual type of cartilage in the assay system. Thus, with articular cartilage, it appears that growth hormone *in vitro* has the direct action of depressing glycosaminoglycan synthesis and that somatomedin may enhance incorporation of ^{35}S-sulphate into high molecular weight keratan sulphate and not into chondroitin sulphate (Smith, Duckworth, Bergenholtz and Lemperg 1975).

The ultrastructural changes after cortisone treatment are in accord with the biochemical effects of the hormone on cartilage and on the synthesis of matrix components by the chondrocyte: not only is ground substance lost from the matrix but there is also diminished incorporation of macromolecule precursors (see Sections 3.4–3.6, and Chapter 3) into the cell (Layton 1951; Bostrom and Odeblad 1953; Mankin, Zarins and Jaffe 1972). Shaw and Lacey (1973) have demonstrated that corticosteroids, in doses comparable (proportionate to body weight) with those used clinically in patients, induce fibrillation on young rabbit knee joints, and attribute this to the effect of wear on cartilage in which the matrix has been depleted by inhibition of sulphomucin synthesis. Recovery of cartilage damaged by prior administration of papain is prevented by corticosteroids, which have a systemic action on other joints as well as local effects, when injected intra-articularly. Shaw and Lacey urge caution in the clinical use of corticosteroids in the presence of progressive degenerative joint disease.

2.8. Immunogenicity of Chondrocytes

Cartilage has long been considered an immunologically privileged tissue. Homografts containing viable cells have been found to survive for long periods at non-articular sites in man and lower animals (Gibson, Curran and Davies 1957). Immunological studies have demonstrated that such grafts are only weakly antigenic (Craigmyle 1958). The poor antigenicity of cartilage has been explained on the basis either of an absence of transplantation antigens or of the protective effect of the matrix (Bacsich and Wyburn 1947). However, it has now been shown that cells isolated from articular cartilage do carry major transplantation antigens (Elves 1974), the reaction of the chondrocytes and of lymphocytes to antibodies being similar. On the other hand, various components of the matrix are also known to be antigenic. Thus the non-helical regions of tropocollagen (Traub and Piez 1971) and the core proteins of proteoglycans (Baxter and Muir 1972), particularly near the attachment of keratan sulphate chains (Keiser and de Vito 1974), are significantly though poorly antigenic. Although immunoglobulin penetrates articular cartilage (see Chapter 4), these antigenic sites are probably shielded in the intact tissue from antibody by steric exclusion due to the extended glycosaminoglycan side-chains of the proteoglycans. Similarly, the proteoglycans protect the cells from the lymphoid system of the host. Thus, protective effects have been demonstrated using isolated chondrocytes with varying amounts of matrix remaining around each cell following controlled papain digestion (Elves 1974). Similarly, resynthesized ground substance has been found to prevent cell death in cartilage exposed to antiserum following experimental depletion of the matrix (Millroy and Poole 1974; Fell 1975). Therefore, despite the weak antigenicity of the matrix itself, it appears that its overall immunological property *in vivo* is to act as a shield for the cells. The feasibility of using grafts of chondrocytes to repair cartilage defects in animals is being investigated experimentally by Bentley (1976, personal communication), with a view to the possible use of this procedure in man.

2.9. Cell Degeneration and Cell Necrosis

Difficulties in interpretation can arise when electron microscopy of a cartilage cell shows features which deviate from the patterns usually obtained from normal healthy chondrocytes. There are several reasons for caution before accepting such an appearance as evidence that the cell is degenerate. First, structural damage can occur from delay in fixation or from faults in techniques during handling and preparation of the specimen: damage of this sort can, for example, produce localized electron-lucent areas of 'cytoplasmic oedema', empty except for embedding medium; it can also cause breakage of membranes and swelling of mitochondria (Toner and Carr 1968, pp. 88–95). Second, an oblique or tangential sectioning effect can give a false impression of discontinuity in a membrane, simulating a true break in nuclear or cytoplasmic membranes or simulating fragmentation of an organelle (Toner and Carr 1968, pp. 88–95). Third, it seems possible that genuine structural imperfections of a minor, focal nature can develop in the cytoplasm in a healthy living cell: for example, the multilayered electron-dense membranous formations seen in the chondrocyte-like cells of human nucleus pulposus fixed in glutaraldehyde may perhaps be explicable on this basis (Meachim and Cornah 1970). Finally, the occurrence of an occasional lysosome or lysosomal derivative may sometimes represent nothing more than an attempt to dispose of an organelle which has become superfluous or effete.

Cell degeneration and cell necrosis are as much functional and biochemical concepts as they are structural states, and thus there are limitations in a purely morphological approach to the recognition of these phenomena. Moreover, in electron microscopy the distinction between a degenerate and a necrotic cell is to some extent arbitrary. Degenerate cells show structural deterioration of their cytoplasm, but their nuclear architecture appears unaltered; in necrotic cells the distinguishing feature is a structural deterioration of the nucleus (Ghadially and Roy 1969, p. 42).

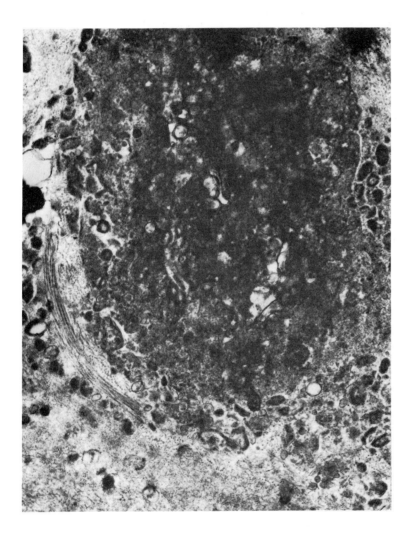

Figure 2.11 Debris of a cell which has undergone necrosis.
Transmission electron micrograph ×25 000.
Glutaraldehyde.

Occasionally the cytoplasm of a chondrocyte shows an extensive structural deterioration which can be regarded as evidence that the cell was undergoing a degenerative change. The change alters the normal appearance of cytoplasmic structures such as endoplasmic reticulum and mitochondria, but not that of the nucleus. In man such cells are uncommon in mature non-fibrillated cartilage and no comprehensive classification of their ultrastructural patterns is available.

Necrotic cells are more easily recognized. In a necrotic chondrocyte the nucleus shows an abnormal homogeneous appearance with a crenated outline. In a more advanced form of necrotic change, the outlines of nucleus and cytoplasm become blurred, and the cell can then appear as a large, irregularly shaped mass amongst which normal organelles and normal cytomembranes are no longer apparent. Complete disintegration of a necrotic cell can appear as a focal aggregate of remnants of organelles and cytomembranes, together with rounded membranous bodies and lipidic debris.

Examples of a necrotic or a completely disintegrated cell are sometimes seen on electron microscopy of adult human articular cartilage (Figure 2.11). They can occur both in fibrillated and in non-fibrillated areas. Thus electron microscopy demonstrates that the death of a chondrocyte can take place within the cartilage matrix, and that it can do so beneath an intact articular surface.

3. CHONDROCYTE METABOLISM AND ENZYME HISTO-CHEMISTRY

Like other living cells, chondrocytes carry out a complex variety of chemical reactions mediated by enzymes. These enzymatic reactions provide the metabolic pathways which are concerned, for example, in respiration and glycolysis, glycogen and lipid metabolism, and the synthesis and degradation of the ground substance. With the probable exceptions of matrix degradation and of the conversion of procollagen to tropocollagen, most of the enzymatic reactions take place entirely within the cell and their efficient co-ordination during metabolic activity must imply a high degree of organization within the chondrocyte and within its individual organelles; an ultrastructural basis for this organization of function at the subcellular level is provided by the various intracellular organelles seen on electron microscopy.

The enzymes of chondrocytes can be studied by histochemical and biochemical techniques. Although chondrocytes were among the first mammalian cells to be studied histochemically, little direct investigation of their metabolism and enzyme histochemistry has been carried out on human articular cartilage. In consequence, much of our information depends on the results of work done on cells in other types of hyaline cartilage and in other species. The metabolic activity of articular cartilage has been studied by manometric and by radioisotope methods, and the results obtained by these methods are supplemented by the information which has been obtained by histochemical techniques.

3.1. Respiration and Glycolysis

3.1.1. Metabolic Pathways. Since cartilage lacks blood vessels, the diffusion distances from nutritional source to tissue cell are much greater in cartilage than in well vascularized tissues (see Chapter 8). The relative importance of the avascular environment and of intrinsic factors in the chondrocyte in determining the type of metabolism is not known. The amounts of nutrient in the chondrocyte environment are likely to be small, although direct measurements of the concentrations of metabolites in cartilage *in vivo* have been few. However, in small fragments of young articular cartilage grown in rabbit ear chambers, measurements with microelectrodes show that oxygen gradients are steep compared with those in vascular fibrous tissue (Silver 1975). Values for oxygen tension in the centre of these 0.5 mm blocks (much thinner and therefore better oxygenated than the articular cartilage of the human knee or hip, for example) are only 5–8 mmHg, about one-third of that in the space between capillaries in soft tissue. Glucose concentration is only slightly lower than in soft tissue, however. Such information about the pericellular environment is compatible with data concerning chondrocyte metabolism acquired by earlier workers.

Bywaters (1937) made a systematic study of equine joint tissues and was the first to observe a low but measurable oxygen utilization by articular cartilage. On a per cell basis, oxygen uptake is about one-fiftieth that of liver or kidney, although the rate of glycolysis is comparable to that of other tissues. These observations, taken together with the paucity of cells in the tissue, underline the difficulties in studying cartilage respiration and metabolism.

Nevertheless, a number of enzyme systems have been investigated. In the glycolytic pathway, lactic and triose-phosphate dehydrogenases have been observed in bovine articular cartilage (Lutwak-Mann 1940; Rosenthal, Bowie and Wagoner 1942a). Activity of the direct oxidation pathway (pentose cycle) was postulated by Lutwak-Mann, who observed a requirement for coenzyme II (nicotinamide adenine dinucleotide phosphate, NADP) in glucose oxidation in articular cartilage. This pathway exists in epiphyseal plate chondrocytes (Kuhlmann 1960; Bernstein, Leboeuf and Cahill 1961) although on the basis of glucose-6-phosphate dehydrogenase activity (a key enzyme in the pentose cycle) it accounts for only a small proportion of total glucose oxidation. Glucose-6-phosphate dehydrogenase is found histochemically in murine articular cartilage (Balogh, Dudley and Cohen 1961), but the resultant pathway is probably important only for the generation of NADPH and pentose sugars, utilized in the synthesis of lipids and nucleic acids.

Succinic dehydrogenase has been demonstrated manometrically in bovine articular cartilage (Rosenthal *et al.* 1942a). Histochemically there is much less activity of succinic than of lactic dehydrogenase (Figure 2.12) in articular cartilage of both mouse

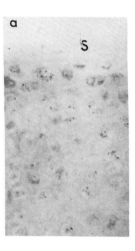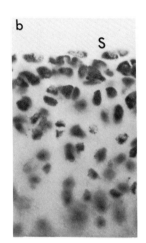

Figure 2.12 Young adult rabbit femoral condylar cartilage showing (a) a low succinic dehydrogenase activity seen as a dark punctate stain, and (b) high lactic dehydrogenase activity. S = articular surface.
Nitro-blue tetrazolium technique, frozen sections ×360.

(Balogh *et al.* 1961) and rabbit (Stockwell 1966), a finding in accord with the difference between oxygen uptake and glycolytic rate observed manometrically. Other enzymes of the Krebs tricarboxylic acid cycle have also been shown histochemically in articular cartilage, and cytochrome oxidase has been found in invertebrate cartilage (Person and Fine 1959).

3.1.2. Ageing Changes. It is believed that ageing affects the respiration of articular chondrocytes. In bovine carpal and tarsal cartilage, Rosenthal, Bowie and Wagoner (1941) found that the glycolytic rate remains constant with increasing age at about 1.7–2.1 μg glucose per 10^6 cells per hour (calculated from their results allowing for the water content and specific gravity of the tissue). Oxygen uptake, however, shows a decline with age from 0.15 in the immature and 0.12 in the young adult to 0.06 μl oxygen per 10^6 cells per hour in aged animals. Further investigation demonstrated that the decrease in oxygen uptake is due to a diminution of the 'oxygen-activating component' (cytochrome) while the 'substrate-activating component' (dehydrogenase) remains relatively constant (Rosenthal, Bowie and Wagoner

1942b). This interpretation of the effect of age on cell metabolism, while probably correct, assumes that all cells in the cartilage are similar. The aged tissue investigated by Rosenthal showed a lower cell density as compared with the young adult, and, as discussed in Section 4.3, this may imply that there was a preferential loss of superficial (zone 1) cells in the aged cartilage slices. If heterogeneity were to exist between cells of different zones as regards oxygen utilization, although this has not yet been demonstrated, then the above results might alternatively reflect a loss of superficial cells.

3.1.3. Zonal Variation. Most of the evidence concerning zonal variations in metabolism suggests that superficial cells (zone 1) are less active than those in the deep layers (zones 2 and 3). The 'lesser' ability of the superficial cells to incorporate sulphate is quoted in human articular cartilage (Collins and McElligott 1960). Similarly, histochemical observations in murine articular cartilage sectioned vertical to the joint surface suggest that NAD and NADP reductase activity is reduced in cells of the superficial zone compared with the deeper zones (Balogh *et al.* 1961). With respect to autoradiographic and histological assessment of the superficial chondrocytes it must, however, be stressed that vertical sections do not show these flattened discoidal cells to advantage (Arlet *et al.* 1958). Nevertheless, quantitative estimation of lactic dehydrogenase activity in human articular cartilage suggests that this is lower per cell in the superficial than in the deeper layers (Stockwell, unpublished). No data exist on zonal variations in oxygen requirement and respiratory gas tensions within articular cartilage, and sulphate uptake merits further study in man (see Figure 2.15).

3.2. Glycogen and Lipid Metabolism

Enzymes associated with glycogen metabolism—glycogen synthetase (Takeuchi and Glenner 1961; Grillo, Okuno, Price and Foa 1964) and phosphorylase (Cobb 1952)—and with lipid metabolism—lipase (Montagna 1949) and lecithinase (Levine and Follis 1949)—have been demonstrated histochemically in chondrocytes. Dihydrolipoic dehydrogenase, involved in the formation of acetyl-coenzyme A compounds, has been found in epiphyseal and tracheal cartilage (Balogh 1964); the enzyme displays more activity in the central than the peripheral cells. This parallels the distribution of lipid and glycogen in the tissue. In rabbit articular cartilage there is slight activity of β-hydroxybutyric dehydrogenase, involved in β-oxidation of fatty acids, and of soluble a-glycerophosphate dehydrogenase, concerned with the formation of a-glycerophosphate from intermediates of glycolysis. There is little zonal variation in these enzymes. Non-specific esterase activity is minimal in rabbit articular cartilage and is located in the deep hypertrophic cells of the unossified epiphysis in the immature tissue and in some cells of zones 2 and 3 of aged tissue (Figure 2.13). This contrasts with non-articular hyaline cartilage, where most cells have a considerable esterase activity, especially during ageing (Stockwell 1966).

Figure 2.13 Non-specific esterase activity (seen as a dark stain) is found in the deep cells (zone 3) of young adult rabbit articular cartilage (a), but in the superficial cells of aged tissue (b). In non-articular hyaline (xiphisternal) cartilage, esterase activity is minimal in the young adult (c), but most aged cells (d) possess considerable activity, thus differing from aged articular chondrocytes. P = perichondrium.

a-Naphthyl acetate as substrate, frozen sections ×180.

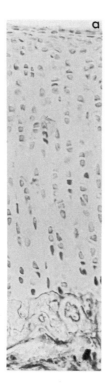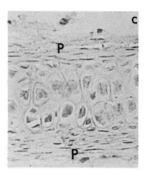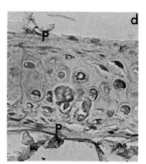

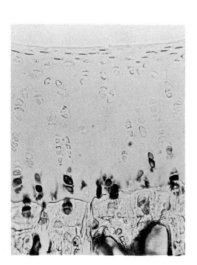

Figure 2.14 The deep cells (zone 3) of aged rabbit femoral condylar cartilage exhibit considerable alkaline phosphatase activity.

a-Naphthyl phosphate as substrate, frozen section ×180.

3.3. Alkaline Phosphatase

As detected histochemically, alkaline phosphatase is present only in the deeper cells of articular cartilage (Zorzoli 1948; Shaw and Martin 1962). In rat (Morse and Greep 1951) and rabbit articular cartilage (Stockwell 1966), activity persists into old age (Figure 2.14). Biochemical studies (Ali and Bayliss 1974) of normal human articular cartilage have not detected differences in activity between the superficial and deeper zones, possibly because the activity is too low to be detected by such an estimation. Estimates of enzyme activity in the full thickness of uncalcified articular cartilage demonstrate that this rises dramatically in osteoarthrosic cartilage (Ali and Evans 1973). This may be related to an increased tendency of the abnormal tissue to exaggerated mineralization and hence, as in the normal, may be associated with a continuous process of remodelling at the basal osseo-chondral junction. A specific member of the alkaline phosphatase group, 5-nucleotidase, is present in chondrocytes. Lutwak-Mann (1940) finds that articular cartilage slices metabolize adenosine-5-phosphate to hypoxanthine, the ultimate oxidation product of this pathway being uric acid. In immature bovine articular cartilage, Otte (1958) localizes 5-nucleotidase to the cells of the superficial zone, although activity is found in all zones in the adult.

3.4. Proteoglycan Synthesis

Proteoglycan metabolism has been investigated in considerable detail. Within the cell, much is known of the sites of synthesis of proteoglycans. The protein moiety is assembled in the rough endoplasmic reticulum. Autoradiographic evidence locates the synthesized polysaccharide moiety within the Golgi complex (Neutra and Leblond 1966) and suggests that sulphation of the polymer also occurs in this organelle (Revel and Hay 1963; Godman and Lane 1964; Perlman, Telser and Dorfman 1964). Activation of sulphate prior to its incorporation into the polysaccharide molecule is facilitated by cytoplasmic enzymes which are not membrane-bound, found in the supernatant fraction of the intracellular fluid (Horwitz and Dorfman 1968). Further information may be obtained in Chapter 3, Section 4.7.

3.4.1. Autoradiographic Studies of Sulphate Incorporation. It has been shown that articular chondrocytes have the ability to incorporate sulphate, and that the incorporated sulphate is 'fixed' in the cell in a form which cannot be removed by subsequent dialysis. This property of sulphate fixation is related to the synthesis and sulphation of glycosaminoglycan. The process can be studied by use of sulphate labelled with a radioactive tracer isotope (^{35}S-sulphate). Quantitative radiochemical techniques estimate the amount of sulphate fixed by the cartilage in a given period of time; autoradiography permits localization of sulphate-fixing cells (Figure 2.15) and makes it possible to observe the subsequent movement of the labelled material from such cells out into the matrix. By these means sulphate uptake can be studied *in vivo*, or *in vitro* using cartilage slices incubated in an artificial medium; in man observations are limited to those made *in vitro*. Cartilage samples obtained at operation or necropsy show a decline in sulphate-fixing ability as the interval after somatic death increases, and for this reason use of cartilage obtained at operation is preferable (Mankin and Lippiello 1970).

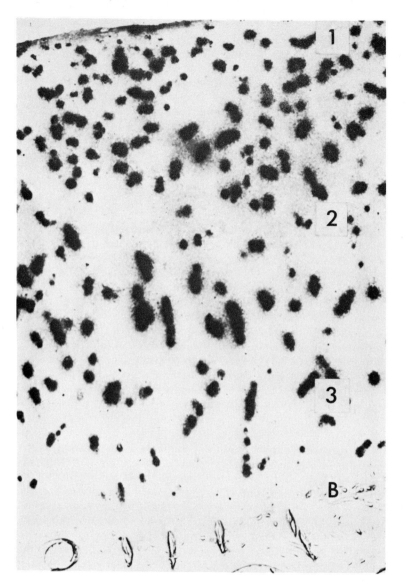

Figure 2.15 Autoradiograph demonstrating sulphate ($^{35}SO_4$) uptake *in vitro* by non-fibrillated articular cartilage from a woman aged 65 years. The black images mark the site of sulphate-fixing cells; inactive cells are not shown. The articular surface is at the top left; in this subject sulphate uptake was not confined to the intermediate (2) and deep (3) uncalcified layers; there was also uptake by a proportion of the superficial layer (1) cells. Inactive calcified layer and subchondral bone (B) ×100.

On autoradiography of adult human articular cartilage (Figure 2.15) an intense image is obtained over the cells of the intermediate and deep uncalcified layers (zones 2 and 3). In contrast, the cells of the superficial layer (zone 1) of the cartilage, when considered as a group, sometimes have a low affinity for sulphate (Collins and McElligott 1960), but it should be noted that the findings in the superficial layer vary from cell to cell and from specimen to specimen (Figure 2.15). Quantitative radiochemistry shows that, in the absence of fibrillation, ageing during adult life has no appreciable effect on sulphate uptake in human articular cartilage: cartilage from the central part of the head of the adult humerus often has at most only a superficial fibrillation and its sulphate uptake is unchanged with age (Collins and Meachim 1961); in contrast, adult human patellar cartilage shows an apparent increase in sulphate uptake with advancing age (McElligott and Collins 1960), but this apparent increase is associated with the frequent development of deep fibrillation and matrix softening at this site and with cell population changes due to cluster formation.

If indeed sulphate uptake per cell is increased in fibrillated cartilage, then this is probably stimulated, *inter alia*, by the local depletion of the matrix ground substance. Thus *in vivo* using papain (McElligott and Potter 1960), and in organ culture using hyaluronidase (Hardingham, Fitton-Jackson and Muir 1972) to produce experimental depletion of matrix ground substance, it has been shown that the synthesis of proteoglycans by the chondrocytes is considerably increased. This suggests that chondrocytes react to changes in the matrix in which they are embedded (see also Sections 4.6 and 8.2). Recent work by Wiebkin and Muir (1975) has shed some light on possible modes of interaction. It appears that in isolated articular chondrocytes in suspension culture, hyaluronic acid (but not cartilage proteoglycans, free chondroitin sulphate or lysozyme) significantly reduces the rate of ^{35}S-sulphate incorporation but also increases the proportion of radioactive sulphate bound within the cells. Wiebkin and Muir suggest that hyaluronic acid interacts with proteoglycans on the cell surface by a similar mechanism to that involved in proteoglycan aggregation: as a consequence, secretion of proteoglycan is diminished. It might be speculated that the chondrocyte synthesizes and secretes proteoglycans at a maximum rate (possibly only for a limited time period) when such hyaluronic acid–proteoglycan aggregates are not prevented from moving away from the cell rapidly (as might occur in a pericellular environment in a matrix depleted of its ground substance). When the matrix has its correct complement of proteoglycans, the secretion rate is reduced to normal levels because newly secreted proteoglycan (complexed with hyaluronic acid) remains in contact or close proximity with the chondrocyte plasma membrane for a relatively longer time. This response to matrix proteoglycan depletion would benefit the cells in at least two ways: first, chondrocytes surrounded by proteoglycans are inaccessible to potentially lethal macromolecules; second, they are less at risk from mechanical damage, since proteoglycan increases the compressive stiffness of the matrix.

3.4.2. Polysaccharide Synthesis and the Functional Heterogeneity of Chondrocytes. Zonal variations in chondrocyte function relating to respiratory enzyme activity and, possibly, to sulphate incorporation have already been noted. With regard to the synthesis of the carbohydrate skeleton of the glycosaminoglycans, several histochemical studies have used the activity of the enzyme uridine diphosphate (UDP)-glucose dehydrogenase as an index to cell function. This enzyme is active in the converson of UDP-glucose to UDP-glucuronic acid, the source of the glucuronic acid component of the disaccharide repeating unit of chondroitin sulphate. In non-articular cartilage, the maximum activity is in the peripheral cells and is reduced or absent in the central cells (Balogh and Cohen 1961). Thus, paradoxically, UDP-glucose dehydrogenase activity is maximal where the chondroitin sulphate concentration is lowest. However, in articular cartilage, no marked differences have been noted between the superficial and deeper zones (Lenzi, Berlanda, Flora, Aureli, Rizzotti, Balduini and Boni 1974; Sprinz and Stockwell 1976).

Apart from interzonal variation, it appears that there may be a functional heterogeneity between the chondrocytes within a single zone. Alcian blue–critical electrolyte concentration (CEC) studies of adult canine humeral head cartilage (Kincaid, Van Sickle and Wilsman 1972) suggest that there are random variations between chondrocytes, particularly within the intermediate and deep zones (2 and 3). The cells are Alcian-blue-positive or negative in the ratio 1:1, both staining alternatives occurring within an isogeneous group. Furthermore, Kincaid *et al.* suggest that some Alcian-blue-positive cells produce predominantly chondroitin sulphate, while others produce both chondroitin sulphate and keratan sulphate. Enzyme histochemistry reveals that most enzymes, such as NAD diaphorase and succinate and other dehydrogenases are equally active in all chondrocytes. However, UDP-galactose-4-epimerase shows a high activity in some chondrocytes and a low activity in others (Wilsman and Van Sickle 1971), giving a similar staining heterogeneity to the pattern obtained with Alcian blue. This result is in accord with the biochemical function of the enzyme which catalyses the conversion of UDP-glucose to UDP-galactose in the biosynthetic pathway of chondroitin sulphate.

Further evidence has been obtained in adult rat articular cartilage by Mazhuga and Cherkosova (1974), who comment that two adjacent chondrocytes in the middle zone may differ in their morphology, showing reciprocal variation in the amount of rough endoplasmic reticulum and of glycogen. From the results of radioisotope incorporation studies, these authors conclude that in the rat about half of the middle zone chondrocytes (those with much glycogen) are highly active in producing proteoglycans while the rest synthesize collagen together with some proteoglycan.

Further evidence is needed before the significance of these studies can be evaluated fully. If indeed there are real differences between chondrocytes at any given time of sampling, then either the chondrocyte population is not homogeneous or individual chondrocytes undergo cyclical changes in function.

3.5. Collagen Synthesis

The molecular unit of the collagen fibre, tropocollagen, is synthesized within the cell as the precursor form, procollagen, which contains a random coil extension at both the N- and C- terminal ends of the triple helix. Like other proteins, the constituent amino-acids are incorporated into the polypeptide chains, the process being mediated by the ribosomes. Subsequently, some proline and lysine residues within the polypeptide chain undergo hydroxylation, a process which, *inter alia*, requires vitamin C. Hydroxy-proline, the characteristic amino-acid of collagen, is now known to have a special role in the stabilization of the tropocollagen molecule and of the collagen fibril, in addition to its general contribution as a ring compound in the tripeptide repeating sequence of the polypeptide. Hydroxy-lysine can be the site of attachment of a number of short carbohydrate side-chains. It has already been mentioned that cartilage has a special form of collagen—type II or $(a_1II)_3$—unique to the tissue. Collagen structure and metabolism are fully discussed in Chapter 3, Section 5.

3.5.1. Collagen Secretion and Fibre Formation. Collagen monomer, as procollagen, is produced intracellularly and collagen fibres are formed extracellularly. There has been some controversy over the intermediate processes involved: at least three routes from the site of synthesis to the extracellular matrix have been postulated:

(a) On the basis of electron autoradiographic observations of ^{3}H-proline incorporation, Revel and Hay (1963) concluded that synthesized material passes out of the cell through the membranes and vacuoles of the Golgi complex.

(b) Other workers contended that the pathway was more direct, i.e. from the endoplasmic reticulum cisternae out into the extracellular matrix without traversing the Golgi complex (Ross and Benditt 1965).

(c) A third hypothesis suggested that the synthesized product passed directly from the ground cytoplasm (cytosol) to the extracellular matrix (Cooper and Prockop 1968) since it was thought that when collagen hydroxylation was arrested experimentally (Prockop and Kivirikko 1967), the material—protocollagen—accumulated external to the endoplasmic reticulum.

The most recent evidence indicates that collagen is secreted via the Golgi complex, as occurs normally with proteins in other secretory cells. Using the odontoblast as the model cell, Weinstock and Leblond (1974) have shown that collagen is passed out of the cell in the region of the intradentinal process (which does not contain granular endoplasmic reticulum) in smooth-walled vesicles derived from the Golgi apparatus. Studying ^{3}H-proline uptake in fibroblasts, Ehrlich, Ross and Bornstein (1974) have found that colchicine causes intracellular retention of the label and an increase in the number of Golgi vacuoles, suggesting that this organelle is associated with an intracellular feedback inhibition of collagen synthesis. Lastly, in fibroblasts prepared so that antibodies could gain entrance to cytoplasmic organelles, both the rough endoplasmic reticulum cisternae and the Golgi complex become labelled by ferritin-conjugated anti-procollagen (Nist, von der Mark, Hay, Olsen, Bornstein, Ross and Dehm 1975). Thus there seems to be no doubt that the Golgi membranes and vacuoles are involved in secretion of collagen.

Ghadially and Roy (1969, p. 50) point out that there is debate as to where monomeric collagen aggregates to form collagen fibrils detectable with the electron microscope. Thus there is evidence of collagen apparently found intracellularly which might suggest an intracellular location of fibrillogenesis: Sheldon and Kimball (1962) believe that portions of collagen fibrils can occur within the vacuoles of the Golgi apparatus of chondrocytes, and it is possible that the banded structures they illustrate in their electron micrographs may in fact be a form of collagen (Cornah, Meachim and Parry 1970). However, portions of banded collagen fibres observed within the profile of the cell can be attributed either to collagenase-mediated degradation of ingested material during rapid tissue remodelling or to the artefactual appearance of enclosure within the cell due to the plane of sectioning (Perez-Tamayo and Rojkind 1973). It appears to be unlikely that fibrillogenesis occurs intracellularly since the procollagen molecule (the intracellular form) remains soluble in physiological conditions suitable for the aggregation of tropocollagen into fibrils; conversion of procollagen to tropocollagen requires an *extra*cellular enzyme (Layman and Ross 1973). Further information on the process of fibrillogenesis may be found in Chapter 3, Section 5.2.5.

3.5.2. Collagen Metabolism in Adult Articular Cartilage. Much of the investigation of the synthesis of tropocollagen by Prockop and his colleagues has been carried out using embryonic chondrocytes, and there appears to be little information concerning the process in the adult articular chondrocyte. Repo and Mitchell (1971) have published evidence that collagen synthesis may in fact occur in normal articular cartilage of mature rabbits. In man the turnover of collagen is very low in normal adult compared with immature tissue (see also Chapter 3, Section 5.2).

3.5.3. Other Matrix Constituents. Little or nothing is known of the synthesis of matrix constituents other than proteoglycan or collagen. However, the overall synthesis of protein in cartilage may be assessed by the rate of incorporation of glycine. It should be noted that glycine incorporation at least partly reflects the synthesis of non-collagenous protein of the proteoglycan ground substance, and is not valid as a measure solely of the rate of collagen synthesis (Mankin and Lippiello 1969).

Studies of glycine incorporation in rabbit articular cartilage suggest that protein synthesis per unit DNA falls to a low but steady value in the normal adult (Mankin and Baron 1965). The situation in fibrillated cartilage is not clear. In canine hip joints, there is evidence of a decrease in glycine incorporation per unit DNA (Mankin and Laing 1967), while in the human hip joint there appears to be an increase in glycine incorporation per unit DNA in fibrillated cartilage (Mankin and Lippiello 1970). The possible effect of the loss from fibrillated cartilage of relatively inactive superficial cells upon apparent changes in the uptake of sulphate in fibrillated cartilage is discussed in Section 8.2.1: similar considerations may be relevant to the measurement of protein synthesis.

3.6. Degradation

Although hydrolytic enzymes of a general type, such as acid phosphatase, have been detected both histochemically (Burstone 1960) and biochemically (Ali and Evans 1973) in articular cartilage, more study has been devoted to those which degrade the macromolecules of the matrix. Degradation could vary in its severity from complete loss of the macromolecule—the process resulting in small fragments which either diffuse out of the tissue or are taken up by the chondrocytes and digested intracellularly—to less severe changes resulting in damaged macromolecules which may remain *in situ* but which are inadequate to sustain the normal physicochemical properties required of the matrix.

3.6.1. Collagen. There appears to be no evidence that collagenase occurs in cartilage: indeed, cartilage (type II) collagen is in any case much more resistant to the enzyme than other forms of collagen (Dingle 1975). However, cathepsin B_1, a thiol proteinase present in human and rabbit articular cartilage (Ali and Bayliss 1974), is capable of degrading collagen (Burleigh, Barrett and Lazarus 1974), as well as proteoglycan (Morrison, Barrett, Dingle and Prior 1973). The low pH optimum of this enzyme implies that its action on collagen would take place in intracellular vacuoles. Other proteolytic enzymes might also break down cartilage collagen provided it had become denatured (Ali 1970, personal communication). Such mechanisms may permit a very limited collagen turnover in adult articular cartilage, as observed in the rabbit (Repo and Mitchell 1971).

3.6.2. Proteoglycan. It is helpful to consider the structure of the protein–polysaccharide complexes in terms of the parts of the molecule which could theoretically be attacked enzymatically. Thus the long hyaluronic acid 'thread' of the hyaluronate–proteoglycan complex might be severed by the action of hyaluronidase; the protein cores of the attached proteoglycans (or of separate proteoglycan monomers) could be broken down by proteolytic enzymes, and the chondroitin sulphate side-chains of the proteoglycan also degraded by hyaluronidase: extensive degradation of chondroitin sulphate would require sulphatases and enzymes such as β-N-acetyl-D-glucosaminidase and β-D-glucuronidase in addition. There are, however, no clear indications as to how keratan sulphate might be degraded (Leaback 1974).

In practice, hyaluronidase has not been detected in cartilage (Bollet, Handy and Sturgill 1963; Leaback 1974) and even if the enzyme is present, it is probable that it could not gain access to the central hyaluronate of the large complexes (Dingle 1975). The apparent absence of hyaluronidase implies also that breakdown of chondroitin sulphate side-chains must be through the action of the lysosomal exo-glycosidases, glucosaminidase and glucuronidase, although it is thought that they are unlikely to be very effective extracellularly (Leaback 1974). The lack of hyaluronidase, which most readily degrades the intact polysaccharides, suggests that it may be necessary to invoke non-enzymatic chemical mechanisms; this may be particularly important in the case of the hyaluronate in the large complexes. Both glucosaminidase (Pugh and Walker 1961) and glucuronidase (Gubisch and Schlager 1961) have been detected histochemically in cartilage. In rabbit articular cartilage, glucosaminidase is equally active in the cells of all zones (Sprinz and Stockwell 1976), although acid phosphatase is much less active in the superficial than in the deep zone.

Degradation of proteoglycans into small fragments can be achieved most effectively by scission of the protein core (Dingle and Burleigh 1974). Indeed, of all the digestive enzymes the proteases have excited most interest, following the observation that hypervitaminosis A leads to the dissolution of the cartilage matrix (Fell and Mellanby 1952), through the potentiation of lysosomal protease (Fell and Dingle 1963). The evidence for the existence of proteolytic activity in articular cartilage is partly biochemical (Ali 1964; Fessel and Chrisman 1964) and partly electron-histochemical (Chrisman 1967). It has been suggested that proteases have a role in the turnover of matrix ground substance, which occurs as a normal physiological phenomenon in adult articular cartilage (Mankin and Lippiello 1969), and that their activity is increased in fibrillated cartilage (Ali and Evans 1973). A number of proteases, termed cathepsins, with acid pH optima, have been detected in hyaline and elastic cartilage. In articular cartilage, cathepsin D is thought to be the main autolytic enzyme and is found in the chondrocytes (Ali and Evans 1973). Cathepsin B_1 is also present in articular cartilage (Ali and Bayliss 1974) and may have particular significance because of its ability to degrade collagen as well as proteoglycan. Like most degradative enzymes, they are of lysomal origin. Thus immunocytochemical methods have demonstrated the localization of cathepsin D in lysosomes (Dingle 1973) and this is corroborated by the finding in human articular cartilage that a rise in cathepsin D activity is accompanied by a parallel rise in acid phosphatase activity (Ali and Bayliss 1974).

Catheptic activity on a tissue wet weight basis is much less in human articular cartilage than in rabbit ear cartilage, for example, but is about the same when compared per unit DNA. Activity of cathepsins is raised in fibrillated, as compared with intact, articular cartilage (Ali and Evans 1973; Ali and Bayliss 1974), whether activity is expressed on a wet weight or DNA basis.

3.6.3. Site of Degradation. It is considered at present that lysosomal enzymes of the chondrocyte, especially the cathepsins, provide the basis for degradation mechanisms endogenous to cartilage tissue. Clearly, therefore, if matrix components are to be enzymatically degraded in the course of physiological turnover or during pathological change, either the matrix macromolecules must come to the cell or the cellular enzymes must go to the macromolecules. There are obviously difficulties here in cartilage, a tissue with a low cell density (see Section 4) and comparatively large distances between the cells.

Fell (1969) and Dingle (1973) believe that breakdown of matrix in cartilage and bone may be a two-stage process. Their results indicate that in the first stage, enzymes derived from the cell partly digest certain components of the matrix. Certainly there is electron-histochemical evidence that proteolytic activity occurs in the pericellular matrix of articular cartilage (Chrisman *et al.* 1967). More recently, immunoenzymic methods, employing a purified antiserum to the enzyme, have located cathepsin D in living cartilage in the approximate area of the matrix to which the enzyme had been released (Poole, Hembry and Dingle 1974). In the second stage the smaller and diffusible breakdown products are taken into the cells by pinocytosis or phagocytosis, and digestion completed within the lysosomal system.

The second stage of intracellular digestion within the lysosomal vacuoles is fully compatible with what is known of such relevant matters as the availability of enzymes and pH optima within the vacuole. However, the first stage involves certain structural and biochemical difficulties, such as the mode of transfer of the enzymes to sites in the matrix and the pH optima of the enzymes. Dingle (1973, 1975) has noted three hypothetical mechanisms by which transfer of enzymes into the matrix might occur:

(a) from the open end of an incompletely fused secondary lysosome (the 'regurgitation' hypothesis);
(b) from a primary lysosome which has fused with a modified portion of the cell's limiting membrane and then discharged its content to the exterior;
(c) by enzymes bound to the limiting cell membrane and brought into contact with matrix macromolecules at some distance from the main cell body by means of long cell processes.

As regards the first and second possibilities, the low pH optimum of the cathepsins makes it desirable that there should be acidic conditions in the immediate vicinity of the cell. However, although cartilage has near-anaerobic metabolism and releases lactic acid, the 'average' hydrogen ion concentration in 0.5 mm thick blocks of growing cartilage is found to be at the higher end of the soft tissue range—pH 6.95–7.4 (Silver 1975).

The third hypothetical mechanism not only has the above implications and affects physicochemical aspects of the enzyme action, but also suggests that the distance which the projecting cell processes extend into the territorial matrix is of considerable importance.

Whatever may be the mechanism of enzymatic degradation, cellular control of the matrix probably diminishes with increasing distance from the cell. Thus the tissue cell density must be an important factor affecting production, degradation and turnover of matrix macromolecules.

4. THE NUMBER OF CHONDROCYTES

It is well known that the cell content of cartilage is small, the cells occupying 0.1–0.01 of the volume of the tissue (Hamerman and Schubert 1962). The cellularity of tissues may be estimated by counting cell nuclei in histological sections. The method is subject to considerable error, arising, for example, from tissue shrinkage during preparation, variation in section thickness, possible obliquity in sectioning, and observer inaccuracy. However, the error involved is probably no worse than that in DNA estimations where cartilage is under investigation, in view of the paucity of cells in the tissue (for the two methods used in parallel, see Mankin and Baron 1965). Where only small amounts of tissue are available, cell-counting may be the method of choice, as, for example, in the estimation of cell density in the different zones of articular cartilage. Much of the published data on the cellularity of articular cartilage is based on this method.

By counting cells in vertical sections, it is found that the cell density of the full thickness of the uncalcified tissue (i.e. excluding zone 4) of adult (31–89 years) human femoral condylar cartilage is $14.5\pm3.0\times10^3$ cells per mm^3 (Stockwell 1967a, cell counts corrected for nuclear height). However, many factors must be taken

Table 2.1. Cellularity of articular cartilage. Maturation changes and zonal variation.

Species	Source of tissue	Age (years)	Cells ($\times10^{-3}$)/mm³			Reference
			Full thickness	Superficial zone	Deeper zones	
Man	Not stated	Not stated	43	—	—	Bywaters 1937
	Humeral head	25–44	—	432*	160*	Meachim and
		45–64	—	416*	192*	Collins 1962
		65–84	—	432*	192*	
	Patella	Adult	—	—	109*	
	Femoral condyle	Newborn	101	217	84	Stockwell
		21–40	14	38	12	1967a
		41–60	16	40	14	(corrected for
		61–80	14	33	12	nuclear height)
Cattle	Metatarso-	6 months	133	—	—	Rosenthal et
	and meta-	1–7	47	—	—	al. 1941
	carpophalan-	8–11	34	—	—	
	geal joints					
Horse	Carpal joints	Adult	31–99	—	—	Bywaters 1937
Rabbit	Femoral	Fetal	294	—	—	Bywaters 1937
	condyle	Adult	128	—	—	Bywaters 1937
		$2\frac{1}{2}$ months	1600*	—	—	Barnett et al.
		$\frac{3}{4}$–6 years	700*	—	—	1963
		$1\frac{1}{2}$–$2\frac{1}{2}$ months	255	—	—	Mankin and
		5–10 months	226	—	—	Baron 1965
		1–2 years	192	—	—	

* Cells per mm^2 of section, calculated from authors' data.

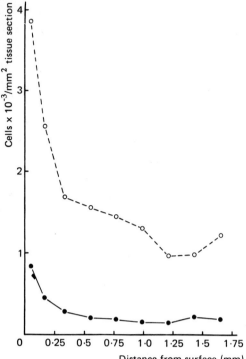

Figure 2.16 Variation of cell density with distance from the articular surface of human femoral condylar cartilage: ○ — — — — ○, newborn; ●———●, young adult.

into account in considering the cellularity of normal articular cartilage in general. There is evidence that the degree of maturity of the individual, zonal variations within the tissue, age, the anatomical site of the joint under investigation and the species studied may all affect the cell density (Table 2.1). In addition, the presence of degenerative change in the tissue may influence the cell content.

4.1. Maturation Changes

At birth the cartilage of the human femoral condyle is relatively cellular, containing about 100×10^3 cells per mm^3; this count is similar to that found in newborn non-articular hyaline cartilage (Stockwell 1967a). During the growth period, the cell density of articular cartilage falls gradually to the adult level (Bywaters 1937; Barnett, Cochrane and Palfrey 1963; Mankin and Baron 1965). It may be noted that the temporary cartilage of the unossified epiphysis should not be included in studies relating to maturation changes of the overlying permanent or 'true' articular cartilage. Difficulties arise in defining the boundary between permanent and temporary cartilage. Thus at least in the case of the value given for the cell density of newborn human cartilage, some epiphyseal cartilage has been included in the study. Therefore, as may be seen from Figure 2.16, the magnitude of the change in cell density during maturation is probably even greater than that quoted above, since newborn articular cartilage is more cellular than the temporary epiphyseal cartilage.

This growth change might be due to a reduction in the absolute number of cells, i.e. cell deaths outnumbering cell addition by mitoses, the latter occurring either within the cartilage (Elliott 1936; Mankin 1964) or at the periphery in the marginal transitional zone (Tonna 1961). Alternatively, the growth change might result from the interposition of additional matrix, causing cell spread. There is no information on the absolute number of cells in articular cartilage, but estimations in costal cartilage suggest little change in the absolute number of cells during maturation (Stockwell 1967a). Hence it is believed that matrix interposition is the principal explanation for the fall in cell density. This belief would not be inconsistent with the demonstration of occasional remnants of necrotic cells, since cell necrosis could, in theory, be balanced by the production of new cells by mitotic activity.

The changes in cell density (or conversely, in the volume of tissue occupied or perhaps controlled by one cell) must be associated with fundamental changes in cell metabolism, nutrition and mechanical stresses, of which little is known. It is emphasized that major differences between immature and mature tissue involving metabolism and other cell functions must be viewed in the light of differences in cellularity, if valid conclusions are to be made about changes in the individual cell (Bywaters 1937; McElligott and Collins 1960). A similar comment applies to conclusions based on studies of fibrillated cartilage.

4.2. Zonal Variation

Little is known of possible differences between the various parts of the same joint although the cartilage of the zenith of the femoral head is less cellular than that of the inferomedial region (Vignon 1973). However, there is some information on variation between the horizontal zones of the cartilage, a variation which is important because of apparent differences in the matrix-synthesizing capability of the cells of the different zones (Sections 2.6 and 3.4).

Cells are most numerous near the articular surface, and the number of cells per unit volume diminishes with increasing distance from the surface to a depth of 0.5 mm or more (in human femoral condylar cartilage), beyond which the number remains relatively unchanged (Figure 2.16). However, in femoral head cartilage (Vignon 1973) there is a slight increase in cellularity near the 'tidemark' at the base of zone 3. There are few cells in the basal calcified zone. In young adult human articular cartilage there are two to three times as many cells per unit volume in the superficial as in the deep uncalcified zone. Estimations for both the humeral head and the femoral condylar cartilage are in substantial agreement (Table 2.1), although cell density appears to be a little higher in the former. The same pattern of change with depth is observed in newborn tissue (Figure 2.16) and in other species, and in other cartilages such as in the intervertebral disc (Maroudas, Stockwell, Nachemson and Urban 1975).

The tissue immediately below the joint surface is slightly more cellular than is that of the rest of the superficial zone: in the superficial 0.12 mm the value is 49×10^3 cells per mm^3 (as compared with 38×10^3 in the superficial 0.22 mm), and this value agrees closely with the cell frequency found in tangential sections of the surface (Stockwell, unpublished). It is of interest (Clarke 1971a) that in the head of the femur the cell frequency near the surface of the articular cartilage is approximately equal to the frequency of the small depressions seen on the surface using scanning electron microscopy (Chapter 1, Section 2.6).

The higher cell density in the superficial layer (zone 1) is probably associated *inter alia* with nutritional conditions and metabolic requirements. Although the superficial cells have not yet been assigned a specific role, it may be speculated that they could act as a metabolic 'sink' to ensure the proper environment for the deeper tissue. Whatever the reason for the elevated cell density in this zone, it is worth reflecting that as a result, one-third of all cells lying beneath a given area of the articular surface are situated within the superficial 0.22 mm (in human femoral condylar cartilage).

There is no evidence to support the view that the cells of zone 1 represent a cell reserve or 'cambium layer': thus usually they do not proliferate in response to fibrillation in human articular cartilage (Meachim and Collins 1962) or in response to experimental scarification of rabbit cartilage (Meachim 1963).

4.3. Ageing

It is commonly believed that the cell content of cartilage falls with age. This is true in the case of human costal cartilage, where a decrease of 25% occurs after the third decade (Stockwell 1967a); a similar decline appears to take place in horse nasal cartilage (Galjaard 1962, Figure 18). In the case of human articular cartilage, there is no dispute that cellularity is less in aged adult than in immature tissue. The question is whether this difference reflects a change which occurs in articular cartilage throughout adult life in addition to a change confined to the period of growth and maturation; as mentioned earlier (Section 4.1) the cell density of articular cartilage diminishes greatly during the growth period (Stockwell 1967a). Here it is relevant to note that skeletal development is not completed until the age of 18–20 years in terms of epiphyseal closure, and that cartilage maturation, both morphological and biochemical, may not be complete until even later than this.

In addition, cartilage fibrillation is associated with alterations in cell density. Since fibrillation is age-related, becoming more extensive with increasing age, the associated changes in cellularity will, in this sense, also be age-related. The following account is therefore concerned with ageing changes in man after the age of 25–30 years in samples free from overt fibrillation.

In the case of the larger joints in man, there is no significant change during ageing (31–89 years) in the cell density of full-thickness femoral condylar cartilage; results from humeral head cartilage (25–84 years) are in keeping with this (Table 2.1). In the femoral condylar cartilage a diminution does occur with age in the superficial layer, but a small increase occurs in the deeper tissue (also observed in humeral head cartilage) which balances the loss in the superficial layer (Stockwell 1967a). Biochemical evidence derived from cell mass estimations in human articular cartilage similarly indicates that the total number of cells is constant during ageing of the larger joints (Miles and Eichelberger 1964). It is of interest that ageing also has no effect on the uncalcified thickness of articular cartilage from the humeral (Meachim 1971) or the femoral head (Vignon 1976, personal communication), provided that fibrillated samples are excluded.

Complications can arise, however, from separate consideration of changes:

(a) in the superficial layer, 0.22–0.25 mm thick (zone 1);
(b) in the deeper uncalcified layers (zones 2 and 3).

If the cellularity of the superficial layer (zone 1) is considered in isolation, a different picture would seem to emerge. Thus, as noted above, the cell density of this layer diminishes during true ageing in human femoral condylar cartilage (Stockwell 1967a). Results from humeral head cartilage suggest that this loss of superficial layer cellularity may be more a feature of cartilage samples showing age-related minor irregularities of articular surface contour ('minimal fibrillation') than of samples where the surface is still 'histologically intact' (Meachim and Collins 1962). However, the loss of cellularity seems greater than can be attributed merely to surface contour damage: thus one could regard the diminished cellularity beneath the surface as an 'ageing' or 'regressive' change (Meachim, Ghadially and Collins 1965).

It is also possible that the findings for full-thickness cellularity may differ between large and small joints. It is not established with any certainty that this remains unaltered during ageing in the smaller joints of man or in the joints of other species. Loss of superficial cells has been observed in the ageing rabbit femoral condyle (Barnett et al. 1963); cell death occurs in situ (Davies, Barnett, Cochrane and Palfrey 1962) with no evidence of the desquamation at the surface postulated by Ogston (1875). In such small joints, with articular cartilage less than 0.5 mm thick, it is possible that a loss in the superficial zone might have a significant effect on the cell density calculated for the full thickness of the tissue.

In a more general context, much of the evidence for a supposed decline in full-thickness cellularity with age appears to be based either on the comparison of the immature with the mature (i.e. a measure of the effect of maturation rather than of ageing) or on tissue where early degenerative change cannot be ruled out. Loss of superficial cells accompanies, and may also precede, the early stages of cartilage fibrillation, and the use of the light microscope is sometimes required to detect the early stage of 'histological' fibrillation. The evidence so far presented for the stability of the overall cellularity of human articular cartilage during ageing is at variance with earlier findings in bovine metatarsal and metacarpal cartilage (Rosenthal et al. 1941), where a significant reduction from 47 to 34×10^3 cells per mm^3 was observed during the true ageing period. The bovine data were based on cell counts made on vertical sections of horizontal slices less than 0.5 mm thick shaved from the joint surfaces. These slices probably did not extend to the full depth of the articular cartilage, and thus the superficial layer probably formed an artificially high proportion of the thickness of the slice, especially at the periphery of the block. The authors state that bovine joints of the age studied were arthritic; hence it is probable that even in nearly normal areas of the joints there were degenerative changes. Thus reduced cellularity in the superficial layer, due to ageing and perhaps also to degenerative changes, might have had a disproportionate effect on the overall cellularity of the samples.

4.4. Variation in Different Joints of the Same Species

Meachim and Collins (1962) found that the deeper part of adult human non-fibrillated cartilage is rather more cellular at the upper humerus than on the patella (Table 2.1). There is probably little difference between the human femoral condylar and humeral head cartilage with respect to the superficial zone, although in the deep tissue the humeral cartilage seems to be more cellular (Table 2.1); from the data available it is not possible to compare the cell densities for the full thickness, since full-thickness cell density was not determined for the humeral head cartilage.

A number of measurements in adult human joints (Table 2.2) with articular cartilage covering a wide range of thickness (Stockwell 1971a) suggest that there are marked differences in cell density of the uncalcified tissue. Thick articular cartilage from the larger joints is less cellular than thin cartilage from smaller joints. A similar trend is observed in other species; in the cat, cartilage from the metatarsophalangeal joint is more cellular than that from the femoral condyle.

4.5. Species Differences

Data for four species are included in Table 2.1 although different joints are involved. The cell density of rabbit cartilage is considerably higher than that of human, bovine or horse cartilage, suggesting that the smaller the animal the higher the cell density. A survey of young adult articular cartilage of the femoral condyle in a number of species (Table 2.2) suggests an inverse relationship between species size and the cellularity of the cartilage (Stockwell 1971a). Nevertheless it is of interest that different anatomical joints in species of a different order of size may have similar cell densities. For example, cartilages of the cat metatarsophalangeal joint and the rat shoulder joint have approximately the same cellularity (Table 2.2); it is noteworthy that the articular cartilage is very nearly of the same thickness (Figure 2.17). This is also observed in the case of the mouse femoral condyle and the human incudomalleolar joint (Figure 1.1). However, there may still be variation in the *distribution* of the cells; for example, cells arranged

Table 2.2. Cellularity of young adult articular cartilage. Variation between species and joints. Results are shown for the cell density of the whole thickness of the uncalcified cartilage. (Data from Stockwell 1971a)

Species	Source of cartilage	Cells $(\times 10^{-3})/mm^3$
Mouse	Femoral condyle	334±41
Rat	,,	265±57
Rabbit	,,	188±56
Cat	,,	108±33
Dog	,,	44±12
Sheep	,,	53±13
Cow	,,	20±4
Man	,,	14±3
,,	Humeral head	15±4
,,	Interphalangeal joint	21±2
,,	Auditory ossicles	595±109
Cat	Metatarsal head	146±13
Rat	Humeral head	119±4

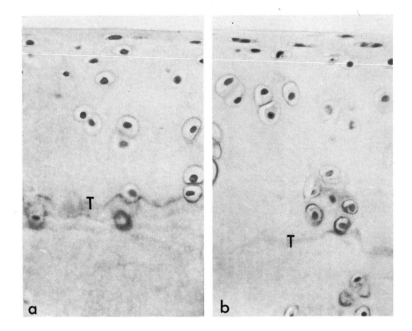

Figure 2.17 Articular cartilage from species of a dissimilar size, but from joints with cartilage of approximately the same thickness and cell density. T = junction of uncalcified with calcified cartilage. (a) Cat metatarsal head, (b) rat humeral head ×420.
   Haematoxylin and eosin.

in columns in the deeper zones of articular cartilage are more prevalent in weight-bearing joints (Barnett 1963).

4.6. The Relationship of Cell Density and Cartilage Thickness

As with cartilage thickness (Simon 1970), the cell density of articular cartilage from a given joint is related to the species size. Indeed, the evidence from different joints of the same species as well as from the same joint in different species suggests that cell density is in fact more closely related to cartilage thickness than to species size (Stockwell 1971a). Thus, local physiological and mechanical factors may be as important as species characteristics in determining cell density.

   The approximately inverse relationship (Figure 2.18) between cell density and cartilage thickness implies that the absolute number of cells lying beneath 1 mm^2 of articular surface will be relatively constant. For all adult joints studied, this value is $26\pm9\times10^3$ cells. It is possible that the constancy of the cell number may be dependent on nutritional factors. Such scanty evidence as exists suggests that the rate of glycolysis per cell in articular cartilage is approximately the same in different species (Bywaters 1937). Hence the glucose requirement of the cartilaginous tissue deep to a unit area of articular surface may also be rather constant in different species and joints. This would imply that conclusions

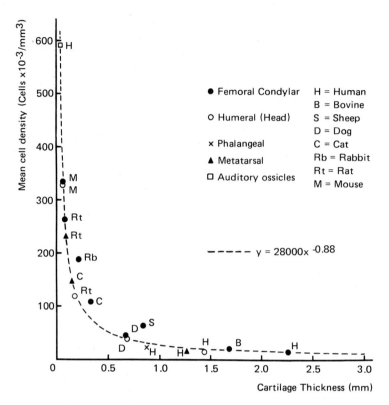

Figure 2.18 Relationship between the cell density and the thickness of adult articular cartilage in various species and joints. The calcified zone (zone 4) was not included in the measurements and calculations.

regarding the adequacy of nutrition of cartilage in any one joint surface could be applied to human joints in general and to joints of other species (see Chapter 8, Section 3). An alternative suggestion could be that cell population is 'controlled' to a constant level by a hypothetical 'communication system' between the cells.

The inverse relationship between cartilage thickness and cartilage cellularity may be an important clue to the way in which cell population and thickness is 'controlled' in the uncalcified part of articular cartilage. As there is a relatively constant total number of cells beneath a unit area of the articular surface, thickness variation in the uncalcified tissue must be mainly dependent on alterations in the amount of extracellular matrix. This suggests a second hypothesis, that the amount of matrix is influenced by the local biomechanical requirements of the tissue. Microstresses within the tissue resulting from joint function may act as stimuli to the cells. The appropriate amount of matrix (at any given stage during growth or in adult life) could thus result from the rate of matrix synthesis and turnover regulated by these stimuli. If the stimuli were reduced or absent, as for example in experimental or therapeutic joint immobilization or perhaps under prolonged zero gravity conditions, then the amount of matrix might be expected to diminish and the cartilage to become thinner. The normal variation in cartilage thickness between species, and between different joints in the same species, may thus partly reflect local requirements; variation in thickness between different sites in the same joint may also be explained on this basis.

Consistent with the above hypothesis, the cartilage on the zenith (superior pole) of the human femoral head is thicker and less cellular than that inferomedial to the fovea (inferior pole), while the anterior and posterior aspects (anterior and posterior poles) have intermediate values (Vignon, Meunier, Boissel, Arlot, Patricot and Vignon 1973). It is tempting to relate these differences to topographical variation in local biomechanical environment. Vignon et al. (1973) suggest that the amount of matrix synthesized by chondrocytes is regulated by the amount of static and dynamic compressive loading on the cartilage. Simon, Friedenberg and Richardson (1973) put forward a somewhat different concept. From studies on canine joints, they suggest that the thickness of articular cartilage is inversely related to the congruence of joint surfaces, and that this relationship tends to equalize the load per unit area when 'congruent' and 'incongruent' articulations are compared. They suggest that 'congruent' surfaces have thin cartilage which deforms only a small amount, but that the area of surface in contact is sufficiently large to distribute the load and thus maintain low stress levels in the tissue. For 'incongruent' surfaces, in contrast, a thick cartilage would allow enough deformation to increase the surface area under compression, thus sufficiently decreasing tissue stress. This concept and that of Vignon et al. are both in keeping with the hypothesis that the amount of matrix produced locally is influenced by the local biomechanical requirements.

5. THE SIZE OF CHONDROCYTES

It is well known that in the epiphyseal plate of growth cartilage the chondrocytes towards the metaphyseal end of the cell columns are considerably enlarged compared with those near the epiphysis. The hypertrophy of these chondrocytes is associated with considerable changes in their activity (Kuhlman 1960). In adult articular cartilage, the cells are not uniform in size but appear to be larger the further they are from the surface. Here also the activity of the deeper cells is greater than that of the superficial cells, at least as regards sulphate utilization as assessed in vertical sections of autoradiographs.

Published values for the size of adult chondrocytes are uncommon. Leidy (1849) gives dimensions for human articular chondrocytes equivalent to $28 \times 11 \mu m$, while Barnett, Davies and Mac-

Conaill (1961) state that the diameter is 30–40 μm. Although in non-articular cartilage chondrocyte diameters may approach these values, in young adult rabbit articular cartilage the cell size appears to be much smaller. The dimensions for the major and minor axes of chondrocyte profiles observed with the electron microscope are given as 10–20 μm and 3–5 μm respectively for the superficial zone, and 11 μm and 6 μm respectively for the deeper zones (Davies *et al.* 1962). Measurements of adult chondrocytes (in vertical section of the articular cartilage) using light microscopy confirm that the most superficial discoidal cells are of this order of size. In human femoral condylar cartilage their profiles are about 14 μm long and 3 μm deep; they are of a similar dimension in a number of species and in different anatomical joints (Stockwell, unpublished). Measurements in sections cut tangential to the surface also confirm these findings. Clarke (1971a, b) finds slightly larger diameters (10–40 μm) for superficial lacunae in young adult human hip joint cartilage, using the scanning electron microscope.

The size of the deeper cells is more variable and more difficult to determine. Inspection of published electron micrographs of adult chondrocyte profiles in man (and other species) suggests that they are of a similar size to those of rabbit articular cartilage. This would lead to the rather unexpected theoretical conclusion that the volume of a superficial cell (regarded as a regular oblate spheroid, i.e. discoidal) is greater than that of a deeper cell (a prolate spheroid or ovoid). However, using the light microscope, measurements give larger dimensions for the deep cell than those suggested by the electron micrographs studied. In human articular cartilage, estimates from electron micrographs indicate chondrocyte diameters of 10 μm $\times$ 7 μm, while light microscopy measurements give 19 μm $\times$ 12 μm. The discrepancy is partly to be attributed to the difficulties of determining precisely the cell boundary with the light microscope and the necessarily rather selective profiles shown in electron micrographs; moreover there are technical problems in determining the exact (rather than the stated) magnification of an electron micrograph.

These values for cell size, taken together with those for cell density (Table 2.2), yield estimates of the volume of tissue occupied by the cells as 0.4% and 2% (for electron and light microscopy measurements respectively). The results of this calculation are consistent with the range of cell volume as a fraction of tissue volume given in Section 4. Where cell density is high, as for example in rabbit articular cartilage, the percentage cell volume is increased (4% and 13% of total tissue volume, respectively, for electron and light microscopy). Finally, it is of interest that there appears to be a degree of inverse relationship between cell density and cell size: this relationship applies whether cell size is estimated from electron microscopy or determined by light microscopy (Stockwell 1971b).

6. REPLICATION AND REPLACEMENT OF CHONDRO-CYTES

Evidence for cell replacement by mitotic division in articular chondrocytes can be sought by several techniques. Histological preparations can be examined for cells showing morphological signs that the nucleus is undergoing mitosis ('mitotic figures'). By administering colchicine to an animal, the potential number of cells showing these morphological signs can be artificially increased, since the drug arrests mitotic division before its completion. Techniques using the radioactive nucleoside tritiated thymidine (^{3}H-thymidine) are based on the incorporation of this substance into DNA during the synthesis of DNA which occurs before mitotic division. These methods have provided little evidence of cell replacement in the normal tissue, although the maintenance of the cell population in adult articular cartilage is of obvious importance.

6.1. Immature Tissue

In immature articular cartilage, chondrocytes undergo mitosis. Harris and Russell (1933) plotted a 'mitotic anulus' around the osseous centre of the epiphysis, and state that the cells become progressively older on passing from the region of cell division towards the joint surface. Elliott (1936) describes a zone of maximal mitotic activity at a distance of about three to four cell diameters from the joint surface in the newborn rat and mouse, but situated rather more deeply in the half-grown cat and dog. Graphs of depth against frequency of mitosis suggested the presence of stimulatory and inhibitory factors, both decreasing with distance from the surface, the latter more rapidly than the former. In a systematic study in the rabbit, Mankin (1964) describes two zones of cell division in the immature epiphysis: (a) adjacent to the superficial zone, and (b) near the osseous centre. The number of mitoses per cent of total cells decreases from 0.16 in the newborn to 0.003 in the older immature animal. Using ^{3}H-thymidine, Tonna (1961) suggests that a significant contribution is made to the growth of the articular cartilage by cell proliferation at the marginal transitional zone where joint capsule, periosteum and cartilage merge. Evidence for diurnal variation in mitotic activity has been produced for rat epiphyseal growth cartilage (Simmons 1964), but Mankin (1964) was unable to find statistically significant evidence for this in rabbit articular cartilage.

6.2. Adult Articular Cartilage

Most observers are agreed that mitoses cannot be found in adult, non-fibrillated articular cartilage, an exception being the inter-pubic articular cartilage during pregnancy in mice (Crelin 1957). Studies using ^{3}H-thymidine incorporation support this conclusion. Autoradiographs of adult rabbit articular cartilage following intra-articular injection of thymidine show no evidence of uptake, although the same procedure produces positive results in the immature animal (Mankin 1963b). Again, months after the administration of thymidine to young rats, articular chondrocytes are still loaded with the material, whereas in tissues with rapidly multiplying cells it is progressively diluted and no trace is seen within a month of the initial incorporation (Tonna and Cronkite 1964).

The older concept of cell replacement by amitosis in adult articular cartilage seems to have died a natural death in the light of modern genetic knowledge (for a discussion see Mankin 1963b). Nevertheless, there is as yet no final refutation of this postulated mode of cell division, at least in articular cartilage, and the bizarre nuclear forms which appeared to substantiate the original view have been observed in ageing chondrocytes at the ultrastructural level (Barnett *et al.* 1963) as well as with the light microscope.

Although mitoses have not been observed in adult, non-fibrillated tissue, it may be that the cells divide very infrequently, so seldom as to make the phenomenon virtually impossible to observe (Mankin 1963b). This hypothesis appears to be tenable in view of evidence such as the exponential decline of the mitotic index during maturation in the rabbit and the slight increase in cell density of the deeper zones of human articular cartilage during ageing (although this is statistically insignificant and might alternatively result from matrix loss). Furthermore, it appears that thymidine incorporation can occur *in vitro* in the articular cartilage of the human femoral head in elderly subjects (Mankin and Lippiello 1970), although the investigators concerned exercise caution as to whether the tissue they examined should be regarded as normal.

6.3. Experimentally Induced Cell Replication

There is little doubt that cell division of articular chondrocytes may be induced under certain abnormal conditions. Chondrocytes enzymatically released from adult human knee joint cartilage are said to undergo rapid proliferation if grown as monolayer cultures but not if they are first aggregated into pellets, when intercellular matrix is formed (Manning and Bonner 1967). However, the behaviour of cultured chondrocytes is dependent on other factors, such as the duration of culture, as well as the initial cell density (Holtzer, Chacko, Abbott, Holtzer and Anderson 1970). If articular cartilage is experimentally damaged, mitoses are said to occur (Seggel 1904; Fasoli 1905). More recently, Trias (1961) described mitoses in adult rabbit articular cartilage in areas adjacent to necrotic regions produced by prolonged pressure, and also in tissue recovering from incomplete damage. Crelin and Southwick (1964) illustrate mitoses found exclusively in the outer half of rabbit articular cartilage after mild compression-fixation; they remark that the number of mitoses observed, even after colchicine arrest, is remarkably small compared with that expected from the number of lacunae containing multiple cells. Rothwell and Bentley (1973) have demonstrated that chondrocyte multiplication can occur in human fibrillated cartilage.

7. REPAIR OF ARTICULAR SURFACES

There are many causes of partial or complete loss of articular cartilage from an area of the joint surface. For example, in an area of deep fibrillation the cartilage can thin, or even be lost completely so as to expose the underlying bone; in the disease osteochondritis dissecans a segment of cartilage with underlying bone can separate from the joint surface, leaving a crater-like defect; in certain other diseases, such as rheumatoid arthritis, 'erosive' thinning of the cartilage can occur; and in an acute episode of intra-articular trauma, cartilage can be fractured and disintegrate. Cartilage may also be deliberately removed from part of the joint surface during the surgical operation of joint debridement in man and during experimental procedures in animals.

Cartilage damage can also occur in which there is matrix splitting but no actual thinning of the material. This is seen in some examples of superficial fibrillation in human joints, and can be produced experimentally in animals by scarification of an articular surface.

After cartilage has been damaged in one or other of the above ways, can it subsequently be repaired? Repair would imply replacement of a defect by new living tissue, or restoration of matrix continuity across gaps due to splits in non-thinned cartilage. Before considering this question, it is helpful to distinguish between two types of damage (DePalma, McKeever and Subin 1966): first, a part-thickness split or defect in which the calcified interface of the chondro-osseous junction is still intact (Figure 2.19); second, a full-thickness defect, localized or extensive in area, which extends completely through cartilage down into the subarticular bone in at least one segment of its base (Figure 2.19). The

Figure 2.19 Situations which can be used to study the potential for repair of articular surfaces in animals and in man. Note the important difference between situations 3 and 4: in 4 the repair process is subject to much more exacting requirements, since the new tissue which grows out of the gap in the bone plate is not protected by a cushion of old cartilage and also is required to re-cover an adjacent exposed surface of calcified cartilage or bone.

    1.   Part-thickness   splits   (Meachim 1963)

    2.   Localized   full-thickness   defect (Carlson 1957; DePalma *et al.* 1966)

    3.   Localized   full-thickness   defect (DePalma *et al.* 1966)

    4.   Extensive   full-thickness   defect (Meachim and Roberts 1971)

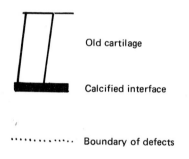

Old cartilage

Calcified interface

Boundary of defects

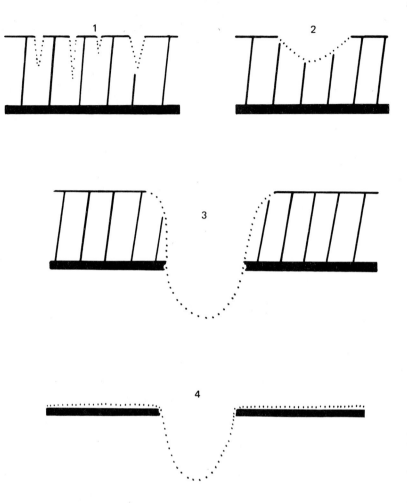

possibilities for repair depend to some degree on which type of defect is present. Two potential mechanisms for repair merit discussion: (a) intrinsic repair, and (b) extrinsic repair.

7.1. Intrinsic Repair

Healing dependent entirely on the activity of surviving chondrocytes adjacent to a split or defect can be termed 'intrinsic repair'. In such circumstances healing is exceptional in adults: observations on traumatized cartilage in man (Collins 1949; Landells 1957) and in animals (DePalma *et al.* 1966) indicate that the cells of mature hyaline articular cartilage have only a limited capacity to repair articular surfaces; this conclusion is in line with Collins' account (1949) of the changes seen in human deeply fibrillated cartilage. However, those chondrocytes which have not undergone degeneration or necrosis due to the damage can initially 'react' to it. This reactive response has been observed both in deeply fibrillated cartilage in man (Meachim and Collins 1962) and in experimentally traumatized cartilage in animals (Meachim 1963). The response does not normally lead to any significant replacement of lost tissue, and the reacting cells can in turn eventually degenerate. This chondrocyte reaction may show one or more of the following features; it should be made clear that not all the features mentioned are observed in every case.

Chondrocyte multiplication can occur, as evidenced in man by autoradiographic studies using tritiated thymidine (Rothwell and Bentley 1973), and cell proliferation can sometimes lead to the formation of abnormally multicellular rounded clusters of chondrocytes in animal and in human articular cartilage (Carlson 1957; Meachim and Collins 1962; Meachim 1963). Features consistent with increased metabolic and synthetic activity have been observed during radiochemical and ultrastructural studies of experimentally traumatized cartilage in animals (Meachim 1963; Fuller and Ghadially 1972), although this cell activity tends to diminish with time if surviving cells eventually degenerate.

In addition to the cellular changes noted above, 'matrix flow' is seen at the edges and in the floor of part-thickness cartilage defects in immature rabbits (Ghadially, Ailsby and Oryschak 1974). Flowing and streaming of material under load-bearing and shearing forces may perhaps be responsible for this phenomenon. It rounds off the edges of the defect, and also causes matrix to flow into the hollow of the defect. Scanning electron microscopy then demonstrates numerous sheets, bands and rope-like and thread-like formations over the floor of the part-thickness defect. In theory, a similar 'matrix flow' might close the gap across a narrow vertical split, produced by fibrillation or by experimental scarification, thus healing it.

Concerning the potential for intrinsic repair of articular cartilage, the key question is the effectiveness of any cell proliferation, new ground substance synthesis and matrix flow which may occur, in terms of restoring the extracellular matrix. Here the limiting factor would seem to be that of also forming new collagen framework. Although the base of a part-thickness defect can show on electron microscopy an ultrathin cover of what appear to be fine collagen fibres (Fuller and Ghadially 1972), no significant filling-in of the defect is seen. There is, however, evidence that intrinsic healing can be artificially promoted by the use of aspirin (Chrisman 1969) and, more especially, by the use of growth hormone. With growth hormone, the base of an experimental part-thickness defect shows a covering layer of collagen sufficiently well developed to be apparent by polarizing light microscopy (Chrisman 1975); similarly, obliteration of vertical splits produced by scarification may be seen (Chrisman 1975).

7.2. Extrinsic Repair

In addition to the limited intrinsic healing capability of the damaged cartilage itself, there is another possible source from which a cartilage defect can be repaired: new non-osseous tissue can sometimes gain access to the articular surface (Landells 1957). This 'extrinsic repair' can reach the surface by two routes (Landells 1957). First, it can grow out from the region of the subarticular bone plate (Figure 2.20). This phenomenon can be demonstrated

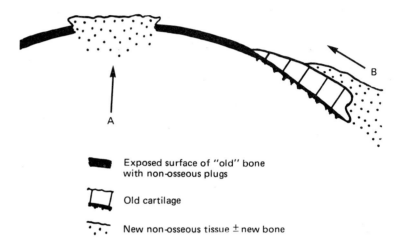

Figure 2.20 Two potential routes by which non-osseous extrinsic repair tissue can reach the articular surface: A—by growth from soft tissue spaces in the subarticular bone plate; B—by spread from juxta-articular or synovial soft tissue at the joint margin. Both methods of extrinsic repair can be accompanied by new bone formation at the deep aspect of the new tissue.

Exposed surface of "old" bone with non-osseous plugs

Old cartilage

New non-osseous tissue ± new bone

in full-thickness cartilage defects made experimentally in animals (DePalma *et al.* 1966) or surgically in man (Insall 1967), and it can occur naturally at a human articular surface (Meachim and Osborne 1970). A gap, not necessarily complete, in the subarticular bone, provides the source of the new tissue; this source is not, by definition, available in part-thickness defects. In man, such gaps can develop in late-stage osteoarthrosis, in osteochondritis dissecans and following intra-articular fracture. They can also be produced artificially by drilling the subchondral bone plate during human surgery or during experimental procedures in animals. If the gap in the bone is produced artificially, care must be taken to avoid additional tissue damage from thermal necrosis due to the drilling (Matthews and Hirsch 1972), since this may counteract the repair potential. From the bone gap, extrinsic tissue of subarticular origin can grow into a full-thickness cartilage defect, and repair it with a new non-osseous surface segment; in parallel with this process, new bone formation can restore osseous continuity in the subarticular plate, thus providing a well formed bony base beneath the new segment of surface tissue.

The second route of extrinsic repair (Figure 2.20) is by growth of new non-osseous tissue, on to a surface of old cartilage or exposed bone, from a juxta-articular or synovial source at the joint margins: this phenomenon is a potential source for the repair both of full-thickness and of part-thickness defects, especially when they are sited near an articular margin.

7.3. Chondrogenesis in Extrinsic Repair Tissue

Extrinsic repair tissue is of variable, and sometimes mixed, histological pattern. It can be fibrous or loose-textured; of a pattern 'intermediate' between that of fibrous tissue and cartilage; chondroid'; fibrocartilaginous; or hyaline cartilaginous. Where it is cartilaginous, the new tissue appears to be avascular. In man, any repair cartilage which forms in osteoarthrosis is nearly always fibrocartilaginous rather than truly hyaline (Meachim and Osborne 1970). Similarly, a fibrocartilaginous type of repair is described and illustrated by Landells (1957) in his study of the changes following trauma to the human joint surface. Experimentally induced repair cartilage in animals can, however, sometimes be of a hyaline pattern (DePalma et al. 1966; Campbell 1969). In practice it is not always possible to make a sharp distinction between hyaline and fibrocartilage, and histological identification of the various types of repair cartilage is sometimes based on subjective criteria.

There appear to be at least two ways in which chondrogenesis can develop within extrinsic repair tissue. First, it may occur as a component of fracture healing or other osteogenic response. Thus, in the case of repair of full-thickness cartilage defects in experimental rabbits the findings strongly suggest that this example of cartilage formation of subarticular origin commences as an integral part of the osteochondrogenic response to fracture of the subarticular bone plate, the drill hole being, in effect, the equivalent of a small fracture (Meachim 1972b). Similarly, at least some instances of human reparative chondrogenesis at articular surfaces seem to commence where there is active osteogenesis at the same site. A second, alternative, mode of chondrogenesis is by metaplasia of reparative fibrous tissue, with modulation of fibroblasts to chondrocytes; this second mode can probably occur independently of an osteogenic response.

In experimental animals, an initial chondrogenesis can be observed in the healing both of full-thickness articular cartilage

119

defects and of 'control' defects made in the para-articular bone plate. However, in contrast to the findings at the articular surface, it is exceptional for para-articular reactive and reparative changes to give rise to plaques of cartilaginous texture abutting directly on to the synovial cavity (Meachim 1972b). Several suggestions can be put forward to account for the development and persistence of such plaques in the repair tissue at the articular, but only exceptionally at the para-articular, surface. One possible explanation might be a chemical effect, mediated through the synovial fluid, from substances liberated by synovial intima or by the old cartilage retained at the margins of the operation site. An alternative, more attractive, possibility might be a mechanical effect from contact with the opposing surface, this effect either acting directly on the cells near the surface of the repair tissue or acting indirectly by causing diminished vascularity and decreased oxygen tension in their environment. In this context it is of interest, and perhaps of relevance, to note that low oxygen concentration promotes cartilage formation in organ cultures of embryonic chick cartilage (Shaw and Bassett 1967). In the case of articular surface defects, Salter (1973, personal communication) has shown that the amount of joint movement may have an important influence on the degree of cartilaginous repair.

7.4. Re-covering of Exposed Bone

In a localized full-thickness defect of the sort studied experimentally by DePalma *et al.* (1966), a 'cushion' of old cartilage is retained at the sides of the defect, and the gap in the underlying bone is of similar diameter to that in the cartilage (Figure 2.19). Meachim and Roberts (1971) have, in contrast, studied the repair of more extensive full-thickness defects, where the potential for extrinsic repair in experimental animals is subjected to more exacting requirements. In their study, the articular cartilage was removed from most of the patellar groove of the rabbit distal femur, except for a narrow rim retained at the edges. Several drill holes were then made into the underlying bone, but these occupied approximately one-third only of the total area of exposed bone surface (Figure 2.19). Thus the new tissue growing from the subarticular region is not initially protected by a cushion of old cartilage (Figure 2.20); moreover, there is a requirement to re-cover adjacent non-drilled bone. In these more exacting circumstances a potential for repair is still apparent. By quantitative methods it was possible to show that new non-osseous surface tissue had not just covered the sites of the drill holes, but also had a potential to spread from the drilled sites to a variable extent over the adjacent non-drilled exposed surface bone (Figures 2.21 and 2.22). This is seen in both immature and mature animals. A

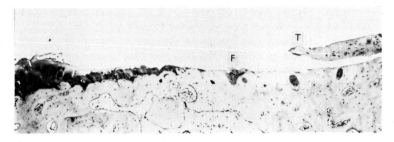

Figure 2.21 Repair potential in an extensive full-thickness defect (experimental situation 4 in Figure 2.19). Tongue of new chondroid tissue (T) growing over a non-drilled area of rabbit articular surface from which the original cartilage had been excised. The new tissue originated from a drill hole (not shown) made into bone plate beyond and to the right of the field seen in the photomicrograph. Note also the tiny focus of new tissue (F) which has formed where cartilage excision, without local drilling, has exposed an intertrabecular space in the bone plate. The edge of the original cartilage, partly excised, is seen on the left of the field.

Toluidine blue ×55.

(Reproduced from Meachim and Roberts (1971) by courtesy of the Editor, *Journal of Anatomy*.)

variable proportion of the new surface tissue was fibrocartilaginous or hyaline cartilaginous (Figure 2.22), the rest being fibrous or intermediate in pattern; 100% re-covering of an extensive defect by new tissue of cartilaginous texture was not observed in any of the animals used. In parallel with this experimental study, it was possible to demonstrate that there is in man a potential for extrinsic repair of extensive full-thickness cartilage defects of the sort seen in late-stage osteoarthrosis (Meachim and Osborne 1970). Such repair of human osteoarthrosic articular surfaces is variable in extent and in histological texture; it is usually overwhelmed or severely counteracted by a destructive mechanism.

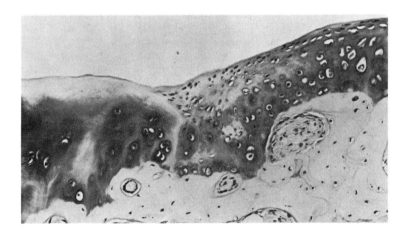

Figure 2.22 Repair potential in an extensive full-thickness defect (experimental situation 4 in Figure 2.19). In this field cartilaginous repair tissue (right) has fused with the rim of old cartilage (left) retained at the margin of the operation site.

Toluidine blue ×150.

(Reproduced from Meachim and Roberts (1971) by courtesy of the Editor, *Journal of Anatomy*.)

However, it would seem that the potential for repair can sometimes be released by surgical procedures such as osteotomy. Both in man and in experimental animals, the repair of extensive defects has to be assessed quantitatively: this assessment is made in terms of the percentage area of initially exposed bone now re-covered; the thickess of the new surface tissue; the relative proportions of cartilaginous and non-cartilaginous texture in the new tissue; and its functional and clinical effectiveness as a covering material protecting bone. Also, there is evidence which strongly suggests that in man an initially satisfactory re-covering of an extensive defect may in time be overwhelmed by the continued destructive action of the osteoarthrosic process.

The possibilities of inducing repair by transplanting isolated chondrocytes into articular cartilage defects have been explored in experimental animals. Chesterman and Smith (1968) found that isolated adult articular chondrocytes do not produce repair, but Bentley and Greer (1971) find that, while articular chondrocytes are rejected, isolated epiphyseal chondrocytes transplanted into experimental defects can multiply and form new cartilage. The success of such allografts is probably due to the more rapid production of matrix by epiphyseal than by articular chondrocytes, thus protecting them from the host antibodies (see Section 2.8).

8. CELLULAR CHANGES IN CARTILAGE FIBRILLATION

Cartilage fibrillation and allied phenomena occur naturally in many mammalian species. The histological pattern varies, at least in detail, according to the species examined (Meachim and Illman 1967). Thus caution is needed when the results of histological and metabolic studies in animals are used in the interpretation of cartilage changes in man. The account which follows is based on studies of adult human articular cartilage from the knee, hip and shoulder joints; where necessary, reference is also made to the findings in experimentally induced cartilage changes in rabbits. The findings refer to fibrillation, and allied changes (Chapter 1), in cartilage still presenting a surface exposed to the joint cavity, uncovered by new fibrous or osseous tissue. Examination with the light microscope of histological sections of human fibrillated cartilage shows that the overall pattern of the cells varies from specimen to specimen. The findings are influenced by the depth to which fibrillation extends into the cartilage, and they also vary within the section according to which horizontal layer (zone) of the cartilage is examined. Necrotic and reactive cell changes can both occur (Weiss and Mirrow 1972). In the superficial layer (zone 1) degenerative and necrotic changes are usually the dominant feature; however, where the deeper layers (zones 2 and 3) are affected necrosis of some of the deeper cells can be accompanied by evidence of a 'reactive response' in others (Figures 2.23 and 2.24). Necrotic and 'reactive' changes can be closely intermingled on the microscopic scale, within the same small segment of cartilage; this is pertinent to metabolic studies of fibrillated or otherwise damaged cartilage, since quantitative observation of cellular activity in segments of such cartilage will sometimes merely show the sum of the two variable and contrasting effects of degeneration and reaction.

This lack of uniformity in the cell changes in damaged cartilage imposes a difficulty when interpreting electron micrographs. A sample suitable for study under the transmission electron microscope represents only a small area of tissue. Thus, in order to obtain a comprehensive impression of the ultrastructural changes in a specimen, it is necessary to examine a series of samples from the specimen and to correlate the findings with the overall pattern of the cells as shown by histological sections examined with the light microscope. On electron microscopy, changes in cell density and cell distribution are seen: they reflect changes already apparent from examination of histological sections, and for quantitative study of such changes light microscopy is actually a more suitable technique. In terms of the morphology of individual cells, the chondrocytes of fibrillated cartilage show basically similar ultra-

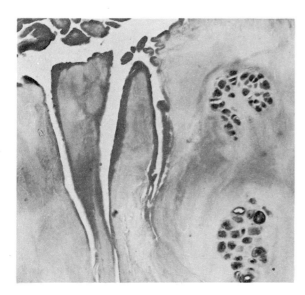

Figure 2.23 Deep fibrillation on the superior aspect of a femoral head. Chondrocyte necrosis, seen on the left of the field, contrasts with multicellular cluster formation, seen on the right of the field. ×150.

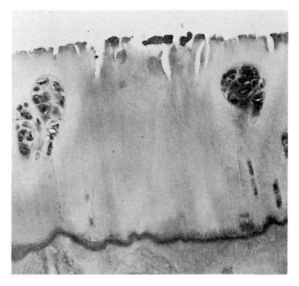

Figure 2.24 A cartilage segment from near that shown in Figure 2.23. Here the cartilage is thinned but the surface thus exposed shows a relatively shallow splitting. Cell clusters are seen, but the acellular appearance of the central part of the field suggests that chondrocyte necrosis is also present. ×150.

structural features to those seen within chondrocytes of non-fibrillated samples (Roy and Meachim 1968); however, in fibrillation the ultrastructure of the cell can become modified in various ways.

Before considering the effects of fibrillation and allied changes, such as smooth-surfaced destructive thinning, on nuclear counts obtained from sections of adult human articular cartilage, it is helpful to recapitulate the mechanisms by which a change in the number of viable cells per unit volume of tissue could occur: (a) by cell necrosis within the cartilage; (b) by loss of cells from shedding into the joint cavity; (c) by cell proliferation; (d) by an alteration in the relative amount of matrix without any change in the total number of cells.

All four mechanisms may be operative in fibrillated cartilage; indirect evidence will be presented which involves the first three. It is also relevant to note here that nuclear counts made on histological sections of fixed tissue are not necessarily an accurate reflection of the actual number of viable cells present in life per unit volume of fresh unfixed cartilage (Stockwell 1967a).

The lack of uniformity in the cell changes in non-intact cartilage has an important implication when interpreting the results of metabolic studies, and it is useful if such studies include histological data on the cartilage samples used. It is then possible to take into account effects attributable to population changes in cell density and cell distribution, and thus to consider how far the results might imply a quantitative change in the individual metabolic activity of the 'average cell' in the sample. Histology is also necessary to confirm that repair tissue has not been inadvertently included in the material studied.

It should be noted here that cartilage undergoing destructive thinning does not always show the deep vertical splitting typical of fibrillation, but may instead show only shallow splitting or present an almost smooth surface (Figures 2.23 and 2.24).

8.1. Degenerative and Necrotic Changes

8.1.1. Superficial Fibrillation. In areas of adult human articular cartilage showing superficial fibrillation there is typically a reduction in the nuclear count (Table 2.3) obtained from the affected superficial layer (zone 1); multicellular rounded clusters are not seen; and the surface layer cells which remain usually show no tendency to proliferate (Meachim and Collins 1962). It has been suggested that this reduction in cell density can in some instances begin at a stage before surface fibrillation becomes detectable by light microscopy (Meachim et al. 1965).

Superficial fibrillation is not associated with any obvious alteration in the cellularity (Table 2.3) of the underlying deeper (zones 2

Table 2.3. Cellularity of adult human articular cartilage from head of humerus. Nuclear counts (nuclei per field $1/16$ mm^2 in area) of the superficial layer (0.25 mm depth) and of the deeper, uncalcified layers (zones 2 and 3) were made. The results are shown according to age for samples in which the articular surface appeared intact when examined under the light microscope; counts from samples with superficial fibrillation are shown separately. Joints with evidence of rheumatoid disease have been excluded. (Data from Meachim and Collins 1962)

State of articular surface	Age group (years)	No. of persons	Average number of nuclei per standard field	
			Superficial layer	Deeper layers
Intact	25–44	9	27	10
Intact	45–64	14	26	12
Intact	65–84	9	27	12
Superficial fibrillation	All ages	10	19	11

and 3) cartilage (Meachim and Collins 1962) and it has no appreciable effect on the amount of sulphate fixed by a full-thickness sample of uncalcified tissue (Collins and Meachim 1961). The absence of a demonstrable quantitative effect on sulphate uptake may be due to the facts that only a proportion of the cells are lost in the superficial layer (Meachim and Collins 1962) and that this layer, when considered as a whole, appears to have a reduced affinity for sulphate on comparison with that of the deeper tissue (Collins and McElligott 1960).

There is circumstantial evidence that necrosis of chondrocytes within the cartilage can contribute to the reduction of cell density in the superficial layer which accompanies, and may also precede, fibrillation (Chapter 1, Section 8.1): histological sections of the affected area show a variable number of cells in which nuclear staining is altered or lost, and 'empty' lacunae are often seen (Meachim et al. 1965).

8.1.2. Deep Fibrillation. Where fibrillation extends deeply into the tissue, there is evidence from electron microscopy of necrosis of some of the deeper cells (zones 2 and 3). Zimny and Redler (1969) have reported that necrotic remnants of deep cells are frequently seen. No quantitative data are available, but the implication of their report is that necrosis occurs more frequently amongst the deeper layer cells in fibrillated than in non-fibrillated cartilage. In deeply fibrillated or otherwise thinned cartilage the influence of this cell necrosis on the overall appearance of the tissue can be overshadowed by the presence of reactive changes amongst other deeper cells, although in other instances necrotic changes only are seen (Figures 2.23 and 2.24).

8.1.3. Cell Shedding. Although cell shedding into the joint cavity is not seen in non-fibrillated cartilage, chondrocytes can sometimes become exposed at the joint surface in fibrillated areas, due to disintegration of the matrix (Meachim and Roy 1969); such cells, or their necrotic remnants, can then be shed into the joint. Another type of cell shedding occurs when a tag of fibrillated matrix which contains chondrocytes separates from the main cartilage mass (Collins and McElligott 1960).

8.1.4. 'Degenerative Changes' within Individual Chondrocytes. When considering the ultrastructure of the individual chondrocyte, no sharp distinction can be made between cells from fibrillated and from non-fibrillated samples. Moreover, individual instances of cell degeneration and of cell necrosis in fibrillated cartilage have their counterpart in examples of these phenomena encountered occasionally in non-fibrillated specimens. Three examples from amongst a number of patterns of 'cytoplasmic degeneration' which have been seen in fibrillated cartilage are described in the account which follows, and their specificity in relation to fibrillation is discussed. In these examples it is helpful to recall that there are limitations in a purely morphological approach to the recognition of 'degenerative changes' in a chondrocyte.

(a) A type of 'hydropic degeneration' can sometimes occur in human articular chondrocytes near a fibrillated surface (Roy and Meachim 1968). The affected cells show swollen mitochondria with disorientated cristae. Their cytoplasm can also show a variety of membrane-lined degenerative inclusions, some of which contain multilayered membranous formations, and many of which appear to derive from the swollen mitochondria. In a proportion of the affected cells the cisternae of the rough endoplasmic reticulum are abnormally dilated and irregular. A similar type of chondrocyte degeneration has been described in healthy articular cartilage from rabbits (Palfrey and Davies 1966) and in rabbit articular cartilage in experimental chronic haemarthrosis (Roy 1968).

(b) Cells containing multiple electron-dense bodies in their cytoplasm have been observed in deeply fibrillated cartilage (Figure 2.25); such structures are infrequent in the cells of non-fibrillated specimens and of those showing only a superficial fibrillation (Roy and Meachim 1968). The morphology of the electron-dense bodies would be consistent with lysosomes. In a cell from deeply fibrillated cartilage they can occur in association with

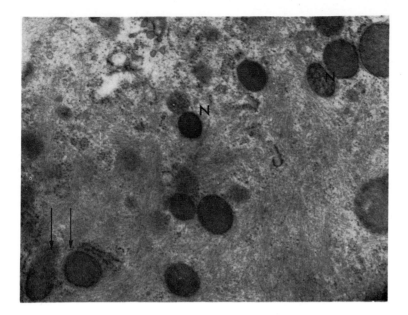

Figure 2.25 Multiple electron-dense bodies (N) in the cytoplasm of a cell from deeply fibrillated cartilage. It is probable that at least some of these bodies derive from mitochondrial degeneration (arrows).

Transmission electron micrograph ×25 000.

Osmium.

structures which appear to be abnormal mitochondria, and it is probable that at least some of them are derived from mitochondrial degeneration.

(c) As noted previously, intracytoplasmic fine filaments are a normal feature of adult human articular chondrocytes. In rabbit articular cartilage intracytoplasmic filaments are seen more commonly in older than in young animals (Barnett *et al.* 1963) and they can therefore be regarded as a feature of ageing. In adult man the filaments occur both in fibrillated and in non-fibrillated cartilage and thus their presence is not a specific consequence of fibrillation. However, it has been found that they can be more abundant in the cells of fibrillated patellar cartilage than in non-fibrillated samples (Zimny and Redler 1969), and this observation would be in keeping with the view that the accumulation of unusually large amounts of filaments in a cell represents a degenerative or involutionary change in the cytoplasm (Meachim and Roy 1967).

8.2. Reactive Changes

8.2.1. Multicellular Rounded Clusters.
In areas of cartilage showing deep fibrillation the deeper (zones 2 and 3) chondrocytes in the affected area often form abnormal multicellular rounded clusters (Figure 2.26), although this phenomenon is not invariably seen. The average nuclear count obtained from a deeply fibrillated area amongst which there are clusters is usually higher than that

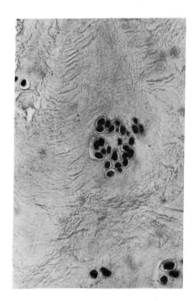

Figure 2.26 A multicellular rounded cluster from deeply fibrillated cartilage ×300.

Haematoxylin and eosin.

obtained from comparable non-fibrillated areas of zones 2 to 3 cartilage in the same specimen; also the larger the clumps, the greater is the increase in average nuclear count from the affected area (Meachim and Collins 1962). Thus it would seem that deeply fibrillated cartilage is sometimes populated by more cells than in non-fibrillated areas lying at a corresponding depth in the section. The findings suggest that the multicellular clusters represent a proliferation of chondrocytes and are not merely due to the redistribution of a numerically stable population. Meachim and Collins (1962) were unable to find mitotic figures in histological sections of fibrillated cartilage, probably because in man the cell clusters evolve at a relatively slow rate. More recently, radiochemical studies by Mankin and Lippiello (1970) and by Rothwell and Bentley (1973), employing ^{3}H-thymidine and other tracer materials, have demonstrated that cartilage fibrillation is in fact associated with cell replication in the tissue.

The cell density within a cluster in human fibrillated femoral condylar cartilage lies in the range $100–600 \times 10^3$ per mm^3. Preliminary findings suggest that the cellularity is inversely proportional to the distance of the cluster from the edge of the fissure (Stockwell, unpublished). This is reminiscent of the relationship in normal cartilage between cell density of the whole tissue and cartilage thickness (Section 4.6) and also of the zonal variation of cell density with respect to distance from the articular surface (Stockwell 1971a). The situation in fibrillated cartilage is complicated by the irregularity of the fissures and by changes in the composition of the matrix.

An important advance in understanding the nature of chondrocyte clusters was made by Collins and McElligott. They investigated fibrillated cartilage using quantitative and autoradiographic *in vitro* techniques employing radioactive ^{35}S-sulphate as a tracer material (McElligott and Collins 1960; Collins and McElligott 1960); these techniques study cellular activity in the synthesis and sulphation of proteoglycan ground substance (Section 3.4.1). Collins and McElligott observed that the multicellular rounded clusters often have an intense image over them in sulphate autoradiographs (Figure 2.27). By radiochemical assays they also observed that deep fibrillation is associated with an increase in sulphate uptake per unit dried weight of patellar cartilage, this quantitative effect being attributable at least partly to an increase in tissue cellularity (Meachim and Collins 1962) and not necessarily indicating an increase in the individual metabolic activity of the 'average cell' in the sample. It was concluded that the clusters are not a degenerative phenomenon: they can contain metabolically active cells and apparently form as a reactive response to the changes in the adjacent matrix (Chapter 1, Section 9.1.2). A study of experimentally induced cartilage disintegration in rabbits subsequently gave indirect evidence in support of this conclusion

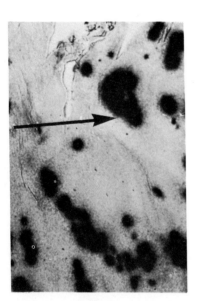

Figure 2.27 Autoradiograph showing black images indicative of sulphate (^{35}SO$_4$) uptake *in vitro* by multicellular rounded clusters (arrow) in deeply fibrillated cartilage. ×100.

(Meachim 1963). It was originally suggested that the stimulus which caused this reactive response was a depletion of acid glycosaminoglycans within the ground substance near the cells. The recent demonstration of an interrelationship between cell density and thickness in normal cartilage (Section 4.6) suggests an additional factor. In fibrillated cartilage localized regions of 'thin' cartilage are produced both between the fissures and also deep to the base of the clefts. *Inter alia*, this would increase the surface area available for diffusion from the synovial fluid. Viewed teleologically, cluster formation might represent an attempt (not necessarily effective) to restore the normal ratio of cell density to cartilage thickness. Conversely, is the absence of cluster formation by the superficial cells of mildly fibrillated cartilage explicable because the cartilage has not yet thinned?

The investigation by Collins and McElligott was made on specimens of cartilage obtained at necropsy. More recently, Mankin and Lippiello (1970) have extended these results in a study of cartilage metabolism in specimens obtained from femoral heads removed during surgical operations. Using DNA content as an indication of the cell population, they have shown that sulphate uptake per unit weight of DNA is increased in fibrillated cartilage as compared with a control tissue. Studies of protein synthesis gave similar results. It is relevant to comment that the results do not necessarily indicate an increase in the individual metabolic activity of the 'average cell' in the sample: in the fibrillated specimens some of the superficial cartilage would have been absent, having been lost by matrix disintegration. Since the superficial layer contains relatively more cells than the deeper tissue (Meachim and Collins 1962) and since it often has a relatively low affinity for sulphate (Collins and McElligott 1960), an apparent increase in sulphate uptake per unit weight of DNA in the sample might occur simply as a mathematical consequence of loss of superficial cells. A further difficulty in interpretation arises from the possibility that in some of the osteoarthrosic samples studied the fibrillated 'old' cartilage is likely to have been admixed with new non-osseous tissue of extrinsic origin (Meachim and Osborne 1970; Meachim 1972a).

There is also evidence from electron microscopy which indicates metabolic activity amongst the deeper cells of fibrillated cartilage. In an ultrastructural study of adult human patellar cartilage, Zimny and Redler (1969) compared the cells in fibrillated softened cartilage with those in smooth firm samples. Representative specimens were examined from the superficial, middle and deep layers. In the fibrillated cartilage the deep-layer cells are frequently seen in clusters. They can show a well developed rough endoplasmic reticulum and Golgi apparatus, features which were interpreted by Zimny and Redler as evidence of synthetic and secretory activity.

However, evidence of cell multiplication based on DNA synthesis and evidence of metabolic activity based on biochemical and ultrastructural features of the resultant daughter cells in a cluster does not ensure that they will be capable of synthesizing matrix components of the correct nature or quantity. Nor do the cells in a cluster necessarily remain active and viable throughout the life history of the cluster. Observations on experimentally induced cartilage damage in rabbits indicate that a cluster can eventually become metabolically inactive (Meachim 1963) and a similar phenomenon probably occurs in man. While it is a reasonable conclusion that the cell clusters often present in fibrillated cartilage are formed by cell replication and that this is a reactive phenomenon (Meachim and Collins 1962; Meachim 1963; Mankin and Lippiello 1970), there is reason to believe that this response is not sufficient for repair (Collins and McElligott 1960).

8.2.2. Aggregates of Elongated Cells. Although multicellular round clusters (Figure 2.26), when present, are the typical pattern of reactive response amongst the chondrocytes of fibrillated cartilage, occasionally a second much less common pattern of cellular change, apparently proliferative in nature, is seen (Meachim, unpublished). The individual cells which characterize this response are elongated in outline (Figure 2.28), unlike those within the

Figure 2.28 An elongated cell (right) adjacent to a cleft (upper left) in deeply fibrillated cartilage.

Transmission electron micrograph ×6300.

Glutaraldehyde.

130

round clusters. They are found arranged in irregular aggregates amongst which there is a variable amount of intercellular matrix. Some aggregates comprise only a few cells, but in others numerous cells, sometimes closely packed, are apparent. In the larger aggregates most of the cells can have their long axes aligned in the same direction ('cell swarms'). In certain instances it is possible that the cells are derived from extrinsic repair tissue rather than intrinsically within the cartilage.

In histological sections of fibrillated cartilage, one or more localized areas on the slide occasionally show this pattern of response, usually amongst zone 2 and 3 cells near fissures. It is possible that the phenomenon may be related to an ultrastructural change described by Zimny and Redler (1969) within the superficial and middle layer cells of fibrillated patellar cartilage. They report that many of the superficial cells can acquire a structural resemblance to proliferating fibroblasts, and that many of the middle layer cells can somewhat resemble stationary fibroblasts, while in others glycogen can disappear and endoplasmic reticulum become more prominent.

A similar fibroblastic transformation of chondrocytes takes place in articular cartilage explants exposed to complement-sufficient antiserum in culture. If the explants are cultured first in the presence of soft connective tissue the cartilage matrix becomes depleted; during subsequent culture in antiserum, antibodies can gain access to the chondrocytes. Some cells are killed but many survive; provided that collagen as well as proteoglycan has been degraded, the surviving chondrocytes transform into elongated fibroblasts (Fell 1975). The mechanism of this transformation is not understood, but the fibroblastic form seems to be resistant to the effects of antiserum since the cells are healthy and actively mitotic; furthermore, their surfaces do not react with IgG. The capacity of these cells to regenerate the matrix is reduced or absent, however. It is relevant to note that there are similarities between the elongated cells of fibrillated cartilage *in vivo* described by Zimny and Redler (1969), the fibroblastic transformation *in vitro* described by Fell, and the cells of the 'dedifferentiated' phase in tissue cultures of chondrocytes described by Holtzer *et al.* (1970). 'Dedifferentiation' *in vitro* occurs after a period of some two weeks during which the cells have been active in matrix synthesis. The 'dedifferentiated' cell resembles a 'fibroblast' morphologically and, though able to proliferate, no longer exhibits the capacity to synthesize the 'luxury' molecules of the matrix. The condition can be reproduced by incubating functional chondrocytes in a medium containing BUDR (5-bromo-2-deoxyuridine, a thymidine analogue). The inhibition of matrix deposition is reversible in the progeny of the 'BUDR-cell'.

It is also possible that the flattened superficial cells of normal articular cartilage may have something in common with the 'fibroblastic', 'dedifferentiated' cell. In addition to certain ultra-structural aspects of the superficial cells and their reduced capacity to incorporate sulphate, their response to antiserum also is in accord with this view. If articular cartilage explants are cultured in complement-sufficient antiserum after prior degradation of the matrix with trypsin, the peripheral cells of the explants (i.e. those bordering on the cut surface of the explant blocks) are killed (Millroy and Poole 1974). The inner chondrocytes survive and regenerate new capsules of ground substance which apparently protect the cells against the antiserum by excluding the large antibody molecules. It is of interest that most of the cells of the superficial zone survive, though necessarily peripheral in the explant block. However, this fibroblastic-like resistance to the lethal effects of the antiserum is only relative, since if the matrix of the explant is perhaps more completely depleted by prior culture in the presence of soft connective tissue (Fell 1975) the superficial chondrocytes succumb and die.

Such speculations on the nature of the cells of the superficial zone may be related to an unanswered problem concerning the reaction of articular chondrocytes to fibrillation changes. How is it that chondrocytes situated deeply in the tissue apparently can react by forming cell clusters and deeply staining matrix while superficial chondrocytes (zone 1) do not?

8.3. Metabolic Changes with Special Reference to Proteoglycan Depletion

Evidence has already been presented of a reduction in the amount of proteoglycan both in fibrillated cartilage (Chapter 1, Section 9.1.2) and in the microscopic foci undergoing regressive change (Chapter 1, Section 8.1.1). It is of interest to consider the involvement of the chondrocytes in these changes in the ground substance, although this discussion does not imply that the suggested cellular mechanisms are necessarily the same in cartilage fibrillation and in regressive change, nor that any such mechanism is *sui generis*. There may be underlying causes for the cell changes as yet undiscovered; for example, intrinsic or extrinsic ageing or genetic factors.

8.3.1. Possible Causes for the Reduction in the Amount of Proteoglycan.
Since there is normally a physiological turnover of proteoglycan (Mankin and Lippiello 1969) the reduced amount of proteoglycan might be due to a failure of the chondrocytes to manufacture glycosaminoglycan, or to excessive loss of proteoglycan after it has been manufactured, or to a combination of both factors. Failure of synthetic activity could be at least partly responsible for reduction of glycosaminoglycan content in regions

where necrosis of chondrocytes is found. Thus cell loss is usually a dominant feature in a fibrillated superficial layer (Meachim *et al.* 1965) and, similarly, extensive necrosis of deeper cells can sometimes occur in deeply fibrillated cartilage. The age-dependent reduction in respiratory power (Section 3.1.2) could theoretically be associated with a more insidious failure of synthetic activity; local changes in the matrix causing adverse nutritional conditions for the cell might also be considered.

However, at least in deeply fibrillated cartilage a simple synthetic failure will not always explain the proteoglycan changes, since there is evidence that often many of the deeper cells in such an area are still metabolically active (Collins and McElligott 1960; Mankin and Lippiello 1970). Additional explanations must therefore be sought. One possibility is that the proteoglycan manufactured by the chondrocytes may be qualitatively different (McDevitt and Muir 1976); however, this may not be the major factor, at least with respect to the polysaccharide moiety (Bollet and Nance 1966). Second, it is possible that proteoglycan 'leaks out' of the cartilage as a consequence of damage to the structural integrity of the matrix from mechanical effects during fibrillation (Maroudas 1970, personal communication). A third view, now widely held following the work of Chrisman and others, is that excessive degradation of the proteoglycan by proteolytic enzyme activity occurs. This could result either from an increase in the activity of degradative enzymes normally concerned in the physiological remodelling of cartilage matrix (Mankin and Lippiello 1969), or from abnormal degradative enzyme systems coming into play.

8.3.2. Enzymatic Degradation. The enzymes concerned in proteoglycan degradation are believed to be mainly or entirely of intrinsic origin within the cartilage and not of extrinsic origin from joint fluid. As discussed in Section 3, the site and manner of their action on the matrix in normal and in fibrillated cartilage is not fully understood. However, the breakdown of matrix in cartilage is believed to be a two-stage process (Fell 1969; Dingle 1973). In the first stage, matrix macromolecules are reduced to smaller fragments outside the cell; in the second stage, fragments are phagocytosed by the cell and digestion is then completed in the lysosomes. Studies on experimental models of cartilage and bone in organ culture (Fell 1969) suggest that in such cartilage, extracellular digestion is more important than intracellular digestion. However, in both stages, the enzymes involved are considered to be lysosomal either in localization or in origin, and thus it is relevant next to discuss the role of lysosomes in cartilage fibrillation.

8.3.3. Significance of Lysosomes in Fibrillation. Proteolytic activity in articular cartilage is elevated in fibrillation (Ali and Evans 1973) and, in histochemical studies, reaction products attributed to protease activity are seen more often in fibrillated than in normal specimens (Chrisman *et al.* 1967). Histological studies using immunofluorescent techniques also suggest excessive degradation by enzyme activity, both in superficial and in deep fibrillation. There is immunocytochemical evidence for the origin of the proteolytic enzymes in lysosomes, although experimental studies in rabbits using enzyme histochemical techniques at the ultrastructural level suggest that intracellular proteases are not all located within these structures (Chrisman 1967, 1969). The morphological evidence from electron microscopy of human articular cartilage is in itself inconclusive although three ultrastructural phenomena have been described which might indicate a 'lysosomal disturbance'.

However, each of these phenomena could be attributable to degenerative and necrotic changes occurring in chondrocytes as a secondary and incidental feature of cartilage fibrillation, and none of them offers morphological proof that proteoglycan depletion is basically due to lysosomal enzyme activity. The relevant observations have been mentioned previously, and can be summarized as follows:

(a) Zimny and Redler (1969) observed that necrotic remnants of deep cells are frequently seen in fibrillated patellar cartilage. They have stated that the necrotic remnants 'are characterized by many lysosomes'.

(b) Roy and Meachim (1968) observed, in deeply fibrillated cartilage, cells containing multiple electron-dense bodies (Figure 2.25) possibly derived from mitochondrial degeneration. They have suggested that these bodies may be lysosomes. Such bodies are an infrequent finding in non-fibrillated cartilage and in cartilage showing only superficial fibrillation.

(c) Meachim (1967) described large 'complex bodies' (Figure 2.8) in human articular chondrocytes: it has been suggested that these inclusions might be lysosomal derivatives, possibly concerned in intracellular breakdown of ingested matrix material. However, they are an uncommon finding and they can occur both in non-fibrillated and in fibrillated specimens.

The significance of these three ultrastructural observations is debatable, particularly as they are not supported by enzyme histochemical data on the 'lysosome-like' structures which have been seen. Moreover, the possibility of excessive activity of lysosomal enzymes is basically a biochemical concept, and there are limitations in a purely morphological approach to the recognition of this phenomenon.

There are three hypothetical ways in which lysosomal enzymes might play a part in the ground substance changes in fibrillated cartilage: release into the extracellular matrix during disintegration of degenerate and necrotic chondrocytes, release into the extracellular matrix from cells which are still healthy and structurally intact, and release into matrix material ingested or engulfed by chondrocytes for intracellular breakdown. Electron microscopy of human articular cartilage has not so far given any definite evidence for any of these mechanisms: it is also relevant to emphasize again that some of the lysosome-like structures which have been seen could represent nothing more than the end-product of intracellular digestive and degenerative processes.

Chrisman obtained ultrastructural histochemical data from rabbit cartilage which suggests that much of the degradative enzyme produced in the cells is not kept segregated in the lysosomes. He reports that in the rabbit the amount of enzyme reaction product is increased in articular cartilage rendered chondromalacic by experimental scarification (Meachim 1963). It is found both intracellularly and extracellularly. Although some of the intracytoplasmic reaction product occurs within membrane-bound electron-dense bodies morphologically consistent with lysosomes, much more of it occurs in areas of cytoplasm not surrounded by a limiting membrane. The extracellular reaction product is prominent and is seen as a pericellular 'halo' in the matrix (Chrisman 1967, 1969). The findings in the rabbit chondromalacic cartilage are apparently not attributable to abnormal intracellular seepage of enzyme from damaged lysosomes, since it would seem that a similar distribution of reaction product is found within the chondrocytes of normal rabbit cartilage. Some of Chrisman's findings would, however, be consistent with an extracellular release *in vivo* of enzyme which was initially segregated in lysosomes.

8.4. Conclusions

Several possible factors, not mutually exclusive, can be suggested to account for the reduced amount of proteoglycan which is observed in the intercellular matrix of fibrillated cartilage. These factors are:

(a) Necrosis of some of the chondrocytes, with diminished synthesis of new ground substance proteoglycan. This mechanism undoubtedly plays a part in the superficial zone (zone 1), and may sometimes also be concerned in the deeper uncalcified zones (zones 2 and 3).

(b) Leakage of proteoglycan from the cartilage simply as a consequence of damage to the structural integrity of the fibrous network of the matrix.

(c) Synthesis by the cells of proteoglycan qualitatively different from that usually manufactured in adult articular cartilage (McDevitt and Muir 1976).

(d) Increased degradation of proteoglycan after it has been synthesized, attributable to lysosomal enzymes acting extracellularly, and also perhaps actually within the chondrocytes.

When considering the above possibilities it is often assumed that proteoglycan metabolism is fundamentally 'faulty' in fibrillated cartilage, and that the reduced amount of intercellular acid glycosaminoglycans is due primarily to a 'biochemical lesion'. However, biochemical factors closely inter-relate with mechanical factors in the pathogenesis of cartilage fibrillation. To elaborate further, it is helpful to make a distinction between (a) events occurring during the initial development of fibrillation and (b) events occurring after histological fibrillation is established in the tissue.

(a) Concerning the initial development of fibrillation, the exact time sequence of events is debatable, since the order in which the cells, intercellular matrix and cartilage surface become altered is not at present fully known. The primary event may not be the same in every case. In man it may in theory be one or more of the following changes: an excessive extracellular release of lysosomal degradative enzymes, perhaps in response to 'microtrauma'; an altered or diminished synthesis of proteoglycan, again perhaps in response to 'microtrauma'; structural damage directly to the superficial matrix, due to mechanically induced fragmentation of its collagen fibre network. In experimental osteoarthrosis in dogs (McDevitt and Muir 1976) the initial events, prior to histologically detectable fibrillation on Indian ink staining, may be fibre network separation (as evidenced by thickening of the tissue) and altered proteoglycan synthesis. Whichever the initial event in man, it is likely to result eventually in microscopic foci of surface fraying and of cartilage softening.

(b) Once fibrillation is established, necrosis of some of the cells, from mechanical factors or other cause, will in itself potentiate a local reduction in the amount of proteoglycan synthesis. Where cell necrosis is accompanied by viable cell cluster formation, such clusters may represent an exaggerated form of reactive remodelling, attributable to a profound local alteration in the biochemical environment of the tissue, and perhaps stimulated by pathological thinning of the cartilage. If this hypothesis of 'reactive remodelling' (to mechanical damage and environmental change) is the correct explanation for the clusters, it would not be surprising if they showed an increased activity of degradative enzymes, possibly with an alteration in the type of proteoglycan manufactured by the cells. Viable chondrocytes which had not formed clusters might perhaps also participate in a 'reactive reponse'. Reduction in the amount of proteoglycan, from enzymatic degradation by viable cells or reduced synthesis by necrotic cells or both causes, will further weaken the collagen network. This will tend to set up a vicious cycle of ground substance changes and of collagen network disintegration from mechanical effects during day-to-day use of the joint. The continued progression of this cycle is not always inevitable and not always relentless (Meachim 1975). However, in some subjects it can at certain sites progress to give a complete loss of uncalcified cartilage with osteoarthrosic bone exposure. The reasons why this progression at such sites occurs more readily in some subjects than in others are not fully known, and the main factor responsible may not be the same in every individual. Both in progressive lesions and in those of limited progression, the low capacity of adult articular chondrocytes and chondrocyte clusters to repair a damaged collagen fibre network hampers their attempts to retard the disintegration of the cartilage.

REFERENCES AND BIBLIOGRAPHY

Akeson W. H., Eichelberger L. and Roma M. (1958) Biochemical studies of articular cartilage. II: Values following the denervation of an extremity. *J. Bone Jt Surg.* **40A,** 153.

Ali S. Y. (1964) The degradation of cartilage matrix by an intracellular protease. *Biochem. J.* **93,** 611.

Ali S. Y. and Bayliss M. T. (1974) Enzymic changes in human osteoarthrotic cartilage. *Normal and Osteoarthrotic Articular Cartilage,* Ed. by S. Y. Ali, M. W. Elves and D. H. Leaback, p. 189. Institute of Orthopaedics, London.

Ali S. Y. and Evans L. (1973) Enzymatic degradation of cartilage in osteoarthritis. *Fed. Proc.* **32,** 1494.

Arlet J., Mole J. and Barriuso J. (1958) Etudes histologiques concernant le cartilage articulaire de bovide a l'etat frais. 1: Criteres de vitalite des chondrocytes. *Revue Rhumat.* **25,** 565.

Bacsich P. and Wyburn G. M. (1947) The significance of the mucoprotein content on the survival of homographs of cartilage and cornea. *Proc. R. Soc. Edin.* **B62,** 321.

Balogh K. (1964) Dihydrolipoic dehydrogenase activity: a step in the formation of acyl-coenzyme A demonstrated histochemically. *J. Histochem. Cytochem.* **12,** 404.

Balogh K. and Cohen R. B. (1961) Histochemical localisation of uridine diphosphoglucose dehydrogenase in cartilage. *Nature (Lond.)* **192,** 1199.

Balogh K., Dudley H. R. and Cohen R. B. (1961) Oxidative enzyme activity in skeletal cartilage and bone. *Lab. Invest.* **10,** 839.

Barland P., Janis R. and Sandson J. (1966) Immunofluorescent studies of human articular cartilage. *Ann. rheum. Dis.* **25,** 156.

Barnett C. H. (1963) Morphology and electron microscopy of normal articular cartilage. *Cytological Aspects of Joint Tissues.* Arthritis and Rheumatism Council Symposium, London.

Barnett C. H., Cochrane W. and Palfrey A. J. (1963) Age changes in articular cartilage of rabbits. *Ann. rheum. Dis.* **22,** 389.

Barnett C. H., Davies D. V. and MacConaill M. A. (1961) *Synovial Joints: their structure and mechanics.* Longmans Green, London.

Baxter E. and Muir H. (1972) The antigenicity of cartilage proteoglycans: the relationship of the antigenic determinants present in Smith degraded and intact proteoglycans. *Biochim. biophys. Acta* **279,** 276.

Bentley G. and Greer R. B. (1971) Homotransplantation of isolated epiphyseal and articular cartilage chondrocytes into joint surfaces of rabbits. *Nature (Lond.)* **230,** 385.

Bernstein D. S., Leboeuf B. and Cahill G. F. (1961) Studies on glucose metabolism in cartilage in vitro. *Proc. Soc. exp. Biol. Med.* **107,** 458.

Bollet A. J. and Nance J. L. (1966) Biochemical findings in normal and osteoarthritic articular cartilage. II: Chondroitin surface concentration and chain length, water, and ash content. *J. clin. Invest.* **45,** 1170.

Bollet A. J., Handy J. R. and Sturgill B. C. (1963) Chondroitin sulphate concentration and protein-polysaccharide composition of articular cartilage in osteoarthritis. *J. clin. Invest.* **42,** 853.

Bostrom H. and Odeblad E. (1953) The influence of cortisone upon the sulphate exchange of chondroitin sulphuric acid. *Ark. für Kemi* **6,** 39.

Burleigh M. C., Barrett A. J. and Lazarus G. S. (1974) Cathepsin Bl. *Biochem. J.* **137,** 387.

Burstone M. S. (1959) Acid phosphatase activity of calcifying bone and dentin matrices. *J. Histochem. Cytochem.* **7,** 147.

Burstone M. S. (1960) Histochemical observations on enzymatic processes in bones and teeth. *Ann. N.Y. Acad. Sci.* **85,** 431.

Bywaters E. G. L. (1937) The metabolism of joint tissues. *J. Path. Bact.* **44,** 247.

Campbell C. J. (1969) The healing of cartilage defects. *Clin. Orthop.* **64,** 45.

Carlson H. (1957) Reactions of rabbit patellary cartilage following operative defects. *Acta orthop. Scand.* Suppl. 28.

Chesterman P. J. and Smith A. U. (1968) Homotransplantation of articular cartilage and isolated chondrocytes. *J. Bone Jt Surg.* **50B,** 184.

Chrisman O. D. (1967) *Cartilage: degradation and repair,* Ed. by C. A. Bassett, p. 81. Nat. Acad. Sci. Nat. Res. Council, Washington DC.

Chrisman O. D. (1969) Biochemical aspects of degenerative joint disease. *Clin. Orthop.* **64,** 77.

Chrisman O. D. (1975) The effect of growth hormone on established cartilage lesions. *Clin. Orthop.* **107,** 232.

Chrisman O. D., Semonsky C. and Bensch A. (1967) Cathepsins in articular cartilage. *The Healing of Osseous Tissue,* Ed. by R. A. Robinson, p. 169. Nat. Acad. Sci. Res. Council, Washington DC.

Clarke I. C. (1971a) Human articular surface contours and related surface depression frequency studies. *Ann. rheum. Dis.* **30,** 15.

Clarke I. C. (1971b) Surface characteristics of human articular cartilage—a scanning electron microscope study. *J. Anat. (Lond.)* **108**, 23.

Cobb J. D. (1952) The morphological distribution of glycogen and glycoprotein in the cells and extracellular material of growing bones. Quoted by G. Gomori (1952) *Microscopic Histochemistry,* p. 197. University Press, Chicago.

Collins D. H. (1949) *The Pathology of Articular and Spinal Disease,* pp 74–115. Edward Arnold, London.

Collins D. H. and McElligott T. F. (1960) Sulphate ($^{35}SO_4$) uptake by chondrocytes in relation to histological changes in osteo-arthritic human articular cartilage. *Ann. rheum. Dis.* **19**, 318.

Collins D. H. and Meachim G. (1961) Sulphate ($^{35}SO_4$) fixation by human articular cartilage compared in the knee and shoulder joints. *Ann. rheum. Dis.* **20**, 117.

Collins D. H., Ghadially F. N. and Meachim G. (1965) Intra-cellular lipids of cartilage. *Ann. rheum. Dis.* **24**, 123.

Cooper G. W. and Prockop D. J. (1968) Intracellular accumulation of protocollagen and extrusion of collagen by embryonic cartilage cells. *J. Cell Biol.* **38**, 523.

Cornah M. S., Meachim G. and Parry E. W. (1970) Banded structures in the matrix of human and rabbit nucleus pulposus. *J. Anat. (Lond.)* **107**, 351.

Craigmyle M. B. L. (1958) Regional lymph node changes induced by cartilage homo- and heterografts in the rabbit. *J. Anat. (Lond.)* **92**, 74.

Crelin E. S. (1957) Mitosis in adult cartilage. *Science* **125**, 650.

Crelin E. S. and Southwick W. O. (1964) Changes induced by sustained pressure in the knee-joint articular cartilage of adult rabbits. *Anat. Rec.* **149**, 113.

Daughaday W. H., Hall K., Raben M. S., Salmon W. D., van den Brande J. L. and van Wyk J. J. (1972) Somatomedin: proposed designation for sulphation factor. *Nature (Lond.)* **235**, 107.

Davies D. V., Barnett C. H., Cochrane W. and Palfrey A. J. (1962) Electron microscopy of articular cartilage in the young rabbit. *Ann. rheum. Dis.* **21**, 11.

DePalma A. F., McKeever C. D. and Subin D. K. (1966) Process of repair of articular cartilage demonstrated by histology and autoradiography with tritiated thymidine. *Clin. Orthop.* **48**, 229.

De Duve C. and Wattiaux R. (1966) Functions of lysosomes. *Ann. Rev. Physiol.* **28**, 435.

Dingle J. T. (1973) The role of lysosomal enzymes in skeletal tissues. *J. Bone Jt Surg.* **55B**, 87.

Dingle J. T. (1975) The secretion of enzymes into the pericellular environment. *Phil. Trans. R. Soc. Lond. B* **271**, 315.

Dingle J. T. and Burleigh M. C. (1974) Connective tissue and its changes in disease. *Trans. ophthal. Soc. U.K.* **94**, 696.

Ehrlich H. P., Ross R. and Bornstein P. (1974) Effects of anti-microtubular agents on the secretion of collagen. A biochemical and morphological study. *J. Cell Biol.* **62**, 310.

Eichelberger L., Akeson W. H. and Roma M. (1958) Biochemical studies of articular cartilage. I: Normal values. *J. Bone Jt Surg.* **40A**, 142.

Eichelberger L., Roma M. and Moulder P. V. (1959) Biochemical studies of articular cartilage. III: Values following the immobilization of an extremity. *J. Bone Jt Surg.* **41A**, 1127.

Elliott H. C. (1936) Studies on articular cartilage. I: Growth mechanisms. *Amer. J. Anat.* **58**, 127.

Elves M. W. (1974) A study of the transplantation antigens on chondrocytes from articular cartilage. *J. Bone Jt Surg.* **56B**, 178.

Fasoli G. (1905) Sul comportamento della cartilagini nelle ferite. *Archo sci. Med.* **29**, 365.

Fell H. B. (1969) Role of biological membranes in some skeletal reactions. *Ann. rheum. Dis.* **28**, 213.

Fell H. B. (1975) The role of mucopolysaccharides in the protection of cartilage cells against immune reactions. *Phil. Trans. R. Soc. Lond. B* **271**, 325.

Fell H. B. and Dingle J. T. (1963) Studies on the mode of action of excess of vitamin A. 6: Lysosomal protease and the degradation of cartilage matrix. *Biochem. J.* **87**, 403.

Fell H. B. and Mellanby E. (1952) Effect of hypervitaminosis A on embryonic limb bones cultivated in vitro. *J. Physiol. (Lond.)* **116**, 320.

Fessel J. M. and Chrisman O. D. (1964) Enzymatic degradation of chondromucoprotein by cell-free extracts of human cartilage. *Arthritis Rheum.* **7**, 398.

Fuller J. A. and Ghadially F. N. (1972) Ultrastructural observations on surgically produced partial-thickness defects in articular cartilage. *Clin. Orthop.* **86**, 193.

Galjaard H. (1962) Histochemisch en interferometrisch onderzoek van hyalien kraakbeen. Thesis, University of Leyden.

Ghadially F. N. and Roy S. (1969) *Ultrastructure of Synovial Joints in Health and Disease.* Butterworths, London.

Ghadially F. N., Meachim G. and Collins D. H. (1965) Extra-cellular lipid in the matrix of human articular cartilage. *Ann. rheum. Dis.* **24**, 136.

Ghadially F. N., Mehta P. N. and Kirkaldy-Willis W. H. (1970) Ultrastructure of articular cartilage in experimentally produced lipoarthritis. *J. Bone Jt Surg.* **52A**, 1147.

Ghadially F. N., Ailsby R. L. and Oryschak A. F. (1974) Scanning electron microscopy of superficial defects in articular cartilage. *Ann. rheum. Dis.* **33**, 327.

Gibson T., Curran R. C. and Davies W. B. (1957) The survival of living homografts in man. *Transplant. Bull.* **4**, 105.

Godman G. C. and Lane N. (1964) On the site of sulfation in the chondrocyte. *J. Cell Biol.* **21**, 353.

Green W. T. and Ferguson R. J. (1975) Histochemical and electron microscopic comparison of tissue produced by rabbit articular chondrocytes *in vivo* and *in vitro. Arthritis Rheum.* **18**, 273.

Grillo T. A. I., Okuno G., Price S. and Foa P. P. (1964). The activity of uridine disphosphate glucose–glycogen synthetase in some embryonic tissues. *J. Histochem. Cytochem.* **12**, 275.

Gubisch W. and Schlager F. (1961) Fermente im Knochen- und Knorpel-gewebe. III Mitteilung: β-D-Glucuronidase. *Acta Histochem.* **12**, 69.

Hamerman D. and Schubert M. (1962) Diarthrodial joints, an essay. *Amer. J. Med.* **33**, 555.

Hardingham T. E., Fitton-Jackson S. and Muir H. (1972) Replacement of proteoglycans in embryonic chick cartilage in organ culture after treatment with testicular hyaluronidase. *Biochem. J.* **129**, 101.

Harris H. A. and Russell A. E. (1933) Atypical growth in cartilage as a fundamental factor in dwarfism amd achondroplasia. *Proc. R. Soc. Med.* **26**, 779.

Hart J. A. L. (1968) Cilia in articular cartilage. *J. Anat. (Lond.)* **103**, 222.

Holtzer H., Chacko S., Abbott H., Holtzer S. and Anderson H. (1970) Variable behaviour of chondrocytes in vitro. *Chemistry and Molecular Biology of the Intracellular Matrix,* Ed. by E. A. Balazs, Vol. 3, p. 1471. Academic Press, London.

Horwitz A. L. and Dorfman A. (1968) Subcellular sites for synthesis of chondromucoprotein of cartilage. *J. Cell Biol.* **38**, 358.

Insall J. N. (1967) Intra-articular surgery for degenerative arthritis of the knee. A report of the works of the late K. H. Pridie. *J. Bone Jt Surg.* **49B**, 211.

Ishikawa H., Bischoff R. and Holtzer H. (1969) Formation of arrowhead complexes with heavy meromysin in a variety of cell types. *J. Cell Biol.* **43**, 312.

Kawiak J., Moskalewski S. and Darzynkiewicz Z. (1965) Isolation of chondrocytes from calf cartilage. *Exp. Cell Res.* **39**, 59.

Keiser H. and de Vito J. (1974) Immunochemical studies of fragments of bovine nasal cartilage proteoglycan subunits. *Conn. Tiss. Res.* **2**, 273.

Kincaid S. A., van Sickle D. C. and Wilsman N. J. (1972) Histochemical evidence of a functional heterogeneity of the chondrocytes of adult canine articular cartilage. *Histochem. J.* **4**, 237.

Kuhlman E. (1960) A microchemical study of the developing epiphyseal plate. *J. Bone Jt Surg.* **42A**, 457.

Landells J. W. (1957) The reactions of injured human articular cartilage. *J. Bone Jt Surg.* **39B**, 548.

Layman D. L. and Ross R. (1973) The production and secretion of procollagen peptidase by human fibroblasts in culture. *Archs Biochem. Biophys.* **147**, 451.

Layton L. L. (1951) Cortisone inhibition of mucopolysaccharide synthesis in the intact rat. *Archs Biochem. Biophys.* **32**, 224.

Leaback D. H. (1974) Studies on some glycosidases from the chondrocytes of articular cartilage and from certain other cells and tissues. *Normal and Osteoarthrotic Articular Cartilage,* Ed. by S. Y. Ali, M. W. Elves and D. H. Leaback, p. 73. Institute of Orthopaedics, London.

Leidy J. (1849) Article I: On the intimate structure and history of the articular cartilages. *Amer. J. med. Sci.* (New Series) **17**, 277.

Lenzi L., Berlanda P., Flora A., Aureli G., Rizzotti M., Balduini C. and Boni M. (1974) Vitamin A induced arthritis in rabbits: an experimental model for the study of human disease. *Normal and Osteoarthrotic Articular Cartilage,* Ed. by S. Y. Ali, M. W. Elves and D. H. Leaback, p. 243. Institute of Orthopaedics, London.

Levine M. D. and Follis R. H. (1949) Lecithinase activity of epiphyseal cartilage of the foetal pig. *Fed. Proc.* **8**, 458.

Lutwak-Mann C. (1940) Enzymes in articular cartilage. *Biochem. J.* **34**, 517.

McDevitt C. A. and Muir H. (1976) Biochemical changes in the cartilage of the knee in experimental and natural osteoarthritis in the dog. *J. Bone Jt Surg.* **58B**, 94.

McElligott T. F. and Collins D. H. (1960) Chondrocyte function of human articular and costal cartilage compared by measuring the *in vitro* uptake of labelled (^{35}S) sulphate. *Ann. rheum. Dis.* **19**, 31.

McElligott T. F. and Potter J. L. (1960) Increased fixation of sulphur-35 by cartilage *in vitro* following depletion of the matrix by intravenous papain. *J. exp. Med.* **112**, 743.

Mankin H. J. (1963a) Localization of tritiated cytidine in articular cartilage of immature and adult rabbits after intra-articular injection. *Lab. Invest.* **12**, 543.

Mankin H. J. (1963b) Localization of tritiated thymidine in articular cartilage of rabbits. III: Mature articular cartilage. *J. Bone Jt Surg.* **45A**, 529.

Mankin H. J. (1964) Mitosis in articular cartilage of immature rabbits. *Clin. Orthop.* **34**, 170.

Mankin H. J. and Baron P. A. (1965) The effect of ageing on protein synthesis in articular cartilage of rabbits. *Lab. Invest.* **14**, 658.

Mankin H. J. and Laing P. G. (1967) Protein and ribonucleic acid synthesis in articular cartilage of osteoathritic dogs. *Arthritis Rheum.* **10**, 444.

Mankin H. J. and Lippiello L. (1969) The turnover of adult rabbit articular cartilage. *J. Bone Jt Surg.* **51A**, 1591.

Mankin H. J. and Lippiello L. (1970) Biochemical and metabolic abnormalities in articular cartilage from osteo-arthritic human hips. *J. Bone Jt Surg.* **52A**, 424.

Mankin H. J., Zarins A. and Jaffe W. L. (1972) The effect of systemic corticosteroids on rabbit articular cartilage. *Arthritis Rheum.* **15**, 593.

Manning W. K. and Bonner W. M. (1967) Isolation and culture of chondrocytes from human adult articular cartilage. *Arthritis Rheum.* **10**, 235.

Marcus R. E. (1973) The effect of low oxygen concentration on growth glycolysis and sulfate incorporation by articular chondrocytes in monolayer culture. *Arthritis Rheum.* **16**, 646.

Maroudas A., Bullough P. G., Swanson S. A. V. and Freeman M. A. R. (1968) The permeability of articular cartilage. *J. Bone Jt Surg.* **50B**, 166.

Maroudas A., Stockwell R. A., Nachemson A. and Urban J. (1975) Factors involved in the nutrition of the human lumbar intervertebral disc: cellularity and diffusion of glucose *in vitro*. *J. Anat. (Lond.)* **120**, 113.

Matthews L. S. and Hirsch C. (1972) Temperatures measured in human cortical bone when drilling. *J. Bone Jt Surg.* **54A**, 297.

Mazhuga P. and Cherkosova V. V. (1974) Adaptive distribution of specific biosynthesis in a homogeneous population of the articular cartilage chondrocytes. *Z. mikrosk.-anat. Forsch.* **88**, 364.

Meachim G. (1963) The effect of scarification on articular cartilage in the rabbit. *J. Bone Jt Surg.* **45B**, 150.

Meachim G. (1967) The histology and ultrastructure of cartilage. *Cartilage: degradation and repair,* Ed. by C. A. L. Bassett, p. 3. Nat. Acad. Sci. Nat. Res. Council, Washington DC.

Meachim G. (1971) Effect of age on the thickness of adult articular cartilage at the shoulder joint. *Ann. rheum. Dis.* **30**, 43.

Meachim G. (1972a) Articular cartilage lesions in osteoarthritis of the femoral head. *J. Path.* **107**, 199.

Meachim G. (1972b) Repair of the para-articular bone plate in the rabbit knee. *J. Anat. (Lond.)* **113**, 359.

Meachim G. (1975) Cartilage fibrillation at the ankle joint in Liverpool necropsies. *J. Anat. (Lond.)* **119**, 601.

Meachim G. and Collins D. H. (1962) Cell counts of normal and osteo-arthritic articular cartilage in relation to the uptake of sulphate ($^{35}SO_4$) in vitro. *Ann. rheum. Dis.* **21**, 45.

Meachim G. and Cornah M. S. (1970) Fine structure of juvenile human nucleus pulposus. *J. Anat. (Lond.)* **107**, 337.

Meachim G. and Illman O. (1967) Articular cartilage degeneration in hamsters and in pigs. *Z. Versuchstierk.* **9**, 33.

Meachim G. and Osborne G. V. (1970) Repair at the femoral articular surface in osteoarthritis of the hip. *J. Path.* **102**, 1.

Meachim G. and Roberts C. (1971) Repair of the joint surface from subarticular tissue in the rabbit knee. *J. Anat. (Lond.)* **109**, 317.

Meachim G. and Roy S. (1967) Intracytoplasmic filaments in the cells of adult human articular cartilage. *Ann. rheum. Dis.* **26**, 50.

Meachim G. and Roy S. (1969) Surface ultrastructure of mature adult human articular cartilage. *J. Bone Jt Surg.* **51B**, 529.

Meachim G., Ghadially F. N. and Collins D. H. (1965) Regressive changes in the superficial layer of human articular cartilage. *Ann. rheum. Dis.* **24**, 23.

Mehta P. N. and Ghadially F. N. (1973) Articular cartilage in corn oil-induced lipoarthrosis. *Ann. rheum. Dis.* **32**, 75.

Miles J. S. and Eichelberger L. (1964) Biochemical studies of human cartilage during the aging process. *J. Amer. Geriatr. Soc.* **12**, 1.

Millroy S. J. and Poole A. R. (1974) Pig articular cartilage in organ culture. Effects of enzymatic depletion of the matrix on response of chondrocytes to complement-sufficient antiserum against pig erythrocytes. *Ann. rheum. Dis.* **33**, 500.

Montagna W. (1949) Glycogen and lipids in human cartilage with some cytochemical observations on the cartilage of the dog, cat and rabbit. *Anat. Rec.* **103**, 77.

Morrison R. I. G., Barrett A. J., Dingle J. T. and Prior D. (1973) Cathepsins B1 and D. Action on human cartilage proteoglycans. *Biochim. biophys. Acta* **302**, 411.

Morse A. and Greep R. O. (1951) Effort of abnormal metabolic states upon the histochemical distribution of alkaline phosphatase in the tibia of the albino rat. *Anat. Rec.* **111**, 193.

Neutra M. and Leblond C. P. (1966) Radioautographic comparison of uptake of galactose-H and glucose-H in the Golgi region of various cells secreting glyco-proteins or mucopolysaccharides. *J. Cell Biol.* **30**, 137.

Nist C., von der Mark K., Hay E. D., Olsen B. R., Bornstcin P., Ross R. and Dehm P. (1975) Location of pro-collagen in chick corneal and tendon fibro-blasts with ferritin-conjugated antibodies. *J. Cell Biol.* **65**, 75.

Ogston A. (1875) On articular cartilage. *J. Anat. Physiol.* **10**, 49.

Oryschak A. F., Ghadially F. N. and Bhatnagar R. (1974) Nuclear fibrous lamina in the chondrocytes of articular cartilage. *J. Anat. (Lond.)* **118**, 511.

Otte P. (1958) Histochemischer Nachweis einer spezifischen 5-Nucleotidase in Gelenk-knorpel. *Hoppe-Seylers Z. physiol. Chem.* **310**, 103.

Palfrey A. J. and Davies D. V. (1966) The fine structure of chondrocytes *J. Anat. (Lond.)* **100**, 213.

Perez-Tamayo R. and Rojkind M. (1973) *Molecular Pathology of Connective Tissues*. Dekker, New York.

Perlman R. L., Telser A. and Dorfman A. (1964) The biosynthesis of chondroitin sulfate by a cell-free preparation. *J. biol. Chem.* **239**, 3623.

Person P. and Fine A. (1959) Oxidative metabolism of cartilage. *Nature (Lond.)* **183**, 610.

Poole A. R., Hembry R. M. and Dingle J. T. (1974) Cathepsin D in cartilage: the immunohistochemical demonstration of extracellular enzyme in normal and pathological conditions. *J. Cell Sci.* **14**, 139.

Pritchard J. J. (1952) A cytological and histochemical study of bone and cartilage formation in the rat. *J. Anat.* **86**, 259.

Prockop D. J. and Kivirikko K. I. (1967) Relationship of hydroxyproline excretion in urine to collagen metabolism. *Ann. intern. Med.* **66**, 1243.

Pugh D. and Walker P. G. (1961) Localization of *N*-acetylglucosaminidase in tissues. *J. Histochem. Cytochem.* **9**, 242.

Repo R. U. and Mitchell N. (1971) Collagen synthesis in mature articular cartilage of the rabbit. *J. Bone Jt Surg.* **53B**, 541.

Revel J. P. and Hay E. D. (1963) An autoradiographic and electron microscopic study of collagen synthesis in differentiating cartilage. *Z. Zellforsch.* **61**, 110.

Rosenthal O., Bowie M. A. and Wagoner G. (1941) Studies on the metabolism of articular cartilage. 1: Respiration and glycolysis in relation to its age. *J. cell. comp. Physiol.* **17**, 221.

Rosenthal O., Bowie M. A. and Wagoner G. (1942a) The nature of the dehydrogenatic ability of bovine articular cartilage. *J. cell. comp. Physiol.* **19**, 15.

Rosenthal O., Bowie M. A. and Wagoner (1942b) The dehydrogenatic ability of bovine articular cartilage in relation to its age. *J. cell. comp. Physiol.* **19**, 333.

Ross R. (1975) Connective tissue cells, cell prolifera-tion and synthesis of extracellular matrix—a review. *Phil. Trans. R. Soc. Lond. B* **271**, 247.

Ross R. and Benditt E. P. (1965) Wound healing and collagen formation. V. Quantitative electron mic-roscopy radioautographic observations of proline-H utilization by fibroblasts. *J. Cell Biol.* **27**, 83.

Rothwell A. G. and Bentley G. (1973) Chondrocyte multiplication in osteoarthritic articular cartilage. *J. Bone Jt Surg.* **55B**, 558.

Rouget C. (1859) Des substances amyloides; de leur role dans la constitution des tissus des animaux. *J. de la Physiol.* **2**, 308.

Roy S. (1968) Ultrastructure of articular cartilage in experimental haemarthrosis. *Archs Path.* **86**, 69.

Roy S. and Meachim G. (1968) Chondrocyte ultra-structure in adult human articular cartilage. *Ann. rheum. Dis.* **27**, 544.

Sacerdotti C. (1900) Uber das Knorpelfett. *Virchows Arch. path. Anat. Physiol.* **159**, 152.

Salmon W. D. and Daughaday W. H. (1957) A hor-monally controlled serum factor which stimulates sulfate incorporation by cartilage *in vitro*. *J. Lab. clin. Med.* **49**, 825.

Schajowicz F. and Cabrini R. L. (1958) Histochemical distribution of succinic dehydrogenase in bone and cartilage. *Science* **131**, 1043.

Scherft J. P. and Daems W. (1967) Single cilia in chondrocytes. *J. Ultrastruct. Res.* **19**, 546.

Seggel R. (1904) Experimentelle Beitrage zur Anatomie und Pathologie der Gelenkknorpels. II: Studien uber Knorpelwunden und Defecte. *Dt. Z. Chir.* **75**, 453.

Shaw J. L. and Bassett C. A. L. (1967) The effects of varying oxygen concentrations on osteogenesis and embryonic cartilage *in vitro*. *J. Bone Jt Surg.* **49A**, 73.

Shaw N. E. and Lacey E. (1973) The influence of corticosteroids on normal and papain treated articular cartilage in the rabbit. *J. Bone Jt Surg.* **55B**, 197.

Shaw N. E. and Martin B. F. (1962) Histological and histochemical studies on mammalian knee joint tissues. *J. Anat. (Lond.)* **96**, 359.

Sheldon H. and Kimball F. B. (1962) Studies on cartilage. III: The occurrence of collagen within vacuoles of the Golgi apparatus. *J. Cell Biol.* **12**, 559.

Sheldon H. and Robinson R. A. (1960) Studies on cartilage. II: Electron microscope observations on rabbit ear cartilage following administration of papain. *J. biophys. biochem. Cytol.* **8**, 151.

Silberberg M., Silberberg R. and Hasler M. (1964). Ultrastructure of articular cartilage in mice treated with somatotrophin. *J. Bone Jt Surg.* **46A**, 766.

Silberberg M., Silberberg R. and Hasler M. (1966). Fine structure of articular cartilage in mice receiving cortisone acetate. *Archs Path.* **82**, 569.

Silberberg R. (1968) Ultrastructure of articular cartilage in health and disease. *Clin. Orthop.* **57**, 233.

Silberberg R. and Hasler M. (1971). Submicroscopic effects of hormones on articular cartilage of adult mice. *Archs Path.* **91**, 241.

Silberberg R. and Hasler M. (1972) Effect of testosterone propionate on the ultrastructure of articular cartilage in mice. *Growth* **36**, 17.

Silver I. A. (1975) Measurement of pH and ionic composition of pericellular sites. *Phil. Trans. R. Soc. Lond. B* **271**, 261.

Simmons D. J. (1964) Circadian mitotic rhythm in epiphyseal cartilage. *Nature (Lond.)* **202**, 906.

Simon W. H. (1970) Scale effects in animal joints. 1. Articular cartilage thickness and compressive stress. *Arthritis Rheum.* **13**, 244.

Simon W. H., Friedenberg S. and Richardson S. (1973) Joint congruence. A correlation of joint congruence and thickness of articular cartilage in dogs. *J. Bone Jt Surg.* **55A**, 1614.

Sledge C. B. (1973) Growth hormone and articular cartilage. *Fed. Proc.* **32**, 1503.

Smith A. U. (1965) Survival of frozen chondrocytes isolated from cartilage of adult animals. *Nature (Lond.)* **205**, 782.

Smith R. E. and Farquhar M. G. (1966) Lysosome function in the regulation of the secretory process in cells of the anterior pituitary gland. *J. Cell Biol.* **31**, 319.

Smith T. W. D., Duckworth T., Bergenholtz A. and Lemperg R. K. (1975) Role of growth hormone in glycosaminoglycan synthesis by articular cartilage. *Nature (Lond.)* **253**, 269.

Sprinz R. and Stockwell R. A. (1976) Changes in articular cartilage following intra-articular injection of tritiated glyceryl trioleate. *J. Anat. (Lond.)* **122**, 91.

Srivistava V. M. L., Malemud C. J. and Sokoloff L. (1974) Chondroid expression by rabbit articular cells in spinner culture following monolayer culture. *Conn. Tiss. Res.* **2**, 127.

Stockwell, R. A. (1966) The Ageing of Cartilage. Thesis, University of London.

Stockwell, R. A. (1967a) The cell density of human articular and costal cartilage. *J. Anat. (Lond.)* **191**, 753.

Stockwell R. A. (1967b) The lipid and glycogen content of rabbit articular hyaline and non-articular hyaline cartilage. *J. Anat. (Lond.)* **102**, 87.

Stockwell R. A. (1967c) Lipid content of human costal and articular cartilage. *Ann. rheum. Dis.* **26**, 481.

Stockwell R. A. (1971a) The interrelationship of cell density and cartilage thickness in mammalian articular cartilage. *J. Anat (Lond.)* **109**, 411.

Stockwell R. A. (1971b) Cell density, cell size and cartilage thickness in adult mammalian articular cartilage. *J. Anat. (Lond.)* **108**, 584.

Takeuchi T. and Glenner G. G. (1961) Histochemical demonstration of uridine diphosphate glucose-glycogen transferase in animal tissues. *J. Histochem. Cytochem.* **9**, 304.

Toner P. G. and Carr K. E. (1968) *Cell Structure*, pp. 88–95. Livingstone, Edinburgh.

Tonna E. A. (1961) The cellular component of the skeletal system studied autoradiographically with tritiated thymidine (H^3TDR) during growth and ageing *J. biophys. biochem. Cytol.* **9**, 813.

Tonna E. A. and Cronkite E. P. (1964) A study of the persistence of H^3-thymidine label in the femora of rats. *Lab. Invest.* **13**, 161.

Traub W. and Piez K. A. (1971) The chemistry and structure of collagen. *Adv. Protein Chem.* **25**, 243.

Trias, A. (1961) Effects of persistent pressure on the articular cartilage. *J. Bone Jt Surg.* **43B**, 376.

Vignon E. (1973) Le Vieillissement du Cartilage Articulaire et l'Arthrose Etude Morphometrique. Thesis, University of Lyon.

Vignon E., Meunier P., Boissel J. P., Arlot M., Patricot L. M. and Vignon G. (1973) Quantitative histological study of human femoral cartilage: changes in relation to the pressure areas. *Proc. IXth Eur. Symp. Calc. Tiss.* Facta-Pubn, Vienna, p. 115.

Weinstock M. and Leblond C. P. (1974) Synthesis, migration and release of precursor collagen by odontoblasts as visualized by radioautography after (^{3}H) proline administration. *J. Cell. Biol.* **60,** 92.

Weiss C. and Mirrow S. (1972) An ultrastructural study of osteoarthritic changes in the articular cartilage of human knees. *J. Bone Jt Surg.* **50A,** 954.

Weiss C., Rosenberg L. and Helfet A. J. (1968) An ultrastructural study of normal young adult human articular cartilage. *J. Bone Jt Surg.* **50A,** 663.

Wiebkin O. W. and Muir H. (1975) Influence of the cells on the pericellular environment. *Phil. Trans. R. Soc. Lond. B* **271,** 283.

Wilsman N. J. and van Sickle D. C. (1971) Histochemical evidence of a functional heterogeneity in neonatal canine epiphyseal chondrocytes. *Histochem. J.* **3,** 311.

Zimny M. L. and Redler I. (1969) An ultrastructural study of patellar chondromalacia in humans. *J. Bone Jt Surg.* **51A,** 179.

Zorzoli A. (1948) The histochemical localisation of alkaline phosphatase in demineralised bones of mice of different ages. *Anat. Rec.* **102,** 445.

3. Biochemistry

I. H. M. Muir

1. INTRODUCTION

This Chapter describes the structure, formation and breakdown of the two principal components of the matrix of cartilage: proteoglycans and collagen. These molecules account for a large part of the matrix and, together with water, endow cartilage with its physical characteristics.

Biochemical data concerning certain aspects of human adult articular cartilage are limited and therefore, for this Chapter, some information has had to be drawn from other cartilaginous tissues, from immature material and from other species.

Cartilage is a strong tissue, carrying considerable loads, and it is therefore at first sight surprising that its water content (in adult human femoral condylar cartilage) is no less than 65–75%, being highest near the joint surface where it can rise to over 80% (Maroudas, Muir and Wingham 1969). The water content of patellar cartilage is similar (Linn and Sokoloff 1965). It is, however, precisely the presence of this water, in conjunction with proteoglycans and collagen, which makes cartilage tough and resilient. As was first pointed out by Fessler (1960), a random macromolecular mesh (such as a solution of proteoglycans), when placed within a fibrous network (such as collagen) so that the macromolecules cannot move, will impede the free flow of water within the tissue when an external force is applied. Provided the collagen network is able to entrap the proteoglycans, the resistance to the flow of interstitial water will depend upon the concentration, configuration and entanglement of the proteoglycan molecules. The contribution made by proteoglycans and by collagen to the physicochemical and mechanical properties of cartilage is discussed in Chapters 4, 5 and 6. In this Chapter a detailed examination of the biochemistry of proteoglycans and collagen is provided since this is central to an understanding of how cartilage functions and what happens when it degenerates.

2. THE COMPOSITION OF CARTILAGE MATRIX

2.1 Overall Composition

Collagen accounts for about half the dry weight (which is about 20–30% of the wet weight) of human adult articular cartilage (Bollet, Handy and Sturgill 1963; Anderson, Ludowieg, Harper and Engleman 1964); but the amount increases to almost the whole of the dry weight in the superficial layer, a fact shown when tangential sections, 200 μm in thickness, from human femoral condyles, are analysed separately (Maroudas et al. 1969; Muir, Bullough and Maroudas 1970; Kempson, Muir, Pollard and Tuke 1973). The proteoglycan content of cartilage varies roughly inversely with the collagen content, being lowest in the superficial layer (Maroudas et al. 1969; Kempson et al. 1973; Lemperg, Larsson and Hjertquist 1974) where the total dry weight is to a large extent accounted for by collagen and proteoglycan. In deeper layers, however, sometimes as much as half the dry weight is not accounted for by these substances (Muir et al. 1970). This discrepancy has been attributed to the presence of some material which, it may be inferred, does not contain appreciable amounts of hexosamine or negative groups (Muir et al. 1970) since in each layer the fixed negative charge correlates well with the total glycosaminoglycan content determined by the total hexosamine and uronic acid contents (Maroudas et al. 1969). Since glycoproteins stain with the periodic acid–Schiff reagent and since (Chapter 1, Section 4.5) this staining is least evident in the superficial zone and more intense in deeper layers (where the discrepancy is largest), some of the dry weight unaccounted for by collagen and proteoglycans may be due to a glycoprotein: this material has so far attracted little attention, but it is distributed roughly inversely to the collagen both in human femoral condyles (Muir et al. 1970) and in the cartilage of nasal septum (Szirmai, de Tyssonsk and Gardell 1967).

The proportion of the matrix composed of collagen as against proteoglycan varies from individual to individual, topographically within the tissue (Figure 3.1) and with maturity (Table 3.1).

2.2. Topographical Variation

There are marked differences, which cannot be correlated with age or sex, between the cartilages of different individuals with respect to the amount of collagen in the surface layer, the relationship between collagen content and depth from the joint surface, and the total collagen in the full thickness of cartilage. There is also a marked difference both in the total amount and in the topographical distribution of chondroitin sulphate and keratan sulphate in the cartilages of different individuals, while neighbouring regions of cartilage from the same joint show a rather similar pattern of distribution of chondroitin sulphate, keratan sulphate and collagen (Maroudas et al. 1969; Muir et al. 1970). The conclusion that the compositional topography of femoral condylar cartilage may be a characteristic of the individual has since been confirmed in many instances (Kempson et al. 1973). The topographical pattern may be genetically determined or may result from unknown factors that affect the composition of the cartilage during each individual's development. The inheritable character of degenerative joint disease is evident in certain strains of mice (Sokoloff, Crittenden, Yamamoto and Gay 1962) which suggests that in man the particular make-up of the cartilage of a joint may predispose some individuals to osteoarthrosis.

Topographical variation in the distribution of chondroitin and keratan sulphates has been demonstrated by histochemical methods (Chapter 1, Section 4.3.1) which correlate well with chemical analyses of serial sections of human femoral condylar cartilage (Stockwell and Scott 1967). The extent of this variation, not only in relation to depth from the joint surface but also with respect to the proximity of the matrix to each cell or group of cells, has been shown using the CEC method (Stockwell and Scott 1965) (see Chapter 1, Section 4.3.1). As discussed later in this Chapter, proteoglycans in cartilage vary particularly with respect to the relative proportions of chondroitin sulphate and keratan sulphate that they contain. The results of histochemical studies would indicate that the distribution of these different varieties of proteoglycans is not uniform even through small regions of the matrix (Stockwell 1970), which may be one reason why degenerative changes are initially localized. Variation has also been observed in the full thickness composition of articular cartilage at different sites of the femoral head (Kempson, Muir, Swanson and Freeman 1970).

2.3. Age Variation

Although the evidently complex macromolecular organization of cartilage matrix reduces somewhat the value of chemical analysis of the whole tissue, such analysis has shown that in adult human articular cartilage in the absence of osteoarthrosis; collagen, chondroitin sulphate and water contents do not change significantly after growth has ceased (Anderson et al. 1964; Miles and Eichelberger 1964; Linn and Sokoloff 1965; Bollet and Nance 1966; Miller, van der Korst and Sokoloff 1969) and there is no

Table 3.1. Composition of knee joint cartilage of pigs of different ages (Simunek and Muir 1972a)

	Fetus	10 weeks	25 weeks	3 years	5 years
Dry weight (% of wet wt)	14.6	25.5	29.9	34.7	36.3
Uronic acid (g/100 g dry wt)	7.6	3.05	3.04	3.1	2.85
Collagen (g/100 g dry wt)	19.6	38.2	49.0	52.7	54.6
Molar ratio glucosamine/ galactosamine	1:26.9	1:30.2	1:17.0	1:4.1	1:3.9

Figure 3.1 Variation with depth from the articular surface of the contents of collagen (○), chondroitin sulphate (△) and keratan suphate (□) in cartilage from normal femoral condyles. Four comparable areas were taken from one knee of six individuals, matched for age and sex into three pairs (a), (b) and (c). Numbers and letters above graphs denote age and sex. (Reproduced from Kempson *et al.* (1973) by permission.)

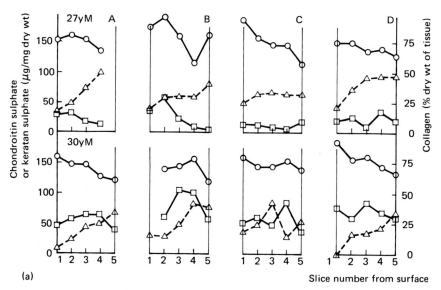

(a)

148

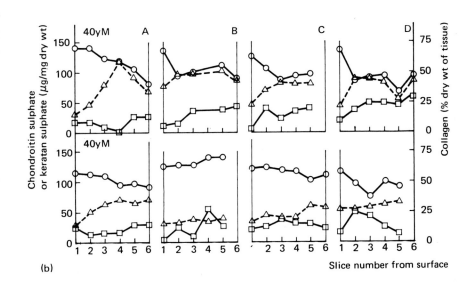

(b)

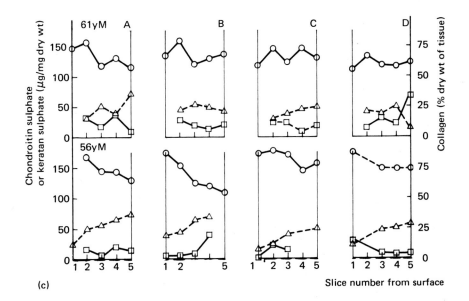

Slice number from surface

(c)

149

loss of elasticity (Sokoloff 1966) with increasing age although the lengths of the chains of chondroitin sulphate decrease somewhat with advancing age in human articular cartilage (Hjertquist and Wasteson 1972). During the third and fourth decades, however, there appears to be an abrupt increase in keratan sulphate content in the deep layer near the calcified zone (Stockwell 1970). The cell density of normal human articular cartilage which does not change after maturity is reached, declines during development (Chapter 2, Section 4.1) when there are substantial changes in the chemical composition of joint cartilage (Campo and Tourtellotte 1967) and in the physical state and composition of the proteoglycans (Simunek and Muir 1972a). It is probable that all these changes are largely attributable to changes in epiphyseal cartilage, which are outside the scope of this book.

3. GLYCOSAMINOGLYCANS OF CARTILAGE

The term 'glycosaminoglycan', formerly 'mucopolysaccharide', refers to long unbranched carbohydrates made up largely of repeating disaccharide units of which one sugar is glucosamine or galactosamine and the other hexuronic acid or, in the case of keratan sulphate, galactose. Apart from hyaluronic acid, all are sulphated to a lesser or greater extent. Three such glycosaminoglycans are present in cartilage, in proportions that vary with the type of cartilage and with age. With the possible exception of hyaluronic acid, the glycosaminoglycans do not exist free but are attached to protein and represent the carbohydrate moieties of proteoglycans. Many of the details of carbohydrate structure were established before this fact was known.

3.1. Chondroitin Sulphate

Chondroitin sulphate consists of repeating units of glucuronic acid and N-acetylgalactosamine (Figure 3.2). The average chain of chondroitin sulphate comprises 25–30 disaccharide repeating units. The distribution of sulphate residues along the chain is not uniform as there are fewer in the vicinity of the linkage of carbohydrate to protein (Wasteson and Lindahl 1971). There is almost one sulphate group per disaccharide in one of two isomeric positions: in chondroitin 4-sulphate the sulphate is attached to C_4 and in chondroitin 6-sulphate to C_6 of the galactosamine residues (Figure 3.2). Both forms occur in articular cartilage, although the latter predominates in adult articular cartilage (Mankin and Lippiello 1971; Lust and Pronsky 1972; Hjertquist and Lemperg 1972; Lemperg *et al.* 1974). The proportion of chondroitin 4-sulphate increases in human osteoarthrosis (Mankin, Dorfman, Lippiello and Zarijns 1971).

(a)

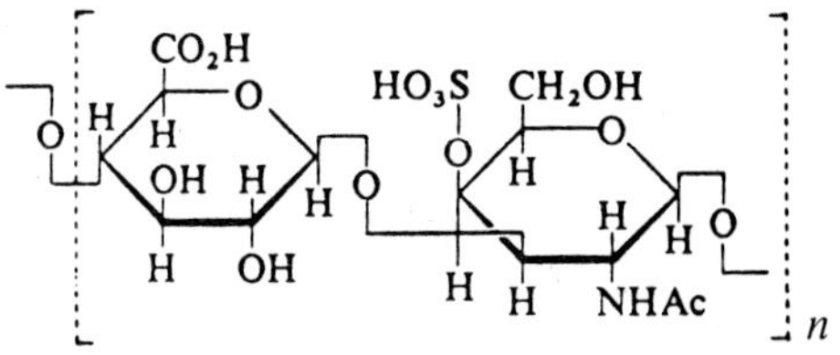

(b)

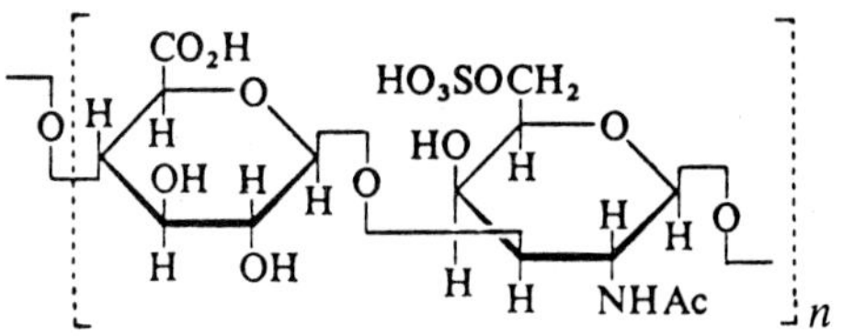

Figure 3.2 The repeating disaccharide units of (a) chondroitin 4-sulphate and (b) chondroitin 6-sulphate.

Specific degradative enzymes named chondroitinase AC (Saito, Yamagata and Suzuki 1968) and chondroitinase C (Michelacci and Dietrich 1976) have been used to estimate the proportions of each chondroitin sulphate isomer. These enzymes are produced by the organism *Flavobacterium heparinum* (Yamagata, Saito, Habuchi and Suzuki 1968) and the former is now commercially available. The results suggest that the isomers are not present as separate chains but that chondroitin sulphate is a hybrid in which the sulphate groups occupy one or other isomeric position along the same chain depending on the type of cartilage examined (Seno, Anno, Yaegashi and Okayama 1975; Mourao, Rosenfeld, Laredo and Dietrich 1976; Mourao and Dietrich 1973). Chondroitin 6-sulphate appears to predominate in human articular cartilage whereas in growth cartilage there are approximately equal proportions of the 4 and 6 isomers according to the results of chondroitinase degradation (Mourao *et al.* 1976).

The biological significance of the position of the sulphate group is not known. Both chondroitin sulphate isomers display highly ordered helical conformations when stretched films of these compounds are examined by x-ray fibre analysis. In chondroitin 6-sulphate, however, the sulphate groups project further from the chain than in chondroitin 4-sulphate (Isaac and Atkins 1973; Atkins 1977). Chondroitin 6-sulphate may therefore interact more strongly than chondroitin 4-sulphate with the basic groups of collagen and other proteins (Section 6). In this context it is notable that the proteoglycans of normal articular cartilage which contain predominantly chondroitin 6-sulphate are rather more resistant to extraction than those of other kinds of hyaline cartilage.

The first definitive chemical evidence that chondroitin sulphate is covalently attached to protein through serine residues was obtained by Muir (1958) who also showed that the linkage is labile to alkali after which chondroitin sulphate entirely free of amino acids is obtained. Subsequently it was shown that the alkaline degradation involved a β-carbonyl elimination reaction in which serine is converted to dehydroalanine and the chondroitin sulphate chains are liberated from protein (Figure 3.3). From this it follows that the chondroitin sulphate chains are attached to the hydroxyl groups of serine residues (Anderson, Hoffman and Meyer 1965).

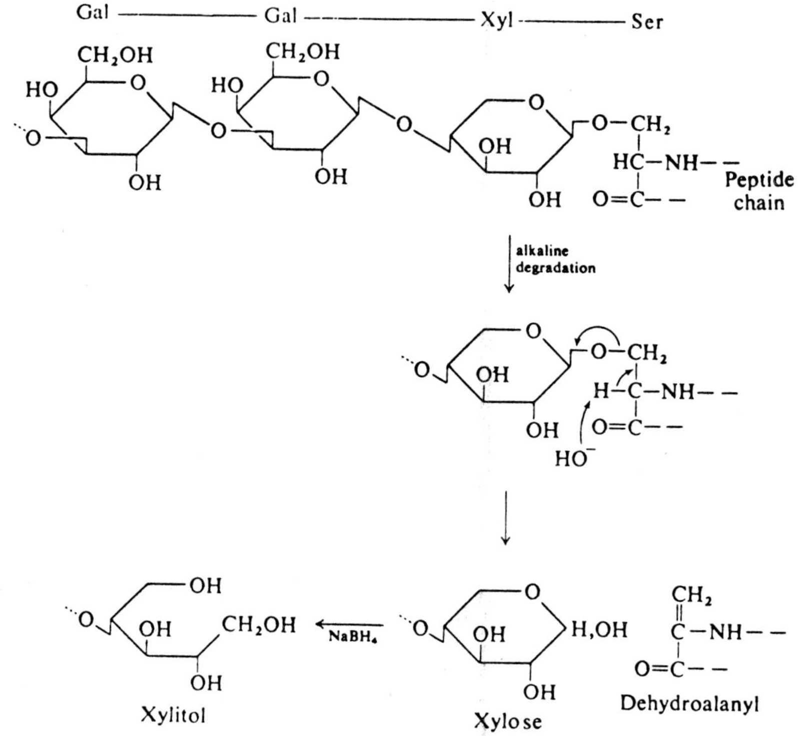

Figure 3.3 The linkage region of chondroitin 4- or 6-sulphate, dermatan sulphate, heparin and heparan sulphate to protein. Alkaline degradation results in the cleavage of the xylosyl-serine linkage by a β-carbonyl elimination reaction. If this is carried out in the presence of sodium borohydride, the xylose residue at the reducing terminal of each chain is reduced to xylitol.

A bridge structure consisting of a trisaccharide sequence of neutral sugars links the chondroitin sulphate chain itself to the serine residues (Figure 3.3). The complete structure of this feature has been established by the work of Rodén and his co-workers (Rodén and Armand 1966; Lindahl and Rodén 1966; Rodén and Smith 1966; Helting and Rodén 1968). It is also present in all other sulphated glycosaminoglycans of animal origin which contain hexuronic acid such as heparin. The special feature of the linkage region is the presence of xylose at the reducing end. This sugar, which had not previously been found in animal polysaccharides, is important in co-ordinating the biosynthesis of carbohydrate and protein (Section 4.6.1).

3.2. Keratan Sulphate

Keratan sulphate, which does not contain uronic acid, consists essentially of disaccharide repeating units of N-acetylglucosamine and galactose (Figure 3.4). Hence molar ratios of

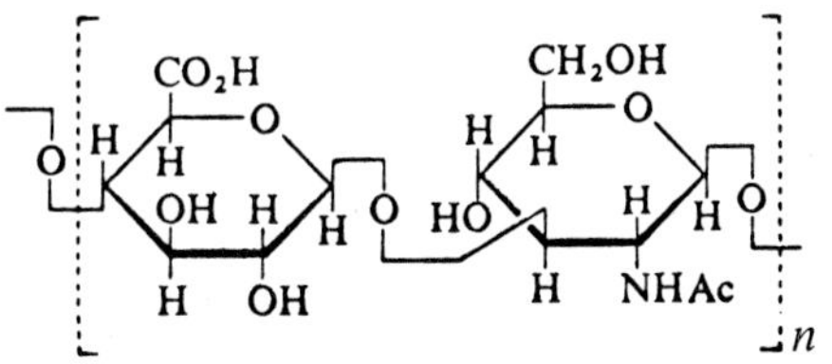

Figure 3.4 The repeating disaccharide unit of keratan sulphate.

glucosamine/galactosamine may be used to determine the proportions of keratan sulphate and chondroitin sulphate in proteoglycans and less precisely in whole cartilage. Keratan sulphate is much more variable than is chondroitin sulphate both in chain length and in the degree of sulphation (reviewed by Muir and Hardingham 1975). Corneal and skeletal keratan sulphates are distinguished on the basis of their linkage to protein (Seno, Meyer, Anderson and Hoffman 1965) and have been termed keratan sulphate I and keratan sulphate II respectively. The latter is much more variable in structure and in degree of sulphation (Mathews and Cifonelli 1965). There appear to be roughly two populations; one has one sulphate group per disaccharide repeating unit, while the other ('over-sulphated') has considerably more sulphate (Hjertquist and Lemperg 1972). The sulphate groups are located on C_6 of half the galactose and more than half the glucosamine residues (Bhavanandan and Meyer 1968). The chains of skeletal keratan sulphate are shorter and more variable in length than are chondroitin sulphate chains with weight-average molecular weights of 5000–10 000 corresponding to about 13 disaccharide repeating units (Hascall and Riolo 1972; Robinson and Hopwood 1973). There is an excess of galactose over glucosamine (Gregory and Rodén 1961; Bhavanandan and Meyer 1967) and there are branch points along the chain where the extra galactose is attached.

Small amounts of fucose (Bhavanandan and Meyer 1968) and sialic acid (Toda and Seno 1970; Hascall and Riolo 1972) are also present in terminal positions.

Skeletal keratan sulphate, which contains small amounts of galactosamine, appears to be linked to protein through galactosamine residues which are attached to the hydroxyl groups of serine and threonine on the proteoglycan core protein (Bray, Lieberman and Meyer 1967; Tsiganos and Muir 1967; Hopwood and Robinson 1974). This linkage, like the chondroitin sulphate–protein linkage, is labile to alkali (Seno et $al.$ 1965) and undergoes a β-elimination reaction in which keratan sulphate chains are liberated from protein. It is concluded that the main keratan sulphate chain is attached to C_6 of the galactosamine residue and that there is also a substituent on C_3 (Figure 3.5) (Bray et $al.$ 1967;

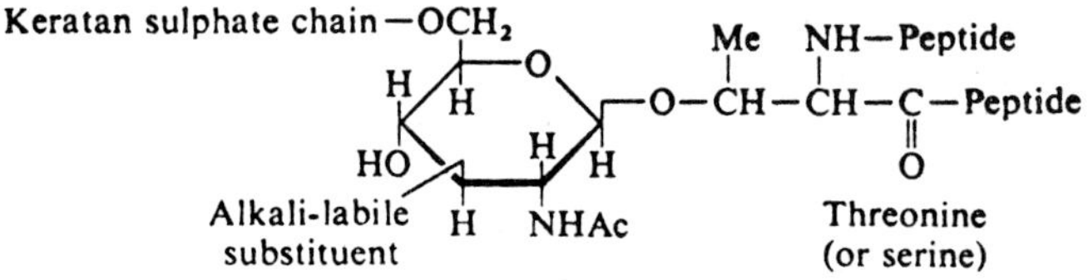

Figure 3.5 The possible linkage of skeletal keratan sulphate (KS-II) to protein from N-acetylgalactosamine to threonine or serine. Mannose is also present in the linkage region.

Seno and Toda 1970) which appears to be neuraminyl-galactosyl disaccharide (Hopwood and Robinson 1974). Substitution on C_3 makes the galactosamine unstable in alkali so that much of it is lost during the β-elimination reaction (Seno and Toda 1970). Small amounts of mannose are also present close to the linkage region. There may also be some additional alkali-stable linkages which appear to involve glutamic acid and glutamine (Heinegård 1972b; Hopwood and Robinson 1974). The branched structure and the presence of mannose, fucose and sialic acid (Toda and Seno 1970) liken keratan sulphate to typical glycoprotein oligosaccharides.

3.3. Hyaluronic Acid

Although hyaluronic acid is ubiquitous in other types of connective tissue, it was at first thought to be absent from cartilage. However, Hjertquist and Lemperg (1972), when examining the total glycosaminoglycan composition of articular cartilage by the cetylpyridinium chloride microfractionation procedure of

Antonopoulos, Gardell, Szirmai and de Tyssonsk (1964), found a minor fraction that separated in the position of hyaluronic acid. Hyaluronic acid has since been isolated from cartilage and identified unequivocally by rigorous chemical proof (Hardingham and Muir 1974a; Hascall and Heinegård 1974a).

Hyaluronic acid is the only non-sulphated glycosaminoglycan. It is made up of repeating disaccharide units of N-acetylglucosamine and glucuronic acid in which the glycosidic linkages are of the same configuration as those of chondroitin sulphate (Figure 3.6) but the unbranched chains are much longer than those of chondroitin sulphate. Molecular weights, which can be as much as a few million, vary in different tissues and also according to the method of preparation. Hyaluronic acid, however, does not occur as a multichain proteoglycan. This is shown by the facts that its viscosity in solution is unaffected by proteolytic digestion (Ogston and Sherman 1959) and that electron micrographs show it to consist of single chains (Fessler and Fessler 1966). The question whether single chains are linked to peptide remains in doubt, however, because even after extensive purification the protein content could not be reduced to less than 2% (Scher and Hamerman 1972). Proteins tend to associate with hyaluronic acid, however, which makes it extremely difficult to remove the last traces of contaminating proteins.

In cartilages of various kinds, hyaluronic acid represents less than 1% of the total uronic acid. In human femoral condyles chondroitin sulphate accounts for about 5–7% of the dry weight (Maroudas et al. 1969; Kempson et al. 1973) so that only about 0.05% of the dry weight is due to hyaluronic acid. In cartilage, hyaluronic acid plays an essential role in the aggregation of proteoglycans and is mostly present not in the free state but as a component of proteoglycan aggregates (Section 4.2). The ability of proteoglycans to interact with hyaluronic acid is restricted to proteoglycans of cartilage and hence proteoglycan aggregation would appear to have some special function in cartilage that is not yet understood (but see Section 4.3.4).

Hyaluronic acid is abundant in embryonic tissues where it appears to be associated with morphogenesis (Toole, Jackson and Gross 1972). At the onset of differentiation and chondrogenesis the amount of hyaluronic acid decreases sharply (Toole 1972). In low concentrations down to 1 ng/ml, hyaluronic acid inhibits chondrogenesis in vitro (Toole et al. 1972) and the effect is entirely specific to hyaluronic acid. It is notable that hyaluronic acid at comparably low concentrations inhibits the synthesis of proteoglycan by stationary cultures of chondrocytes from adult (Wiebkin and Muir 1973, 1975) or embryonic (Solursh, Vaerewyck and Reiter 1974; Handley and Lowther 1976) cartilage, whereas confluent cultures of fibroblasts or synovial cells from adult tissues are unaffected (Wiebkin and Muir 1973).

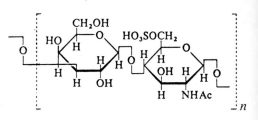

Figure 3.6 The repeating disaccharide unit of hyaluronic acid.

4. THE PROTEOGLYCANS

4.1. General Structure

The term 'proteoglycan' (known previously as protein–polysaccharide or chondromucoprotein) refers to macromolecules of connective tissue constructed of a protein core to which a large number of glycosaminoglycan chains are attached laterally. Protein comprises only 10–20% of the weight of the molecule, 80–90% being due to chondroitin sulphate with lesser but variable amounts of keratan sulphate. This general structure was first proposed by Mathews and Lozaityte 1958) and, on different grounds, by Partridge, Davis and Adair (1961). It is consistent with the effects of proteolytic enzymes first shown by Muir (1958). When cartilage is extracted at neutral pH and in the absence of proteolytic enzymes a product is obtained which gives a viscous solution and which retains about 10% of protein even when extensively purified. The protein has a characteristic amino-acid composition in which serine, glycine, proline and glutamic acid predominate. On treatment with proteolytic enzymes, the viscosity is lost and the protein content markedly reduced, although after exhaustive proteolysis most of the serine is retained (Muir 1958).

The average chain weight of chondroitin sulphate is about 20 000, and 50–100 such chains attached to a protein core will result in a composite molecule of molecular weight 1–3 million (Luscombe and Phelps 1967a; Eyring and Yang 1968; Rosenberg, Hellmann and Kleinschmidt 1970). Light-scattering measurements indicate the weight-average molecular weight of nasal cartilage proteoglycans to be 2.3×10^6 (Pasternack, Veis and Breen 1974). The general structure shown schematically in Figure 3.7 is now widely accepted and accords with the electron microscopical appearance of single molecules spread by a special technique and visualized by negative staining (Rosenberg et al. 1970). The current model for cartilage proteoglycans has a central core protein with an average molecular weight of 20 000 to which about 100 chondroitin sulphate and 50 keratan sulphate chains are attached (Hascall and Sajdera 1970; Hascall and Riolo 1972). Enzymes, such as testicular hyaluronidase, that degrade the chondroitin sulphate side-chains have less effect on the physical properties of proteoglycans than have proteolytic enzymes (Cessi and Bernardi 1965; Luscombe and Phelps 1967b). A molecule constructed as shown in Figure 3.7 will fall apart when only a few peptide bonds are cleaved, which explains why the release of proteinases by inflammatory cells is so destructive in rheumatoid arthritis, and why intravenous injections of crude papain into rabbits causes a loss of metachromasia of cartilage and collapse of

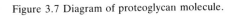

Figure 3.7 Diagram of proteoglycan molecule.

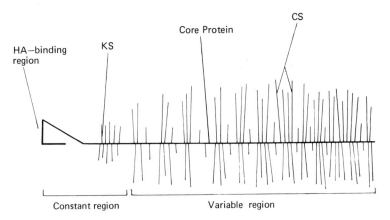

the ears (Thomas 1956). Limiting viscosity measurements show that proteoglycans occupy solution volumes 30–50 times their dry weight (Hascall and Sajdera 1970; Pasternack *et al.* 1974), which enables large amounts of water to be retained in the tissue. Proteoglycans in solution can be reversibly compressed (Hascall 1979) and *in vivo* they occupy far less than the maximum solvent volume. In cartilage they therefore exert a swelling pressure that is constantly restrained by the collagen network in which they are entrapped, whereas the breakdown products, being smaller than the parent proteoglycans, are able to diffuse out of the tissue and are lost. The functional importance of proteoglycans in cartilage is illustrated in certain chicken and mouse mutants. In nanomelic chicks, proteoglycans specific to cartilage are lacking, the chondrocytes are abnormally close together and the severe skeletal deformities that result are lethal, usually before hatching (Mathews 1967; Pennypacker and Goetinck 1976). In branchiomorphic mice, which have foreshortened limbs, the proteoglycans are undersulphated and the reduction in charge density reduces their molecular domains (Orkin, Pratt and Martin 1976).

Cartilage proteoglycans contain keratan sulphate as well as chondroitin sulphate which are attached to the same protein core (Seno *et al.* 1965; Heinegård and Gardell 1967; Hoffman, Mashburn and Meyer 1967; Tsiganos and Muir 1967; Hascall and Riolo 1972; Heinegård 1972b) although the relative proportions of each may vary widely from molecules containing largely chondroitin sulphate (Muir and Jacobs 1967) to those containing almost as much keratan sulphate as chondroitin sulphate (Pedrini 1969; Tsiganos, Hardingham and Muir 1971). Proteoglycans are very heterogeneous and in any given cartilage the population of

157

molecules shows a continuous range of chemical composition and molecular size that is characteristic of the tissue and changes during development and ageing.

4.2. The Extraction of Proteoglycans from Cartilage Matrix

Nearly all the extraction procedures have been developed for use with bovine nasal cartilage and cannot be applied to other kinds of cartilage with exactly the same results. Since the essential function of proteoglycans in cartilage results from their entrapment in the collagen network, they do not readily diffuse out of sliced tissue when extracted with salt solutions of physiological ionic strength (Shatton and Schubert 1954) unless the collagen network is disrupted by high speed homogenization (Malawista and Schubert 1958). Much of the earlier work on proteoglycans was initiated by Schubert and his associates (e.g. Gerber, Franklin and Schubert 1960; Pal and Schubert 1965; Pal, Doganges and Schubert 1966) who employed high speed homogenization to achieve efficient extraction when about 65% of the proteoglycan was extracted from bovine nasal cartilage. The proteoglycans, however, were heterogeneous and separated on centrifugation into a rapidly sedimenting fraction (termed PPH) while the other (named PP-L) remained in the supernatant. Various subfractions were obtained which were operationally defined but were not discrete fractions (Rosenberg, Pal, Beale and Schubert 1970). The terms PP-L and PP-H were used in much of the literature up to 1970.

High shearing forces degrade polymers of large molecular weight (Harrington and Zimm 1965) and hence methods employing high speed homogenization have been superseded and replaced by dissociative extraction procedures first introduced by Sajdera and Hascall (1969), who examined systematically the effect of ionic strength and type of salt on the efficiency of extraction. The most effective salts all showed optimal concentrations (Figure 3.8) which are the same for different types of cartilage. Mason and Mayes (1973) showed that the extracting efficiency of different cations is related to their degree of solvation. At high salt concentrations they compete for the available water in the tissue and alter the interaction of proteoglycans with collagen. The results of Herbage, Lucas and Huc (1974) suggest that changes in the conformation of collagen which precede denaturation are important in releasing proteoglycan from the tissue since the optimum salt concentration for extraction decreased with temperature and could be related to the denaturation of collagen as shown by x-ray diffraction. This suggests that proteoglycans are not merely entrapped in the collagen network but are also associated with collagen in some definitive way which probably involves a variety of co-operative interactions. Such

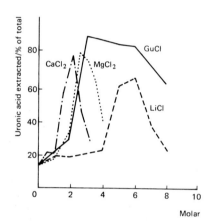

Figure 3.8 Results of the extraction of sliced bovine nasal cartilage with solutions of various electrolytes for 20 h at 25°C. Guanidinium chloride (GuCl), LiCl and CaCl₂ were buffered with 0.05 ml/litre (0.05M) Tris-HCl at pH 7.5; MgCl₂ solutions were unbuffered (pH 5–6). (Reproduced from Sajdera and Hascall (1969) by courtesy of the American Society of Biological Chemists)

158

interactions are dissociated by solutions of guanidine hydro-chloride, and Sajdera and Hascall (1969) found this to be the most effective extractant. Guanidine hydrochloride shows an optimum concentration at about 4 mol/litre (4 M) (Figure 3.8) when 80–85% of the proteoglycans are extracted from sliced bovine nasal cartilage without disruption of the tissue, the remaining 15–20% being resistant to further extraction. In young bovine articular cartilage the proportion of residual proteoglycan is somewhat higher (Rosenberg, Pal and Beale 1973) and in pig articular cartilage it varies roughly with the collagen content (Simunek and Muir 1972a). The proteoglycans resistant to extrac-tion must be very strongly bound to collagen in some unknown way. They may be solubilized by treatment of the tissue with hydroxylamine (Pal and Schubert 1965) and are released when the collagen itself is digested with bacterial collagenase (Brandt and Muir 1971b). The products from either of these treatments are partially degraded and attempts to demonstrate covalent bonds between proteoglycans and collagen have proved inconclusive. Multiple non-covalent co-operative bonds are often extremely strong. This is particularly true when their direction is orientated as may be the case with collagen and proteoglycans because of the structural feature of these substances as suggested by electron optical studies (see Section 6.3). Proteoglycans resistant to extrac-tion may be partially solubilized from guinea-pig costal cartilage by adding EDTA to the solution of 4 mol/litre (4M) guanidine hydrochloride (Lohmander 1975). Compared with the extractable proteoglycans, inextractable proteoglycans in costal cartilage are of comparatively slow turnover (Lohmander 1977) and have higher glucosamine contents (Lohmander 1975). This is also true of proteoglycans of dog articular cartilage (McDevitt and Muir 1975).

Irrespective of the type of cartilage, age or method of extraction, proteoglycans are very heterogeneous and polydisperse. Sequen-tial extraction of pig articular cartilage gives products of increasing hydrodynamic size, protein and keratan sulphate contents at each step. The proteoglycans extracted at later steps are larger and richer in keratan sulphate (assessed by molar ratios of glucosamine/galactosamine) and in protein (Brandt and Muir 1971b; Simunek and Muir 1972a) than those extracted earlier at lower salt concentrations (Tables 3.2 and 3.3). Raising the salt concentration sequentially in the stepwise extraction procedure increases the overall yield and range of variation amongst the proteoglycans. Discrete fractions are not obtained, however, although at each extraction step the range itself is restricted. This is also true for other types of cartilage, including laryngeal (Tsiganos and Muir 1969; Hardingham and Muir 1974a; Harding-ham, Ewins and Muir 1976), nasal (Mayes, Mason and Griffin 1973) and costal (Lohmander 1975) cartilages. The minority of

Table 3.2 Protein content and glucosamine/galactosamine molar ratios of proteoglycans extracted sequentially from pig knee joint car-tilage with 0.15 mol/litre (0.15M) sodium acetate buffer pH 6.8 (Brandt and Muir 1971a)

Extract No.	Protein content (% of dry weight)	Glucosamine/ galactos- amine
1	7.1	1:30
2	9.5	1:12
3	9.9	1:10
4	13.2	1:9
5	12.5	1:7.8

Table 3.3 Molar ratios of glucosamine/galactosamine of proteoglycans in three sequential extracts of pig knee joint cartilage of increasing age (Simunek and Muir 1972a)

Extracting solution	Age of animals				
	Fetus	10 wk	25 wk	3 yr	5 yr
1. 0.15 mol/litre (0.15M) sodium acetate	1:11.7	1:29.5	1:19.2	1:6.5	1:3.0
2. 2 mol/litre (2M) calcium chloride	1:13.0	1:12.5	1:8.7	1:3.3	1:2.5
3. 2 mol/litre (2M) calcium chloride	–	1:12.4	1:6.5	1:4.7	1:2.4

proteoglycans that may be extracted with 'non-dissociative' solutions of physiological or low ionic strength are of smaller size and differ in several respects, including chemical composition, from proteoglycans that require 'dissociative' conditions for extraction. The latter exist as aggregates (Section 4.3) in cartilage and must be dissociated before they can be extracted. On dialysis to low ionic strength they reassociate into aggregates. Extraction at pH 4.5 gives the maximum proportion of aggregates (Hardingham and Muir 1974a) and the addition of proteinase inhibitors to the extracting solutions, as well as during the dialysis, increases the proportion of aggregates, particularly when tissues such as chondrosarcoma with high proteinase activity are being extracted (Oegema, Hascall and Dziewiatkowski 1975). Proteinase inhibitors are now used routinely in investigations of aggregation.

4.3. Proteoglycan Aggregation

A unique feature of cartilage proteoglycans is their ability to form multimolecular aggregates of very high molecular weight of the order of 50 million. Detailed evidence of aggregation of highly purified proteoglycans was produced by Hascall and Sajdera (1969), although it had been proposed much earlier (Mathews and Lozaityte 1958). It was only with the development of efficient non-disruptive methods of extraction and purification by density gradient centrifugation that unequivocal results were obtained by Hascall and Sajdera (1969). They showed that proteoglycan extracted with dissociating solvents such as 4 mol/litre (4M) guanidinium chloride when dialysed and then purified by caesium chloride density gradient centrifugation contained a fast and a more slowly sedimenting component in the analytical ultracentrifuge. When subjected to a second density gradient centrifugation under *dissociative* conditions in the presence of 4 mol/litre (4M) guanidine hydrochloride about 25% of the protein, originally associated with the proteoglycan, now separated at the top of the gradient, whilst in the analytical ultracentrifuge the fast-sedimenting component had disappeared. This showed that aggregation is not a simple self-association but involves binding to other specific non-proteoglycan components. Since density gradient centrifugation is now widely used and as it employs a principle for the separation of molecules that may be unfamiliar it is described in outline in the following sections (4.3.1 and 4.3.3).

4.3.1. Equilibrium Density Gradient Centrifugation of Proteoglycans. Equilibrium density gradient centrifugation in caesium chloride was first used to purify proteoglycans by Franek and Dunstone (1966). In this method molecules are separated according to their buoyant density in a concentrated caesium chloride gradient. Since the buoyant density of carbohydrates, particularly of polyanionic glycosaminoglycans, is much higher than that of proteins, molecules may be separated according to differences in the proportions of carbohydrate to protein; those containing the most carbohydrate separate at the bottom of the gradient whilst those richer in protein towards the top at lower densities. The usefulness of this method was examined by Hascall and Sajdera (1969) for the purification of nasal cartilage proteoglycans. These contain about 90% of glycosaminoglycans and have buoyant densities of about 1.8 g/ml whereas contaminating proteins such as collagen have buoyant densities around 1.3 g/ml and may be removed at the top of the gradient (Figure 3.9). Density gradient

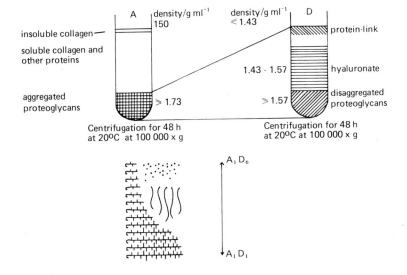

Figure 3.9 Equilibrium density gradient centrifugation in caesium chloride.
A. *Associative conditions*. Starting density usually 1.6 g/ml or less.
D. *Dissociative conditions*. Lower fraction from associative gradient mixed with an equal volume of 7.5 mol/litre (7.5M) guanidine hydrochloride at pH 5.8. Starting density adjusted to 1.5 g/ml with caesium chloride. Separation in the dissociative gradient of molecules of decreasing size and buoyant density depicted on the right.

centrifugation is now generally carried out in two stages: the first under 'associative' conditions to purify proteoglycans; the second under 'dissociative' conditions to dissociate and separate the constituents of proteoglycan aggregates.

4.3.2. Associative Density Gradient Centrifugation.

Proteoglycans extracted with dissociating solutions such as 4 mol/litre (4M) guanidine hydrochloride or 2 mol/litre (2M) calcium chloride are first dialysed to low ionic strength at pH 5.8 to allow aggregates to reassociate. Caesium chloride is then added to the buffered solution to give an appropriate starting density which depends on the proportion of carbohydrate to protein in the proteoglycan under investigation. Articular cartilage proteoglycans have a lower proportion of glycosaminoglycan to protein than proteoglycans of nasal cartilage and hence a somewhat lower starting density is employed than that used with nasal cartilage proteoglycans (Rosenberg et al. 1973; Rosenberg 1974; McDevitt and Muir 1975). The solution is then centrifuged at about $1 \times 10^5 g$ for 48 h to form the caesium chloride gradient. As the majority of proteoglycans contain much more carbohydrate than other constituents cartilage, they separate at the bottom in the densest part of the gradient, whilst other constituents such as collagen separate near the top of the gradient and may be removed. Proteoglycans from normal articular cartilage when purified in this way, consist of at least two sedimenting species in the analytical ultracentrifuge, a fast-moving component with sedimentation coefficients (S^0) of 60–70 and a slower component of S^0 16 (Rosenberg et al. 1973).

4.3.3. Dissociative Density Gradient Centrifugation.

Purified proteoglycans from the associative density gradient consisting of aggregated and non-aggregated molecules are mixed with an equal volume of 7.5 mol/litre (7.5M) guanidinium chloride, the density adjusted to 1.5 g/ml with caesium chloride and the centrifugation repeated as before. Any aggregated proteoglycans are dissociated into three constituents—proteoglycan, hyaluronic acid and 'protein-link'—which separate at different buoyant densities (Figure 3.9). The majority of proteoglycans generally separate near the bottom of the gradient but a minority with lower carbohydrate/protein ratios are distributed through the gradient (Tsiganos et al. 1971). The proportion varies with the type and age of the cartilage. Proteoglycans fractionated in this way are extensively heterogeneous in chemical composition and molecular size (Hardingham and Muir 1974a; Lohmander 1975; Hardingham et al. 1976; Rosenberg, Wolfenstein-Todel, Margolis, Pal and Strider 1976; Heinegård 1977). A simple terminology has been introduced to identify the various density gradient fractions which are numbered from the bottom upwards (Heinegård 1972a). Thus associative density gradient fractions are termed A_1, A_2, A_3, etc., and dissociative density gradient fractions A_1D_1, A_1D_2, A_1D_3, etc. and A_2D_1, A_2D_2, A_2D_3, etc. (Figure 3.9). Fractions that are subsequently fractionated in various ways may then be identified by additional letters or numbers (Lohmander 1975; Heinegård 1977).

4.3.4. The Role of Hyaluronate.
It was first thought that the 'protein-link' which separated at the top of the second dissociative gradient linked together proteoglycans into aggregates (Hascall and Sajdera 1969; Rosenberg *et al.* 1970; Rosenberg *et al.* 1973). It has since been recognized, however, that aggregation depends upon a highly specific interaction of proteoglycans with hyaluronic acid, first discovered in 1972 by Hardingham and Muir (1972a). Hyaluronic acid accounts for less than 1% of the total uronic acid in laryngeal (Hardingham and Muir 1974a) or nasal (Hascall and Heinegård 1974a) cartilage, and when proteoglycan aggregates are dissociated it separates in the middle of the second dissociative gradient (Figure 3.9) (Hardingham and Muir 1973a, 1974a).

The interaction of proteoglycan and hyaluronic acid leads to an increase in hydrodynamic size and to a large increase in viscosity (Hardingham amd Muir 1972a; Hascall and Heinegård 1974a) and requires as little as 0.01% of hyaluronic acid to be detectable (Hardingham and Muir 1972a). The interaction is entirely specific to hyaluronate and no comparable effects are produced by other polyanions—even close isomers of hyaluronic acid such as chondroitin, i.e. desulphated chondroitin sulphate (Hascall and Heinegård 1974b)—nor does it depend on the presence of divalent metal ions as it is unaffected by the presence of EDTA (Hardingham and Muir 1972a). Proteoglycan aggregation of this kind has been shown in cartilage from a variety of anatomical sites, including articular cartilage (Tsiganos and Muir 1973; Rosenberg *et al.* 1973, 1976).

Using viscometry and gel chromatography to measure changes in hydrodynamic size resulting from the interaction of proteoglycans with hyaluronate, the stoichiometry of the interaction was established (Hardingham and Muir 1972a). When there is a large excess of proteoglycans over hyaluronate, as occurs in cartilage, a large number of proteoglycans interact with a single chain of hyaluronic acid. The interaction increases as the proportion of hyaluronate increases until it reaches an optimum at about 150:1 (w/w). Since the effect diminishes with higher proportions of hyaluronate, proteoglycans do not appear to cross-link hyaluronate chains and hence possess only a single binding site (Hardingham and Muir 1972a). Under conditions which favour binding and with proteoglycans in excess, hyaluronate can bind about 250 times its weight of proteoglycan. Using average molecular weights for proteoglycan of 2.5×10^6 and for hyaluronic acid of 5×10^5, a model for the complex was deduced (Figure 3.10) and it was

163

Figure 3.10 Model of the proteoglycan–hyaluronic acid complex. PG: proteoglycan; HA: hyaluronic acid; CS:
chondroitin sulphate; KS: keratan sulphate.

PG mol. wt 2.5 x 10^6
HA mol. wt 0.5 x 10^6

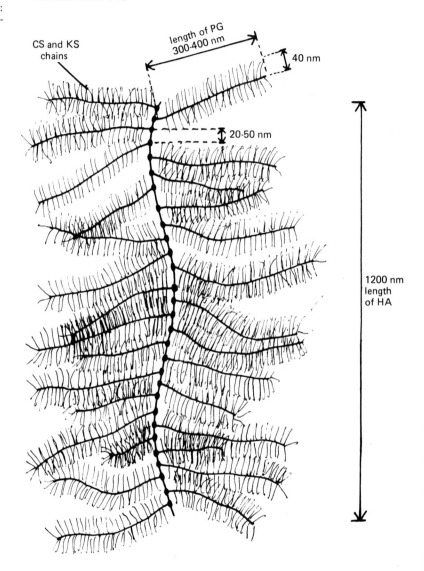

CS and KS
chains

length of PG
300-400 nm

40 nm

20-50 nm

1200 nm
length
of HA

calculated that each molecule of proteoglycan would occupy a region on the hyaluronate chain of about 20 nm in length (Hardingham and Muir 1974b). Similar conditions based on the amount of hyaluronate and aggregate in nasal (Hascall and Heinegård 1974a) and laryngeal (Muir and Hardingham 1975) cartilage suggest that the average distance between proteoglycan molecules in aggregates is much greater than 20 nm and hence that the hyaluronate in cartilage may not be saturated with proteoglycans.

Oligosaccharides derived from hyaluronate by digestion with testicular hyaluronidase, above a critical size are strong competitive inhibitors of proteoglycan–hyaluronate complex formation. Decasaccharides are the smallest oligosaccharides to compete strongly with hyaluronate, whereas octasaccharides and smaller oligosaccharides are virtually ineffective (Hardingham and Muir 1973b; Hascall and Heinegård 1974b). The binding of each proteoglycan therefore involves only 5 nm of the hyaluronate chain. Proteoglycan molecules cannot be packed as closely as this along the hyaluronate chain, because of the steric hindrance of the numerous chondroitin sulphate chains which are attached laterally to the core protein (Mathews and Lozaityte 1958; Partridge et al. 1961), the chains being fully extended by electrostatic repulsion. However, when most of the chondroitin sulphate is removed by digestion of proteoglycans with chondroitinase, the resulting core proteins may be packed five times more closely along the hyaluronate chain (Hascall and Heinegård 1974b) indicating that, with intact proteoglycans, closeness of packing at saturation is limited by steric interference of chondroitin sulphate chains on adjacent molecules. That chondroitinase-treated proteoglycans are able to interact with hyaluronate shows that the chondroitin sulphate chains themselves play no part in the interaction with hyaluronate; nor are aggregates dissociated by chondroitinase digestion (Hascall and Heinegård 1974a), the hyaluronate in the aggregate being largely protected from attack by chondroitinase.

At maximum density of packing, when they are about 20 nm apart, the proteoglycan molecules must lie perpendicular to the hyaluronate chain, so that the binding site must be at one end of the core protein. The hyaluronate chain acts as a thread holding together numerous proteoglycan molecules (Figure 3.10); the overall size of the aggregate depends largely on the length of the hyaluronate chain, as does the size of the proteoglycan hyaluronate complex prepared from hyaluronate of different chain length (Swann, Powell, Broadhurst, Sordillo and Sotman 1976). Thus in nasal cartilage the aggregates are larger and the hyaluronate chains longer than in tracheal cartilage (Hascall and Heinegård 1974a). Aggregates of bovine articular cartilage (Rosenberg et al. 1973) are smaller than those of bovine nasal cartilage, presumably because the hyaluronate chains are shorter. The model shown in Figure 3.10 is consistent with published electron micrographs of aggregates which appeared before the involvement of hyaluronate was known (Rosenberg, Hellmann and Kleinschmidt 1970). It is also compatible with the results of electric birefringence measurements of molecular parameters in solution of free proteoglycan and of proteoglycan bound to hyaluronate as portrayed in Figure 3.10 (Foweraker, Isles, Jennings, Hardingham and Muir 1977).

Reduction of disulphide bridges interferes with aggregation (Hascall and Sajdera 1969). The tertiary structure of the hyaluronate-binding region of the core protein is maintained by five to seven intramolecular disulphide bridges (Hardingham *et al.* 1976). When these are reduced and alkylated, interaction with hyaluronate is abolished, without change in molecular size or in protein content. If the reduced proteoglycan is not alkylated, the loss of interaction is largely reversible on re-oxidation (Hardingham *et al.* 1976). This indicates that the hyaluronate-binding region is resistant to denaturation and it is remarkably stable to heating (Hardingham and Muir 1975). On the other hand, it is very sensitive to specific chemical modification of basic and aromatic amino-acids (Hardingham *et al.* 1976).

Certain lysine, arginine and tryptophan residues are essential for interaction with hyaluronate. It would appear that about one-third of the arginine residues of the core protein are directly involved in the interaction, and indirectly about one-third of the tryptophan residues (Hardingham *et al.* 1976). About half the lysine residues of the hyaluronate-binding region are also directly involved and, when hyaluronate is present, these residues are partially protected from chemical substitution (acetylation and dansylation) (Heinegård and Hascall 1977, personal communication). Modification of varying proportions of the carboxyl groups of hyaluronate oligosaccharides shows that interaction with proteoglycan in competition with hyaluronate is abolished when less than 40% of the carboxyl groups are modified (Christner, Brown and Dziewiatkowski 1977). *N*-Acetylglucosamine residues are also essential since chondroitin does not compete with hyaluronate (Hascall and Heinegård 1974b) although it has the same glycosidic linkages and differs only in containing *N*-acetylgalactosamine in place of *N*-acetylglucosamine. These results show that the effective binding site is of limited size and of precise shape, allowing the maximum number of subsite interactions to take place in a small area of the molecule. The whole hyaluronate-binding region, on the other hand, has a molecular weight of about 60 000 and may be obtained by cyanogen bromide cleavage of dissociated proteoglycans. As it lacks glycosaminoglycan chains it is of low buoyant density and separates at the top of a caesium chloride density gradient (Heinegård 1977). In the intact aggregate the hyaluronate-binding region is relatively protected from proteolysis and can be isolated by mild tryptic digestion from chondroitinase-treated aggregates (Heinegård and Hascall 1974a).

The amino-acid composition of the hyaluronate-binding region differs significantly from that of the whole core protein, particularly in containing more aspartic acid, arginine, methionine and cystine and less serine, glycine and proline (Heinegård and Hascall 1974a; Heinegård 1977). About 60% of the amino-acids of the remainder of the core protein from nasal cartilage consists of approximately equimolar amounts of serine, glycine, proline and glutamic acid (Heinegård and Hascall 1974a).

Although proteoglycans are extremely heterogeneous in chemical composition and molecular size (Section 4.4) it is assumed that as the interaction with hyaluronate is very specific and restricted to proteoglycans of cartilage, proteoglycans which are able to interact with hyaluronate possess the same hyaluronate-binding region. It is therefore suggested that the core protein is constructed of an invariant hyaluronate-binding region, devoid of glycosaminoglycan chains and a variable region to which chondroitin sulphate and keratan sulphate are attached in varying proportions (Heinegård and Hascall 1974a; Hardingham *et al.* 1976; Heinegård 1977). A minority of the proteoglycans in normal cartilage, however, are unable to interact with hyaluronate (Hardingham and Muir 1974a). These appear to lack the hyaluronate-binding region and may belong to a different class of proteoglycan (Hardingham *et al.* 1976) (Section 4.4.1).

4.3.5. The Role of 'Protein-link'. The binding of proteoglycan to hyaluronate appears to be an equilibrium which lies well in favour of complex formation under physiological conditions of ionic strength, pH and temperature (Hardingham and Muir 1972a, 1975). The complex, however, is unstable in the ultracentrifuge unlike the aggregate (Gregory 1973) which, in addition to hyaluronate, contains a third component, the 'protein-link', which accounts for about a quarter of the protein of the aggregate (Hascall and Sajdera 1969). The protein-link stabilizes the aggregate so that it is not in equilibrium with its dissociation products (Hardingham and Muir 1975) and hence aggregates are unaffected by oligosaccharides of hyaluronate which dissociate the proteoglycan–hyaluronate complex (Hascall and Heinegård 1974b). In the aggregate, but not in the complex, hyaluronate is protected from attack by leech hyaluronidase (an enzyme which specifically degrades hyaluronate) (Hardingham and Muir 1975). Similarly, in the aggregate the hyaluronate-binding region survives tryptic digestion and the hyaluronate is partially protected from chondroitinase digestion (Heinegård and Hascall 1974a). The protein-link fraction binds to proteoglycan but it does not promote proteoglycan aggregation on its own (Tsiganos, Hardingham and Muir 1972). It is also able to bind to hyaluronate in the absence of proteoglycan and appears in aggregates in 1:1 ratio with the hyaluronate-binding region as deduced from partial degradation of aggregates (Heinegård and Hascall 1974a). When aggregates from nasal cartilage are dissociated, the lowest density fraction at the top of the gradient (Section 4.3.3) contains two proteins which are separable on polyacrylamide gel electrophoresis (Keiser, Shulman and Sandson 1972) and have approximate molecular weights of 40 000 and 50 000 (Hascall and Heinegård 1974a). However, it seems unlikely that the protein-link consists functionally of more than one constituent. Aggregates prepared from a rat chondrosarcoma which has high levels of proteolytic activity, contain only the protein-link of 40 000 molecular weight (Oegema, Hascall and Dziewiatkowski 1975) and there is evidence that proteolytic cleavage converts the larger into the smaller (Hascall 1979). Proteoglycan aggregation as currently envisaged is depicted diagrammatically in Figure 3.11.

Figure 3.11 Diagram of proteoglycan aggregation.

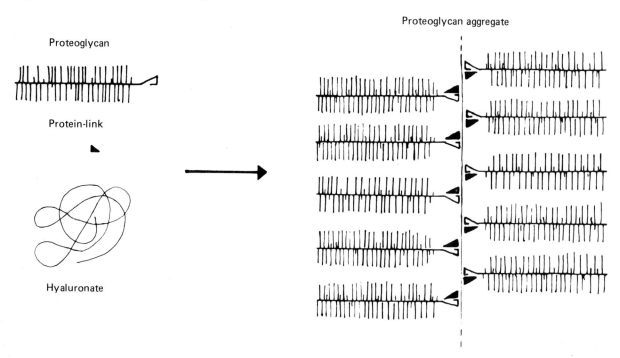

The biological function of proteoglycan aggregation is not yet known but, as it is restricted to proteoglycans of cartilage, it presumably has a role which is peculiar to the function of cartilage. It is notable that the proportion of aggregates is reduced in experimental canine osteoarthrosis (Muir 1977). The large size of aggregates immobilizes them very effectively in the collagen network and they have to be dissociated before the proteoglycans can be extracted. (On subsequent dialysis they re-associate into aggregates.) That aggregates are present in cartilage *in situ* is shown by the fact that mild papain treatment of whole cartilage gives a product which may be isolated without the use of dissociating solutions, which has protein still attached to hyaluronate and resembles the product formed from aggregates themselves by mild papain treatment (Hascall and Heinegård 1974a). Aggregates are more resistant to degradative enzymes than are free proteoglycans and their solutions within the collagen network may be less compressible. Aggregates may also indirectly play some part in regulating proteoglycan synthesis by chondrocytes which are influenced by hyaluronate when it is free, but not when it is bound up in aggregates (Wiebkin, Hardingham and Muir 1975) (Section 4.8).

4.4. Heterogeneity of Proteoglycans

Attempts to prepare discrete fractions of proteoglycans by a variety of physical methods have invariably failed and it would appear that in any given cartilage the population of proteoglycans exhibits a continuous range of chemical composition and molecular size. Part of the heterogeneity described in earlier work, however, is attributable to aggregation before this was understood, but even disaggregated proteoglycans are extremely heterogeneous.

There appear to be three types or classes of proteoglycans in cartilage, each class being itself heterogeneous: there are proteoglycans which form aggregates (generally the majority), those which cannot do so, and those which resist extraction even with strongly dissociating solvents (Section 4.2).

By applying standard sequential extraction procedures to articular cartilage, it is evident that each class of proteoglycan, at a given age, has an overall composition which is distinct, although protein and keratan sulphate contents of all three classes increase with age (Simunek and Muir 1972a). The relative proportions of each class also change with age, particularly during development, and also in some pathological conditions (Simunek and Muir 1972b), including experimentally induced osteoarthrosis (McDevitt and Muir 1976).

4.4.1. Non-aggregating Proteoglycans. Non-dissociating solutions of low ionic strength (Section 4.2) extract essentially only the minority of proteoglycans that cannot form aggregates and are unable to interact with hyaluronate and from which no hyaluronate may be dissociated (Hardingham and Muir 1974a; Hardingham *et al.* 1976). Such proteoglycans are of relatively low molecular weight, of about $2-3 \times 10^5$ (Tsiganos and Muir 1969), and contain less protein and keratan sulphate than the majority of proteoglycans which are not extracted by solutions of low ionic strength (Brandt and Muir 1969, 1971a; Simunek and Muir 1972a; Mayes *et al.* 1973; Hardingham and Muir 1974a). They are also heterogeneous, and when normal articular cartilage is homogenized at low speed and extracted serially with 0.15 mol/litre (0.15M) sodium acetate, progressively larger molecules of increasing protein and keratan sulphate content are extracted (Table 3.2) in diminishing yield until no more are extracted (Brandt and Muir 1971a). The relative proportion of proteoglycans extractable at low ionic strength is appreciably greater than normal in some pathological conditions (Simunek and Muir 1972b; McDevitt and Muir 1976).

The amino-acid compositions of non-aggregated proteoglycans suggest that the hyaluronate-binding region is incomplete or lacking (Hardingham *et al.* 1976). It has been suggested that this is because of degradation by endogenous proteinases during the extraction at low ionic strength (Oegema *et al.* 1975; Heinegård 1977). However, the following evidence is against this. Prolonging the time of extraction beyond 3 hours does not increase the yield from laryngeal cartilage, nor is it reduced by the presence of proteinase inhibitors in the extracting solutions. Moreover, similar yields of non-aggregating proteoglycans (together with aggregating species) are obtained when dissociating solutions of high ionic strength are used for the extraction (Hardingham and Muir 1974a). The results of biosynthesis experiments *in vitro* do not reveal any precursor–product relationships between the three classes of proteoglycan and thus do not indicate that the non-aggregating species is derived from aggregating proteoglycans (Hardingham and Muir 1972b). Similar conclusions may be drawn from biosynthesis experiments with guinea-pig costal cartilage *in vivo* (Lohmander 1977).

Sequential extraction of nasal (Mayes *et al.* 1973) and costal (Lohmander 1975) cartilage with solutions of low ionic strength followed by dissociative solutions of high ionic strength, suggest that the three classes of proteoglycan are of general occurrence in cartilage. Non-aggregating proteoglycans may not be phenotypic of differentiated chondrocytes but may represent proteoglycans produced by mesenchymal cells in general. Proteoglycans produced by cultures of prechondrogenic cells from very early chick embryos are not aggregated nor are they able to interact with hyaluronate (de Luca, Heinegård, Hascall, Kimura and Caplan 1977). Differentiation of mesenchymal cells is prevented and the synthesis of cartilage matrix suppressed by bromodeoxyuridine (Abbott and Holtzer 1968). Bromodeoxyuridine reversibly arrests the synthesis by differentiated chondrocytes of proteoglycans typical of cartilage but not the synthesis of proteoglycans of relatively small size that are produced by non-differentiated mesenchymal cells (Dorfman, Levitt, Schwartz and Ho 1975).

4.4.2. Aggregating Proteoglycans. The majority of proteoglycans are extractable only under dissociating conditions (usually 4 mol/litre (4M) guanidine hydrochloride; Sajdera and Hascall 1969) when non-aggregating proteoglycans are also extracted. Dissociative density gradient centrifugation does not separate the two species of proteoglycan (Hardingham and Muir 1974a), and hence if cartilage is extracted first with solutions of low ionic strength to remove non-aggregating proteoglycans (usually about 5–10% of the total in adult articular cartilage; Simunek and Muir 1972a; McDevitt and Muir 1976), almost all the proteoglycan extracted subsequently in 4 mol/litre (4M) guanidine hydrochloride reassociates into aggregates when dialysed to low ionic strength. On dissociative density gradient centrifugation (Section 4.3.3) the proteoglycans mostly separate at the bottom of the gradient (A_1D_1) from hyaluronate which separates in the middle of the gradient between 1.45 and 1.57 g/ml (Figure 3.9) (Tsiganos *et al.* 1972; Gregory 1973; Hardingham and Muir 1974a). However, a minor proportion of proteoglycans of lower buoyant density are distributed through the gradient. Some are of a buoyant density similar to hyaluronate and hence do not separate from hyaluronate. On dialysis to low ionic strength they interact with it and form a complex, which is large and therefore excluded from Sepharose 2B, whereas the majority of proteoglycans at the bottom of the gradient, where there is no hyaluronate, are not excluded (Tsiganos *et al.* 1971; Heinegård 1972a). This result was at first confusing before hyaluronate was identified in the middle of the dissociative gradient (Hardingham and Muir 1973a, 1974a).

Compared with non-aggregating proteoglycans, proteoglycans dissociated from aggregates contain more protein and more keratan sulphate relative to chondroitin sulphate and are of larger average molecular size (Hardingham and Muir 1974a). Although such proteoglycans sediment unimodally in the ultracentrifuge (Hascall and Sajdera 1969), they are extremely heterogeneous in size and chemical composition when examined by density gradient centrifugation (Heinegård and Hascall 1974a; Lohmander 1975; Hardingham *et al.* 1976; Heinegård 1977) or rate-zonal centrifugation (Hoffman, Mashburn, Hsu, Trivedid and Diep 1975).

In these studies proteoglycans from nasal or laryngeal cartilage were used. However, the heterogeneity of proteoglycans of bovine articular cartilage has recently been examined by density gradient centrifugation by Rosenberg and co-workers (Rosenberg *et al.* 1976). The findings parallel those obtained with other types of cartilage. The proteoglycans exhibit a range of molecular size and chemical composition through the dissociative density gradient, the largest molecules with sedimentation constants of 14.35 separate at the bottom and the smallest of only 5.75 at the top. Chondroitin sulphate content increases with molecular size whereas protein and keratan sulphate content decrease. The protein content of molecules of lowest molecular weight is about 30%, which is about three times more than in the largest proteoglycans. The amino-acid compositions also change gradually through the gradient; cysteine, methionine and aspartic acid contents increase with protein content and diminishing molecular size. Serine and glycine contents change in the opposite way and increase with molecular size and chondroitin sulphate content. Since chondroitin sulphate chains are attached to serine residues on the core protein (Section 3.1) and since the sequence Ser-Gly on the core protein is always needed for recognition by the xylosyltransferase that initiates chondroitin sulphate chain synthesis (Baker, Rodén and Stoolmiller 1972) (Section 4.6.1), molecules with higher chondroitin sulphate contents will contain more serine and glycine than those with less chondroitin sulphate.

The results obtained with proteoglycans of bovine articular cartilage, as with those from other types of cartilage, are in keeping with the suggestion that the core protein consists of an invariant hyaluronate-binding region devoid of chondroitin sulphate and a region of variable length to which the chondroitin sulphate chains are attached (Figure 3.7). Electron microscopic studies of proteoglycans from articular cartilage support this idea and show molecules varying in length from 100 to 400 nm (Rosenberg, Hellmann and Kleinschmidt 1975). Proteoglycans from guinea-pig costal cartilage are similar in appearance (Thyberg, Lohmander and Heinegård 1975). Aggregating pro-

Figure 3.12 Three sizes of proteoglycan, showing constant hyaluronate-binding region and shorter chondroitin-sulphate-binding region with decreasing size.

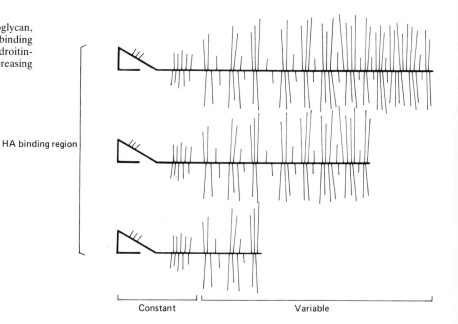

HA binding region

Constant   Variable

172

teoglycans from a series in which the hyaluronate-binding region is present in molecules of all sizes (Figure 3.12), and the ability to interact with hyaluronate is not restricted to any particular size of proteoglycan (Swann *et al.* 1976). Core proteins prepared by chondroitinase digestion of proteoglycans of decreasing buoyant density are progressively smaller in size and from all molecules the hyaluronate-binding region can be cleaved by cyanogen bromide digestion. The hyaluronate-binding region represents a large proportion of the total protein in proteoglycans of low buoyant density (Heinegård 1977), so that the amino-acid composition of proteoglycans of lowest molecular weight from articular cartilage (Rosenberg *et al.* 1976) resembles the composition of the hyaluronate-binding region isolated by partial degradation of large proteoglycans of nasal cartilage (Heinegård and Hascall 1974a). The series of proteoglycans depicted in Figure 3.12 can vary in range of size and range of keratan sulphate content according to the type of cartilage and it is not known whether there is an identical series in the cartilage of different joints or whether this varies in weight-bearing and non-weight-bearing areas of the same joint. The non-aggregating proteoglycans, however, do not fit into the series because, although of high chondroitin sulphate content, they are relatively small.

The lengths of chondroitin sulphate chains do not vary appreciably amongst proteoglycans of different buoyant density (Heinegård 1977). Partial degradation of proteoglycans with trypsin and chymotrypsin shows the chondroitin sulphate chains to be located in groups or clusters of up to eight chains along the core protein. In the clusters only a few amino-acids separate the chains which have a similar distribution of lengths in all clusters (Heinegård and Hascall 1974b). In proteoglycans of lower buoyant density there appear to be fewer clusters and more single chains (Heinegård 1977), which implies that the density of clusters increases with distance from the hyaluronate-binding site (Figure 3.7).

Keratan sulphate chains are shorter than chondroitin sulphate chains, and vary in length with molecular weights of 5 to 10×10^3 (Hascall and Riolo 1972; Robinson and Hopwood 1973). Heinegård and Axelsson (1977) have performed an extensive series of partial degradation experiments with proteoglycan aggregates and dissociated proteoglycans from nasal and tracheal cartilages. Using trypsin, chymotrypsin and chondroitinase ABC in various sequences and also hydroxylamine to produce fragments derived from different parts of the core protein, they conclude that keratan sulphate is located in three different regions. About 20% is attached to the core protein close to the clusters of chondroitin sulphate chains, about 60% is located in a region proximal to the hyaluronate-binding region where there are few chondroitin sulphate chains, and the remaining 10–20% is attached to the hyaluronate-binding region itself (Figure 3.7). Whether keratan sulphate is distributed in the same way in proteoglycans of articular cartilage remains to be established. The structure in Figure 3.7 would explain why proteoglycans of smaller molecular size contain higher proportions of keratan sulphate and protein relative to chondroitin sulphate and hence are of lower buoyant density than larger proteoglycans; most of the keratan sulphate should be located in or around the invariant hyaluronate-binding region, which is present in molecules of all sizes that are capable of interacting with hyaluronate (Figure 3.12).

The function of keratan sulphate is unknown. It is not essential for binding to hyaluronate since proteoglycans from a rat chondrosarcoma which interact with hyaluronate lack keratan sulphate (Oegema *et al.* 1975). The keratan sulphate content of proteoglycans of articular and other types of cartilage increases with age throughout all fractions, and it is notable that in osteoarthrosis the reverse change takes place both in human (Mankin and Lippiello 1971) and in experimental canine osteoarthrosis (McDevitt and Muir 1974, 1975, 1976).

4.4.3. Inextractable Proteoglycans. The proteoglycans which resist extraction with dissociating solutions can only be defined operationally. Their composition may be inferred from the glycosaminoglycans isolated after complete proteolysis of cartilage residues from which extractable proteoglycans have been removed. In articular cartilage such proteoglycans contain a higher proportion of keratan sulphate relative to chondroitin sulphate than extractable proteoglycans (McDevitt and Muir 1975). The relative proportion of keratan sulphate increases with age in these as in the extractable proteoglycans and they also may be heterogeneous. The possibility that the keratan sulphate contributes to their insolubility in some way and increases their interaction with insoluble proteins, particularly collagen, might be inferred from the fact that the proportion of inextractable proteoglycans increases with age as does the keratan sulphate content of articular cartilage (Simunek and Muir 1972a). Conversely, in natural and experimental canine osteoarthrosis (McDevitt and Muir 1974, 1975, 1976; McDevitt, Gilbertson and Muir 1977) the proportion of extractable proteoglycans increases as the keratan sulphate content of the articular cartilage decreases. Isolated keratan sulphate chains themselves, however, have no effect on collagen fibrillogenesis and do not interact with collagen (Obrink 1973a). On balance, therefore, it appears that the keratan sulphate of inextractable proteoglycans does not contribute to their insolubility which may depend on some unknown structural feature.

4.5. Antigenicity of Proteoglycans

Proteoglycans of cartilage are weakly antigenic (reviewed by Herman and Carpenter 1975). Although they contain only 5–15% of protein, the antigenicity is attributable to the protein moiety since it is destroyed by tryptic or papain digestion (White, Sandson, Rosenberg and Schubert 1963; Loewi and Muir 1965) whereas digestion with hyaluronidase enhances antigenicity (Loewi and Muir 1965; Brandt, Tsiganos and Muir 1973). Neither chondroitin sulphate (Boake and Muir 1955; Sandson, Rosenberg and White 1966) nor keratan sulphate (Quinn and Cerroni 1957; Sandson et al. 1966) is itself antigenic nor do the neutral sugars of the linkage region (Section 3.1) influence antigenicity, as the entire chain may be removed by a chemical procedure (Smith degradation) which leaves the protein core intact, without effect on antigenicity (Baxter and Muir 1972).

Immunological methods have been used to investigate the structure of proteoglycans, but the interpretation of results of earlier work is uncertain because proteoglycans were not purified by density gradient centrifugation. The presence of antigenic determinants common to proteoglycans from different species is attributable to that part of the core protein which resists digestion by trypsin and chymotrypsin since this is similar in proteoglycans from different species (Mathews 1971). Keiser and De Vito (1974) have recently examined the antigenicity of proteoglycans prepared by density gradient centrifugation and fragmented by digestion with trypsin and chymotrypsin. There appear to be two species-common determinants, the stronger of which is in a region enriched with keratan sulphate and the weaker is probably due to the amino-acid sequences around chondroitin sulphate chains. These results provide some independent evidence for the suggestion of Heinegård and Axelsson (1977) that chondroitin sulphate and much of the keratan sulphate are located in different parts of the molecule. Species-specific determinants are attributable to the protein-link (Di Ferrante, Donnelly and Sajdera 1972; Keiser et al. 1972; Keiser and Sandson 1974). In the intact aggregate the protein-link does not react with antibody, and only does so when aggregates are dissociated (Di Ferrante et al. 1972). This is consistent with the model depicted in Figure 3.11 where the protein-link is placed in the inner part of the aggregate and hence is relatively inaccessible.

Small non-aggregating proteoglycans which are retarded on Sepharose 6B and which contain very little keratan sulphate react directly with antibody without prior digestion with hyaluronidase. In this they are unlike the larger excluded proteoglycans (Tsiganos and Muir 1969). To show this difference in behaviour of proteoglycans clearly, Brandt, Tsiganos and Muir (1973) removed the small proteoglycans of pig articular cartilage from the remainder by gel chromatography on Sepharose 6B. The larger excluded proteoglycans then did not react with or inhibit antibody until digested with hyaluronidase. Submitting the proteoglycans to dissociative density gradient centrifugation does not confer reactivity on the larger proteoglycans so that their lack of reactivity is not attributable to aggregation. Partial proteolysis with trypsin and chymotrypsin, however, produces fragments which inhibit antibody (Baxter and Muir 1972). It would thus appear that in the larger proteoglycans the antigenic determinants are inaccessible or buried in some way. This suggests some difference in structure or shape between the small and larger proteoglycans that is not explained by the model shown in Figure 3.7.

The antigenicity of proteoglycans rarely involves disease. In relapsing polychondritis, however, where there is localized inflammation of non-articular cartilage, patients show cell-mediated immunity to purified proteoglycan (Rajapakse and Bywaters 1974).

4.6. Proteoglycan Synthesis

Studies both *in vivo* (Gross, Mathews and Dorfman 1960) and *in vitro* (Campo and Dziewiatkowski 1962) show that the protein and carbohydrate moieties of proteoglycans are formed and metabolized in parallel. Inhibitors of protein synthesis arrest the formation both of the protein moiety and of chondroitn sulphate but the inhibitors do not interfere with the activity of enzymes already formed before the inhibitor was introduced (Telser, Robinson and Dorfman 1965) and hence inhibition of chondroitin sulphate synthesis occurs after a delay (Cole and Lowther 1969) the effect being secondary rather than direct. The formation of the core protein is thus the first step in the biosynthesis (Telser *et al.* 1965).

There is considerable information about the intracellular stages in the synthesis of proteoglycans and the subject has been comprehensively reviewed (Stoolmiller and Dorman 1969; Rodén 1970; Rodén and Schwartz 1975).

4.6.1. Chondroitin Sulphate. The first step in chondroitin sulphate synthesis is the transfer of xylose, the first sugar of the linkage region (Figure 3.3) to the serine residues of the core protein (Robinson, Telser and Dorfman 1966). The predominance of glycine and glutamic acid in proteoglycans arises from the need to have the appropriate sequence around those serine residues (about half the total) which are glycosylated (Baker *et al.* 1972). The next step, the attachment of galactose to the xylose residues already bound to core protein, has been shown with a cell-free enzyme system (Robinson *et al.* 1966). With the use of exogenous competitive acceptors and a cell-free enzyme system, Helting and Rodén (1969a, b) have now shown that the addition of the three sugars of the linkage region and of the first glucuronic acid of the chondroitin sulphate chain itself, are brought about by separate enzymes specific for each glycosylation step. The specificities of these enzymes were tested both towards the acceptor and the group transferred and it was shown that the exact structure of the linkage region was ensured by the specificities of these enzymes, which enabled each sugar to be added in turn. If there were an error at any step, the next sugar could not be transferred. The linkage region therefore provides a mechanism for co-ordinating the synthesis of the chondroitin sulphate and protein moieties of the proteoglycans, because chondroitin sulphate chain synthesis can begin only when core protein has been formed to which the first sugar, xylose, can be transferred. This process can be bypassed in the presence of β-D-xylosides (Robinson, Brett, Tralaggan, Lowther and Okayama 1975; Schwartz, Galligani, Ho and Dorfman 1974) which act as acceptors for the galactosyltransferase that attaches the first galactose of the linkage region to xylose. Thus β-D-xylosides prevent production of proteoglycan molecules by competing with the natural galactose acceptor, the xylosylserine residues on the core protein, with the result that free chondroitin sulphate chains are formed. If the xyloside is a fluorescent compound such as 4-methylumbelliferyl-β-D-xyloside, chondroitin sulphate chains are formed which are fluorescent (Dondi and Muir 1976).

The formation of the major part of the chondroitin sulphate chain, which consists of disaccharide repeating units (Figure 3.2), is brought about by two enzymes whose specificities have been determined with the use of the cell-free enzyme system from chick embryo cartilage acting on exogenous acceptors of known structure (Telser, Robinson and Dorfman 1966). The enzyme specificities ensure that glucuronic acid and *N*-acetylgalactosamine are added alternately to the nascent carbohydrate chain. The work of Richmond, De Luca and Silbert (1973b) indicates that the synthesis of individual chains proceeds rapidly to completion without accumulation of small sized intermediate products.

The location of the various transferases involved in the synthesis of chondroitin sulphate has been shown by Horwitz and Dorfman (1968), who fractionated rough from smooth membranes of chick cartilage cells. They showed that the rough membranes, where protein synthesis takes place, have the highest specific activity for the xylose and galactose transferases. Both rough and smooth membranes have similar specific activities for the enzymes involved in the formation of the chondroitin sulphate chains themselves, while the activity of the sulphotransferase was several times higher in the smooth than in the rough membranes. On the basis of these observations, Horwitz and Dorfman concluded that, after formation of the core protein by conventional mechanisms of protein synthesis, the linkage region sugars are added mainly at the rough membranes of the endoplasmic reticulum. The chondroitin sulphate chains are then elongated and completed as the proteoglycan molecule proceeds through the membrane system of the cell to the Golgi vesicles, and sulphation, being the last of the transferase reactions, takes place mainly when the molecule has reached the smooth membranes.

That the glycosyl transferases catalysing consecutive steps in the synthesis of chondroitin sulphate are arranged in adjacent positions on membranes of the endoplasmic reticulum is indicated from evidence from affinity chromatography. Xylosyl transferase covalently attached to a support has a high affinity for the enzyme transferring the first galactose of the linkage region. When the latter is bound to the xylosyl transferase the specific activity of the galactosyl transferase is increased (Schwartz and Rodén 1975). As in many monosaccharide interconversions the uridine nucleotide derivatives of the sugars are involved in all these transfer reactions, in some of which further control mechanisms operate. Uridine diphosphate-glucuronic acid (UDP-glucuronic acid), which is needed for chondroitin sulphate synthesis, is formed from UDP-glucose by UDP-glucose dehydrogenase. UDP-xylose, which is required to start chain synthesis, is in turn formed from UDP-glucuronic acid by decarboxylation. Neufeld and Hall (1965) have shown that UDP-xylose specifically inhibits UDP-glucose dehydrogenase and hence, should the synthesis of core protein lag behind, UDP-xylose would accumulate because there would be no core protein to which the xylose could be transferred. The accumulation of UDP-xylose would then inhibit the formation of UDP-glucuronic acid, which in turn would stop more UDP-xylose being formed. The xylose of the linkage region therefore provides a feedback control mechanism for co-ordinating carbohydrate and protein synthesis in proteoglycans. In this context, it may perhaps be significant that other proteoglycans which contain uronic acid, including heparin, possess the same linkage region as do proteoglycans containing chondroitin sulphate.

In common with other biological sulphation reactions, sulphation of glycosaminoglycans requires 3-phosphoadenosine-5-phosphosulphate (PAPS) as an intermediate (D'Abramo and Lipmann 1957). It appears that the sulphation of chondroitin sulphate does not proceed via sulphated monosaccharides because, although UDP-*N*-acetylgalactosamine sulphate has been isolated from tissues which are actively forming chondroitin sulphate, it is not an intermediate (Suzuki and Strominger 1960). Moreover, Perlman, Telser and Dorfman (1964) showed that chain synthesis can proceed in the absence of sulphation if no

PAPS is added to a cell-free extract of chick cartilage. Sulphation therefore follows, but is not an obligatory stage in, chain synthesis. The studies of Richmond, De Luca and Silbert (1973a) suggest that sulphation is an 'all or nothing' process and that the sulpho-transferase is located close to glycosyl transferases so that chain elongation and sulphation closely follow each other. That all these enzymes are membrane-bound with definite locations suggests that their spatial arrangement has thermodynamic advantages for the formation of large molecules by an assembly-line process, since if the reactions took place in free-solution the concentration of reactants would have to be sufficiently high to overcome the random distribution of precursors and reactants within the solution. Enzymes involved in the synthesis of other complex proteins, where additional groups are added to the polypeptide chains, are similarly localized on membranes.

4.6.2. Keratan Sulphate. In contrast with chondroitin sulphate synthesis, little is known about the synthesis of keratan sulphate, because first, although keratan sulphate has resemblances to other glycosaminoglycans, its exact structure is not known so that the conclusive identification of a reaction product is very difficult; and secondly, because purified degradative enzymes specific for cartilage keratan sulphate (Hirano and Meyer 1971, 1973; Fakada and Matsumura 1976) have not been generally available.

From both *in vivo* (Davidson and Small 1963) and *in vitro* (Hardingham and Muir 1972b) studies, keratan sulphate appears to have a slower turnover rate than chondroitin sulphate. Since keratan sulphate and chondroitin sulphate are part of the same molecule in cartilage proteoglycans, the difference in turnover of the average population of each type of glycosaminoglycan suggests that proteoglycans rich in keratan sulphate are metabolized more slowly than those rich in chondroitin sulphate. Those which resist extraction in canine articular cartilage contain more keratan sulphate than extractable proteoglycans and become labelled *in vivo* more slowly (McDevitt and Muir 1975; McDevitt 1977). Similarly, in guinea-pig costal cartilage extraction-resistant proteoglycans have a much slower turnover rate than extractable proteoglycans (Lohmander 1977) although each glycosaminoglycan has a 'slow' and a 'fast' metabolic component (Lohmander, Antonopoulos and Friberg 1973).

4.7. Metabolism of Proteoglycans

The chemical heterogeneity of proteoglycans is reflected in their metabolic heterogeneity. The existence of proteoglycan molecules of different size might suggest that the smaller arise from the larger by partial degradation during normal turnover. The evidence from *in vitro* and *in vivo* studies does not support this idea, however. The *in vitro* studies of Hardingham and Muir (1972b) show no precursor–product relationship between smaller and larger molecules, and the work of Kleine, Heinrich and Goetz (1973, 1974) indicates that in calf rib cartilage there appear to be four unrelated metabolic pools of chondroitin sulphate proteoglycans differing in extractability and chemical composition and that label is not transferred from one pool to another. In guinea-pig rib cartilage labelled *in vivo* there are two major metabolic pools: a fast pool with half-life of 3 days and a slow pool with half-life of 60–70 days. Molecules with fast turnover are enriched in low ionic strength extracts and those of slowest turnover in the cartilage residue. There was no evidence for precursor–product relationships between different fractions (Lohmander 1977), which agrees with the idea of distinct, unrelated classes of proteoglycan (Section 4.4). Another factor which contributes to the metabolic heterogeneity of proteoglycans in human articular cartilage is that the turnover of proteoglycans varies betweem different joints, in different regions of the same joint and at different depths from the articular surface as shown by Maroudas (1975) *in vitro*. Moreover, the relative rates of synthesis of different classes of proteoglycan may not be the same throughout the joint, which introduces a further cause of metabolic heterogeneity. The synthetic activity of individual chondrocytes does not seem to be closely co-ordinated, and may be influenced by the cell's immediate surroundings and location which could affect the diffusion of nutrients and hormones such as somatomedin.

Thus, precise turnover rates are probably of little significance, and discrepancies between the results of different workers might arise from a variety of factors which may be difficult to control or assess (see Chapter 4, Section 5).

4.8. Metabolic Control Mechanisms

The mechanism which controls overall production of proteoglycans and the synthesis of one variety as opposed to another is not understood, and to maintain a steady state the rate of synthesis must equal the loss. The chondrocyte appears to respond to loss of proteoglycans from the matrix by increased synthesis. Such a response has been clearly shown in embryonic cartilage of chick limb-bone rudiments grown in organ culture. When these rudiments are treated with papain (Bosmann 1968) or hyaluronidase (Fitton-Jackson 1970), so that much of the proteoglycan is lost from the matrix, the chondrocytes respond by very rapid synthesis of new matrix constituents. When returned to a normal medium after removing the enzymes, the uronic acid and hexosamine of the matrix are entirely restored within a few days (Hardingham,

Fitton-Jackson and Muir 1972). Since the initial response is dose-dependent (Fitton-Jackson 1970), the cells must possess a sensitive mechanism for assessing the chemical composition of their matrix. The same response occurs *in vivo* in the cartilage of young animals since intravenous papain causes a loss of chondroitin sulphate from cartilage which is subsequently replaced (McCluskey and Thomas 1959).

The small amount of hyaluronic acid in cartilage may function in controlling proteoglycan synthesis as well as in the aggregation of proteoglycans. When present in the medium in concentrations as low as 1×10^{-4} μg/ml, hyaluronic acid reduces proteoglycan synthesis by isolated chondrocytes in suspension cultures. This inhibitory effect is restricted to chondrocytes and is not shown by fibroblasts from synovium or skin (Wiebkin and Muir 1973). Hyaluronic acid affects embryonic chondrocytes in a similar way (Toole 1973; Solursh, Vaerewyck and Reiter 1974). The effect is specific to hyaluronate and its larger oligosaccharides and is not shown by chondroitin (chemically desulphated chondroitin sulphate) which is a close analogue of hyaluronate. Hyaluronic acid already combined with proteoglycan either in the aggregate or in the complex has no effect (Wiebkin *et al.* 1975). Hyaluronic acid binds to the cell surface from which it may be removed by mild trypsin treatment (Wiebkin and Muir 1975), and the effect of hyaluronate is abolished by treatment of the cells with trypsin but not chondroitinase. Together these results suggest that hyaluronate interacts with a component on the cell surface that may be proteoglycan (Wiebkin *et al.* 1975).

Hyaluronic acid has no effect, however, on overall protein synthesis by cultured chondrocytes from embryonic cartilage (Handley and Lowther 1976). It is possible in the presence of β-D-xylosides to divorce chondroitin sulphate synthesis from the synthesis of core protein, with the result that free chondroitin sulphate chains are produced (Section 4.6.1). It is notable that, under these circumstances, hyaluronate does not inhibit chain synthesis, and Handley and Lowther (1976) therefore suggest that hyaluronate may either depress the synthesis of core protein or perhaps repress the activity of the xylosyltransferase which attaches xylose to serine residues on the core protein.

The production of collagen and proteoglycans must somehow be co-ordinated *in vivo*, but over short periods of time *in vitro*, synthesis of the two macromolecules is not closely integrated. When collagen synthesis is arrested in the presence of *aa'*-dipyrridyl (Section 6.1), chondroitin sulphate synthesis is unaffected (Bhatnagar and Prockop 1966). Conversely, when proteoglycan synthesis in cartilage slices is disrupted by the presence of β-D-xylosides, neither collagen synthesis nor the distribution of newly formed collagen is affected (Dondi and Muir 1976).

4.9. Breakdown

During normal turnover, the breakdown of proteoglycans must be brought about by enzymes produced by chondrocytes themselves. The structure of proteoglycans makes them particularly vulnerable to attack by proteolytic enzymes (Figure 3.7). Different proteolytic enzymes reduce the viscosity of proteoglycan solutions to varying degrees (Muir 1958).

Lysosomal proteinases have been extensively investigated in recent years and cathepsins B, D and G and lysosomal elastase are now well characterized. Each is capable of degrading proteoglycans in epiphyseal and articular cartilage and producing fragments of varying size from isolated proteoglycans (Morrison, Barrett, Dingle and Prior 1973; Malemud and Janoff 1975; Keiser, Greenwald, Feinstein and Janoff 1976). Proteinases active at neutral pH, identified in cartilage of human patella, are probably the principal enzymes involved in the normal turnover of proteoglycans (Sapolsky, Howell and Woessner 1974; Sapolsky, Keiser, Howell and Woessner 1976). Pure cathepsin D, which is active at acid pH, has no activity against proteoglycan at pH 7 or above (Woessner 1973).

Hyaluronidase has been identified in synovial tissues and fluids but not in cartilage (Bollet, Bonner and Nance 1963). Hyaluronidase of low pH optimum is also found in lysosomes (Aronson and Davidson 1968) where, in combination with a sulphatase, β-N-acetylhexosaminidase and β-glucuronidase, it must assist in degrading chondroitin sulphate chains to completion (Muir 1973). The absence of partially degraded chondroitin sulphate chains in costal cartilage cultures where partially degraded proteoglycans were identified (Wasteson, Lindahl and Hallén 1972) suggests that hyaluronidase, which has an acid pH optimum, does not participate in extracellular degradation during normal turnover of proteoglycans in cartilage matrix.

Intact proteoglycans are entrapped in the collagen network, but once they are partially degraded they are able to diffuse out of the tissue into the circulation and are removed by the liver and degraded completely (Wood, Wusteman and Curtis 1973). The liver is capable of degrading all the chondroitin sulphate being turned over in the body (Wood *et al.* 1973) and only a small proportion reaches the urine from the circulation as chondroitin sulphate chains (Revell and Muir 1972). Some of the proteoglycan being catabolized may also be taken up by chondrocytes and degraded by lysosomal enzymes. Connective tissue cells are capable of ingesting $^{35}SO_4$-chondroitin sulphate (Saito and Uzman 1971a, b) and experiments with cultures of costal cartilage show that when the chondroitin sulphate moiety of proteoglycans is broken down it is completely degraded with the release of inorganic sulphate (Wasteson *et al.* 1972).

In organ culture the soft tissues of the joint are active in the production of proteinases that destroy the matrix of cartilage, particularly in the presence of immune complexes (Fell and Barratt 1973; Poole, Barratt and Fell 1973). Human polymorphonuclear neutrophils contain two proteinases which act at neutral pH and rapidly release $^{35}SO_4$ from articular cartilage *in vitro* (Malemud and Janoff 1975). The possible role of these and other proteinases in pathological damage to joint tissues has been considered recently (Barrett 1975; Malemud and Janoff 1975). The situation is complicated by the increasing number of proteinases that are being found and by the existence in the tissues of general and specific inhibitors and activators of the various enzymes.

5. COLLAGEN

5.1. Structure

Early to appear in evolution, collagen has retained its essential features in even the most highly evolved animals and there is a striking conservation of amino-acid sequence in the collagen of mammals as different as man and rat (Click and Bornstein 1970). Although the chemical structure of collagen is known in detail from the results of extensive investigations over many years, some of its features are still obscure. Many reviews covering its chemistry and biology are available (see, for example, Harkness 1961, 1966; Harrington and von Hippel 1961; Ramachandran 1967; Kuhn 1969; Traub and Piez 1971; Gallop, Blumenfeld and Seifter 1972; Miller and Matukas 1974; Bornstein 1974; Martin, Byers and Piez 1975; Miller 1976).

Collagen fibrils are composed of aggregates of molecules known as tropocollagen. Tropocollagen consists of three polypeptide chains wound round one another in a super-helix (Figure 3.13).

Figure 3.13 Diagrammatic representation of the collagen triple helix made up of three *a*-chains.

The basic biological unit of collagen, however, is not tropocollagen, the protein in molecular form, but the ordered association of these molecules which form the microfibrils. The ability to form microfibrils is inherent in the structure of the tropocollagen molecule. The most widely accepted view is that the microfibril consists of five tropocollagen molecules (Section 5.2.5). The formation of cross-links between molecules and between the three polypeptide chains after they have been secreted from the cell confers great stability upon the microfibrils. The resulting network, composed of fibrillar cross-linked material, is ideally suited to provide the tissues with tensile strength. This unique structure makes collagen insoluble and resistant to attack by degradative enzymes, and compared with other proteins it is turned over very slowly in adult tissues, except when remodelling takes place during growth and repair.

Table 3.4 Tissue Distribution of Genetic Types of Collagen

Collagen type	Polypeptide chain composition	Tissue distribution	Hydroxylysine content residues/1000	Percentage hydroxylysine glycosylated
I	$[a_1(I)]_2a_2$	Skin, bone, tendon, dentine	6–8	<20
II	$[aII]_3$	Cartilage, intervertebral discs	20–25	50
III	$[aIII]_3$	Synovial membrane, blood vessels, skin	6–8	15–20
IV	$[aIV]_3$	Basement membranes	60–70	80

(Reproduced from Bailey and Robins (1976) by permission.)

Several distinct molecular species or types of collagen have been identified (Miller 1976) (Table 3.4). Cartilage collagen (Miller 1971b) has intermolecular cross-links, as have other types of collagen (Section 5.2.6). The greater degree of glycosylation of hydroxylysine residues (Strawich and Nimni 1971) may be responsible for the distinct morphology of cartilage collagen where the fibres tend to be thinner than in other types of connective tissue. Attachment of carbohydrate to collagen appears to reduce its aggregation properties. Thus basement membrane collagens which are particularly rich in carbohydrate are not fibrillar.

The rod-shaped structure of the tropocollagen molecule, which is about 300 nm in length, is to a large extent explained by the unique amino-acid composition and sequence of its polypeptide chains (Piez 1968). Glycine accounts for one-third of the amino-acids and the unique amino-acid hydroxyproline, together with proline, account for one-quarter. Throughout a large part of the polypeptide chain glycine occurs at every third residue as part of a tripeptide repeating sequence, Gly-Pro-X, where X may be another amino-acid or hydroxyproline. This sequence gives the polypeptide a unique helical structure to which the amino-acids proline and hydroxyproline provide rigidity because their ring structures prevent free rotation of the C—C bonds in the ring. The small glycine residues in every third position enable the three chains to approach closely at these points.

The various types of collagen have polypeptide chains which differ in amino-acid composition and sequence (for reviews see Miller and Matukas 1974; Gallop and Paz 1975). Cyanogen bromide, which cleaves polypeptide chains at methionine residues, gives a distinctive series of peptides from each type of collagen, which may be used to identify or assess their relative proportions in connective tissue. In addition to basement membrane collagen, which is the least well defined, three types of collagen have been conclusively identified in connective tissue and have been termed type I, II and III (Miller, Epstein and Piez 1971), each one having a characteristic distribution in connective tissue (Table 3.4).

Type I collagen is the commonest and most widely distributed of mammalian collagens and occurs in such tissues as bone, tendon and skin. It differs from other types of collagen in that one of the three polypeptide chains, called $a_2(I)$, is different from the other two identical chains called $a_1(I)$, although all three are of the same molecular weight. In contrast, type II collagen, the collagen in human adult articular cartilage, consists of three identical polypeptide chains termed $a_1(II)$ and it is notable that this type of collagen is phenotypic of cartilage. In animals (Miller and Matukas 1969; Trelstad, Kang, Igarashi and Gross 1970; Miller 1971a; Strawich and Nimni 1971; Eyre and Muir 1975) and man (Miller *et al.* 1971; Eyre and Muir 1977) it is found only in cartilage and intervertebral discs (Eyre and Muir 1974, 1976, 1977). It is not, however, present in all cartilaginous tissues: for example, it has not been identified in the semilunar meniscus of the knee (Eyre and Muir 1975, 1977), which is a typical fibrocartilage. Both type I and type II collagen are present in bovine epiphyseal cartilage (Seyer, Brickley and Glimcher 1974a) and in the articular cartilage of birds (Seyer, Brickley and Glimcher 1974b). In human epiphyseal cartilage the presence of some type I collagen in the columnar hypertrophic zone has been shown by immunofluorescence using antisera specific to each type of collagen (Gay, Muller, Lemmen, Remberger, Matzen and Kuhn 1976). Chondrocytes isolated from young rabbit articular cartilage (Layman, Sokoloff and Miller 1972; Cheung, Harvey, Benya and Nimni 1976) or embryonic chick cartilage (Gay *et al.* 1976) begin to lose the ability to synthesize type II collagen after undergoing cell division and forming monolayers whereas slices of articular cartilage continue to synthesize type II collagen during prolonged culture (Cheung *et al.* 1976). The microenvironment of chondrocytes, as well as cell division, also has an influence on the type of collagen synthesized since type II collagen is produced by chick chondrocytes when they are aggregated into nodules even though they have divided. Type I collagen, on the other hand, is seen at the periphery of such cultures where a pseudo-perichondrium forms and the cells resemble fibroblasts in morphology (Gay *et al.* 1976).

There have been contradictory results from different laboratories concerning the type of collagen in osteoarthrotic cartilage. Thus it has been reported that collagen synthesized *in vitro* by old human osteoarthrotic cartilage, removed at operation for total hip replacement, was type I and not the normal type II collagen (Nimni and Deshmukh 1973). On the other hand, in experimental osteoarthrosis in the dog although the synthesis of collagen was considerably increased, the newly formed collagen, labelled *in vivo*, was type II (Eyre, McDevitt and Muir 1975). Moreover, type I collagen could not be identified with certainty in several specimens of human fibrillated osteoarthrotic knee cartilage (Eyre and Muir unpublished results) using the homologous CNBr-peptides a_1(I)CB2 and a_1(II)CB6 to identify type I and type II collagen respectively. The relative proportions of each collagen may be determined in a mixture of these two peptides from amino-acid analyses, since leucine is exclusive to a_1(I)CB2 while valine and aspartic acid are present only in a_1(II)CB6 but not in a_1(I)CB2 (Eyre and Muir 1974, 1977). (However, the presence of a few per cent of type I collagen in cartilage would not be detected by these methods.) Using specific antisera against each type of collagen, the presence of type I collagen has been shown by immunofluorescence in human osteoarthrotic cartilage as fluorescence within and as halos surrounding those chondrocytes that had formed clusters in fibrillated areas (Gay *et al.* 1976). Generalized fluorescence in the matrix of the cartilage due to type I collagen was not seen, and so no major change in the type of collagen in the matrix had occurred.

This confusion may in part be explained by alterations which occur in collagen as tissues age. These changes affect the chromatographic and electrophoretic behaviour of peptides and a-chains. Since collagen molecules normally have a long half-life in adult cartilage (Section 5.2), carbohydrate may adventitiously become attached to collagen over a long period of time. There is evidence that hexoses react via their carbonyl groups with ε-amino groups of lysine and hydroxylysine residues in collagen, with the result that glycosylamine derivatives accumulate appreciably in older cartilage (Robins and Bailey 1972; Tanzer, Fairweather and Gallop 1972; Robins, Shimokomaki and Bailey 1973). The larger peptides produced by cyanogen bromide digestion of old human tissue do not separate as well as do those obtained from digests of young cartilage (Eyre and Muir 1977) so that definite identification of types of collagen is more difficult in old human tissues.

5.2. Synthesis

In normal adult human cartilage, in comparison with other tissues, there appears to be almost no turnover of collagen as compared with other proteins. To assess metabolic turnover of human tissues, ingenious use has been made of the sudden rise in atmospheric ^{14}C in the Northern Hemisphere resulting from tests of nuclear weapons during 1961 and 1962 (Libby, Berger, Mead, Alexander and Ross 1964). The tissues of subjects coming to autopsy who had been exposed to increased levels of ^{14}C were compared with those of subjects living in the Southern Hemisphere where the levels of ^{14}C had not changed. It was found that the collagen in adult cartilage was unlabelled compared with other body proteins. On the other hand, some turnover of the collagen in adult rabbit articular cartilage has been demonstrated (Repo and Mitchell 1971) although in articular cartilage of mature dogs, synthesis of collagen represents only a few per cent of the total synthesis of protein (Eyre *et al.* 1975). From the slow turnover of collagen it appears reasonable to conclude that, like other collagenous tissues, the collagenous framework of cartilage is mainly laid down prior to maturity and normally changes little thereafter. (See also Chapter 4, Section 5.)

Several of the unique processes involved in collagen synthesis are now fairly well understood, mostly as a result of studies using chick embryo cartilage which is a rich source of the enzymes involved in collagen synthesis. These are: the synthesis of the amino-acids of hydroxyproline and hydroxylysine which are unique to collagen, the method by which the molecules are arranged in the fibril, and the mode of formation of the cross-links (Table 3.5). On the other hand, the mechanism by which collagen is exported from the cell and laid down in the tissues in ordered structures is still obscure, although proteoglycans play some part in this process (Section 6).

5.2.1. The Polypeptide Chain. The three polypeptides are formed independently as complete chains and not by the assembly of subunits (Vuust and Piez 1970, 1972) and are translated simultaneously by the normal processes of protein synthesis (Fessler, Morris and Fessler 1975) (Table 3.5).

The molecule of newly formed collagen (tropocollagen) consisting of three polypeptide chains (*a*-chains) is not secreted as such from the cell but in the form of a soluble precursor. Evidence from a number of different laboratories using tissue culture systems has shown that the newly secreted collagen is larger than tropocollagen (Bellamy and Bornstein 1971; Church, Pfiefer and Tanzer 1971; Layman, McGoodwin and Martin 1971). The collagen

187

Table 3.5 Sequence of events in collagen biosynthesis and fibre formation

Event	Known requirement
Translation of three pro-a-chains simultaneously	Ribosome apparatus
Hydroxylation of some proline and lysine residues (hydroxylation of proline necessary for triple helical conformation)	Two enzymes + O_2 Fe^{2+} ascorbic acid a-oxoglutarate
Glycosylation of hydroxylysine	Specific galactosyl- and glucosyltransferases + galactose and glucose
Detachment from ribosomes. Formation of interchain disulphide bonds. Removal of NH-terminal extension peptides (during export from cell)	Procollagen peptidase
Removal one at a time of COOH-terminal extension peptides containing S–S bonds to form tropocollagen (does not occur if collagen underhydroxylated)	Other specific peptidases
Intramolecular cross-links	Amine oxidase + Cu^{2+}
Aggregation of five tropocollagen molecules to form microfibril (nucleation phase)	Spontaneous at 37°C, probably modulated by proteoglycans
Fibrillogenesis: (a) Linear growth of microfibril by addition of tropocollagen molecules (precipitation phase) (b) Lateral growth by association of microfibrils to produce collagen fibre	Spontaneous at 37°C and perhaps modulated by proteoglycans
Intermolecular cross-links develop when microfibrils are formed and during and after fibrillogenesis (cross-links initially reducible with borohydride)	Amine oxidase + Cu^{2+}
Linking of fibres to form collagen network	Perhaps by interaction with proteoglycans and glycoproteins

precursor contains cysteine (absent from tropocollagen) and is stabilized by interchain disulphide bonds (Burgeson, Wyke and Fessler 1972; Dehm, Jimenez, Olsen and Prockop 1972). Its conversion to tropocollagen is time-dependent (Bellamy and Bornstein 1971). It was originally thought that the peptide containing cysteine was an extension at the NH_2-terminal end, which could be cleaved by the action of pepsin (Dehm *et al.* 1972) and converted to tropocollagen. The removal of the extension peptide *in vivo* was thought to be brought about by an extracellular peptidase known as procollagen peptidase which was specific for collagen precursors. Evidence for this was obtained from a study of an inherited disorder in cattle known as dermatosparaxis, which is characterized by an extreme fragility of the skin. The collagen fibres are poorly organized and electron micrographs show that normal fibres are not formed (O'Hara, Read, Romane and Bridges 1970). The collagen in the tissues of affected animals resembles the collagen precursor isolated from tissue cultures (Lapière, Lenaers and Kohn 1971). In the last few years, considerable confusion has surrounded the structure of the collagen precursor and how it may be converted to collagen.

This confusion is now largely resolved, since it has been realized that the conflicting results of different laboratories arose because of endogenous proteases in the culture systems which were breaking down the collagen precursor to varying degrees. When the isolation and purification was carried out in the presence of a number of protease inhibitors, a much larger collagen precursor was isolated which had extensions at both ends of the helical collagen chain. The disulphide bonded region was located, not in the NH-terminal peptide, as previously supposed, but in the COOH-terminal peptide (Byers, Click, Harper and Bornstein 1975; Fessler *et al.* 1975; Davidson, McEneary and Bornstein 1975; Monson, Click and Bornstein 1975; Murphy, von der Mark, McEneary and Bornstein 1975). This had already been suggested by Tanzer and co-workers (1974) who found several intermediate forms of the collagen precursor produced by a cloned cell line from dermatosparaxic calves which had peptide extensions at both ends of the collagen molecule. The current view of procollagen is that it is considerably larger than tropocollagen in that the extension peptide at the NH-terminal end has 200 residues and at the COOH-terminal end 340 residues, so that the precursor chains each have molecular weights of 150 000, compared with 100 000 for tropocollagen. The extension peptides contain no hydroxyproline or hydroxylysine and have amino-acid compositions quite different from that of tropocollagen itself. Moreover, each extension peptide is immunologically distinct from the other and from tropocollagen (Murphy *et al.* 1975; Nist, von der Mark, Hay, Olsen, Bornstein, Ross and Dehm 1975). To establish the interrelationship of the peptides and how they are synthesized, ingenious use has been made of tadpole collagenase which cleaves at one position all three a-chains of the collagen molecule into two unequal pieces (Fessler *et al.* 1975; Byers *et al.* 1975). Pulse label experiments showed that three procollagen a-chains are translated simultaneously, the whole process taking about 5.3 min (Fessler *et al.* 1975). The formation of the disulphide bonds take place after pro-a-chains are completed and detached from ribosomes (Harwood, Bhalla, Grant and Jackson 1975) and occurs whether or not the pro-a-chains are hydroxylated (Fessler and Fessler 1974).

The conversion of procollagen to tropocollagen appears to take place in a number of steps, the first being the removal of the NH-terminal extension peptides which takes place when procollagen is exported from the cell (Morris, Fessler, Weinstock and Fessler 1975). This is followed by cleavage, one at a time, of the COOH-terminal extension peptides which are attached to each other by disulphide bridges (Davidson *et al.* 1975). Underhydroxylated procollagen is not cleaved to collagen, however, until hydroxylation is restored in the presence of ferrous iron (Fe^{2+}) (Fessler and Fessler 1974). At least two and perhaps several enzymes are needed for these conversions, one of which is procollagen peptidase which cleaves the NH-terminal peptide only (Table 3.5). It is not active against the COOH-terminal peptide (Davidson *et al.* 1975). In dermatosparaxic cattle which lack procollagen peptidase (Lenaers, Ansay, Nusgens and Lapière 1971), the procollagen retains the NH-terminal peptides but not the COOH-terminal peptides and therefore lacks the disulphide bonds (Kohn, Isersky, Zupnick, Lenaers, Lee and Lapière 1974).

The majority of these studies have been made on type I collagen produced by cultures of embryonic bone. Very similar extension peptides attached at the NH-terminal and COOH-terminal ends of type II procollagen have, however, been identified using cultures of embryonic chick cartilage (Fessler *et al.* 1975; Olsen, Hoffman and Prockop 1976).

The metabolic fate of the extension peptides, which are of considerable size, is unknown. The procollagen with the COOH-extension peptides has a relatively prolonged existence and disulphide bridges may play some role in fibre formation by conferring stability upon the molecule (Fessler *et al.* 1975) which does not aggregate spontaneously as does tropocollagen. It has been suggested that procollagen peptides may exert some feedback control on collagen synthesis, as human fibroblasts deficient in procollagen peptidase produced excessive amounts of collagen (Lichtenstein, Martin, Kohn, Byers and McKusick 1973). That one-third of such a large precursor molecule should merely be discarded seems unduly wasteful in view of the early evolution of collagen. It may reflect a common evolutionary origin with some other essential protein, or the extension peptides may have an essential and perhaps independent function that is not yet known.

5.2.2. The Hydroxylation of Proline. From the work particularly of Prockop and his co-workers, the hydroxylation of proline in collagen is now well understood (for reviews see Rosenbloom and Prockop 1969; Prockop 1969, 1970). The reaction requires molecular oxygen, ferrous iron, a-oxoglutarate and ascorbic acid. A form of collagen called protocollagen which lacks hydroxyproline may be produced if oxygen is absent or if the ferrous iron is chelated with aa'-dipyrridyl (Table 3.5). The enzyme bringing about the reaction has been partially purified from chick embryo cartilage and shown to hydroxylate synthetic polypeptides with the structure (Pro-Gly-Pro)$_3$ as well as protocollagen itself (Kivirikko and Prockop 1967b).

Synthetic polypeptides have been used to study the characteristics of this enzyme. It does not act on the tripeptide Pro-Gly-Pro, but becomes progressively more active when polytripeptides of increasing molecular weight up to 4000 are used as substrates (Kivirikko and Prockop 1967a). The proline residues in the second position after glycine, which is where hydroxyproline occurs in collagen, are preferentially hydroxylated (Kivirikko and Prockop 1967a). Not all prolines in this position become hydroxylated, however, because the affinity of the enzyme for the substrate decreases as hydroxylation proceeds (Juva and Prockop 1969) and so a strictly homogeneous product never results from this process (Bornstein 1967; Butler 1970). The reaction takes place while nascent chains are still attached to ribosomes (Harwood *et al.* 1975) and also when the polypeptides have been released from the ribosomes (Bhatnagar, Rosenbloom, Kivirikko and Prockop 1967). The triple-stranded conformation of collagen is not necessary for activity (Kivirikko, Bright and Prockop 1968), indeed hydroxylation requires the peptides to be in the non-helical configuration and the enzyme is inhibited by poly-L-proline of the same helical conformation as the polypeptide chains of collagen. By using polyprolines of different molecular weights it has been concluded that the inhibition site on the enzyme can accommodate 150–200 prolyl residues (Prockop and Kivirikko 1969). If hydroxylation is prevented, the resulting protein, known as protocollagen, accumulates within the cell (Bhatnagar, Kivirikko and Prockop 1968) and the extension peptides are not cleaved (Fessler and Fessler 1974).

5.2.3. The Hydroxylation of Lysine. Some of the lysines in collagen are also hydroxylated. This reaction needs the same co-factors as the hydroxylation of proline but appears to be performed by a different enzyme (Weinstein, Blumenkrantz and Prockop 1969) although lysine and proline are hydroxylated in parallel (Rosenbloom and Prockop 1969; Harwood *et al.* 1975) (Table 3.5). The number of hydroxylysine residues in collagen is to some extent variable (Bornstein 1967; Miller *et al.* 1969; Butler 1970), just as is the number of hydroxyproline residues, and is higher in cartilage collagen than in collagen from skin (Miller *et al.* 1969; Steven, Broady and Jackson 1969; Strawich and Nimni 1971).

5.2.4. Glycosylation. Many of the hydroxylysine residues of cartilage collagen have a disaccharide, glucosyl-galactose, attached to the hydroxyl group (Butler and Cunningham 1966; Spiro 1969). It has been suggested that attachment of carbohydrate may be necessary for extrusion of procollagen from the cell (Bosmann and Eylar 1968), which might explain why protocollagen accumulates within the cell when hydroxylation is prevented (Bhatnagar *et al.* 1968). Uitto and Prockop (1974) have suggested, however, that the formation of the triple helical conformation (which requires a minimal level of hydroxylation of proline) is a prerequisite for the secretion of the molecule at an optimal rate. Separate enzymes transfer galactose and glucose, both of which are specific for the glycosylation of collagen (Bosmann and Eylar 1968; Hagopian, Bosmann and Eylar 1968) (Table 3.5), but the degree of glycosylation is not uniform. In pulse label experiments with chick embryo cartilage *in vitro*, Blumenkrantz, Rosenbloom and Prockop (1969) showed that the formation of hydroxylysine and the attachment of the sugars were discrete sequential steps, the transfer of galactose preceding the transfer of glucose. The proportion glucosyl-galactosyl-hydroxylysine to galactosyl-hydroxylysine was different at different stages of development of chick embryo cartilage. Since the ratio was reduced by a number of hormones, including thyroid and growth hormone (Blumenkrantz and Prockop 1970), biological conditions appear to influence the carbohydrate heterogeneity of collagen.

5.2.5. The Formation of Fibrils. The assembly of the polypeptide chains of tropocollagen to form a triple helix takes place spontaneously because of the unique tripeptide repeating sequence of much of the polypeptide chains (Section 4.1) but for this to happen the hydroxylation of proline has to reach a critical level (Jimenez, Harsch and Rosenbloom 1973; Uitto and Prockop 1974).

Until the non-helical extension peptides are cleaved, the chains do not aggregate spontaneously and hence the precursor forms of collagen may be transport forms of the protein (Layman *et al.* 1971; Jimenez, Dehm and Prockop 1971) which allow it to move away from the cell before aggregating into fibrils. Normal animal tissues, including cartilage, contain the specific peptidases that remove the extension peptides, whereas in dermatosparaxic cattle procollagen peptidase is absent from affected tissues and in these normal fibres are not formed (O'Hara *et al.* 1970). Thus, the disease results from an enzyme deficiency rather than from a fault in the synthesis of the polypeptide chain of collagen itself (Lapière *et al.* 1971). A similar enzyme deficiency has recently been identified in sheep (Becker, Timpl, Helle and Prockop 1976).

The ability to form fibrils is an inherent property of tropocollagen, although at 4°C and at physiological pH and ionic strength it remains soluble. When warmed to 37°C, however, tropocollagen aggregates into normal banded fibrils. The formation of fibrils takes place in two phases (Table 3.5). In the first, nucleation phase individual molecules aggregate to form the five-stranded microfibril. Once this has taken place, linear growth can proceed in the second phase by the addition of single molecules. Lateral growth is more likely to involve the association of formed microfibrils. This two-phase process allows fibril length and diameter to be controlled independently (Piez 1975) and modulated to different degrees by interactions with proteoglycans.

In normal collagen fibres the tropocollagen molecules face the same way, their side-to-side aggregation being staggered by a quarter of the length of each molecule (Figure 3.14). This

Figure 3.14 Diagrammatic representation of the arrangement of molecules in fibrillar collagen, showing overlap by a quarter the length of each molecule and the position of predominant cross-links. Non-helical regions shown by zig-zag lines at each end.

arrangement explains the characteristic banded pattern, repeated every 64 nm (640 Å), of collagen fibrils viewed in the electron microscope. Various models depicting how the molecules are arranged in the collagen microfibril have been proposed. The five-stranded model originally proposed by Smith (1968) (Figure 3.15) is most widely accepted and is consistent with x-ray diffrac-

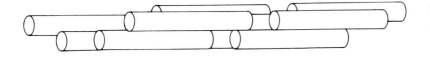

Figure 3.15 Three-dimensional diagrammatic representation of the assembly of five tropocollagen molecules in the microfibril as proposed by Smith (1968).

tion and electron optical studies (reviewed by Piez and Miller 1974). From amino-acid sequence analysis of $a_1(I)$ chains (which have a considerable degree of homology with $a_1(II)$ chains) an axial quarter stagger arrangement of five molecules in the microfibril provides the maximum interaction between polar groups and between hydrophobic groups on adjacent molecules (Fietzek and Kuhn 1975).

There are three levels of coiling in such a five-stranded microfibril: at the first level individual polypeptide chains are coiled in a left-handed helix; at the second level the three polypeptide chains are coiled round each other to form the tropocollagen molecule in a right-handed super-helix; at the third level the five tropocollagen molecules which form the microfibril are assumed to be twisted together in a left-handed super-coil. This structure with three levels of coiling in alternate left- and right-handed directions is analogous to that of a rope in which the lateral compressive forces that develop when it is pulled prevent the strands from slipping past each other (Piez 1975).

Different molecular arrangements may be produced artificially *in vitro*, as for example where the molecules are arranged side-by-side in parallel. This form, known as segment long-spacing or SLS collagen, has been extremely useful in elucidating by electron microscopy the point of attack of degradative enzymes such as animal collagenase (Section 5.3).

5.2.6. The Formation of Cross-links. Once deposited as fibrils, collagen undergoes a slow maturation and becomes increasingly insoluble, as cross-links are formed first at intramolecular level between the three polypeptides and then between the molecules themselves.

The chemistry of these cross-links, which vary in the two situations and in the manner of their formation, has been studied extensively. The results, which have been reviewed recently (Bailey and Robins 1973; Bailey, Robins and Balian 1974), show that cross-links involve the formation of aldehydes by the oxidative deamination of ε-amino groups of lysine and hydroxylysine residues brought about by the action of a monoamine oxidase. The resulting aldehydes may then react with unchanged ε-amino groups of lysine or hydroxylysine on neighbouring molecules to form Schiff bases (Figures 3.16 and 3.17) or with themselves to form aldol condensation products (although these appear to be restricted to the intramolecular cross-links between the polypeptide chains of tropocollagen itself).

Both reaction products are chemically unstable and appear to be intermediates in the formation of stable cross-links. Their proportion is therefore highest in newly formed collagen laid down during growth or in wound-healing tissue. With increasing age, as collagen matures, unstable cross-links are replaced by stable ones whose nature has yet to be elucidated. The unstable cross-links may be converted into stable derivatives *in vitro* by reduction with

Figure 3.16 Cross-link derived from lysine residues.

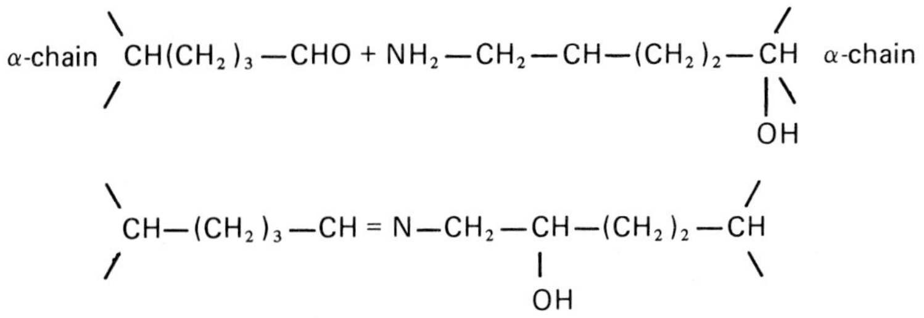

$$\text{\textbackslash}$$

α-chain $CH(CH_2)_3-CHO + NH_2-CH_2-CH-(CH_2)_2-CH$ α-chain

$$CH-(CH_2)_3-CH = N-CH_2-CH-(CH_2)_2-CH$$

Figure 3.17 Cross-link derived from hydroxylysine residues and subsequent Amadori rearrangement.

α-chain $CH-(CH_2)_2-CH-CHO + NH_2-CH_2-CH-(CH_2)_2-CH$ α-chain
$$\qquad\qquad\quad OH \qquad\qquad\qquad\quad OH$$

$$CH-(CH_2)_2-CH-CH = N-CH_2-CH-(CH_2)_2-CH$$
$$\qquad\qquad\quad OH$$

$$CH-(CH_2)_2-C-CH_2-NH-CH_2-CH-(CH_2)_2-CH$$
$$\qquad\qquad\qquad\| \qquad\qquad\qquad\quad OH$$
$$\qquad\qquad\qquad O$$

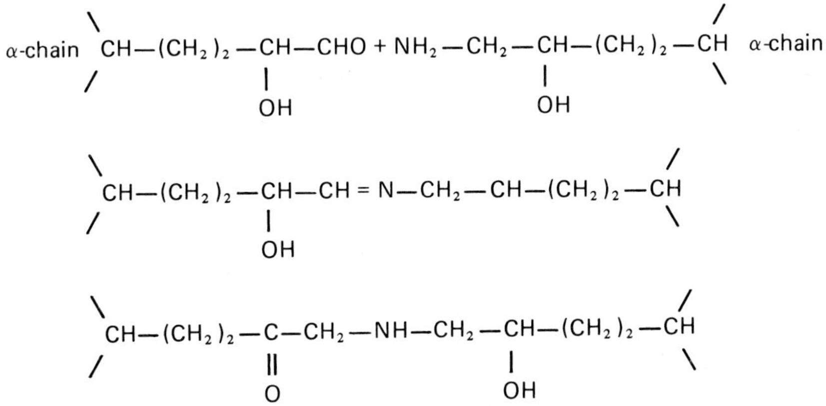

borohydride but there is no reliable evidence that the unstable cross-links become reduced *in vivo* on conversion to stable cross-links.

The chemical structures of the intermediate cross-links have been inferred from the products isolated after borohydride reduction and acid hydrolysis of collagen. In cartilage collagen (type II) the predominant cross-links are formed by the interaction of the aldehyde derived from hydroxylysine with another unchanged hydroxylysine on a neighbouring molecule (Davis and Bailey 1971; Miller 1971b). In this case, however, the reaction product is more stable than a Schiff's base, because it spontaneously undergoes the Amadori rearrangement to a more stable keto derivative (Figure 3.17) (Robins *et al.* 1973) and it may be isolated directly without borohydride reduction (Miller and Robertson 1973), which confirms that Schiff's bases actually exist *in vivo*.

In the microfibril tropocollagen molecules are arranged head-to-tail, but overlapping by a quarter of the length of each molecule

(Figure 3.14). Intermolecular cross-links should therefore be formed between the NH_2- and COOH-terminal ends of adjacent molecules. A cross-linked peptide of such a kind has been isolated by Miller (Miller 1971b; Miller and Robertson 1973) from chick cartilage collagen after CNBr cleavage and borohydride reduction.

The amine oxidase that brings about the oxidative deamination of the ε-amino groups of lysine and hydroxylysine is a copper-dependent enzyme which has been isolated and partially purified from embryonic chick cartilage (Siegel, Pinnell and Martin 1970). The enzyme is more active on reconstituted collagen fibrils than on soluble collagen (Siegel 1974). It is inactivated by β-aminopropionitrile (BAPN) which binds irreversibly to the enzyme (Narayanan, Siegel and Martin 1972). The characteristics of the enzyme explain the similarities between copper deficiency and experimental lathyrism produced by BAPN, a condition in which newly formed collagen is abnormally soluble (Levene and Gross 1959) because cross-links are not formed (Martin, Gross, Piez and Lewis 1961). The amine oxidase in plasma also requires copper as co-factor but it has no action on tropocollagen.

5.3. Degradation

There is little change in the composition of articular cartilage after skeletal maturity is reached (see Section 2.3) and little turnover of collagen once growth and remodelling have ceased.

The resistance of collagen to most proteolytic enzymes at physiological pH, presumably due to the highly ordered and compact structure of tropocollagen and the microfibril, is lost when collagen is denatured by heating. At body temperature, however, the process whereby collagen is resorbed during the normal remodelling of connective tissue, or is destroyed in pathological conditions, needs explanation. Gross and Lapière (1962) showed that, during metamorphosis of the tadpole when the tail is being rapidly resorbed, an enzyme is released which can attack native mammalian tropocollagen fibrils *in vitro*. All three chains of the triple helix are attacked simultaneously, breaking the molecules into two unequal pieces (Figure 3.18), one-quarter and three-quarters the length of the original as shown in electron micrographs of segment long-spacing fibrils (SLS) (Gross and Nagai 1965). The effect of the enzyme on collagen is to lower the denaturation temperature so that denaturation proceeds spontaneously at body temperature, thus rendering the collagen susceptible to ordinary proteolysis. This enzyme has since been identified in mammalian connective tissue undergoing resorption (Perez-Tamayo 1970), in the involuting uterus (Jeffrey and Gross 1970) and in wound-healing tissue (Grillo and Gross 1967) as well as in a variety of normal and pathological human tissues (reviewed

Figure 3.18 Site of cleavage of collagen
molecule by animal collagenase.

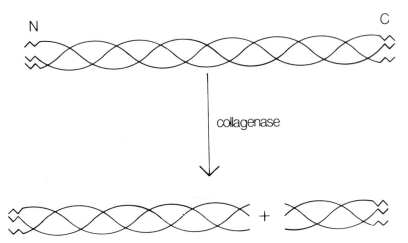

by Harris and Krane 1974a, b, c; Harris and Cartwright 1977).
Collagenase is released into the medium by cultures of rheumatoid
synovium (Evanson, Jeffrey and Krane 1968; Lazarus, Decker,
Oliver, Daniels, Multz and Fullmer 1968). The enzyme, which has
a molecular weight of 33 000, is dependent on calcium and is
active over a wide range of pH from 5 to 9.5, with an optimum at
pH 8–8.5 (Woolley, Glanville, Crossley and Evanson 1975). It
cleaves types I, II and III collagens in solution into quarter and
three-quarter length fragments, but type II collagen of cartilage is
much more resistant than the other types of collagen (Woolley,
Lindberg, Glanville and Evanson 1975a). Collagen in intact
cartilage is also attacked (Woolley, Lindberg, Glanville and Evanson 1975b) and cartilage proteoglycans do not inhibit the enzyme
(Woolley and Evanson 1977a).

There are two proteins in serum that are potent inhibitors of
collagenase: a_2-macroglobulin which is a general inhibitor of
proteinases, and a β_1-protein of molecular weight 40 000 which is a
specific inhibitor of collagenase (Woolley, Roberts and Evanson
1976) and may therefore play a special part in controlling collagenase activity (Woolley, Roberts and Evanson 1975). Latent
collagenase in culture media of rabbit tissues and cells appears to
be an enzyme-inhibitor complex (Sellers, Cartwright, Murphy and
Reynolds 1977).

Partly owing to the presence of these inhibitors, it has been
difficult to establish the precise role of collagenase in collagen
catabolism. To enable immunochemical methods to be used,
Woolley, Crossley and Evanson (1976) have recently prepared
and characterized a highly specific antibody to rheumatoid syno-

vial collagenase. Using this antibody, the collagenases from various human tissues were found to be immunologically identical, whereas the collagenase of granulocytes (Lazarus, Daniels, Brown Bladen and Fullmer 1968) did not react with the antibody. When enzyme activity was inhibited by the protein inhibitors, the antigenicity of the enzyme was masked, and, conversely, reaction with antibody inhibited enzyme activity (Woolley, Crossley and Evanson 1976). Using immunofluorescence with rheumatoid tissue, collagenase was detected at the cartilage–pannus junction and in contiguous regions of the matrix. No fluorescence was detected, however, within chondrocytes or in the matrix farther from the pannus (Woolley and Evanson 1977b). It is suggested that the local imbalance between the production of active enzyme and of specific inhibitors leads to the erosion of cartilage in the rheumatoid joint (Woolley and Evanson 1977b). However, neither the hydroxyproline content nor the extractability of collagen is affected in osteoarthrosis (Bollet, Handy and Sturgill 1963; Anderson *et al.* 1964; Miller *et al.* 1969), suggesting that there is no degradation of mature collagen until late in degenerative joint disease when erosion of cartilage begins. Nevertheless, in experimentally induced osteoarthrosis there is an increased turnover (Repo and Mitchell 1971) and synthesis of collagen (Eyre *et al.* 1975), suggesting that some collagen breakdown and resynthesis is taking place.

6. THE INTERACTION OF PROTEOGLYCANS AND COLLAGEN

There is experimental evidence to suggest that proteoglycans and collagen in cartilage are biologically as well as mechanically interdependent. Thus, proteoglycans may affect fibril formation and stability, and there is evidence that some proteoglycans are closely associated with mature collagen and resist extraction (Section 4.4.3) and hence that they may form an important part of the collagen network in cartilage.

6.1. The Effect of Proteoglycans upon Collagen Synthesis

It might appear that collagen and glycosaminoglycan synthesis are closely interdependent because both syntheses are inhibited to the same extent and at the same time in chick embryo cartilage *in ovo* by hydrocortisone (Ebert and Prockop 1963). Bhatnagar and Prockop (1966) have shown, however, that each synthesis can be separately inhibited in chick cartilage *in vitro* over a short period of time (1–2 hours). Thus in the presence of aa'-dipyrridyl, collagen synthesis is arrested but glycosaminoglycan synthesis proceeds normally. In contrast, in the presence of a glutamine analogue, 6-diazo-5-oxonorleucine (DON), glycosaminoglycan synthesis is inhibited, but collagen synthesis proceeds normally and the subsequent extrusion of collagen from the cells is unaffected as shown by autoradiography. Similarly in adult pig cartilage *in vitro* the synthesis of collagen and proteoglycans are not closely interrelated processes, since interference with one does not affect the other over a period of 20 hours (Doni and Muir 1976) (Sections 4.6.1 and 4.8). Over somewhat longer periods of time, however, inhibition of glycosaminoglycan synthesis was noted when collagen synthesis was inhibited by *aa'*-dipyrridyl (Rokosova-Cmuchalova and Bentley 1968).

6.2. The Effect of Proteoglycans upon Collagen Fibril Formation

The interaction of collagen and proteoglycans is functionally of great importance, but the way in which they interact is not well understood, although it depends mainly on electrostatic interactions (reviewed by Muir and Hardingham 1975). In general, interaction increases with the charge density and chain length of the glycosaminoglycan, whether interaction is examined by light scattering methods (Obrink 1973a) or by agglutination of collagen-coated red cells (Conochie, Scott and Page-Faulk 1975). Keratan sulphate, however, shows virtually no interaction in either system. The interaction of chondroitin 4-sulphate with tropocollagen (lathyritic) attached to Sepharose has been studied by Obrink, Laurent and Carlsson (1975). The binding which decreased with increasing ionic strength was still appreciable at physiological ionic strength and pH. Each collagen molecule appeared to have at least three binding sites, one being much weaker than the other two.

The formation of fibrils is an inherent property of tropocollagen and is a two-phase process (Section 5.2.5). By adding glycosaminoglycans or proteoglycans before or after the nucleation phase, their influence on each phase may be studied. Proteoglycans that interact with collagen tend to accelerate fibril formation when present during the nucleation phase. On the other hand, cartilage proteoglycans delay fibril formation when added during the phase of linear growth (Obrink 1973b). Proteoglycan aggregates have little influence on fibril formation, however (Lowther and Natarajan 1972), so that the aggregation of proteoglycans may reduce or modulate their influence on fibril formation. Toole and Lowther (1968) have suggested that the proteoglycans secreted in the same vicinity as newly formed collagen may control the diameter and perhaps the orientation of collagen fibrils. It is possible that different proteoglycans in the matrix may affect fibril formation differently and give rise to fibres of varying morphology. This possibility is particularly interesting when the molecular organization of cartilage is considered. The fibres near the surface are more closely packed and of finer diameter than those in the deeper part of cartilage and their thickness increases with depth (Maroudas and Bullough 1968; Weiss, Rosenberg and Helfet 1968; Muir *et al.* 1970). The orientation of the fibres also changes through the matrix (Chapter 1, Section 2.5). At the same time the composition of the proteoglycans changes gradually with depth from the articular surface. This may influence fibre thickness as the proportion of keratan sulphate relative to chondroitin sulphate increases with depth (Maroudas *et al.* 1969; Kempson *et al.* 1973). Chondroitin sulphate, but not keratan sulphate, interacts with collagen (Obrink 1973a; Conochie *et al.* 1975) and hence the strength of interaction of proteoglycans with collagen should vary inversely with keratan sulphate content and this in turn could affect fibre morphology.

During development there appears to be considerable reorganization of collagen at the fibrillar level. Using electron microscopy, Silberberg, Silberberg, Vogel and Wellstein (1961) showed that in the articular cartilage of mice, thin fibrils of 10 nm were present at birth which disappeared by 6 months of age, while in adult cartilage the most abundant fibres were 60–70 nm in diameter. The formation of thicker collagen fibres may result from changes in the composition of the proteoglycan during development. Thus, the keratan sulphate content of the proteoglycans in fetal pig articular cartilage is very low, but increases rapidly during the first few months after birth (Simunek and Muir 1972a). That proteoglycans at different stages of development vary in their interaction with collagen has been shown by Toole and Linsenmayer (1975) using chick embryos. Proteoglycans obtained from limb buds of embryos at the stage when cartilage formation is well advanced interact with collagen to the greatest extent.

In the majority of interaction experiments soluble skin collagen has been used, because it is difficult to obtain soluble collagen from other tissues. However, viscosity studies indicate that there are differences in the way that cartilage proteoglycan interacts with type I collagen of skin and type II collagen of cartilage (Ananthanarayanan and Nimni 1975). It is also realized that to avoid complications due to the presence of even a few cross-links in soluble collagen, collagen from lathyritic animals which has no cross-links should be used in interaction experiments (Obrink 1973b).

6.3. The Effect of Proteoglycans upon Collagen Fibril Stability

It is likely that the thermal stability of soluble collagen *in vivo* before it is laid down as fibrils is increased by interaction with proteoglycans. Thus, in the presence of chondroitin sulphate the melting temperature of soluble collagen rises from 38°C to 46°C (Gelman and Blackwell 1973). Reconstituted collagen fibrils become progressively less soluble as the concentration of proteoglycans is raised (Toole 1969). Compared with the collagens of other tissues, cartilage collagen is more resistant to thermal denaturation (Curtiss and Klein 1963) and to dissolution even in strongly denaturing solutions such as 5 mol/litre (5M) guanidine hydrochloride, 2 mol/litre (2M) CaCl$_2$ or 6 mol/litre (6M) urea (Miller *et al.* 1969; Strawich and Nimni 1971). Both characteristics may depend upon proteoglycan interactions. On the other hand, the intermolecular cross-links of collagen may also contribute to its insolubility, but, against this view, these cross-links increase with age (Section 5.2.6) and yet immature cartilage collagen is only slightly more soluble than the collagen of mature cartilage (Lust, Pronsky and Sherman 1972).

Electron optical studies of cartilage by Smith and his colleagues using bismuth nitrate to visualize proteoglycans, suggest that the complex resulting from the interaction of collagen and proteoglycan is an ordered structure (Serafini-Fracassini and Smith 1966; Smith, Peters and Serafini-Fracassini 1967; Smith 1968; Serafini-Fracassini, Wells and Smith 1970). Proteoglycans are revealed as a line of dots orientated at right angles to the fibre axis, each dot representing a glycosaminoglycan chain. The line of dots was spaced at regular intervals, apparently related to the banding of fibres as shown by conventional phosphotungstic acid staining. This suggests that only certain regions of the collagen fibril take part in the interaction with proteoglycan, in agreement with the presence of three binding sites for chondroitin sulphate on the collagen molecule (Obrink *et al.* 1975).

A minority of the proteoglycan in cartilage appears to be more firmly associated with collagen than the remainder and resists extraction with even strongly dissociating solutions (Section 4.4.3). This fraction may be the proteoglycan which is attached at the postulated sites of high affinity on the collagen fibre. The inextractable proteoglycan fraction which appears to belong to a separate metabolic pool (Hardingham and Muir 1972b; Lohmander 1977) may act as a bonding agent between collagen fibrils, spanning distances between fibrils that would be too great for cross-links to develop. The decreasing tensile fatigue strength of human articular cartilage with increasing age (Weightman 1976) might be due to a gradual reduction in the number of sites of high affinity on the long-lived collagen fibre. The basic groups of collagen which interact with the negative groups of proteoglycans are principally the ε-amino groups of lysine and hydroxylysine. These slowly react with hexoses (Robins and Bailey 1972; Robins *et al.* 1973; Tanzer, Fairweather and Gallop 1972) (Section 4.1) and lose their basic character in older cartilage.

REFERENCES

Abbott J. and Holtzer H. (1968) The loss of phenotypic traits by differentiated cells. V. The effect of 5-bromodeoxyuridine on cloned chondrocytes. *Proc. natn. Acad. Sci. U.S.* **59**, 1144.

Ananthanarayanan S. and Nimni M. E. (1975) Collagen of rat skin and bovine articular cartilage: their hydrodynamic properties during interactions with proteoglycans. *Extracellular Matrix Influences on Gene Expression*, Ed. by H. C. Slavkin and R. C. Greulich, p. 311. Academic Press, New York.

Anderson B., Hoffman P. and Meyer K. (1965) The O-serine linkage in peptides of chondroitin 4- or 6-sulfates. *J. biol. Chem.* **240**, 156.

Anderson C. E., Ludowieg J., Harper H. A. and Engleman E. P. (1964) The composition of the organic component of human articular cartilage. *J. Bone Jt Surg.* **46A**, 1176.

Antonopoulos C. A., Gardell J., Szirmai J. A. and de Tyssonsk E. R. (1964) Determination of glycosaminoglycans (mucopolysaccharides) from tissues on the microgram scale. *Biochim. biophys. Acta* **83**, 1.

Aronson N. N. and Davidson E. A. (1968) Catabolism of mucopolysaccharides by rat liver lysosomes *in vivo. J. biol. Chem.* **243**, 4494.

Atkins E. D. T. (1977) Molecular architecture of the animal and some microbial extracellular polysaccharides. *First Cleveland Symposium on Macromolecules*, Ed. by A. G. Walton. Elsevier, Amsterdam.

Bailey A. J. and Robins S. P. (1973) Development and maturation of the cross-links in the collagen fibres of skin. *Front. Matrix Biol.* **1**, 130.

Bailey A. J. and Robins S. P. (1976) Current topics in the biosynthesis, structure and function of collagen. *Sci. Prog. (Oxf.)* **63**, 419.

Bailey A. J., Robins S. P. and Balian G. (1974) Biological significance of the intermolecular cross-links of collagen. *Nature (Lond.)* **251**, 105.

Baker J. R., Rodén L. and Stoolmiller A. C. (1972) Biosynthesis of chondroitin sulfate proteoglycan. Xylosyl transfer to Smith-degraded cartilage proteoglycan and other exogenous acceptors. *J. biol. Chem.* **247**, 3838.

Barrett A. J. (1975) The enzymic degradation of cartilage matrix. *Dynamics of Connective Tissue Macromolecules*, Ed. by P. M. C. Burleigh and A. R. Poole, p. 189. North-Holland Publ., Amsterdam.

Baxter E. and Muir H. (1972) The antigenicity of cartilage proteoglycans: the relationship of the antigenic determinants present in Smith-degraded and intact proteoglycans. *Biochim. biophys. Acta* **279**, 276.

Becker U., Timpl R., Helle O. and Prockop D. J. (1976) NH₂-terminal extensions on skin collagen from sheep with a genetic defect in conversion of procollagen into collagen. *Biochemistry* **15**, 2853.

Bellamy G. and Bornstein P. (1971) Evidence for procollagen, a biosynthetic precursor of collagen. *Proc. natn. Acad. Sci. U.S.* **68**, 1138.

Bhatnagar R. S. and Prockop D. J. (1966) Dissociation of the synthesis of sulphated mucopolysaccharides and the synthesis of collagen in embryonic cartilage. *Biochim. biophys. Acta* **130**, 383.

Bhatnagar R. S., Kivirikko K. I. and Prockop D. J. (1968) Studies on the synthesis of intracellular accumulation of protocollagen in organ culture of embryonic cartilage. *Biochim. biophys. Acta* **154**, 196.

Bhatnagar R. S., Rosenbloom J., Kivirikko K. I. and Prockop D. J. (1967) Dissociation of the synthesis of sulphated mucopolysaccharides and the synthesis of collagen in embryonic cartilage. *Biochim. biophys. Acta* **149**, 273.

Bhavanandan V. P. and Meyer K. (1967) Studies on keratosulfates. Methylation and partial acid hydrolysis of bovine corneal keratosulfate. *J. biol. Chem.* **242**, 4352.

Bhavanandan V. P. and Meyer K. (1968) Studies on keratosulfates. Methylation, desulfation and acid hydrolysis studies on old human rib cartilage keratosulfate. *J. biol. Chem.* **243**, 1052.

Blumenkrantz N. and Prockop D. J. (1970) Variations in the glycosylation of the collagen synthesized by chick embryo cartilage. *Biochim. biophys. Acta* **208**, 461.

Blumenkrantz N., Rosenbloom J. and Prockop D. J. (1969) Sequential steps in the synthesis of hydroxylysine and the glycosylation of hydroxylysine during the biosynthesis of collagen. *Biochim. biophys. Acta* **192**, 81.

Boake W. C. and Muir H. (1955) The non-antigenicity of chondroitin sulphate. *Lancet* **ii**, 1222.

Bollet A. J. and Nance J. L. (1966) Biochemical findings in normal and osteoarthritic articular cartilage. II. Chondroitin sulphate concentration and chain length, water and ash content. *J. clin. Invest.* **45**, 1170.

Bollet A. J., Bonner W. M. and Nance J. L. (1963) The presence of hyaluronidase in various mammalian tissues. *J. biol. Chem.* **238**, 3522.

Bollet A. J., Handy J. R. and Sturgill B. C. (1963) Chondroitin sulphate concentration and protein-polysaccharide composition of articular cartilage in osteoarthritis. *J. clin. Invest.* **42**, 853.

Bornstein P. (1967) Comparative sequence studies of rat skin and tendon collagen. I. Evidence for incomplete hydroxylation of individual prolyl residues in normal proteins. *Biochemistry* **6**, 3082.

Bornstein P. (1974) The biosynthesis of collagen. *Ann. Rev. Biochem.* **43**, 567.

Bosmann H. B. (1968) Cellular control of macromolecular synthesis: rates of synthesis of extracellular macromolecules during and after depletion by papain. *Proc. R. Soc. Lond. B* **169**, 399.

Bosmann H. B. and Eylar E. H. (1968) Attachment of carbohydrate to collagen. Isolation, purification and properties of the glucosyltransferase. *Biochem. biophys. Res. Comm.* **30**, 89.

Brandt K. and Muir H. (1969) Characterisation of protein-polysaccharides of articular cartilage from mature and immature pigs. *Biochem. J.* **114**, 871.

Brandt K. and Muir H. (1971a) Heterogeneity of protein-polysaccharides of porcine articular cartilage. *Biochem. J.* **121**, 261.

Brandt K. and Muir H. (1971b) Heterogeneity of protein-polysaccharides of porcine articular cartilage. The chondroitin sulphate proteins associated with collagen. *Biochem. J.* **123**, 747.

Brandt K., Tsiganos C. P. and Muir H. (1973) Immunological relationships between proteoglycans of different hydrodynamic size from articular cartilage of foetal and mature pigs. *Biochim. biophys. Acta* **320**, 453.

Bray B. A., Lieberman R. and Meyer K. (1967) Structure of human skeletal keratan sulfate. The linkage region. *J. biol. Chem.* **242**, 3373.

Burgeson R. E., Wyke A. W. and Fessler J. H. (1972) Collagen synthesis by cells. II. Secretion of a disulfide linked material. *Biochem. biophys. Res. Comm.* **48**, 892.

Butler W. T. (1970) Structural studies in collagen. *Chemistry and Molecular Biology of the Intercellular Matrix*, Ed. by E. A. Balazs, Vol. 1, p. 149. Academic Press, New York.

Butler W. T. and Cunningham L. W. (1966) Evidence for the linkage of a disaccharide to hydroxylysine in tropocollagen. *J. biol. Chem.* **241**, 3882.

Byers P. H., Click E. M., Harper E. and Bornstein P. (1975) Interchain disulfide bonds in procollagen are located in a large non-triple helical COOH-terminal domain. *Proc. natn. Acad. Sci. U.S.* **72**, 3009.

Campo R. D. and Dziewiatkowski D. D. (1962) Intracellular synthesis of protein-polysaccharides by slices of bovine costal cartilage. *J. biol. Chem.* **237**, 2729.

Campo R. D. and Tourtellotte C. D. (1967) The composition of bovine cartilage and bone. *Biochim. biophys. Acta* **141**, 614.

Cessi C. and Bernardi G. (1965) The kinetics of enzymatic degradation and the structure of protein-polysaccharide complexes of cartilage. *Structure and Function of Connective and Skeletal Tissue*, p. 152. Butterworths, London.

Cheung H. S., Harvey W., Benya P. D. and Nimni M. E. (1976) New collagen markers of 'derepression' synthesized by rabbit articular chondrocytes in culture. *Biochem. biophys. Res. Comm.* **68**, 1371.

Christner J., Brown M. and Dziewiatkowski D. D. (1977) Interaction of cartilage proteoglycans with hyaluronic acid. The role of the hyaluronic acid carboxyl groups. *Biochem. J.*, **167**, 711.

Church R. L., Pfiefer S. E. and Tanzer M. L. (1971) Collagen biosynthesis: synthesis and secretion of a high molecular weight precursor procollagen. *Proc. natn. Acad. Sci. U.S.* **68**, 2638.

Click E. M. and Bornstein P. (1970) Isolation and characterization of the cyanogen bromide peptides from the $\alpha 1$ and $\alpha 2$ chain of human skin collagen. *Biochemistry* **9**, 4699.

Cole N. N. and Lowther D. A. (1969) The inhibition of chondroitin sulphate-protein synthesis by cycloheximide. *FEBS Letts* **2**, 351.

Conochie L. B., Scott J. E. and Page-Faulk W. (1975) A passive agglutination method using collagen-coated tanned sheep erythrocytes to demonstrate collagen-glycosaminoglycan interaction. *J. Immunol. Methods* **7**, 393.

Curtiss P. H. and Klein L. (1963) Destruction of articular cartilage in septic arthritis. I. *In vitro* studies. *J. Bone Jt Surg.* **45A**, 797.

D'Abramo F. and Lipmann F. (1957) The formation of adenosine-3^1 phosphate-5^1-phosphosulfate in extracts of chick embryo cartilage and its conversion into chondroitin sulphate. *Biochim. biophys. Acta* **25**, 211.

Davidson E. A. and Small W. (1963) Metabolism *in vivo* of connective tissue mucopolysaccharides. III. Chondroitin sulfate and keratosulfate of cartilage. *Biochim. biophys. Acta* **69**, 445.

Davidson J. M., McEneary L. S. G. and Bornstein P. (1975) Intermediates in the limited proteolytic conversion of procollagen to collagen. *Biochemistry* **14**, 5188.

Davis N. R. and Bailey A. J. (1971) Chemical synthesis of the reduced form of an intermolecular cross-link of collagen. *Biochem. biophys. Res. Comm.* **45**, 1416.

Dehm P., Jimenez S. A., Olsen B. R. and Prockop D. J. (1972) A transport form of collagen from embryonic tendon: electron microscopic demonstration of an NH_2-terminal extension and evidence suggesting the presence of cystine in the molecule. *Proc. natn. Acad. Sci. U.S.* **69**, 60.

DeLuca S., Richmond M. E. and Silbert J. E. (1973) Biosynthesis of chondroitin sulfate. Sulfation of the polysaccharide chain. *Biochemistry* **12**, 3911.

De Luca S., Heinegård D., Hascall V. C., Kimura H. and Caplan A. (1977) Chemical and physical changes in proteoglycans during development of chick limb bud chondrocytes grown *in vitro*. *J. biol. Chem.* **252**, 6600.

Di Ferrante N., Donnelly P. V. and Sajdera S. W. (1972) A segregated antigen in cartilage matrix. *J. Lab. clin. Med.* **80**, 364.

Dondi P. and Muir H. (1976) Collagen synthesis and deposition in cartilage during disrupted proteoglycan production. *Biochem. J.* **160**, 117.

Dorfman A., Levitt D., Schwartz N. B. and Ho P. L. (1975) Studies on cartilage differentiation. *Extracellular Matrix Influences on Gene Expression*, Ed. by H. C. Slavkin and R. C. Greulich, p.19. Academic Press, New York.

Ebert P. S. and Prockop D. J. (1963) Effects of hydrocortisone on the synthesis of sulphated mucopolysaccharides and collagen in chick embryos. *Biochim. biophys. Acta* **78**, 390.

Evanson J. M., Jeffrey J. J. and Krane S. M. (1968) Studies on collagenase from rheumatoid synovium in tissue culture. *J. clin. Invest.* **47**, 2639.

Eyre D. R. and Muir H. (1974) Collagen polymorphism: two molecular species in pig intervertebral disc. *FEBS Letts* **42**, 192.

Eyre D. R. and Muir H. (1975) The distribution of different molecular species of collagen in fibrous, elastic and hyaline cartilages of the pig. *Biochem. J.* **151**, 595.

Eyre D. R. and Muir H. (1976) Types I and II collagens in intervertebral disc. Interchanging radial distributions in annulus fibrosus. *Biochem. J.* **157**, 267.

Eyre D. R. and Muir H. (1977) Quantitative analysis of types I and II collagens in human intervertebral discs at various ages. *Biochim. biophys. Acta* **492**, 29.

Eyre D. R., McDevitt C. A. and Muir H. (1975) Experimentally induced osteoarthrosis in the dog. *Ann. rheum. Dis.* **34**, Suppl. 2, 137.

Eyring E. J. and Yang J. T. (1968) Conformation of protein polysaccharide complex from bovine nasal septum. *J. biol. Chem.* **243**, 1306.

Fakada M. N. and Matsumura G. (1976) Endo-β-galactosidase of *Escherichia freundii*. Purification and endoglycosidic action on keratan sulfates, oligosaccharides and blood group active glycoprotein. *J. biol. Chem.* **251**, 6218.

Fell H. B. and Barratt M. E. J. (1973) The role of soft connective tissue in the breakdown of pig articular cartilage cultivated in the presence of complement-sufficient anti-serum to pig erythrocytes. I. Histological changes. *Int. Arch. Allergy* **4**, 441.

Fessler J. H. (1960) A structural function of mucopolysaccharide in connective tissue. *Biochem. J.* **76**, 124.

Fessler J. H. and Fessler L. I. (1966) Electron microscopic visualization of the polysaccharide hyaluronic acid. *Proc. natn. Acad. Sci. U.S.* **56**, 141.

Fessler L. I. and Fessler J. H. (1974) Protein assembly of procollagen and effects of hydroxylation. *J. biol. Chem.* **249**, 7637.

Fessler L. I., Morris N. P. and Fessler J. H. (1975) Procollagen: biological scission of amino and carboxyl extension peptides. *Proc. natn. Acad. Sci. U.S.* **72**, 4905.

Fietzek P. O. and Kuhn K. (1975) Information contained in the amino acid sequence of the α1 (I)-chain of collagen and its consequences upon the formation of the triple helix of fibrils and cross-links. *Mol. Cell. Biochem.* **8**, 141.

Fitton-Jackson S. (1970) Environmental control of macromolecular synthesis in cartilage and bone: morphogenetic response to hyaluronidase. *Proc. R. Soc. Lond. B* **175**, 405.

Foweraker A. R., Isles M., Jennings B. R., Hardingham T. E. and Muir H. (1977) Electric birefringence studies of cartilage proteoglycan aggregation. *Biopolymers* **16**, 1367.

Franek M. D. and Dunstone J. R. (1966) Density-gradient centrifugation in the isolation of polysaccharide-protein complexes from aortic tissue. *Biochim. biophys. Acta* **127**, 213.

Gallop P. M. and Paz M. A. (1975) Post-translational protein modifications, with special attention to collagen and elastin. *Physiol. Rev.* **55**, 418.

Gallop P. M., Blumenfeld O. O. and Seifter S. (1972) Structure and metabolism of connective tissue proteins. *Ann. Rev. Biochem.* **41**, 617.

Gay S., Muller P. K., Lemmen C., Remberger K., Matzen K. and Kuhn K. (1976) Immunohistological study on collagen in cartilage–bone metamorphosis and degenerative osteoarthrosis. *Klin. Wschr.* **54**, 969.

Gelman R. A. and Blackwell J. (1973) Interaction between collagen chondroitin-6-sulfate *Conn. Tiss. Res.* **2**, 31.

Gerber B. R., Franklin E. C. and Schubert M. (1960) Ultracentrifugal fractionation of bovine nasal chondromucoprotein. *J. biol. Chem.* **235**, 2870.

Gregory J. D. (1973) Multiple aggregation factors in cartilage proteoglycan. *Biochem. J.* **133**, 383.

Gregory J. D. and Rodén L. (1961) Isolation of keratosulfate from chondromucoprotein of bovine nasal septa. *Biochem. biophys. Res. Comm.* **5**, 430.

Grillo H. C. and Gross J. (1967) Collagenolytic activity during mammalian wound repair. *Develop. Biol.* **15**, 300.

Gross J. and Lapière C. (1962) Collagenolytic activity in amphibian tissues. A tissue culture assay. *Proc. natn. Acad. Sci. U.S.* **48**, 1014.

Gross J. and Nagai Y. (1965) Specific degradation of the collagen molecule by tadpole collagenolytic enzyme. *Proc. natn. Acad. Sci. U.S.* **54**, 1197.

Gross J., Mathews M. B. and Dorfman A. (1960) Sodium chondroitin sulfate-protein complexes of cartilage. II. Metabolism. *J. biol. Chem.* **235**, 2889.

Hagopian A., Bosmann H. B. and Eylar E. H. (1968) Glycoprotein biosynthesis. The localisation of polypeptidyl: N-acetylgalactosaminyl, collagen glucosyl and glycoprotein: galactosyl transferases in HeLa cell membrane fractions. *Archs Biochem. Biophys.* **128**, 387.

Handley C. J. and Lowther D. A. (1976) Inhibition of proteoglycan biosynthesis by hyaluronic acid in chondrocytes in cell culture. *Biochem. biophys. Acta* **444**, 69.

Hardingham T. E. and Muir H. (1972a) The specific interaction of hyaluronic acid with cartilage proteoglycans. *Biochim. biophys. Acta* **279**, 401.

Hardingham T. E. and Muir H. (1972b) Biosynthesis of proteoglycans in cartilage slices. Fractionation by gel chromatography and equilibrium density-gradient centrifugation. *Biochem. J.* **126**, 791.

Hardingham T. E. and Muir H. (1973a) Hyaluronic acid in cartilage. *Biochem. Soc. Trans.* **1**, 282.

Hardingham T. E. and Muir H. (1973b) Binding of oligosaccharides of hyaluronic acid to proteoglycans. *Biochem. J.* **135**, 905.

Hardingham T. E. and Muir H. (1974a) Hyaluronic acid in cartilage and proteoglycan aggregation. *Biochem. J.* **139**, 565.

Hardingham T. E. and Muir H. (1974b) The function of hyaluronic acid in proteoglycan aggregation. *Normal and Osteoarthrotic Articular Cartilage,* Ed. by S. Y. Ali, M. W. Elves and D. H. Leaback, p. 51. Institute of Orthopaedics, London.

Hardingham T. E. and Muir H. (1975) Structure and stability of proteoglycan aggregates. *Ann. rheum. Dis.* **34**, Suppl. 2, 26.

Hardingham T. E., Ewins R. J. F. and Muir H. (1976) Cartilage proteoglycans. Structure and heterogeneity of the protein core and the effects of specific protein modifications on the binding to hyaluronate. *Biochem. J.* **157**, 127.

Hardingham T. E., Fitton-Jackson S. and Muir H. (1972) Replacement of proteoglycans in embryonic chicken cartilage in organ culture after treatment with testicular hyaluronidase. *Biochem. J.* **129**, 101.

Harkness R. D. (1961) Biological functions of collagen. *Biol. Revs* **36**, 339.

Harkness R. D. (1966) Collagen. *Sci. Prog. (Oxf.)* **54**, 257.

Harrington W. F. and von Hippel P. H. (1961) Formation and stabilization of the collagen-fold. *Archs Biochem. Biophys.* **92**, 100.

Harrington R. E. and Zimm B. H. (1965) Degradation of polymers by controlled hydrodynamic shear. *J. Phys. Chem.* **69**, 161.

Harris E. D. and Cartwright E. C. (1977) Collagenases. *Proteinases of Mammalian Cells and Tissues,* Ed. by A. J. Barrett, p. 249. North-Holland Publ., Amsterdam and Oxford.

Harris F. D. and Krane S. M. (1974a) Collagenase I. *New Engl. J. Med.* **291**, 557.

Harris F. D. and Krane S. M. (1974b) Collagenase II. *New Engl. J. Med.* **291**, 605.

Harris F. D. and Krane S. M. (1947c) Collagenase III. *New Engl. J. Med.* **291**, 652.

Harwood R., Bhalla A. K., Grant M. E. and Jackson D. S. (1975) The synthesis and secretion of cartilage procollagen. *Biochem. J.* **148**, 129.

Hascall V. C. (1979) Interaction of cartilage proteoglycans with hyaluronic acid. *J. Supramol Struct.*

Hascall V. C. and Heinegård D. (1974a) Aggregation of cartilage proteoglycans. I. The role of hyaluronic acid. *J. biol. Chem.* **249**, 4232.

Hascall V. C. and Heinegård D. (1947b) Aggregation of cartilage proteoglycans. II. Oligosaccharide competitors of the proteoglycan-hyaluronic acid interaction. *J. biol. Chem.* **249**, 4242.

Hascall V. C. and Riolo R. L. (1972) Characteristics of the protein-keratan sulfate core and of keratan sulfate prepared from bovine nasal cartilage proteoglycans. *J. biol. Chem.* **247**, 4529.

Hascall V. C. and Sajdera S. W. (1969) Protein-polysaccharide complex from bovine nasal cartilage. The function of glycoprotein in the formation of aggregates. *J. biol. Chem.* **244**, 2384.

Hascall V. C. and Sajdera S. W. (1970) Physical properties and polydispersity of proteoglycans from bovine nasal cartilage. *J. biol. Chem.* **245**, 4920.

Heinegård D. (1972a) Extraction, fractionation and

characterisation of proteoglycan from bovine tracheal cartilage. *Biochim. biophys. Acta* **285,** 181.

Heinegård D. (1972b) Hyaluronidase digestion and alkaline treatment of bovine tracheal cartilage proteoglycans. Isolation and characterisation of different keratan sulfate proteins. *Biochim. biophys. Acta* **285,** 193.

Heinegård D. (1977) Polydispersity of cartilage proteoglycans. Structural variations with size and buoyant density of the molecules. *J. biol. Chem.* **252,** 1980.

Heinegård D. and Axelsson I. (1977) The distribution of keratan sulphate in cartilage proteoglycans. *J. biol. Chem.* **252,** 1971.

Heinegård D. and Gardell S. (1967) Studies on protein-polysaccharide complex (proteoglycans) from human nucleus pulposus. *Biochim. biophys. Acta* **148,** 164.

Heinegård D. and Hascall V. C. (1974a) Aggregation of proteoglycan. III. Characteristics of the proteins isolated from trypsin digests of aggregates. *J. biol. Chem.* **249,** 4250.

Heinegård D. and Hascall V. C. (1974b) Characterisation of chondroitin sulfate isolated from trypsin-chymotrypsin digests of cartilage proteoglycans. *Archs Biochem. Biophys.* **165,** 427.

Helting T. and Rodén L. (1968) The carbohydrate-protein linkage region of chondroitin 6-sulfate. *Biochim. biophys. Acta* **170,** 301.

Helting T. and Rodén L. (1969a) Biosynthesis of chondroitin sulfate. I. Galactosyl transfer in the formation of the carbohydrate-protein linkage-region. *J. biol. Chem.* **244,** 2790.

Helting T. and Rodén L. (1969b) Biosynthesis of chondroitin sulfate. II. Glucuronosyl transfer in the formation of the carbohydrate-protein linkage-region. *J. biol. Chem.* **244,** 2799.

Herbage D., Lucas J. M. and Huc A. (1974) Collagen and proteoglycan interactions in bovine articular cartilage. *Biochim. biophys. Acta* **336,** 108.

Herman J. H. and Carpenter B. A. (1975) Immunobiology of cartilage. *Seminars Arthr. Rheum.* **5,** 1.

Hirano S. and Meyer K. (1971) Enzymatic degradation of corneal and cartilaginous keratosulfates. *Biochem. biophys. Res. Comm.* **44,** 1371.

Hirano S. and Meyer K. (1973) Purification and properties of a keratan sulfate hydrolyzing enzyme, an endo-β-galactosidase. *Conn. Tiss. Res.* **2,** 1.

Hjertquist S. O. and Lemperg R. (1972) Identification and concentraion of the glycosaminoglycans of human articular cartilage in relation to age and osteoarthrosis. *Calc. Tiss. Res.* **10,** 223.

Hjertquist S. O. and Wasteson A. (1972) The molecular weight of chondroitin sulphate from human articular cartilage. *Calc. Tiss. Res.* **10,** 31.

Hoffman P., Mashburn T. A. and Meyer K. (1967) Protein-polysaccharides of bovine cartilage. II. The relation of keratan sulfate and chondroitin sulfate. *J. biol. Chem.* **242,** 3805.

Hoffman P., Mashburn T. A., Hsu D. S., Trivedid D. and Diep J. (1975) Variable nature of cartilage proteoglycans. *J. biol. Chem.* **250,** 7251.

Hopwood J. J. and Robinson H. C. (1974) The structure and composition of cartilage keratan sulfate. *Biochem. J.* **141,** 517.

Horwitz A. L. and Dorfman A. (1968) Subcellular sites for synthesis of chondromucoprotein of cartilage. *J. cell. Biol.* **38,** 358.

Isaac D. H. and Atkins E. D. T. (1973) Molecular conformations of chondroitin-4-sulphate. *Nature New Biol.* **244,** 252.

Jeffrey J. J. and Gross J. (1970) Collagenase from rat uterus. Isolation and partial characterization. *Biochemistry* **9,** 268.

Jimenez S. A., Dehm P. and Prockop D. J. (1971) Further evidence for a transport form of collagen. Its extrusion and extracellular conversion to tropocollagen in embryonic tendon. *FEBS Letts* **17,** 245.

Jimenez S. A., Harsch M. and Rosenbloom J. (1973) Hydroxyproline stabilizes the triple helix of chick tendon collagen. *Biochem. biophys. Res. Comm.* **52,** 106.

Juva K. and Prockop D. J. (1969) Formation of enzyme-substrate complexes with protocollagen proline hydroxylase and large polypeptide substrates. *J. biol. Chem.* **244,** 6486.

Keiser H. and De Vito J. (1974) Immunochemical studies of fragments of bovine nasal cartilage proteoglycans sub-unit. *Conn. Tiss. Res.* **2,** 273.

Keiser H. and Sandson J. (1974) Immunodiffusion and gel-electrophoretic studies of human articular cartilage proteoglycan. *Arthritis Rheum.* **17,** 218.

Keiser H., Shulman H. J. and Sandson J. (1972) Immunochemistry of cartilage proteoglycan: immunodiffusion and gel electrophoretic studies. *Biochem. J.* **126,** 163.

Keiser H., Greenwald R. A., Feinstein G. and Janoff A. (1976) Degradation of cartilage proteoglycan by human leucocyte granule neutral proteases—a model of joint injury. II. Degradation of isolated bovine nasal cartilage proteoglycan. *J. clin. Invest.* **57,** 625.

Kempson G. E., Muir H., Pollard C. and Tuke M. (1973) The tensile properties of the cartilage of human femoral condyles related to the content of collagen and glycosaminoglycans. *Biochim. biophys. Acta* **297**, 465.

Kempson G. E., Muir H., Swanson A. and Freeman M. A. R. (1970) Correlations between stiffness and the chemical constituents of cartilage on the human femoral head. *Biochim. biophys. Acta* **215**, 70.

Kivirikko K. I. and Prockop D. J. (1967a) Hydroxylation of proline in synthetic polypeptides with purified protocollagen hydroxylase. *J. biol. Chem.* **242**, 4007.

Kivirikko K. I. and Prockop D. J. (1967b) Purification and partial characterization of the enzyme for the hydroxylation of proline in protocollagen. *Archs Biochem. Biophys.* **118**, 611.

Kivirikko K. I., Bright H. J. and Prockop D. J. (1968) Kinetic patterns of protocollagen hydroxylase and further studies on the polypeptide substrate. *Biochim. biophys. Acta* **151**, 558.

Kleine T. O., Heinrich B. and Goetz K. (1973) Biosynthesis of chondroitin sulphate proteins. Isolation of four pools differing in their solubility and labelling rates in calf rib cartilage. *FEBS Letts* **31**, 170.

Kleine T. O., Heinrich B. and Goetz K. (1974) Biosynthesis of chondroitin sulphate proteins. Pulse labelling experiments with radiosulfate of four pools in calf rib cartilage. *FEBS Letts* **39**, 255.

Kohn L. D., Isersky C., Zupnick Z., Lenaers A., Lee G. and Lapière C. M. (1974) Calf tendon procollagen peptidase: its purification and endopeptidase mode of action. *Proc. natn. Acad. Sci. U.S.* **71**, 40.

Kuhn K. (1969) The structure of collagen. *Essays in Biochemistry*, Ed. by P. N. Campbell and G. D. Grenville, Vol. 5, p. 59. Academic Press, London.

Lapière C. M., Lenaers A. and Kohn L. D. (1971) Procollagen peptidase: an enzyme exercising the co-ordination of peptides of procollagen. *Proc. natn. Acad. Sci. U.S.* **68**, 3054.

Layman D. L., McGoodwin E. B. and Martin G. R. (1971) Transport form of collagen precursor. *Proc. natn. Acad. Sci. U.S.* **68**, 454.

Layman D. L., Sokoloff L. and Miller E. J. (1972) Collagen synthesis by articular cartilage in monolayer culture. *Exp. Cell Res.* **73**, 107.

Lazarus G. S., Daniels J. R., Brown R. S., Bladen H. A. and Fullmer H. M. (1968) Degradation of collagen by a human granulocyte collagenolytic systems. *J. clin. Invest.* **47**, 2622.

Lazarus G. S., Decker J. L., Oliver C. H., Daniels J. R., Multz C. V. and Fullmer H. M. (1968) Collagenolytic activity of synovium in rheumatoid arthritis. *New Engl. J. Med.* **279**, 914.

Lemperg R. K., Larsson S. E. and Hjertquist S. O. (1974) The glycosaminoglycans of bovine articular cartilage. I. Concentration and distribution in different layers in relation to age. *Calc. Tiss. Res.* **15**, 237.

Lenaers A., Ansay M., Nusgens B. V. and Lapière C. M. (1971) Collagen made of extended α-chains, procollagen in genetically-defective dermatosparaxic calves. *Eur. J. Biochem.* **23**, 533.

Levene C. I. and Gross J. (1959) Alterations in the state of molecular aggregation of collagen induced in chick embryos by β-aminopropionitrile (lathyrus factor). *J. exp. Med.* **110**, 771.

Libby W. F., Berger R., Mead J. F., Alexander G. V. and Ross J. F. (1964) Replacement rates for human tissue from atmospheric radiocarbon. *Science* **146**, 1170.

Lichtenstein J. R., Martin G. R., Kohn L., Byers L. D. and McKusick V. A. (1973) Defect in conversion of procollagen to collagen in a form of Ehlers–Danlos syndrome. *Science* **182**, 298P.

Lindahl F. C. and Rodén L. (1966) The chondroitin sulphate-protein linkage. *J. biol. Chem.* **241**, 2113.

Linn F. C. and Sokoloff L. (1965) Movement and composition of interstitial fluid of cartilage. *Arthritis Rheum.* **8**, 481.

Loewi G. and Muir H. (1965) The antigenicity of chondromucoprotein. *Immunology* **9**, 119.

Lohmander S. (1975) Proteoglycans of guinea pig costal cartilage. Fractionation and characterisation. *Eur. J. Biochem.* **57**, 549.

Lohmander S. (1977) Turnover of proteoglycans in guinea pig costal cartilage. *Archs Biochem. Biophys.* **180**, 96.

Lohmander S., Antonopoulos C. A. and Friberg U. (1973) Chemical and metabolic heterogeneity of chondroitin sulfate and keratan sulfate in guinea pig cartilage and nucleus pulposus. *Biochim. biophys. Acta* **304**, 430.

Lowther D. A. and Natarajan M. (1972) The influence of glycoprotein on collagen fibril formation in the presence of chondroitin sulphate proteoglycan. *Biochem. J.* **127**, 607.

Luscombe M. and Phelps C. (1967a) The composition and physico-chemical properties of bovine nasal septa protein-polysaccharide complex. *Biochem. J.* **102**, 110.

Luscombe M. and Phelps C. (1967b) Action of degradative enzymes on the light fraction of bovine septa protein-polysaccharide. *Biochem. J.* **103**, 103.

Lust G. and Pronsky W. (1972) Glycosaminoglycan contents of normal and degenerate articular cartilage of dogs. *Clin. chim. Acta* **39**, 281.

Lust G., Pronsky W. and Sherman D. M. (1972) Biochemical studies on developing canine hip joints. *J. Bone Jt Surg.* **54A**, 986.

McCluskey R. T. and Thomas L. (1959) The removal of cartilage matrix *in vivo* by papain: prevention of recovery with cortisone, hydrocortisone and prednisolone by a direct action on cartilage. *Amer. J. Path.* **35**, 819.

McDevitt C. A. (1977) A Study of the Structural Macromolecules of Articular Cartilage in Osteoarthrosis. PhD Thesis, University of London.

McDevitt C. A. and Muir H. (1974) A biochemical study of experimental and natural osteoarthrosis. *Biopolymere und Biomechanik von Bindegewebssystemen,* Ed. by F. Hartmann, Ch. Hartung and H. Zeidler, p. 261. Springer-Verlag, Berlin and New York.

McDevitt C. A. and Muir H. (1975) The proteoglycans of articular cartilage in early experimental osteoarthrosis. *Protides of Biological Fluids*, Ed. by H. Peeters, p. 269. Pergamon Press, Oxford and New York.

McDevitt C. A. and Muir H. (1976) Biochemical changes in the cartilage of the knee in experimental and natural osteoarthrosis in the dog. *J. Bone Jt Surg.* **58B**, 94.

McDevitt C. A., Gilbertson E. M. M. and Muir H. (1977) An experimental model of osteoarthrosis. Early morphological and biochemical changes. *J. Bone Jt Surg.* **59B**, 24.

Malawista T. and Schubert M. (1958) Chondromucoprotein: new extraction method and alkaline degradation. *J. biol. Chem.* **230**, 535.

Malemud C. J. and Janoff A. (1975) Identification of neutral proteases in human neutrophil granules that degrade articular cartilage proteoglycan. *Arthritis Rheum.* **18**, 361.

Mankin H. J. and Lippiello L. (1971) The glycosaminoglycans of normal and arthritic cartilage. *J. clin. Invest.* **50**, 1712.

Mankin H. J., Dorfman H., Lippiello L. and Zarijns A. (1971) Biochemical and metabolic abnormalities in articular cartilage from osteoarthritic human hips. II. Correlation of morphology with biochemical and metabolic data. *J. Bone Jt Surg.* **53A**, 523.

Maroudas A. (1975) Glycosaminoglycan turnover in articular cartilage. *Phil. Trans. R. Soc. Lond. B* **271**, 293.

Maroudas A. and Bullough P. (1968) Permeability of articular cartilage. *Nature (Lond.)* **219**, 1260.

Maroudas A., Muir H. and Wingham J. (1969) The correlation of fixed negative charge with glycosaminoglycan content of human articular cartilage. *Biochim. biophys. Acta* **177**, 492.

Martin G. R., Byers P. H. and Piez K. A. (1975) Procollagen. *Adv. Enzymol.* **42**, 167.

Martin G. R., Gross J., Piez K. A. and Lewis M. S. (1961) On the intramolecular cross-linking of collagen in lathyritic rats. *Biochim. biophys. Acta* **53**, 599.

Mason R. M. and Mayes R. W. (1973) Extraction of cartilage protein-polysaccharides with inorganic salt solutions. *Biochem. J.* **131**, 535.

Mathews M. B. (1967) Chondroitin sulphate and collagen in inherited skeletal defects of chickens. *Nature (Lond.)* **213**, 1255.

Mathews M. B. (1971) Comparative biochemistry of chondroitin sulphate-proteins of cartilage and notochord. *Biochem. J.* **125**, 37.

Mathews M. B. and Cifonelli J. A. (1965) Comparative biochemistry of keratosulfates. *J. biol. Chem.* **240**, 4140.

Mathews M. B. and Lozaityte I. (1958) I. Sodium chondroitin-sulfate protein complexes of cartilage. II. Molecular weight and shape. *Archs Biochem. Biophys.* **74**, 158.

Mayes R. W., Mason R. M. and Griffin D. C. (1973) The composition of cartilage proteoglycans. An investigation using high- and low-ionic-strength extraction procedures. *Biochem. J.* **131**, 541.

Michelacci Y. M. and Dietrich C. P. (1976) Chondroitinase C from *Flavobacterium heparinum*. *J. biol. Chem.* **251**, 1154.

Miles J. S. and Eichelberger L. (1964) Biochemical studies of human cartilage during the ageing process. *J. Amer. Geriat. Soc.* **12**, 1.

Miller E. J. (1971a) Isolation and characterisation of a collagen from chick cartilage containing three identical a-chains. *Biochemistry* **10**, 1652.

Miller E. J. (1971b) Collagen cross-linking: identification of two cyanogen bromide peptides containing sites of intermolecular cross-link formation in cartilage collagen. *Biochem. biophys. Res. Comm.* **45**, 444.

Miller E. J. (1976) Biochemical characteristics and biological significance of genetically distinct collagens. *Mol. Cell. Biochem.* **13**, 165.

Miller E. J. and Matukas V. J. (1969) Chick cartilage collagen: a new type of a1-chain not present in bone or skin of the species. *Proc. natn. Acad. Sci. U.S.* **64**, 1264.

Miller E. J. and Matukas V. J. (1974) Biosynthesis of collagen. The biochemist's view. *Fed. Proc.* **33**, 1197.

Miller E. J. and Robertson P. B. (1973) The stability of collagen cross-links when derived from hydroxylysyl residues. *Biochem. biophys. Res. Comm.* **54**, 432.

Miller E. J., Epstein E. W. and Piez K. (1971) Identification of three genetically distinct collagens by cyanogen bromide cleavage of insoluble human skin and cartilage collagen. *Biochem. biophys. Res. Comm.* **42**, 1024.

Miller E. J., van der Korst J. K. and Sokoloff L. (1969) Collagen of human articular and costal cartilage. *Arthritis Rheum.* **12**, 21.

Monson J. M., Click E. M. and Bornstein P. (1975) Further characterisation of procollagen. Purification and analysis of the pro α1-chain of chick bone procollagen. *Biochemistry* **14**, 4088.

Morris N. P., Fessler L. I., Weinstock A. and Fessler J. H. (1975) Procollagen assembly and secretion in embryonic chick bone. *J. biol. Chem.* **250**, 5719.

Morrison R. I. G., Barrett A. J., Dingle J. T. and Prior D. (1973) Cathepsins B$_1$ and D: action on human cartilage proteoglycans. *Biochim. biophys Acta* **302**, 411.

Mourao P. A. S. and Dietrich C. P. (1973) Differences in the content of chondroitin sulfate C and chondroitin sulfate A in the epiphysial growth cartilages of human vertebrae and long bones. *Biochim. biophys. Acta* **320**, 210.

Mourao P. A. S., Rosenfeld S., Laredo J. and Dietrich C. P. (1976) The distribution of chondroitin sulfates in articular and growth cartilages of human bones. *Biochim. biophys. Acta* **428**, 19.

Muir H. (1958) The nature of the link between protein and carbohydrate of a chondroitin sulphate complex from hyaline cartilage. *Biochem. J.* **69**, 195.

Muir H. (1973) Structure and enzymatic degradation of mucopolysaccharides. *Lysosomes and Storage Disease,* Ed. by F. van Hoof and H. G. Hers, Chap. 3, p. 79. Academic Press, London and New York.

Muir H. (1977) A molecular approach to the understanding of osteoarthrosis. *Ann. rheum. Dis.* **36**, 199.

Muir H. and Hardingham T. E. (1975) Structure of proteoglycans. *MTP International Review of Science*, Series 1, Ed. by W. J. Whelan, Vol 5, p.153. Butterworths, London.

Muir H. and Jacobs S. (1967) Protein-polysaccharide of pig laryngeal cartilage. *Biochem. J.* **103**, 367.

Muir H., Bullough P. and Maroudas A. (1970) The distribution of collagen in human articular cartilage with some of its physiological implications. *J. Bone Jt Surg.* **52B**, 554.

Murphy W. J., von der Mark K., McEneary L. S. G. and Bornstein P. (1975) Characterisation of procollagen-derived peptides unique to the precursor molecule. *Biochemistry* **14**, 3242.

Narayaran A. S., Siegel R. C. and Martin G. R. (1972) On the inhibition of lysyl oxidase by β-aminopropionitryl. *Biochem. biophys. Res.*

Comm. **46**, 745.

Neufeld E. F. and Hall C. W. (1965) The inhibition of UDP-D-glucose dehydrogenase by UDP-D-xylose. A possible regulatory mechanism. *Biochem. biophys. Res. Comm.* **19**, 456.

Nimni M. E. and Deshmukh K. (1973) Differences in collagen metabolism between normal and osteoarthritic human articular cartilage. *Science* **181**, 751.

Nist C., von der Mark K., Hay E., Olsen B. R., Bornstein P., Ross R. and Dehm P. (1975) Localization of procollagen in chick corneal and tendon fibroblasts by ferritin-conjugated antibodies. *J. cell. Biol.* **65**, 75.

Obrink B. (1973a) A study of the interactions between monomeric tropocollagen and glycosaminoglycans. *Eur. J. Biochem.* **33**, 387.

Obrink B. (1973b) The influence of glycosaminoglycans on the formation of fibres from monomeric tropocollagen in vitro. *Eur. J. Biochem.* **34**, 129.

Obrink B., Laurent T. C. and Carlsson B. (1975) Binding of chondroitin sulphate to collagen. *FEBS Letts* **56**, 166.

Oegema T. R., Hascall V. C. and Dziewiatkowski D. D. (1975) Isolation and characterisation of proteoglycans from the Swarm rat chondrosarcoma. *J. biol. Chem.* **250**, 6151.

Ogston A. G. and Sherman T. F. (1959) Degradation of the hyaluronic acid complex of synovial fluid by proteolytic enzymes and by ethylenediaminetetraacetic acid. *Biochem. J.* **72**, 301.

O'Hara P. J., Read W. K., Romane W. M. and Bridges C. H. (1970) A collagenous tissue dysplasia of calves. *Lab. Invest.* **23**, 307.

Olsen B. R., Hoffman H. P. and Prockop D. J. (1976) Interchain disulfide bonds at the COOH-terminal end of procollagen synthesized by matrix-free cells from chick embryonic tendon and cartilage. *Archs Biochem.* **175**, 341.

Orkin R. W., Pratt R. M. and Martin G. R. (1976) Undersulfated chondroitin sulfate in the cartilage matrix of brachymorphic mice. *Develop. Biol.* **50**, 82.

Pal S. and Schubert M. (1965) The action of hydroxylamine on the protein-polysaccharides of cartilage. *J. biol. Chem.* **240**, 3245.

Pal S., Doganges P. T. and Schubert M. (1966) The separation of new forms of the protein-polysaccharides of bovine nasal cartilage. *J. biol. Chem.* **241**, 4261.

Partridge S. M., Davis H. F. and Adair G. S. (1961) The chemistry of connective tissue and the constitution of the chondroitin sulphate protein complex in cartilage. *Biochem. J.* **79**, 15.

Pasternack S. G., Veis A. and Breen M. (1974) Solvent-dependent changes in proteoglycan subunit conformation in aqueous guanidine hydrochloride solutions. *J. biol. Chem.* **249**, 2206.

Pedrini V. (1969) Electrophoretic heterogeneity of protein-polysaccharides. *J. biol. Chem.* **244**, 1540.

Pennypacker J. P. and Goetinck P. F. (1976) Biochemical and ultrastructural studies of collagen and proteochondroitin sulfate in normal and nanomelic cartilage. *Develop. Biol.* **50**, 35.

Perez-Tamayo R. (1970) Collagen resorption in carageenin granulomas. *Lab. Invest.* **22**, 137.

Perlman R. L., Telser A. and Dorfman A. (1964) The biosynthesis of chondroitin sulfate by a cell-free preparation. *J. biol. Chem.* **239**, 3623.

Piez K. A. (1968) Cross-linking of collagen and elastin. *Ann. Rev. Biochem.* **37**, 547.

Piez K. A. (1975) The regulation of collagen fibril formation. *Extracellular Matrix Influences on Gene Expression,* Ed. by H. C. Slavkin and R. C. Greulich, p. 231. Academic Press, New York and London.

Piez K. A. and Miller A. (1974) The structure of collagen fibrils. *J. Supramol. Struct.* **2**, 121.

Poole A. R., Barratt M. E. J. and Fell H. B. (1973) The role of soft connective tissue in the breakdown of pig articular cartilage cultivated in the presence of complement-sufficient antiserum to pig erythrocytes. II. Distribution of immunoglobulin (IgG). *Int. Arch. Allergy* **44**, 469.

Prockop D. J. (1969) The intracellular biosynthesis of collagen. *Archs intern. Med.* **124**, 563.

Prockop D. J. (1970) Intracellular biosynthesis of collagen interactions of protocollagen proline hydroxylase with large polypeptides. *Chemistry and Molecular Biology of the Intercellular Matrix*, Ed. by E. A. Balazs, Vol. 1, p. 335. Academic Press, New York.

Prockop D. J. and Kivirikko K. I. (1969) Effect of polymer size on the inhibition of protocollagen proline hydroxylase by polyproline. II. *J. biol. Chem.* **244**, 4838.

Quinn R. W. and Cerroni R. (1957) Antigenicity of chondroitin sulfate. *Proc. Soc. exp. Biol. Med.* **96**, 268.

Rajapakse D. A. and Bywaters E. G. L. (1974) Cell-mediated immunity to cartilage proteoglycan in relapsing polychondritis. *Clin. exp. Immunol.* **16**, 497, 502.

Ramachandran I. (Ed.) (1967) *A Treatise on Collagen,* Vols. 1–3. Academic Press, New York.

Repo R. U. and Mitchell N. (1971) Collagen synthesis in mature articular cartilage of the rabbit. *J. Bone Jt Surg.* **53B**, 541.

Revell P. A. and Muir H. (1972) The excretion and degradation of chondroitin 4-sulphate administered to guinea pigs as free chondroitin sulphate and as proteoglycan. *Biochem. J.* **130**, 597.

Richmond M. E., De Luca S. and Silbert J. E. (1973a) Biosynthesis of chondroitin sulfate. Assembly of chondroitin on microsomal primers. *Biochemistry* **12**, 3904.

Richmond M. E., De Luca S. and Silbert J. E. (1973b) Biosynthesis of chondroitin sulfate. Sulfation of the polysaccharide chain. *Biochemistry* **12**, 3911.

Robins S. P. and Bailey A. J. (1972) Age related changes in collagen. Identification of reducible lysyl-carbohydrate condensation products. *Biochem. biophys. Res. Comm.* **48**, 76.

Robins S. P., Shimokomaki M. and Bailey A. J. (1973) The chemistry of the collagen cross-links. Age related changes in the reducible components of intact bovine collagen fibres. *Biochem. J.* **131**, 771.

Robinson H. C. and Hopwood J. J. (1973) The alkaline cleavage and borohydride reduction of cartilage proteoglycan. *Biochem. J.* **133**, 457.

Robinson H. C., Telser A. and Dorfman A. (1966) Studies on biosynthesis of the linkage region of chondroitin sulphate-protein complex. *Proc. natn. Acad. Sci. U.S.* **56**, 1859.

Robinson H. C., Brett M. J., Tralaggan P. J., Lowther D. A. and Okayama M. (1975) The effect of D-xylose, β-xylosides and β-galactosides on chondroitin sulphate biosynthesis in chicken cartilage. *Biochem. J.* **148**, 25.

Rodén L. (1970) Biosynthesis of acidic glycosaminoglycans (mucopolysaccharides). *Metabolic Conjugation and Metabolic Hydrolysis,* Ed. by W. H. Fishman, Vol. 2, p. 346. Academic Press, New York.

Rodén L. and Armand G. (1966) Structure of the chondroitin-4-sulfate-protein linkage region: isolation and characterisation of the disaccharide 3-*O*-β-glucuronosyl-D-galactose. *J. biol. Chem.* **241**, 65.

Rodén L. and Schwartz N. B. (1975) Biosynthesis of connective tissue proteoglycans. *MTP International Review of Science,* Series 1, Ed. by W. J. Whelan, Vol. 5, p. 96. Butterworths, London.

Rodén L. and Smith R. (1966) Structure of the neutral trisaccharide of the chondroitin-4-sulfate protein linkage region. *J. biol. Chem.* **241**, 5949.

Rokosova-Cmuchalova B. and Bentley J. P. (1968) Relation of collagen synthesis in cartilage. *Biochem. Pharmac. Suppl.* **33**, 315.

Rosenberg L. (1974) Structure of cartilage proteoglycans. *Dynamics of Connective Tissue Macromolecules*, Ed. by P. M. C. Burleigh and A. R. Poole, p. 105. North-Holland Publ., Amsterdam.

Rosenberg L., Hellmann W. and Kleinschmidt A. K. (1970) Macromolecular models of protein-polysaccharide from bovine nasal cartilage based on electron microscopic studies. *J. biol. Chem.* **245**, 4123.

Rosenberg L., Hellmann W. and Kleinschmidt A. K. (1975) Electron microscopic studies of proteoglycan aggregates from bovine articular cartilage. *J. biol. Chem.* **250**, 1877.

Rosenberg L., Pal S. and Beale R. J. (1973) Proteoglycans from bovine proximal humeral articular cartilage. *J. biol. Chem.* **248**, 3681.

Rosenberg L., Pal S., Beale R. J. and Schubert M. (1970) A comparison of protein-polysaccharides of bovine nasal cartilage isolated and fractionated by different methods. *J. biol. Chem.* **245**, 4112.

Rosenberg L., Wolfenstein-Todel C., Margolis R., Pal S. and Strider W. (1976) Proteoglycans from bovine proximal humeral articular cartilage. Structural basis for the polydispersity of proteoglycan subunit. *J. biol. Chem.* **251**, 6439.

Rosenbloom J. and Prockop D. J. (1969) Biochemical aspects of collagen biosynthesis. *Repair and Regeneration*, Ed. by J. E. Dunphy and W. van Winkle, p. 117. McGraw-Hill, New York.

Saito H. and Uzman B. G. (1971a) Uptake of chondroitin sulfate by mammalian cells in culture. II. Kinetics of uptake and autoradiography. *Exp. Cell Res.* **66**, 90.

Saito H. and Uzman B. G. (1971b) Uptake of chondroitin sulfate by mammalian cells in culture. III. Effect of incubation media, metabolic inhibitors and structural analogs. *Exp. Cell Res.* **66**, 97.

Saito H., Yamagata T. and Suzuki S. (1968) Enzymatic methods for the determination of small quantities of isomeric chondroitin sulfates. *J. biol. Chem.* **243**, 1536.

Sajdera S. W. and Hascall V. C. (1969) Protein-polysaccharide complex from bovine nasal cartilage: a comparison of low and high shear extraction procedures. *J. biol. Chem.* **244**, 77.

Sandson J., Rosenberg L. and White D. (1966) The antigenic determinants of the protein-polysaccharides of cartilage. *J. exp. Med.* **123**, 817.

Sapolsky A. I., Howell D. S. and Woessner J. F. (1974) Neutral proteases and cathepsin D in human articular cartilage. *J. clin. Invest.* **53**, 1044.

Sapolsky A. I., Keiser H., Howell D. S. and Woessner J. F. (1976) Metallo-proteases of human articular cartilage that digest cartilage proteoglycan of neutral and acid pH. *J. clin. Invest.* **58**, 1030.

Scher I. and Hamerman D. (1972) Isolation of human synovial-fluid hyaluronate by density-gradient ultracentrifugation and evaluation of its protein content. *Biochem. J.* **126**, 1073.

Schwartz N. and Rodén L. (1975) Biosynthesis of chondroitin sulfate. Solubilization of chondroitin sulfate glycosyltransferases and partial purification of uridine diphosphate-D-galactose:D-xylose galactosyltransferase. *J. biol. Chem.* **250**, 5200.

Schwartz N., Galligani L., Ho P. L. and Dorfman A. (1974) Stimulation of synthesis of free chondroitin sulfate chains by β-D-xylosides in cultured cells. *Proc. natn. Acad. Sci. U.S.* **71**, 4047.

Sellers A., Cartwright E., Murphy G. and Reynolds J. J. (1977) Evidence that latent collagenases are enzyme-inhibitor complexes. *Biochem. J.* **163**, 303.

Seno N. and Toda N. (1970) The carbohydrate-peptide linkage region of keratan sulfate from whale cartilage. *Biochim. biophys. Acta* **215**, 544.

Seno N., Anno K., Yaegashi Y. and Okayama T. (1975) Microheterogeneity of chondroitin sulfates from various cartilages. *Conn. Tiss. Res.* **3**, 87.

Seno N., Meyer K., Anderson B. and Hoffman P. (1965) Variations in keratosulfates. *J. biol. Chem.* **240**, 1005.

Serafini-Fracassini A. and Smith J. W. (1966) Observations on the morphology of the protein-polysaccharide complex of bovine nasal cartilage and its relationship to collagen. *Proc. R. Soc. Lond. B* **165**, 440.

Serafini-Fracassini A., Wells P. J. and Smith J. W. (1970) Studies on the interactions between glycosaminoglycans and fibrillar collagen. *Chemistry and Molecular Biology of the Intercellular Matrix*, Ed. by E. A. Balazs, Vol. 2, p. 1201. Academic Press, New York.

Seyer J. M., Brickley D. M. and Glimcher M. J. (1974a) The isolation of two types of collagen from embryonic bovine epiphyseal cartilage. *Calc. Tiss. Res.* **17**, 25.

Seyer J. M., Brickley D. M. and Glimcher M. J. (1947b) The identification of two types of collagen in the articular cartilage of postnatal chickens. *Calc. Tiss. Res.* **17**, 43.

Shatton J. and Schubert M. (1954) Isolation of a mucoprotein from cartilage. *J. biol. Chem.* **211**, 565.

Siegel R. C. (1974) Biosynthesis of collagen cross-links. Increased activity of purified lysyl oxidase with re-constituted fibrils. *Proc. natn. Acad. Sci. U.S.* **71**, 4826.

Siegel R. C., Pinnell S. R. and Martin G. R. (1970) Cross-linking of collagen and elastin. Properties of lysyl-oxidase. *Biochemistry* **9**, 4486.

Silberberg R., Silberberg M., Vogel A. and Wellstein W. (1961) Ultrastructure of articular cartilage of mice of various ages. *Amer. J. Anat.* **109**, 251.

Simunek Z. and Muir H. (1972a) Changes in the protein-polysaccharides of pig articular cartilage during prenatal life, development and old age. *Biochem. J.* **126**, 515.

Simunek Z. and Muir H. (1972b) Proteoglycans of the knee-joint cartilage of young normal and lame pigs. *Biochem. J.* **130**, 181.

Smith J. W. (1968) Molecular pattern in native collagen. *Nature (Lond.)* **219**, 157.

Smith J. W., Peters T. J. and Serafini-Fracassini A. (1967) Observations on the distribution of the proteinpolysaccharide and collagen in bovine articular cartilage. *J. cell Sci.* **2**, 129.

Sokoloff L. (1966) Elasticity of ageing cartilage. *Fed. Proc.* **25**, 1089.

Sokoloff L., Crittenden L. B., Yamamoto R. S. and Gay G. E. (1962) The genetics of degenerative joint disease in mice. *Arthritis Rheum.* **5**, 531.

Solursh M., Vaerewyck S. A. and Reiter R. S. (1974) Depression by hyaluronic acid of glycosaminoglycan synthesis by cultured chick embryo chondrocytes. *Develop. Biol.* **41**, 233.

Spiro R. G. (1969) Characterisation and quantitative determination of the hydroxylysine-linked carbohydrate units of several collagens. *J. biol. Chem.* **244**, 602.

Steven F. S., Broady K. and Jackson D. S. (1969) Protein-polysaccharide collagen complex of human articular and intercostal cartilage distribution and amino acid composition of protein fractions. *Biochim. biophys. Acta* **175**, 225.

Stockwell R. A. (1970) Changes in the acid glycosaminoglycan content of the matrix of ageing human articular cartilage. *Ann. rheum. Dis.* **29**, 509.

Stockwell R. A. and Scott J. E. (1965) Observations on the acid glycosaminoglycan (mucopolysaccharide) content of the matrix of ageing cartilage. *Ann. rheum. Dis.* **24**, 341.

Stockwell R. A. and Scott J. E. (1967) Distribution of acid glycosaminoglycans in human articular cartilage. *Nature (Lond.)* **215**, 1376.

Stoolmiller A. O. and Dorfman A. (1969) The metabolism of glycosaminoglycans. *Comprehensive Biochemistry,* Ed. by M. Florkin and E. H. Stotz, Vol. 17, p. 241. Elsevier, Amsterdam.

Strawich E. and Nimni E. M. (1971) Properties of a collagen molecule containing three identical components extracted from bovine articular cartilage. *Biochemistry* **10**, 3905.

Suzuki S. and Strominger J. L. (1960) Enzymatic sulfation of mucopolysaccharide in hen oviduct. *J. biol. Chem.* **235**, 257.

Swann D. A., Powell S., Broadhurst J., Sordillo E. and Sotman S. (1976) The formation of a stable complex between dissociated proteoglycan and hyaluronic acid in the absence of link protein. *Biochem. J.* **157**, 503.

Szirmai J. A., de Tyssonsk E. van B. and Gardell S. (1967) Microchemical analysis of glycosaminoglycans, collagen, total protein and water in histochemical layers of nasal septum cartilage. *Biochim. biophys. Acta* **136**, 331.

Tanzer M. C., Fairweather R. and Gallop P. M. (1972) Collagen crosslinks: isolation of reduced N^ε-hexosylhydroxylysine from borohydride-reduced calf skin insoluble collagen. *Archs Biochem. Biophys.* **151**, 137.

Tanzer M. I., Church R. L., Yeager J. A., Wampler D. E. and Park E. D. (1974) Procollagen: intermediate forms containing several types of peptide chains and non-collagen peptide extensions at NH_2 and COOH ends. *Proc. natn. Acad. Sci. U.S.* **71**, 3009.

Telser A., Robinson H. C. and Dorfman A. (1965) The biosynthesis of chondroitin sulfate-protein complex. *Proc. natn. Acad. Sci. U.S.* **54**, 912.

Telser A., Robinson H. C. and Dorfman A. (1966) The biosynthesis of chondroitin sulphate. *Archs Biochem. Biophys.* **116**, 458.

Thomas L. (1956) Reversible collapse of rabbit ears after intravenous papain and prevention of recovery by cortisone. *J. exp. Med.* **104**, 245.

Thyberg J., Lohmander S. and Heinegård D. (1975) Proteoglycans of hyaline cartilage. Electron-microscopic studies of isolated molecules. *Biochem. J.* **151**, 156.

Toda N. and Seno N. (1970) Sialic acid in the keratan sulfate fraction from whale cartilage. *Biochim. biophys. Acta* **208**, 227.

Toole B. P. (1969) Solubility of collagen fibrils formed *in vitro* in the presence of sulphated acid mucopolysaccharide-protein. *Nature (Lond.)* **222**, 872.

Toole B. P. (1972) Hyaluronate turnover during chondrogenesis in the developing chick limb and axial skeleton. *Develop. Biol.* **29**, 321.

Toole B. P. (1973) Hyaluronate and hyaluronidase in morphogenesis and differentiation. *Amer. Zool.* **13**, 1061.

Toole B. P. and Linsenmayer T. F. (1975) Proteoglycan-collagen interaction: possible developmental significance. *Extracellular Matrix*

Influences on Gene Expression, Ed. by H. C. Slavkin and R. C. Greulich, p. 341. Academic Press, New York and London.

Toole B.P. and Lowther D. A. (1968) The effect of chondroitin sulphate-protein on the formation of collagen fibrils *in vitro. Biochem. J.* **109**, 857.

Toole B. P., Jackson G. and Gross J. (1972) Hyaluronate in morphogenesis: inhibition of chondrogenesis *in vitro. Proc. natn. Acad. Sci. U.S.* **69**, 1384.

Traub W. and Piez K. A. (1971) The chemistry and structure of collagen. *Adv. Protein Chem.* **25**, 243.

Trelstad R. L., Kang A. H., Igarashi S. and Gross J. (1970) Isolation of two distinct collagens from chick cartilage. *Biochemistry* **9**, 4993.

Tsiganos C. P. and Muir H. (1967) A hybrid proteinpolysaccharide of keratan sulphate and chondroitin sulphate from pig laryngeal cartilage. *Biochem. J.* **104**, 26c.

Tsiganos C. P. and Muir H. (1969) Studies on proteinpolysaccharides from pig laryngeal cartilage: heterogeneity, fractionation and characterization. *Biochem. J.* **113**, 885.

Tsiganos C. P. and Muir H. (1973) Proteoglycan aggregation in different types of cartilage and its dependance on age. *Connective Tissue and Ageing,* Ed. by H. G. Vogel, Vol. 1, p. 132. Excerpta Medica, Amsterdam.

Tsiganos C. P., Hardingham T. E. and Muir H. (1971) Proteoglycans of cartilage: an assessment of their structure. *Biochim. biophys. Acta* **229**, 529.

Tsiganos C. P., Hardingham T. E. and Muir H. (1972) Aggregation of cartilage proteoglycans. *Biochem. J.* **128**, 121P.

Uitto J. and Prockop D. J. (1974) Synthesis and secretion of under-hydroxylated procollagen at various temperatures by cells subject to temporary anoxia. *Biochem. biophys. Res. Comm.* **60**, 414.

Vuust J. and Piez K. A. (1970) Biosynthesis of the *a*-chains of collagen studied by pulse-labelling in culture. *J. biol. Chem.* **245**, 6201.

Vuust J. and Piez K. A. (1972) A kinetic study of collagen biosynthesis. *J. biol. Chem.* **247**, 856.

Wasteson A. and Lindahl U. (1971) The distribution of sulphate residues in the chondroitin sulphate chain. *Biochem. J.* **125**, 903.

Wasteson A., Lindahl U. and Hallén A. (1972) Mode of degradation of the chondroitin sulphate proteoglycan in rat costal cartilage. *Biochem. J.* **130**, 729.

Weightman B. (1976) Tensile fatigue of human articular cartilage *J. Biomechanics* **9**, 193.

Weinstein E., Blumenkrantz N. and Prockop D. J. (1969) Hydroxylation of proline and lysine in protocollagen involves two separate enzymatic sites.

Biochim. biophys. Acta **191**, 747.

Weiss C., Rosenberg L. and Helfet A. J. (1968) An ultrastructure study of normal young adult human articular cartilage. *J. Bone Jt Surg.* **50A**, 663.

White D., Sandson J., Rosenberg L. and Schubert M. (1963) The antigenicity of the proteinpolysaccharides of human cartilage. *J. clin. Invest.* **42**, 992.

Wiebkin O. W. and Muir H. (1973) The inhibition of sulphate incorporation in isolated adult chondrocytes by hyaluronic acid. *FEBS Letts* **37**, 42.

Wiebkin O. W. and Muir H. (1975) Influence of the cells on the pericellular environment. The effect of hyaluronic acid on proteoglycan synthesis and secretion by chondrocytes of adult cartilage. *Phil. Trans. R. Soc. Lond. B* **271**, 283.

Wiebkin O. W., Hardingham T. E. and Muir H. (1975) The interaction of proteoglycans and hyaluronic acid and the effect of hyaluronic acid on proteoglycan synthesis by chondrocytes of adult cartilage. *Dynamics of Connective Tissue Macromolecules,* Ed. by P. M. C. Burleigh and A. R. Poole, p. 81. North-Holland Publ., Amsterdam.

Woessner J. F. (1973) Purification of cathepsin D from cartilage and uterus and its action on the proteinpolysaccharide complex of cartilage. *J. biol. Chem.* **248**, 1634.

Wood K. M., Wusteman F. S. and Curtis C. G. (1973) The degradation of intravenously injected chondroitin 4-sulphate in the rat. *Biochem. J.* **134**, 1009.

Woolley D. E. and Evanson J. M. (1977a) Effect of cartilage proteoglycans on human collagenase activities. *Biochim. biophys. Acta* **497**, 144.

Woolley D. E. and Evanson J. M. (1977b) Collagenase and its natural inhibitors in relation to the rheumatoid joint. *Conn. Tiss. Res.* **5**, 31.

Woolley D. E., Crossley M. J. and Evanson J. M. (1976) Antibody to rheumatoid synovial collagenase. Its characterisation, specificity and immunological cross-reactivity. *Eur. J. Biochem.* **69**, 421.

Woolley D. E., Roberts D. R. and Evanson J. M. (1975) Inhibition of human collagenase activity by a small molecular weight serum protein. *Biochim. biophys. Res. Comm.* **66**, 747.

Woolley D. E., Roberts D. R. and Evanson J. M. (1976) Small molecular weight β1 serum protein which specifically inhibits human collagenase *Nature (Lond.)* **261**, 325.

Woolley D. E., Glanville R. W., Crossley M. J. and Evanson J. M. (1975) Purification of rheumatoid synovial collagenase and its action on soluble and insoluble collagen. *Eur. J. Biochem.* **54**, 611.

Woolley D. E., Lindberg K. A., Glanville R. W. and Evanson J. M. (1975a) Action of rheumatoid syno-

vial collagenase on cartilage collagen. Different sus-
ceptibilities of cartilage and tendon collagen to
collagenase. *Eur. J. Biochem.* **50,** 437.

Woolley D. E., Lindberg K. A., Glanville R. W. and
Evanson J. M. (1975b) Action of rheumatoid syno-
vial collagenase on cartilage collagen. *Ann. rheum
Dis.* **34,** Suppl. 2, 70.

Yamagata T., Saito H., Habuchi O. and Suzuki S.
(1968) Purification and properties of bacterial
chondroitinases and chondrosulfatases. *J. biol.
Chem.* **243,** 1523.

4. Physicochemical Properties of Articular Cartilage

A. Maroudas

1. INTRODUCTION

The purpose of this Chapter is to describe in quantitative terms the physicochemical properties which are relevant in the study of cartilage nutrition, load bearing and lubrication. Thus the main topics will be the distribution and transport of various types of solutes in cartilage, osmotic pressure and fluid flow. These properties will be discussed, whenever possible, both in relation to one another and with reference to the structure of cartilage.

The extracellular component of cartilage consists primarily of collagen fibres embedded in a gel of proteoglycans and water. Since cells occupy a small fraction of the total volume of human articular cartilage, the physicochemical properties of cartilage are defined mainly by the properties of this matrix. Whilst the collagen network is responsible for the integrity of the tissue and its tensile strength, both fluid and solute transport depend principally on the properties of the proteoglycan–water gel. Because the proteoglycan molecule contains fixed negatively charged groups (carboxylate and sulphate due to chondroitin and keratan sulphates), the gel possesses the typical properties of a polyelectrolyte solution.

Provided autolytic degradation of cartilage is minimized, the structure of the matrix remains unchanged on death, so that it is possible to study its properties *in vitro*. Moreover, articular cartilage does not swell and can be conveniently cut and exposed to solution without any significant loss of its proteoglycans (Maroudas, Muir and Wingham 1969). The methods used to study the properties of articular cartilage *in vitro* are thus relatively simple.

215

Although chondrocyte metabolism has been dealt with in Chapters 2 and 3, the question of the turnover of the main matrix constituents will be dealt with in this Chapter, with special reference to the methodology for both *in vivo* and *in vitro* studies, as this aspect of the subject is dependent upon physicochemical considerations.

2. PHYSICOCHEMICAL PROPERTIES AND CHEMICAL COMPOSITION

Although the chemical constitution of the matrix has already been discussed in Chapters 1 and 3, it is proposed to reconsider here the role of each constituent and the variations in its concentration because these are responsible for the observed variations in the physicochemical properties of the matrix. Each of the major constituents will be discussed in turn.

2.1. Collagen

* A conversion table from the Système International (SI) units is given on page 545.

Collagen fibres form a relatively coarse structure: the fibrils themselves are 30–80 nm (300–800Å)* in diameter (Chapter 1, Section 2.5) and the gaps between them are large (of the order of 100 nm (1000Å) or more; see Figure 1.12, for instance) compared with the 2–10 nm (20–100Å) 'pores' within the proteoglycan–water gel. Moreover, at physiological pH the cartilage collagen behaves as if it contained practically no unneutralized charged groups, as shown in Figure 4.1 (W. D. S. Freeman and Maroudas, in preparation; also Freeman and Maroudas 1975). In this respect, cartilage collagen behaves differently from some of the other collagens; thus reconstituted steer hide collagen has been reported to have a net positive charge (Li and Katz 1976). Both the coarseness of the fibres and their electrical neutrality render collagen physicochemically inert and therefore of less interest than the proteoglycan constituent. However, it is important to bear in mind that it is the relative inextensibility of the collagen fibre network in cartilage which limits the water content of cartilage, even when the latter is excised from the joint.

The variations in the collagen content are relatively small; typical values on a wet basis for normal femoral head cartilage are 20% for the surface, 15% for the middle zone and 18% for the deep zone.

On a wet basis, the collagen content remains constant with ageing. On a dry basis, however, it decreases somewhat due to the increase in the concentration of non-collagenous protein (Venn 1977), most of which appears to be associated with the proteoglycan aggregate (Venn, Bayliss and Maroudas 1978, in preparation).

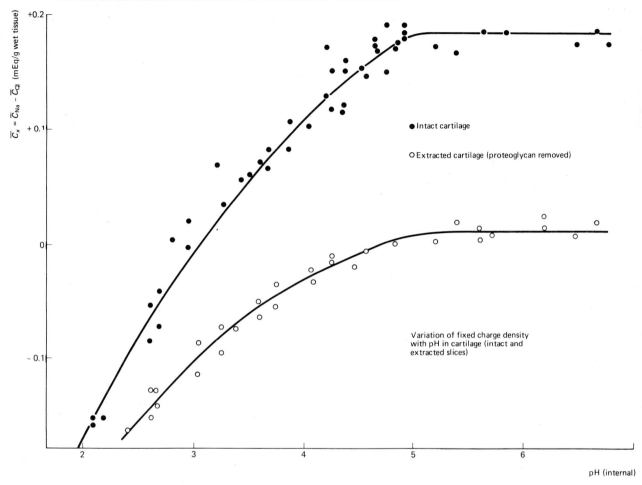

Figure 4.1 Variation of fixed charge density $(\bar{C}_x)$ with internal pH for (●) intact cartilage and (○) cartilage from which the proteoglycan constituent has been removed.

2.2. Water

2.2.1. Water Content. Water is the major constituent of cartilage as it accounts for 60–80% of the wet weight of the tissue (see Chapter 3). The actual water content of a given specimen is determined by the balance between the swelling pressure of the proteoglycans and the tension in the collagen network (see Sections 6.1 and 6.2.5)

Since both the physicochemical and the mechanical properties of cartilage depend on the ratio of the individual solid constituents of the matrix to water, it is very important in any investigation of such properties to measure the water content and to express all concentrations on a wet weight basis.

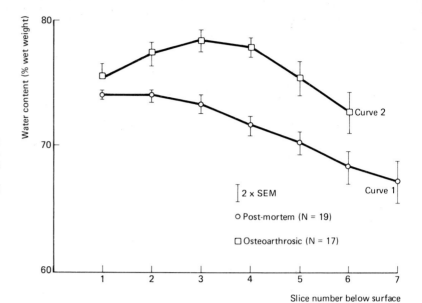

Figure 4.2 Variation in water content as a function of depth in cartilage from normal post-mortem and osteoarthrotic femoral heads.

(Reproduced from Venn and Maroudas (1977) by permission.)

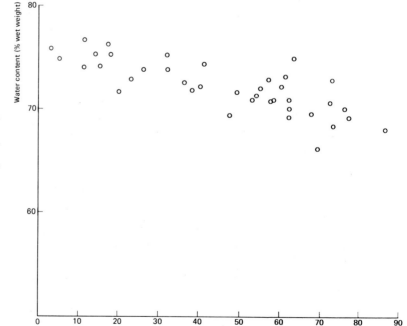

Figure 4.3 Variation with age in the water content of non-fibrillated post-mortem articular cartilage from the superior surface of the normal human femoral head.

(Reproduced from Venn (1977) by permission.)

Figure 4.2 curve 1 shows the variation in the water content with distance from the articular surface for normal cartilage from the femoral head. This presents the same pattern as has been previously observed for the femoral condyle (Maroudas, Muir and Wingham 1969).

Although previous workers found no significant difference in the water content of the normal, non-fibrillated tissue with ageing after maturity has been reached, more recent data appear to indicate that there is a steady decrease in the water content with advancing years (Almeida 1973; Venn 1977; Amado 1976, private communication). Such a trend would be consistent with a greater degree of cross-linking in the collagen fibre network and hence a lower extensibility.

The variation in the water content with age, as determined by Venn (1977), is shown in Figure 4.3. A lowering in the water content with ageing implies that, although on a dry weight basis the concentration of a given constituent may not be changing, on a wet basis there may be an increase.

It has long been known (e.g. Hirsch 1944) that in fibrillated cartilage the water content is higher than in normal. Recently it has been found that the pattern of variation with depth is also different (Venn and Maroudas 1977), as shown in Figure 4.2 curve 2. Thus, whilst in intact cartilage there is a uniform decrease in the water content with depth, in fibrillated tissue the water content shows a maximum in the middle zone, paralleling the fixed charge density (FCD) distribution (see Figure 4.4). Both the above profile and the elevated overall water content can be explained by postulating that the collagen network is damaged, leading to a decrease in the elastic restraint of the latter on the swelling tendencies of the proteoglycan–water gel (Section 6.2.5) (Maroudas 1976a)

The fact that the overall water content is increased in fibrillated tissue means that on a weight basis the concentration of both collagen and the proteoglycans must be lower than in intact cartilage, even if there were no difference in the proportion of these constituents on a dry basis (Venn and Maroudas 1977).

2.2.2. State of Water in Cartilage. The following evidence points to the fact that the extracellular water in cartilage behaves as free water as regards both availability to small solutes and mobility.

First, the partition coefficients of small, uncharged solutes such as amino-acids, urea and glucose are very close to unity when based on the total water content of cartilage (Maroudas 1970). Secondly, as in the case of other small solutes, the diffusion coefficient of tritiated water in cartilage is equal to approximately half its value in free solution; such a reduction can be predicted simply from considerations of increased tortuosity in cartilage as compared with free solution (Maroudas and Venn 1977). Thirdly, the activation energy for the diffusion of tritiated water in cartilage is equal to 16.8 kJ (4.0 kcal), which is the same as in free solution (Maroudas and Venn 1977). Finally, the uptake and desorption of tritiated water can be fitted precisely by a diffusion equation based on a single diffusion coefficient, which shows clearly that the water in cartilage behaves as a single compartment system, i.e. that no part of it is less mobile than the rest (Maroudas and Venn 1977).

The increase in the water content observed in fibrillated cartilage is attributed by the present author to a damaged collagen network. Mankin and Zarins-Thrasher (1975) thought that there was an increase in the proportion of bound water in such tissues, but no evidence for this hypothesis has been found by the present author (Maroudas and Venn 1977).

Although all the water in cartilage is accessible to small solutes and participates in isotopic exchange, some of this water must be associated with collagen fibrils. Thus, it has been reported that in reconstituted steer hide collagen in tendon such intrafibrillar water is present in the ratio of $\simeq$1.2:1 (Katz and Li 1973) to the dry weight of collagen. As far as cartilage is concerned, it is not known what fraction of water is present in the intrafibrillar form or whether this water is available to the proteoglycan molecules. If the proteoglycan molecules were completely absent from the intrafibrillar space, as has been suggested by Wells (1972), the matrix of cartilage would be a two-phase system, with a considerable difference in the osmotic pressure across the surface of the fibril. As a result of this difference in the osmotic pressure, one would expect the intrafibrillar water content to be much lower in cartilage than in materials such as reconstituted collagen or tendon, which contain little proteoglycan.

Whether in reality the extracellular water exists as a two-phase system or not, calculations based on the assumption of a uniform proteoglycan gel involving all of the cartilage water have yielded activity coefficients for NaCl in cartilage which are close to those in an isolated proteoglycan gel of similar concentration (Freeman and Maroudas 1975) (see also Section 3.2.1) and a Gibbs–Donnan osmotic pressure which corresponds well with the measured value in proteoglycan–water gels (Section 3.2.4) (Urban 1977).

2.3. Proteoglycans

Although present in relatively small quantities (approximately 10% w/w or 7% v/v), this is the constituent which is responsible for a number of the most important characteristics of cartilage. The flexible, hydrophilic nature of the glycosaminoglycan chains and their high concentration of negatively charged fixed groups, lead to a high swelling pressure whilst the fine macromolecular mesh ensures a low hydraulic permeability. These two properties allied to the high water content of cartilage combine to make this tissue eminently suitable as a load-bearing material with a low coefficient of friction (see Section 6).

The selective behaviour of the matrix to the penetration of various solutes is also closely dependent on the concentration of negatively charged groups and the fineness of the proteoglycan mesh.

Thus even small variations in the proteoglycan content will lead to considerable changes in the behaviour of the tissue.

2.3.1. Fixed Charge Density. In order to study quantitatively the variation in the physicochemical properties of cartilage with the proteoglycan content, a rapid non-destructive and versatile micro-method for the determination of the latter was needed. Because of the quantitative agreement between the total glycosaminogly-can (GAG) content determined by chemical analysis and that corresponding to the concentration of negatively charged fixed groups as obtained by physical methods (Maroudas *et al.* 1969; Maroudas and Thomas 1970; Venn and Maroudas 1977), it was possible to adopt the latter parameter as a direct measure of the GAG content.

Fixed charge density (FCD) is defined as the concentration of fixed groups in milliequivalents per gram of wet tissue. The two experimental methods (the streaming potential and the tracer cation) which have been used to determine fixed charge density in cartilage have been described in detail in the literature (Maroudas 1968; Maroudas *et al.* 1969; Maroudas and Thomas 1970; Venn and Maroudas 1977) and will be described briefly in Section 3.2.2. The tracer cation method has been found to be more convenient: it is non-destructive, quick and accurate, and specimens of any shape or size can be handled, weighing as little as 1 mg or as much as 1 g.

Using this method, studies have been made of the topographical variations in the total GAG content in cartilage from (a) femoral heads obtained at post-mortem (Maroudas, Evans and Almeida 1973), (b) patellae obtained at post-mortem (Ficat and Maroudas 1975), and (c) osteoarthrotic femoral heads removed for total hip replacement (Venn and Maroudas 1977; Byers, Maroudas, Oztop, Stockwell and Venn 1977).

The following main conclusions emerged from this work.

Intact cartilage from post-mortem hips (femoral heads) has a much higher GAG content than the intact cartilage from the knee (femoral condyles or patellae). Preliminary results have also shown that cartilage from peripheral joints (e.g. talus and inter-phalangeal) has an even lower GAG content than the knee cartilage.

Intact cartilage (i.e. 'intact' as judged by the technique of Byers, Contempomi and Farkas (1970) and by Meachim's procedure involving the use of Indian ink (Meachim 1972; see also Chapter 1, Section 9) showed relatively small variations in fixed charge density over the area of any one joint. In contrast, sites which exhibited signs of fibrillation, however slight, invariably had a much lower fixed charge density. This decrease in fixed charge density at fibrillated sites is due to an increase in the water content, superimposed on a decrease in the GAG concentration, and agrees with the findings of other authors (e.g. Hirsch 1944; Matthews 1953; Bollet and Nance 1966; Hjertquist and Lemperg 1972).

Localized degeneration at a given site does not lead to changes in the GAG content at other sites provided the cartilage surface there is intact. This was observed both in femoral heads and in patellae obtained at post-mortem.

In osteoarthrotic femoral heads, too, there were considerable topographical variations in the GAG content, which usually correlated well with the histology of the tissue (Venn and Maroudas 1977; Byers et al. 1977).

The examples in Figures 4.4, 4.5 and 4.6 illustrate some of the above conclusions.

Figure 4.4 shows a typical variation in FCD with distance from the articular surface for intact cartilage from different sites of the

Figure 4.4 Variation in total glycosaminoglycan content (expressed as FCD) with distance from the articular surface for intact cartilage from different sites of (a) post-mortem femoral head and (b) a patella.

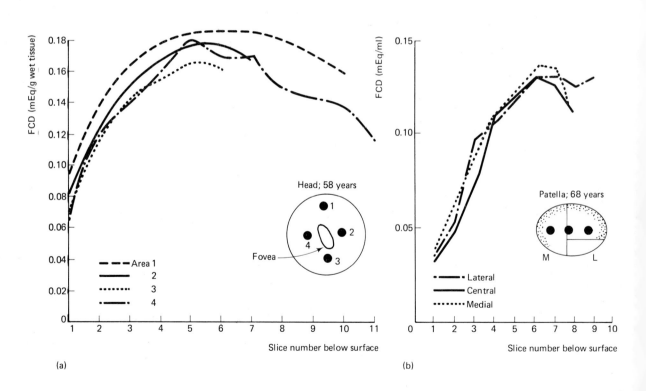

femoral head and the patella. The thin area below the fovea has a somewhat lower FCD than the other sites on the femoral head. The overall level of FCD is higher for the femoral head than for the patella.

Figure 4.5 illustrates the variations in GAG content on a femoral head and a patella with both normal and fibrillated sites.

Figure 4.5 Comparison between the FCD versus depth curves between normal and fibrillated sites from (a) a post-mortem femoral head and (b) patella.

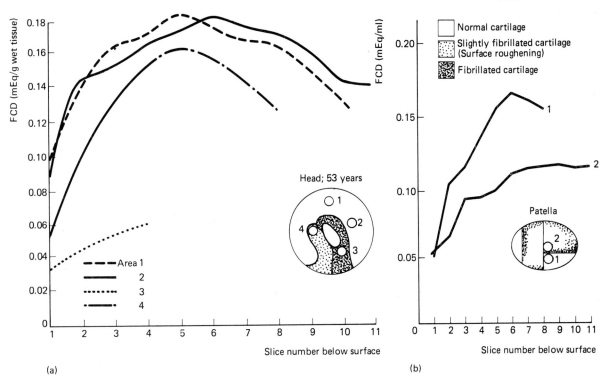

(a)

(b)

Figure 4.6 shows diagrammatically an osteoarthrotic femoral head, with an area of bone exposure present on the superior facet. The cartilage covering the remainder of the joint surface ranged from visually intact to severely fibrillated; the glycosaminoglycan content ranged from practically normal to very low. It is interesting to note that at sites immediately adjacent to the denuded area, cartilage was considerably thinner, but showed only slight fibrillation. Its fixed charge density was much lower than that corresponding to the deep zone of a normal specimen. However, only a few millimetres away from the thinned cartilage, both the appearance and the GAG content were close to normal.

Although in severely fibrillated cartilage, whether present in post-mortem or osteoarthrotic specimens, fixed charge density is considerably lower than in normal cartilage, it is never close to zero, even in the superficial zone.

The lowest level of fixed charge density encountered in any of the specimens in this study was around 0.03 mEq/g of wet tissue. It may be that this represents the same proteoglycan fraction which is so difficult to separate from collagen by extractive biochemical procedures and which is thought to be intimately associated with the collagen fibres (see Chapter 3).

Figure 4.6 Comparison of the GAG content between different sites on an osteoarthrotic femoral head.

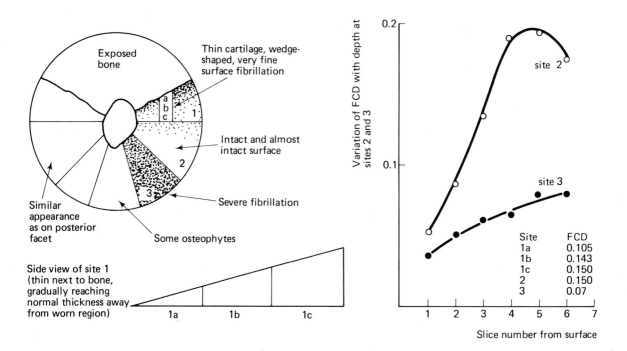

Site	FCD
1a	0.105
1b	0.143
1c	0.150
2	0.150
3	0.07

Venn (1977) has recently studied the variation in fixed charge density with age and found a small increase, particularly up to the age of 40.

The tracer cation method (described in Section 3.2.2) has been adapted to study quantitatively topographical variations in fixed charge density not only on a macro-scale but also on a micro-scale. It is possible, by the use of an x-ray microprobe, to determine simultaneously the total concentrations of negatively charged fixed groups and of sulphur, and to localize the analysed spot to within a few microns. From a knowledge of the relative proportions of negatively charged fixed groups and of sulphur, it is possible to deduce the type of glycosaminoglycan present (Maroudas 1972).

Thus, for instance, the tracer cation method, together with x-ray microanalysis, has made it possible to determine quantitatively

both the fixed charge density and the sulphur content in the first
10 μm of the surface zone. It was shown that the concentration of
negatively charged fixed groups in this layer was low, though by no
means negligible, and that the ratio of fixed charge density to
sulphur equivalents was just under 2, indicating the presence of
more or less pure chondroitin sulphate and no significant amounts
of hyaluronic acid (but see Chapter 3, Section 3.3). Although the
very uppermost surface layer, the so-called 'surface lamina', is
thinner than the analysed section (approximately 2–5 μm as
compared with 10 μm), the presence of significant amounts of
hyaluronic acid in it would have affected the results. Thus it may
be inferred that the protein–hyaluronate in synovial fluid does not
penetrate cartilage to any significant extent, a finding relevant to
the lubrication of cartilage in life (see Section 7 of this Chapter,
and Chapter 7).

Another subject which has interested histochemists is the variation in chemical composition from the pericellular rim to the
interterritorial matrix. Intense staining around cell lacunae
observed with basic dyes has been interpreted by many workers
(Chapter 1, Section 4.3.2) as indicative of a much greater concentration of negatively charged fixed groups in the perilacunar area
than in the interterritorial matrix. Some histochemists (Szirmai
1969), on the other hand, have argued that the differences in
staining represent differences in the amounts of collagen and not
in glycosaminoglycan concentration. Here again it has been possible, by means of x-ray microprobe analysis, to throw more light
on the subject.

Increased amounts of collagen in the pericellular areas, compared with the interterritorial matrix, would be reflected by
differences in the dry mass per unit thickness of a slice of wet
tissue. Since no such differences have been found, it can be
concluded that round at least the majority of cells in articular
cartilage no dense 'basket' of collagen is present. On the other
hand, a somewhat higher fixed charge density has been observed
on the perilacunar rim than in the interterritorial matrix both in
the middle and the deep zones of cartilage. The differences,
however, are not very great (less than 20%) (Maroudas 1972).

Although with the conventional x-ray microprobe which was
used in the above studies a resolution of a few microns is the best
that can be achieved, a combined transmission electron
microscope-microanalyser (EMMA) could give a resolution of the
order of 0.1 μm. With this sort of resolution the present method of
determining fixed charge density could be of much wider use; e.g.
in the localization of glycosaminoglycans with respect to collagen
fibrils in different connective tissues, or in the study of cell
membranes.

The results of fixed charge density measurements have been
described in some detail for two reasons: first, because fixed

charge density itself (or the glycosaminoglycan content with which it can be equated) is the most important parameter as far as solute and fluid transport through the matrix are concerned; and secondly, because fixed charge density micromethods have led to new information on the local variations in the glycosaminoglycan content in normal and degenerate cartilage.

3. DISTRIBUTION OF SUBSTANCES BETWEEN CARTILAGE AND EXTERNAL SOLUTION

In vivo, cartilage is in contact with synovial fluid. The concentration of a solute in cartilage therefore depends on three factors: (a) the concentration of the solute in synovial fluid; (b) the distribution of the solute between synovial fluid (or a solution of equivalent composition) and cartilage; and (c) the consumption of the solute (or production) by the chondrocytes.

The distribution of various solutes between cartilage and external solution has been extensively studied *in vitro* by the present writer and her associates (Maroudas 1970; Maroudas and Evans 1972, 1974; Snowden and Maroudas 1976; Maroudas 1976b). Some results have also been obtained *in vivo* (Maroudas 1975a; Maroudas, unpublished results). The distribution of solutes can be quantitatively described by the distribution coefficient, K, which is defined, on a molal basis, as the ratio of the concentration of a given solute in cartilage water to its concentration in the external solution (or $K = \bar{m}/m$, where $\bar{m}$ = solute concentration in cartilage, in moles solute/1000 g of cartilage water, and m = concentration of solute in external solution, in moles solute/1000 g of water).

3.1. Distribution of Small Non-ionic Solutes

The distribution of a non-ionic solute between cartilage and external solution can be expected to depend primarily on the fraction of free water in cartilage which is accessible to that solute. *In vitro* studies of small solutes such as urea, proline, glucose (Maroudas 1970, 1975a) have shown that the molal distribution coefficients for these solutes are close to unity and are independent of the GAG content. This implies, as has been stated in Section 2.2.2 that all or most of the cartilage water is (a) free and (b) accessible to small solutes.

The total water content includes, of course, intracellular water, which also acts as solvent for small molecules and ions. The selective permeability of cell membranes *in vivo* is not reflected in the *in vitro* studies. However, the overall picture of ionic and non-ionic equilibria in cartilage would be modified relatively little by a different distribution within the chondrocytes as the latter constitute only a small fraction of the total volume, viz. 0.4–2% (Chapter 2, Section 5).

Part of the extracellular water is associated with the collagen fibrils. In reconstituted steer hide collagen the interfibrillar water has been reported to be approximately equal to 1.2 × dry weight of collagen (Katz and Li 1973). If it were of the same order of magnitude in cartilage, it would be equivalent to about 30% of the total water content. Katz and Li (1973) estimate that only a very small fraction of this water (20%) is localized within the helix itself, the rest being intermolecular and more or less equally divided between 'pores' which can hold about 5 water molecules and 'holes' into which some 50 water molecules can fit. Thus most of the collagen water should show limited accessibility to larger molecules but should be freely available to small solutes. This is consistent with our studies on cartilage which do not show any measurable space from which small solutes are excluded.

3.2. Ionic Equilibria

3.2.1. Donnan Equilibrium and the Activity of NaCl in Cartilage.
Since the matrix of cartilage contains negatively charged groups—the sulphate and the carboxylate groups of chondroitin and keratan sulphates—which are not free to move, one may expect a Donnan potential to be set up across the interface when cartilage is immersed in an electrolyte solution. The distribution of mobile ions between cartilage and the external solution would be expected to obey the Donnan equilibrium equation, viz.

$$\left(\frac{a_{cation}}{\bar{a}_{cation}}\right) z_{anion} = \left(\frac{\bar{a}_{anion}}{a_{anion}}\right) z_{cation} \qquad (1)^*$$

* The symbols used in this Chapter are listed on p. 287.

where a = activity of the ion in solution,
$\bar{a}$ = activity of the ion in cartilage,
z = valency of the ion;

and the electroneutrality condition, viz.

$$\bar{C}_{cation} = \bar{C}_{anion} + \bar{C}_{immobile\ anion} \qquad (2)$$

where $\bar{C}$ = concentrations in cartilage in gram equivalents.

It should be noted that activities are related to concentrations by the following equation:

$$a = \gamma m \qquad (3)$$

where γ = activity coefficient,
m = concentration expressed on a molal basis (moles of solute per volume of water).

The departure of γ from unity is a measure of the deviation of the solute from ideal behaviour.

For simple electrolyte solutions, instead of single ionic activity coefficients which cannot be measured directly, one generally uses mean electrolyte activity coefficients, defined by the expression

$$\gamma_{\pm} = \{(\gamma_{z^+})(\gamma_{z^-})\}^{\frac{1}{2z}} \tag{4}$$

Thus for a NaCl solution

$$\gamma_{\pm} = \sqrt{(\gamma_{Na^+})(\gamma_{Cl^-})} \tag{5}$$

By analogy, it is possible to define a mean activity coefficient $\bar{\gamma}_{\pm}$, of Na^+ and Cl^- in cartilage.

Accordingly, for cartilage equilibrated in NaCl solution equation (1) can be expressed in the form

$$\left(\frac{\bar{m}_{Na^+}}{m_{Na^+}}\right)\left(\frac{\bar{\gamma}_{\pm}}{\gamma_{\pm}}\right) = \left(\frac{m_{Cl^-}}{\bar{m}_{Cl^-}}\right)\left(\frac{\gamma_{\pm}}{\bar{\gamma}_{\pm}}\right) \tag{6}$$

where $\bar{m}_{Na^+}$ and $\bar{m}_{Cl^-}$ represent molal concentrations of Na^+ and Cl^- in cartilage, respectively,

m_{Na^+} and m_{Cl^-} represent molal concentrations of Na^+ and Cl^- in external solution,

$\bar{\gamma}_{\pm}$ is the mean electrolyte activity coefficient in cartilage,

$\gamma_{\pm}$ is the mean electrolyte activity coefficient in solution.

Since in external solution $m_{Na^+} = m_{Cl^-} = m_{NaCl}$, equation (6) further reduces to

$$\left(\frac{\bar{\gamma}_{\pm}}{\gamma_{\pm}}\right)^2 = \frac{(m_{NaCl})^2}{(\bar{m}_{Na^+})(\bar{m}_{Cl^-})} \tag{7}$$

The deviation of $(\bar{\gamma}_{\pm}/\gamma_{\pm})$ from unity describes to what extent the behaviour of the electrolyte in the tissue departs from its behaviour in solution.

The values of the mean activity coefficient lie in the range 0.67–0.72 (Table 4.1), as compared with the value 0.755 in a 0.15 mol/litre (0.15M) NaCl solution.

If $\bar{m}_+$ and $\bar{m}_-$ are experimentally determined, the mean ionic activity coefficient in the tissue, $\bar{\gamma}_{\pm}$, can be found from equation (7). Values of $\gamma_{\pm}$, the mean ionic activity coefficient in free solution, are tabulated for numerous electrolytes in Robinson and Stokes (1968). Figure 4.7, which is taken from such data, gives $\gamma_{\pm}$ as a function of $(m)^{\frac{1}{2}}$ for NaCl solutions.

Table 4.1

Typical values of the partition coefficients of Na^+ and Cl^- between cartilage from the femoral head and NaCl solution

FCD	$\dfrac{\bar{m}_{Na^+}}{m_{Na^+}}$	$\dfrac{\bar{m}_{Cl^-}}{m_{Cl^-}}$	$\bar{\gamma}_{\pm}$
0.105	1.66	0.672	0.720
0.120	1.83	0.686	0.675
0.145	1.83	0.610	0.718
0.154	2.04	0.607	0.680
0.162	2.19	0.573	0.670
0.178	2.21	0.540	0.690

228

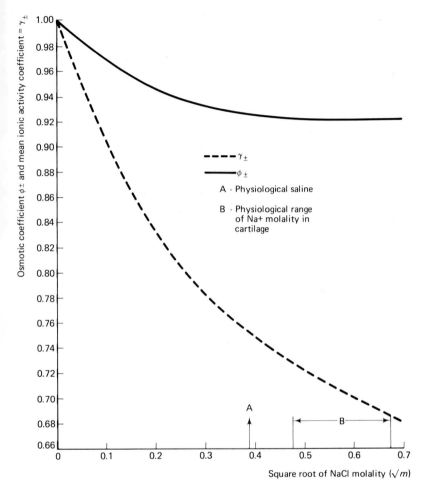

Figure 4.7 Variation in the values of the mean ionic activity coefficient, $\bar{\gamma}_{\pm}$, and the osmotic coefficient, $\varphi_{\pm}$, in free NaCl solution as a function of the square root of concentration at 25°C.

(Data from Robinson and Stokes 1968.) (Reproduced from Urban (1977) by permission.)

Maroudas (1975a) and W. D. S. Freeman and Maroudas (in preparation) found that the values of $\bar{\gamma}_{\pm}$ for NaCl in cartilage as well as in proteoglycan gels lie mostly between 0.65 and 0.72 and that $\bar{\gamma}_{\pm}$ decreases as the fixed charge density increases (Figure 4.8). These values of $\bar{\gamma}_{\pm}$ are very similar to those in aqueous solution at a concentration of NaCl equivalent to $\bar{m}_{+}$, the cation concentration in the internal solution (Maroudas 1975a). It therefore appears that Na$^+$ and Cl$^-$ ions in proteoglycan solutions behave in a similar fashion to those in an aqueous solution of similar concentration of total ionic groups (mobile and fixed).

The knowledge of $\bar{\gamma}_{\pm}$ is important as it can be used to calculate the Donnan contribution to the osmotic pressure of the tissue (see Section 3.2.1).

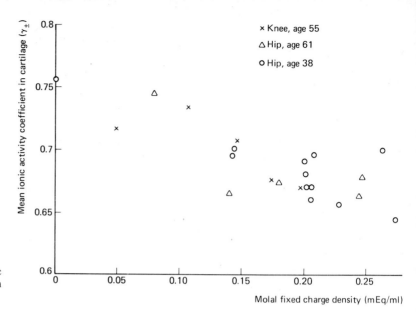

Figure 4.8 Variation in the mean ionic activity coefficient in cartilage, $\bar{\gamma}_{\pm}$, with fixed charge density.

Although there are no rigorous methods for predicting the activity coefficients in polyelectrolyte solutions or gels, various semitheoretical approaches have been developed. It is usual to split the mean activity coefficient of the electrolyte into the contributions of (a) the interactions between the mobile ions only and (b) those between the polyion and the mobile ions. The most complete treatment of the polyion–mobile ion interactions is that due to Manning (1969). Manning derived equations by means of which it is possible to calculate the activity coefficients as well as the osmotic coefficients in a solution of any polyelectrolyte provided the distance between the charges on the polyelectrolyte molecule is known. The closer the charges are to one another, the more 'ion condensation' there is and the less osmotically active the counterions thus become. The cartilage glycosaminoglycans consist of almost equimolar proportions of chondroitin sulphate (CS) and keratan sulphate (KS), the former containing two negatively charged groups per disaccharide unit, whilst the latter contains only one. The mean intercharge distance is thus relatively large (~0.75 nm: Wells 1973) and according to Manning's criteria no counterion condensation should occur.

Manning's theory is applicable only to the case of very low external electrolyte concentration. Modifications of the Manning treatment have been suggested (e.g. Wells 1973; Kwak 1973) which are meant to make the equations suitable for use at higher concentrations of NaCl, including the physiological. According to these modifications the following equation should be employed to relate Manning's activity coefficient of the counterion in a salt-free solution, $\bar{\gamma}^{PM}$, to the mean activity coefficient $\bar{\gamma}_{\pm}$:

$$\bar{\gamma}_{\pm} = \bar{\gamma}^{PM} \times \bar{\gamma}_{\pm}^{MM} \qquad (8)$$

However, there are different interpretations of the term $\bar{\gamma}_{\pm}^{MM}$. Thus, in Wells' equation $\bar{\gamma}^{MM}$ is taken to be the mean activity coefficient of the salt corresponding to the concentration of the co-ion in the polyelectrolyte solution. In Kwak's treatment, on the other hand, $\bar{\gamma}_{\pm}^{MM}$ corresponds to the mean ionic strength of the polyelectrolyte solution. The present writer agrees with the latter (Maroudas 1975a).

Manning (1969) calculated $\bar{\gamma}^{PM}$ as a function of the parameter X which expresses the ratio of the fixed charge density to the concentration of free electrolyte ($X = \bar{C}_X/\bar{C}_{\text{electrolyte}}$). A curve of $\bar{\gamma}^{PM}$ calculated from Manning's theory as modified by Wells is shown in Figure 4.9 for proteoglycans with an intercharge spacing of 0.75 nm. The values of $\bar{\gamma}^{PM}$ calculated from our experimental results for $\bar{\gamma}_{\pm}$ using equation (7) and Wells' interpretation of $\bar{\gamma}_{\pm}^{MM}$ are shown in the same Figure and are seen to lie above the theoretical curve. An even greater discrepancy is observed if $\bar{\gamma}^{MM}$ is calculated at the mean ionic strength of the inner phase, although the latter method of calculation has a more valid theoretical basis (Iwasi and Kwak, 1976). It can thus be concluded that the activity of NaCl in cartilage and in concentrated proteoglycan gels is higher than predicted theoretically by Manning's treatment. Kwak found a similar trend in synthetic polyelectrolyte solutions at high polyelectrolyte concentrations (Kwak 1973).

An important implication of the fact that the activity coefficient of NaCl in cartilage is only slightly below the ideal value is that the Donnan osmotic pressure must be close to the ideal value as well. Hence it must be higher than has been estimated on the basis of model systems (Wells 1973) or from results obtained on very dilute proteoglycan solutions (Preston, Snowden and Houghton 1972). Details on the calculation of the Donnan osmotic pressure from $\bar{\gamma}^{PM}$ are given in Section 3.2.4.

Some consequences and applications of the Donnan equilibrium are described in the following pages.

3.2.2. Tracer Cation Method for the Determination of Negatively Charged Fixed Groups.
The fact that the Donnan equilibrium holds for cartilage equilibrated in very dilute solutions has been used as the basis of a method (the tracer cation method) for the quantitative determination of negatively charged fixed groups in the following way (Maroudas and Thomas 1970). Since the ratio

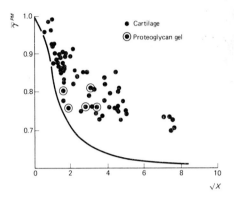

Figure 4.9 Variation of $\bar{\gamma}^{PM}$, the polyion–mobile ion contribution to the activity coefficient of NaCl in cartilage and proteoglycan gels. X is defined as the ratio of fixed charge density to the concentration of free electrolyte in cartilage; $\bar{\gamma}^{PM}$ has been calculated from the formula

$$\bar{\gamma}_{\pm} = \bar{\gamma}^{PM} \times \bar{\gamma}^{MM},$$

where $\bar{\gamma}^{MM}$ is the mean ionic activity of NaCl solution at a concentration corresponding to that of co-ion in cartilage (Maroudas and W. D. S. Freeman, unpublished results).

$\bar{m}_{Na^+}/m_{Na^+}$ is high for cartilage equilibrated in a dilute solution, it follows from equation (7) that the ratio $\bar{m}_{Cl^-}/m_{Cl^-}$ is correspondingly low. This in turn implies that the concentration of free electrolyte in cartilage ($\bar{m}_{Cl^-}$) is very low and hence that, in accordance with equation (2), the concentration of cations in cartilage is practically equal to the concentration of negatively charged fixed groups. Thus by measuring the concentration of these cations one can obtain a value for the total concentration of negatively charged fixed groups.

If fixed charge density is very low (<0.04 mEq/g) the concentration of free electrolyte in cartilage can no longer be neglected and $\bar{m}_{Cl^-}$ has to be determined in addition to $\bar{m}_{Na^+}$, by the use of (^{36}Cl) tracer. Fixed charge density can then be calculated from equation (2). The graph in Figure 4.10 shows the results of an extensive recent study involving both normal and degenerate cartilage, of the correlation between fixed charge density as measured directly by the tracer cation method and as calculated from hexosamine

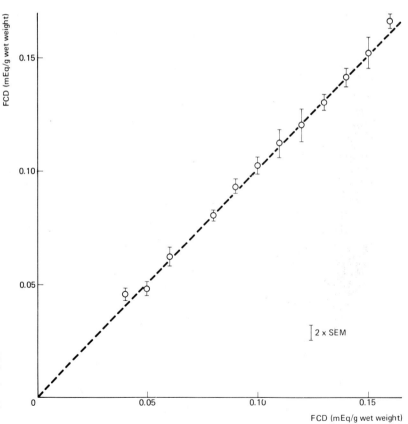

Figure 4.10 Comparison between fixed charge density as measured by the tracer cation method and as obtained from chemical analysis.
(Reproduced from Venn and Maroudas (1977) by permission.)

and uronic acid analysis (Venn and Maroudas 1977). The excellent agreement between the two sets of values at all levels of fixed charge density implies that the majority of the glycosaminoglycans in cartilage show normal charge densities, even in osteoarthrosis. Thus supersulphation or undersulphation, if present at all, cannot affect more than a very small fraction of the glycosaminoglycans.

The fact that all the negatively charged groups of the glycosaminoglycans are available to the sodium ions means that they are not neutralized by the positively charged groups on the collagen molecules. This is entirely in agreement with the finding that at the physiological pH the collagen in cartilage has no net positive charge and that no substantial amount of proteoglycan is involved in electrostatic interactions with it (see p. 217, Fig. 4.1, and Freeman and Maroudas 1975; also W. D. Freeman and Maroudas, in preparation).

3.2.3. Internal pH in Cartilage.

From the Donnan equilibrium (equation (1)) it follows that the hydrogen ion activity must always be higher in cartilage than in external solution. The internal pH in cartilage (p$\bar{\text{H}}$) is given by the formula (Freeman and Maroudas 1975):

$$\text{p}\bar{\text{H}} = \text{pH} + \log K_{\text{Cl}^-} \qquad (9)$$

where pH = pH of external solution
and K_{Cl^-} = molal partition coefficient of the chloride ion between cartilage and external solution.

Femoral head cartilage from the middle zone may be taken as an example with a typical fixed charge density of 0.18 mEq/g and a corresponding K_{Cl^-} of 0.49. Hence pH − p$\bar{\text{H}}$ = 0.31. The internal pH would thus be 0.3 units lower than that of the outside solution. The higher the fixed charge density, the lower will be K_{Cl^-}. Hence the internal cartilage pH decreases as the proteoglycan concentration increases.

Since proteolytic enzymes such as cathepsins B and D have their optima at acid pHs, the lowering of pH due to the Donnan effect in regions of high fixed charge density (e.g. around cell lacunae) might be of physiological significance.

3.2.4. Donnan Osmotic Pressure.

Because of the negatively charged fixed groups in cartilage, the distribution of mobile ionic species is not equal between cartilage and synovial fluid and, in accordance with the Donnan equilibrium, there will always be more ions in cartilage than in synovial fluid. The component of the swelling pressure of cartilage which is due to this excess of ions will be referred to as the ionic or the Donnan contribution to the swelling pressure and can be calculated from the equation

$$\frac{\Delta \pi}{RT} = \frac{\bar{\pi}}{RT} - \frac{\pi}{RT} \qquad (10)$$

where $\bar{\pi}$ and π are the Donnan osmotic pressures of the inner and outer phases respectively. They in turn are given by the expressions

$$\frac{\pi}{RT} = \varphi(m_{Na^+} + m_{Cl^-}) \tag{11}$$

and

$$\frac{\bar{\pi}}{RT} = \bar{\varphi}(\bar{m}_{Na^+} + \bar{m}_{Cl^-}) \tag{12}$$

where φ = osmotic coefficient of NaCl in synovial fluid (since the hyaluronic acid concentration of synovial fluid is very low, the osmotic coefficient will be very close to that in a 0.15 mol/litre (0.15M) NaCl solution),

$\bar{\varphi}$ = osmotic coefficient of NaCl in cartilage.

As for $\bar{\gamma}$, various semi-empirical treatments have been developed for estimating $\bar{\varphi}$ in polyelectrolyte solutions, the most complete treatment being again due to Manning (1969) and modified for use under physiological conditions by Wells (1973) and Kwak (1973). The osmotic coefficient $\bar{\varphi}$ can be split into two independent components, viz.

$$\bar{\varphi} = \bar{\varphi}^{PM} \cdot \bar{\varphi}^{MM} \tag{13}$$

where φ^{MM} is the osmotic coefficient of aqeous solution which can be taken either, in accordance with Wells (1973), at the co-ion concentration or, in accordance with Kwak (1973) and Maroudas (1975a), at the mean ionic strength.

$\bar{\varphi}^{PM}$ is the osmotic coefficient representing the interactions between polyion and counterions. It can either be calculated from the intercharge distance or it can be estimated from the value of $\bar{\gamma}^{PM}$ (calculated from the experimental value of $\bar{\gamma}_\pm$ by the use of equation (8)).

The relation between $\bar{\varphi}^{PM}$ and $\bar{\gamma}^{PM}$ is given by Manning as:

$$\bar{\varphi}^{PM} = 1 + \ln\bar{\gamma}^{PM} \tag{14}$$

$\bar{\varphi}$ can be calculated from equations (13) and (14) and can then be used to obtain $\Delta\pi_{Donnan}$ by means of equations (10) and (12).

Figure 4.11 shows curves of $\Delta\pi_{Donnan}$ calculated by means of equations (12), (13) and (14), $\bar{\gamma}^{PM}$ having been obtained from the experimental values of $\bar{\gamma}_\pm$ (equation (8)), considering $\bar{\gamma}^{MM}$ to correspond (a) to the co-ion concentration in cartilage and (b) to the mean ionic strength. Values calculated theoretically from the intercharge spacing by the Manning–Wells method are also plotted in the same Figure.

Although not many directly measured values of $\Delta\pi_{Donnan}$ are available for comparison, the values obtained by Maroudas (1975a) for femoral head cartilage are given together with those obtained by Urban (1977) for a proteoglycan gel of similar GAG concentrations as well as for the human nucleus pulposus. It can be seen that the experimental values agree most closely with the values calculated by procedure (b) from the experimental $\bar{y}_\pm$.

Experimentally, the following method was used to measure the ionic contribution to the swelling pressure of cartilage.

It can be shown from the Donnan equilibrium equation and the electroneutrality equation (equations (1) and (2), Section 3.2.1) that, if cartilage is equilibrated in concentrated salt solutions, the difference between the number of ions in cartilage and in external solution becomes very small, and hence the ionic contribution to the osmotic pressure should be negligible. Thus, if cartilage is transferred from a 0.15 mol/litre (0.15M) NaCl solution (i.e. physiological saline) into a hypertonic solution (say 1 mol/litre; 1.0M), the swelling pressure within cartilage will decrease by the amount due to its ionic component. One would accordingly expect a certain amount of water to be lost. Experimentally it has indeed been found (Maroudas 1975a) that when a plug of cartilage from the femoral head has been equilibrated in a 1 mol/litre (1.0M) NaCl solution, its water content is 5.0% lower than after equilibration in physiological saline. It has also been found that the same amount of water can be expressed from cartilage in 0.15 mol/litre (0.15M) NaCl solution by the application of an external load of about 0.17 MN/m² (1.7 kg/cm²). It can thus be concluded that the ionic contribution to the swelling pressure of cartilage is approximately 0.17 MN/m² (1.7 kg/cm²) for the cartilage of the femoral head.

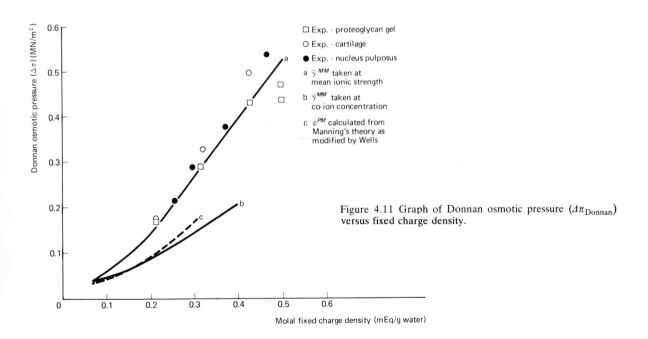

Figure 4.11 Graph of Donnan osmotic pressure ($\Delta\pi_{Donnan}$) versus fixed charge density.

The above method assumes that the total internal cartilage pressure is not dependent on the geometry of the specimen, but only on its water content. For small deformations this assumption is likely to hold.

As water is squeezed out of cartilage, the molal concentration of ionic species in cartilage increases and the Donnan osmotic pressure rises accordingly. When the water content has been reduced by about 30–40%, the Donnan osmotic pressure can rise to as much as 0.5 MN/m² (5 kg/cm²) (Maroudas 1975b).

Other procedures have been developed for the measurement of both the total internal cartilage pressure and the Donnan contribution (Maroudas 1975b) and are discussed in Section 6.2.

Although the Donnan osmotic pressures are relatively low compared with the pressures encountered in joints under load, they do play a part in determining the mechanical properties of cartilage. Their part is discussed in Section 6.4, with special reference to swelling equilibria and the analysis of forces producing creep in cartilage, and again in Chapter 6, Section 3.

3.2.5. Composition of Liquid Expressed from Cartilage. An interesting consequence of the Donnan equilibrium, reported by Linn and Sokoloff (1965), is the decreasing electrolyte concentration which they observed in successive portions of fluid expressed from cartilage under pressure, the composition of the first fraction being close to that of synovial fluid. By considering the liquid expressed at each compression stage as being in thermodynamic (i.e. Donnan) equilibrium with the cartilage at that stage, and by assuming a value for the initial concentration of fixed negative groups in the cartilage, a quantitative expression for the electrolyte composition of each portion of fluid can be derived (Maroudas, unpublished work). Linn and Sokoloff's experimental results were found to agree with these theoretical predictions. It is important to realize that expression of a fluid of a certain composition from cartilage certainly does not imply that fluid of this composition exists in cartilage as a distinct phase; the electrolytes will distribute themselves between the expressed fluid and the fluid remaining in the compressed cartilage so as to satisfy the thermodynamic equilibrium between cartilage and the external solution in contact with it.

3.2.6. Distribution of Various Ions Between Cartilage and External Solution. It can be shown from considerations of the ideal Donnan equilibrium that the following relation should hold between the distribution coefficients of two ions, A and B (Helfferich 1962):

$$\left(\frac{\bar{m}_A}{m_B}\right) = \left(\frac{\bar{m}_B}{m_A}\right)^{z_A/z_B} \tag{15}$$

Departures from this ideal condition are described by the selectivity coefficient K_B^A:

$$K_B^A = \left(\frac{\bar{m}_A}{m_A}\right) \Big/ \left(\frac{\bar{m}_B}{m_B}\right)^{z_A/z_B} \tag{16}$$

If $K_B^A > 1$, the material takes up ion A in preference to ion B, over and above any preference due purely to valency effects, as predicted by equation (15).

A set of values of distribution coefficients for K^+, Ca^{2+}, Na^+, SO_4^{2-}, Cl^- and HPO_4^{2-} are given in Table 4.2. The concentration of these ions in the equilibrating solution corresponded to their concentration in plasma. The selectivity coefficients K_{Na}^K, K_{Na}^{Ca}, $K_{Cl}^{SO_4}$ and K_{Cl}^{HPO4} are also tabulated.

Table 4.2

A. Typical Distribution Coefficients of Na^+, K^+ and Ca^{2+}

Slice from surface	$\dfrac{\bar{m}_{K^+}}{m_{K^+}}$	$\dfrac{\bar{m}_{Ca^{2+}}}{m_{Ca^{2+}}}$	$\dfrac{\bar{m}_{Na^+}}{m_{Na^+}}$	$\left(\dfrac{\bar{m}_{Na^+}}{m_{Na^+}}\right)^2$	$K_{Na^+}^{K^+}$	$K_{Na^+}^{Ca^{2+}}$
1	1.88	3.90	1.5	2.25	1.25	1.74
2	2.50	6.05	1.9	3.60	1.20	1.67
3	2.66	8.60	2.0	4.20	1.33	2.05
4	3.10	9.00	2.2	4.90	1.40	1.85

B. Typical Distribution Coefficients of Cl^-, SO_4^{2-} and HPO_4^{2-}

Slice from surface	$\dfrac{\bar{m}_{SO_4^{2-}}}{m_{SO_4^{2-}}}$	$\dfrac{\bar{m}_{HPO_4^{2-}}}{m_{HPO_4^{2-}}}$	$\dfrac{\bar{m}_{Cl^-}}{m_{Cl^-}}$	$\left(\dfrac{\bar{m}_{Cl^-}}{m_{Cl^-}}\right)^2$	$K_{Cl}^{SO_4^{2-}}$	$K_{Cl}^{HPO_4^{2-}}$
1	0.939	0.990	0.950	0.900	1.04	1.10
2	0.701	0.600	0.711	0.500	1.40	1.20
3	0.410	0.360	0.559	0.312	1.30	1.15
4	0.359	0.410	0.560	0.314	1.14	1.30

An examination of Table 4.2 shows that the selectivity coefficients for K^+, Ca^+, SO_4^{2-} and HPO_4^{2-} all deviate to a greater or lesser extent from unity. Thus $K_{Na}^K \sim 1.3$. This preference of cartilage for K^+ rather than Na^+ is consistent with the observation that most ion exchange materials have a greater affinity for the ion whose hydrated volume is smaller. This effect has been explained by the tendency of the elastic matrix of the ion exchange material to contract and hence to prefer to have smaller ions in its interstices (Helfferich 1962; Marinsky 1966).

As for Ca^{2+}, since it is a divalent ion, its distribution coefficient would be expected to be equal to the square of that for the monovalent Na^+. However, this effect is already taken into account in the definition of the selectivity coefficient. The fact that the latter is greater than unity ($K_K^{Ca} \sim 1.8$) means that cartilage has a greater affinity for Ca^{2+} than that predicted purely from the Donnan equilibrium. This higher affinity is probably due to the presence of stronger electrostatic forces between the divalent calcium and the matrix anions and the slightly smaller hydrated volume of Ca^{2+}. There may also be an interaction between Ca^{2+} and collagen (Li and Katz 1976).

The sulphate ion, being a divalent ion, would be expected to be excluded from cartilage to a greater extent than the chloride ion; thus, in accordance with the Donnan equilibrium, its distribution coefficient between cartilage and solution should be equal to the square of the distribution coefficient for the chloride ion. However, the concentration of the sulphate ion in cartilage is in fact somewhat higher, as shown by values of $K_{Cl}^{SO_4}$ ranging from 1 to 1.4. The same is true of $K_{Cl}^{HPO_4}$.

One general factor which may contribute to the selectivity coefficients of ions given above being greater than unity is the fact that they are all present in much smaller concentrations in the equilibrating medium than Na^+ and Cl^- and selectivity coefficients are known to be concentration-dependent.

From a knowledge of the distribution coefficients of Ca^{2+} and HPO_4^{2-} it is possible to calculate the activity coefficients of these two ions. The mean values of the ratios $\bar{\gamma}_{Ca^{2+}}/\gamma_{Ca^{2+}}$ and $\bar{\gamma}_{HPO_4^{2-}}/\gamma_{HPO_4^{2-}}$ are 0.3 and 0.8 respectively (Benderly and Maroudas 1975). It is clear from these values that the activity of the calcium ion is considerably lower in cartilage than in solution. It also means that the activity product

$$(m_{Ca^{2+}} \cdot \bar{\gamma}_{Ca^{2+}}) \cdot (m_{HPO_4^{2-}} \cdot \bar{\gamma}_{HPO_4^{2-}})$$

is lower in cartilage than it would be in a solution of the same electrolyte composition and that the solubility product of $CaHPO_4$ is not exceeded in spite of the relatively high concentrations of the calcium ion in cartilage (Benderly and Maroudas 1975). From these data one can speculate that the role of proteoglycans in the process of calcification might be to enable the calcium ion to be present in high concentrations in the cartilage matrix, without precipitation of calcium orthophosphate. From this it follows that if the concentration of the proteoglycans were to be reduced in the matrix, the solubility product of $CaHPO_4$ would be exceeded and precipitation would take place.

In life, articular cartilage is in equilibrium with synovial fluid, which in turn is in equilibrium with serum, the electrolyte composition of which is equivalent to that of normal Ringer's solution.

The distribution results given in Table 4.2 thus provide direct information on the concentration of free K^+, Ca^{2+}, SO_4^{2-} and HPO_4^{2-} in cartilage.

It is evident that the distribution coefficients for the cations increase with fixed charge density (Maroudas and Evans 1972) and hence, for any given ion, they increase with distance from the articular surface. However, an average value can be calculated. Thus for K^+ the average distribution coefficient is 2.2 and since the K^+ content in synovial fluid is around 0.0047 Eq/litre the mean concentration of free K^+ in cartilage would be around 0.0105 Eq/litre of water. This value approximates the figures given by Miles and Eichelberger (1964) for the potassium content of knee cartilage, which when expressed on the same basis is in the range 0.011–0.013 Eq/litre of water.

Similarly, since the concentration of Ca^{2+} in synovial fluid is about 0.004 mol/litre (8 mg/100 ml or 0.004 Eq/litre), and its mean distribution coefficient about 7, the concentration of Ca^{2+} in cartilage should be around 0.028 mol/litre (5.6 mg/100 ml or 0.028 Eq/litre) of tissue water. This quantity would of course represent only that Ca^{2+} in cartilage which is in reversible equilibrium with synovial fluid.

The only values for the Ca^{2+} content found in the literature are those determined by Eichelberger, Akeson and Roma (1958) for the articular cartilage of puppies. These authors reported values up to 0.12 mEq/ml for 20–25-week-old puppies, which is equal to half the Na^+ content, and is much higher than the values quoted above. Possibly the samples of cartilage used for these analyses were contaminated with calcium from the calcified zone, as Eichelberger *et al.* stated that they had not mastered perfectly the technique of removing the cartilage without penetrating with the scalpel the zone of calcification or the subjacent bone.

3.2.7. Concentration of Sulphate Ion in Cartilage and Studies of Sulphur Turnover.

It is pertinent at this point to discuss the question of the free sulphate 'pool' in cartilage, with special reference to the rate of sulphate incorporation by the chondrocytes to produce sulphated glycosaminoglycans.

Since the cartilage matrix is in equilibrium with synovial fluid, one cannot speak of an isolated pool of free sulphate ions in cartilage: the sulphate ion concentration is determined purely by (a) the distribution coefficient of SO_4^{2-} between cartilage and synovial fluid, (b) the concentration of SO_4^{2-} in synovial fluid and (c) the consumption of SO_4^{2-} by the chondrocytes. As shown in Chapter 8, Section 3.1, the latter is very small and can be neglected when discussing the inorganic sulphate content of the matrix.

The distribution coefficient of SO_4^{2-} between cartilage and synovial fluid has been found to have the value of 0.58, and since the concentration of SO_4^{2-} in blood serum and in other extracellular fluids including synovial fluid is around 0.0005 mol/litre (0.0005M) (Guyton 1966; Herbai 1970), its concentration in cartilage must be around 0.0003 molal.

If one wishes to estimate the rate of production of sulphated glycosaminoglycans by the chondrocytes in cartilage from a study of ^{35}S uptake, it is necessary to know accurately the mean specific activity of the inorganic sulphate in cartilage throughout the experiment, be it *in vivo* or *in vitro*.

Mankin and Lippiello (1969) based their calculation of the glycosaminoglycan turnover in rabbit articular cartilage on the assumption that cartilage contains 2.86 μmol of sulphate per mg dry weight (i.e. approximately 1.0 mol of sulphate per litre of cartilage water). This figure (which Mankin and Lippiello (1969) deduced by assuming that the rate of sulphate incorporation was independent of sulphate concentration) is higher than that deduced from the distribution coefficient of sulphate by several orders of magnitude. Hence Mankin and Lippiello's estimate that as much as 30% of the glycosaminoglycans present in rabbit cartilage have a half-life of only eight days seems likely to have been too high. This subject is discussed further in Section 5.

3.3. Distribution of Higher Molecular Weight Solutes

It has been shown in Section 2.2.2 that all the water in cartilage appears to behave as solvent water towards small ions and molecules. However, as the molecular weight of the solutes increases, some of the water becomes inaccessible, partly because it is situated within the collagen fibrils and partly because of the steric exclusion exerted by the proteoglycans. In the case of very large solutes it is the latter effect which predominates.

Early work by the present author (Maroudas 1970), carried out chiefly on dextrans 10 and 40, showed the great dependence of the distribution coefficients of large solutes on their size as well as on the glycosaminoglycan content of the cartilage, in accordance with the general principles discovered earlier for solutions of macromolecules (e.g. Ogston 1958).

More recent studies on the distribution of globular proteins of varying size, using iodinated tracer molecules, have yielded more accurate results which are summarized below (Snowden and Maroudas 1976; Maroudas 1976b).

Figure 4.12a shows a graph of the partition coefficient of (^{125}I) iodinated serum albumin versus fixed charge density for both intact and fibrillated slices of hip and knee cartilage as well as for specimens from which some proteoglycans had been extracted by chemical or enzymatic methods (Snowden and Maroudas 1976).

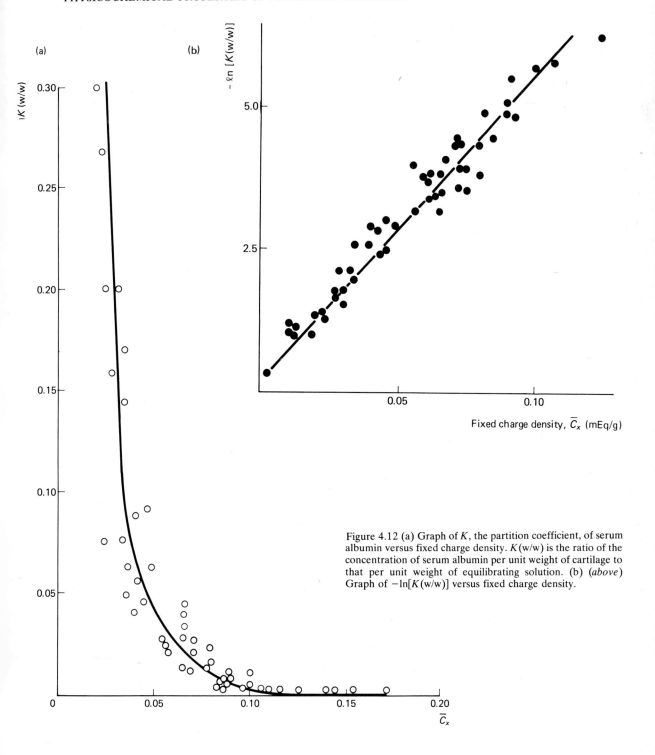

Figure 4.12 (a) Graph of K, the partition coefficient, of serum albumin versus fixed charge density. K(w/w) is the ratio of the concentration of serum albumin per unit weight of cartilage to that per unit weight of equilibrating solution. (b) (*above*) Graph of $-\ln[K(\text{w/w})]$ versus fixed charge density.

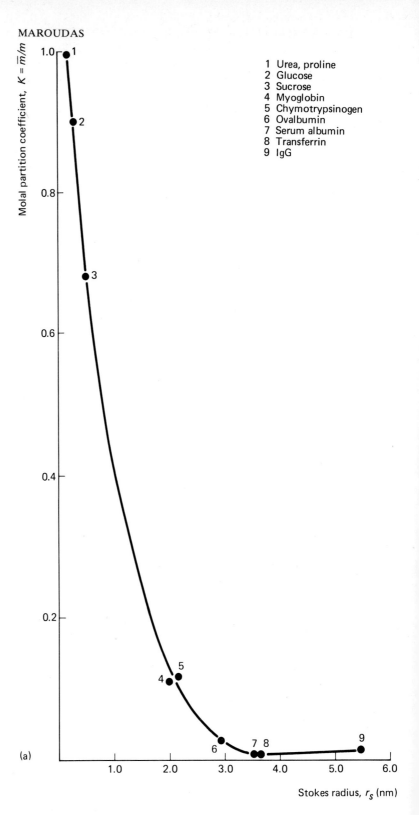

Figure 4.13 (a) Variation of partition coefficients with solute size. (b) (*opposite*) Graph of $(\ln \frac{1}{K})^{\frac{1}{2}}$ versus r_s.

It can be seen that cartilage samples from very different sources follow the same curve, provided the partition coefficient is plotted versus the glycosaminoglycan content.

This can be explained on the basis of the steric exclusion of large solutes by the proteoglycan molecules.

It is thus of interest to examine to what extent the results obtained on cartilage fit Ogston's theory developed for the exclusion of globular solutes by linear rodlike macromolecules in solution. Ogston (1958) derived an equation of the following form for the partition coefficient, K, of a globular solute:

$$K = \exp A C_x (r_x + r_s)^2 \qquad (17)$$

where C_x = concentration of the linear rodlike macromolecules,
r_x = radius of the rodlike macromolecule,
r_s = radius of globular solute,
A = constant.

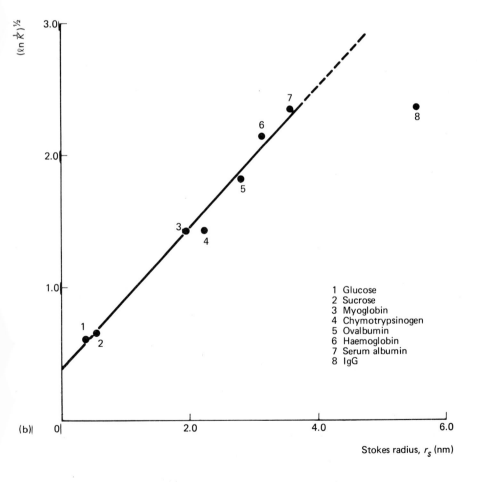

1 Glucose
2 Sucrose
3 Myoglobin
4 Chymotrypsinogen
5 Ovalbumin
6 Haemoglobin
7 Serum albumin
8 IgG

According to equation (17), the logarithm of the partition coefficient should vary linearly with (a) the glycosaminoglycan concentration, or C_x, for a given solute and (b) the expression $(r_x + r_s)^2$ for a range of solutes of different size, but at a given glycosaminoglycan content.

When plotted logarithmically the graph of K versus C_x is indeed a straight line (as shown in the results in Figure 4.12b.). The same is true if the partition coefficients given in Figure 4.13a are replotted as $(\ln 1/K)^{\frac{1}{2}}$ versus r_s (Figure 4.13b), but here the relationship breaks down for the largest solutes.

The reason for the fact that the partition coefficents of IgG are of the same order of magnitude as those of serum albumin, although the former solute is much larger, is not clear. It is possible that there is a small fraction of 'pores' in cartilage which are relatively larger than the rest and considerably larger than either serum albumin or IgG, and that the transport of both the latter species occurs predominantly through these larger pores. Such a view seems to be consistent with the relatively high diffusion coefficient of serum albumin in cartilage (see Section 4.3.3). If serum albumin molecules were moving through spaces only slightly larger than themselves, one would expect a frictional retardation and a lowering of their diffusivity, as had indeed been observed previously with the smaller but much less compact dextrans 10 and 40 (Maroudas 1970).

3.4. Summary

The values of typical partition coefficients for different types of solutes are listed in Table 4.3.

The molal partition coefficients of small non-ionic solutes between cartilage and free solution are close to unity and are practically independent of the GAG content. This implies that all, or most, of the cartilage water, whether inter- or intrafibrillar, is free and accessible to small solutes. If one knows the partition coefficient of a metabolite and its diffusivity (see Section 4), one can calculate whether cellular requirements for this metabolite at any given location within the tissue are fully met by diffusion from the synovial cavity (see Chapter 8).

There is no difference between normal and degenerate cartilage as far as the molal partition coefficients of small non-ionic solutes are concerned.

Monovalent cations such as Na^+ have a partition coefficient in the range 1.5–3.0. This coefficient increases with the glycosaminoglycan concentration, in accordance with the Donnan equilibrium. It should be noted that the activity coefficients of sodium ion in cartilage are only slightly below their values in free solution, which implies that, although the glycosaminoglycans are

Table 4.3 Permeability of cartilage to solutes

Type of solute	Example	Typical molal distribution coefficient ($\bar{m}/m$)		$\bar{D}(cm^2/s) \times 10^6$	Ratio of diffusion coefficient to that in water (D/D_{aq})
		$FCD = 0.08$	$FCD = 0.16$		
Small uncharged	Tritiated water	1.0	1.0	0.6–0.7(8°C) 1.2–1.4 (37°C)	0.40–0.45
	Urea, proline	1.0	1.0	6.0 (25°C) (urea)	0.40–0.45
	Glucose	1.0	0.9	2.4–2.7 (25°C)	0.40–0.45
	Sucrose	1.0	0.9	1.9–2.1 (25°C)	0.40–0.45
Small cations	Na^+	1.5	2.2	4.8–5.5 (25°C)	~ 0.40
	Ca^+	3	9	1.5 (25°C)	~ 0.25
Small anions	Cl^-	0.75	0.53	7.5–8.5 (25°C)	0.40–0.45
	HPO_4^{2-}	0.8	0.5	—	—
	SO_4^{2-}	0.6	0.4	2.8–3.5 (37°C)	0.40–0.45
Large globular proteins	Serum albumin	0.01	0.001	0.1 (8°C) 0.16 (25°C)	0.25
	Transferrin	0.01	0.001	—	—
	IgG	0.01	0.001	0.5 (8°C)	0.20

responsible for the high sodium concentration in cartilage, they do not show strong interactions with this cation. On the basis of the partition data for sodium and chloride ions, it is possible to calculate the ionic contribution to the osmotic pressure of cartilage. The osmotic pressure thus calculated is of the order of 0.17 MN/m² (1.7 atm), which agrees with our experimental values.

In degenerate cartilage, fixed charge density is lower, hence the concentration of cations is lower than in normal tissue. As a result the ionic contribution to the osmotic pressure is considerably reduced.

As for other cations, the hydrogen ion concentration must always be higher in cartilage than in external solution, the difference being a function of the GAG content. The pH is thus lower in cartilage than in synovial fluid: for instance, calculations show that femoral head cartilage from the middle zone will have a pH about 0.3 of a unit lower than that of synovial fluid, purely due to the presence of negatively charged groups. In addition, of course, there will be the effect of lactic acid production by the chondrocytes. However, the latter effect has so far not been quantified.

Most of the proteolytic enzymes which have the ability to degrade cartilage proteoglycans have their optima at acid pHs; a lowering of pH in regions of high glycosaminoglycan content may thus play a part in the control of the local proteoglycan level.

The divalent calcium ion shows a partition coefficient much higher than that of monovalent sodium, particularly in cartilage of high glycosaminoglycan content. This is only partly explicable on the grounds of higher valency and must be partly due to an additional affinity of the cartilage matrix for calcium. The result of this is that cartilage can tolerate a much higher concentration of calcium in the presence of normal phosphate levels without precipitation of calcium orthophosphate than would be possible in an aqueous solution. The role of proteoglycans in the control of calcification might thus be to concentrate the calcium in the matrix without precipitation of calcium phosphate. Once the proteoglycans were lost from the matrix, calcification would set in.

Anions are partly excluded from the cartilage matrix by virtue of the Donnan equilibrium, divalent anions being affected more than monovalent ones.

The partition coefficient of the sulphate ion is particularly relevant in studies of glycosaminoglycan turnover. Using it, one is able to compare the sulphate uptake into the matrix from *in vitro* and *in vivo* [35]S tracer studies and to calculate in each case the actual rate of synthesis of sulphated glycosaminoglycans.

The partition coefficients of large solutes are extremely sensitive to variations in the GAG content: thus a threefold increase in the latter will lead to a hundredfold decrease in the partition coefficient of a substance such as serum albumin. This 'filtering action' may have a number of physiological implications, which are discussed in Chapter 8.

4. THE DIFFUSION OF SOLUTES THROUGH CARTILAGE

4.1. Physicochemical Principles

The transport of a solute from the synovial cavity into cartilage can take place by two mechanisms:

(a) pure diffusion due to a solute concentration gradient;
(b) flow with the solvent (i.e. with water) under the effect of a hydraulic pressure gradient.

Mathematically, this can be expressed in the following form:

$$J = \bar{D}\frac{d\bar{C}}{dx} + \bar{C}\kappa\frac{dp}{dx} \qquad (18a)$$

where
J = total solute flux (mol s^{-1} cm^{-2}),
$\bar{D}$ = diffusion coefficient of the solute inside cartilage,
$\bar{C}$ = equilibrium solute concentration in cartilage,
$d\bar{C}/dx$ = concentration gradient of the solute in cartilage,
κ = hydraulic permeability coefficient,
dp/dx = hydrostatic pressure gradient.

It is shown in Chapter 8, Section 3.3, that the contribution of fluid flow to normal cartilage nutrition is very small compared with diffusion. It is thus the first term in equation (18a) which is the relevant one and we shall consider it in some detail.

The rate of diffusion of solutes from external solution into cartilage and vice versa is governed by three factors: (a) the resistance of a stagnant liquid film at the cartilage/fluid interface (in life this interface is between cartilage and synovial fluid); (b) the distribution coefficient of a solute between cartilage and external solution; and (c) the effective diffusion coefficient of the solute in cartilage.

It has been shown that provided the liquid in contact with the cartilage is vigorously stirred, liquid film resistance can be neglected in comparison with the resistance to diffusion within cartilage itself (Maroudas 1968). It is thus possible to write the expression for the solute permeability in terms of factors (b) and (c) above:

$$\bar{P} = \bar{D}(\bar{C}/C) \qquad (18b)$$

where
$\bar{P}$ = the effective solute flux per unit cross-sectional area of cartilage per unit concentration gradient across it,
$\bar{D}$ = the effective diffusion coefficient of solute in cartilage,
$\bar{C}/C$ = the molar distribution coefficient of solute between cartilage and external solution.

4.2. Methods of Measuring Diffusion Coefficients

The actual mobilities of solutes in cartilage, as characterized by their diffusion coefficients, $\bar{D}$, can be obtained by a number of experimental procedures. Two methods have been used for cartilage, both employing radioisotopes as tracers. One procedure consists in using cartilage as a membrane and determining the flux of a given solute across it (Helfferich 1962; Maroudas 1968, 1970). From such data it is possible to obtain $\bar{P}$ and, hence, calculate $\bar{D}$ from equation (18b) provided the value of the distribution coefficient $\bar{C}/C$ is known.

The second procedure (Crank 1975) consists in measuring the rate of uptake of a given solute by a chunk of cartilage or the rate of desorption of the solute (and this is often experimentally more convenient).

The diffusion coefficient can be obtained directly from the formula (Crank 1975)

$$\bar{D} = \frac{0.049 \times l^2}{t_{\frac{1}{2}}} \tag{19}$$

where l = cartilage thickness in cm
and $t_{\frac{1}{2}}$ = time taken from the beginning of the absorption (or desorption) run, at which half of the solute has been taken up by cartilage or desorbed from it.

There are a number of advantages to this method over the permeability method.

Thus, it can yield information as to whether, for a given solute, the process can legitimately be described in terms of a single diffusion coefficient or whether more than one diffusion coefficient is needed; this happens if there are different 'compartments' in the tissue in which the solute exhibits different mobilities (Maroudas and Venn 1977).

For large molecules contaminated with small amounts of low molecular solute containing the same tracer it is the only method which can be used satisfactorily as it enables a separation between the two components to be achieved.

From the practical point of view, the specimen can be small, irregularly shaped and even fibrillated, but provided it is of uniform thickness and solute concentration it can be handled by the 'desorption' method whereas clamping in a permeability cell may be a problem.

A serious drawback of this method is that for a solute with a high diffusion coefficient the specimen must be of adequate thickness, usually not less than 1 mm, if sufficient accuracy is to be achieved.

4.3. Diffusion Data

4.3.1. Small Non-ionic Solutes. Figure 4.14 shows a typical experimental desorption curve for tritiated water (^3H_2O) (Maroudas and Venn 1977). The diffusion coefficient calculated from the value of $t_{\frac{1}{2}}$ according to equation (19) is 1.20×10^{-5} cm²/s. In the same Figure is shown the theoretical desorption curve, calculated using the $\bar{D} = 1.2 \times 10^{-5}$ cm²/s and a formula given by Crank (1975). It can be seen that both at values of $t < t_{\frac{1}{2}}$ and at $t > t_{\frac{1}{2}}$ there is an excellent agreement between the two curves. This shows that from the point of view of its mobility, the water in cartilage behaves as a one-compartment system, being freely exchangeable with outside solution. The same behaviour was observed in normal as well as in fibrillated specimens and also in cartilage from which proteoglycans had been removed by chemical means (Maroudas and Venn 1977).

Our results thus in no way support the view expressed by Mankin and Zarins-Thrasher (1975) that the excess water present in proteoglycan-depleted specimens of cartilage is 'bound' water.

It should be noted that the rate of diffusion of any solute into or out of a specimen of tissue is very sensitive to the thickness of the specimen. Mankin and Zarins-Thrasher (1975), in their qualitative studies of the exchange of tritiated water, do not appear to have taken the specimen thickness into account: it is possible that the differences they have observed in the rate of loss of ^3H_2O on heating between normal and degenerate cartilage were in reality due to differences in the shape of their specimens.

The diffusion coefficient of 1.2×10^{-5} cm²/s at 37°C was also obtained for tritiated water by the permeability method (Maroudas and Venn 1977). The diffusion coefficient of ^3H_2O in free solution is 3×10^{-5} at 37°C so that $\bar{D}/D = 1.2/3.0 = 0.4$. The same $\bar{D}/D$ ratio was observed for other small non-ionic solutes such as urea and proline (Maroudas 1970, 1975a).

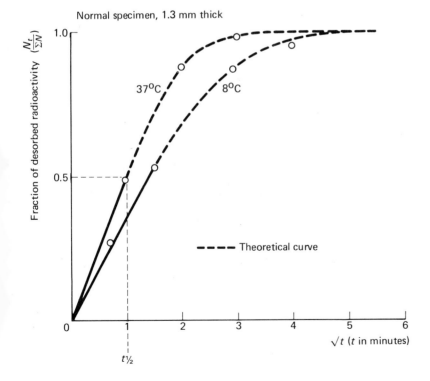

Figure 4.14 Efflux curve for tritiated water. ΣN = total amount of radioactivity taken up by the slice at equilibrium; N_t = amount of radioactivity desorbed up to time t.

(Reproduced from Maroudas and Venn (1977) by permission.)

249

This reduction in the diffusion coefficient in cartilage as compared with free solution can be explained in terms of a reduction in the effective area available to the diffusing molecules and an increase in the tortuosity of the path due to the solids present in the tissue. A formula derived by Mackie and Meares (1955) for porous media and based purely on geometrical considerations relates $\bar{D}$ to D as follows:

$$\frac{\bar{D}}{D} = \frac{(1 - Vs)^2}{(1 + Vs)^2} \qquad (20)$$

where Vs is the volume fraction of solids in cartilage.

If a value of 0.7 is used for the density of collagen and other protein and 0.55 for the proteoglycans, then for a typical specimen of normal femoral head cartilage (70% water; 18% collagen; 8% GAG; 4% non-collagenous protein and mineral) equation (20) gives $\bar{D}/D = 0.45$, which is close to the experimental value.

This agreement indicates that both water and small non-ionic solutes behave in the same way as in free solution, except for the mechanical obstruction provided by the solid constituents of the matrix.

4.3.2. Small Ionic Solutes. The self-diffusion coefficients of anions such as Cl^- and SO_4^{2-} in cartilage are again equal to 35–45% of their value in free solution (Maroudas 1970; Maroudas and Evans 1974), which agrees with the behaviour of small uncharged solutes.

As for cations, an additional reduction in $\bar{D}/D$ due to the existence of electrostatic interactions between the counter-ions and the fixed negatively charged groups should be expected. If, for instance, there were a considerable degree of localization of Na^+ in the vicinity of the fixed groups, this would be reflected in a large decrease in the value of $\bar{D}_{Na^+}$ (Manning 1969). In fact, however, the ratio $\bar{D}/D$ has been found to be at most 10% lower than for Cl^-. This implies that the interactions between Na^+ and the fixed groups of the GAG are relatively weak, which is consistent with the information derived from determination of the activity coefficients of Na^+ and Cl^- in cartilage (see Section 3.2.1).

In summary, for molecules which are too small in comparison with the cross-sectional area of the 'pores' in the proteoglycan–water gel, the movement of the solute is governed chiefly by free diffusion, the ratio of the diffusion coefficient in cartilage to that in water being dependent mainly on the water content of cartilage and the tortuosity of the porous space. The value of the ratio $\bar{D}/D$ is approximately 0.4 (Maroudas 1970; Maroudas and Evans 1974; Maroudas 1975a).

4.3.3. Higher Molecular Weight Solutes. For molecules whose dimensions are not negligible in relation to pore size, the diffusion coefficients depend not only on the friction between the solute and the solvent but also on the friction between the solute molecules and the solid elements in the matrix.

Corrections for such effects have been attempted. Faxen (1922), for instance, calculated the reduction in mobility of a spherical particle in a cylindrical pore by friction with the pore walls. The mobility reduction, expressed in terms of a 'drag factor' F, is:

$$F = 1 - 2.104\frac{d_i}{d_p} + 2.09\left(\frac{d_i}{d_p}\right)^3 - 0.95\left(\frac{d_i}{d_p}\right)^5 \qquad (21)$$

where d_i = diameter of diffusing solute,
d_p = pore diameter.

Since the mean size of the 'pores' in cartilage is of the same order of magnitude as the serum albumin molecule (Maroudas 1970), a considerable reduction in the mobility (F close to zero) would be expected on the basis of Faxen's equation.

Although our early results obtained using solutes such as inulin carboxylic acid, dextran 10 and dextran 40 showed a considerable decrease in the ratio $\bar{D}/D$ with increase in the molecular weight of the solute and a decrease in $\bar{D}/D$ with increase in the GAG content (Maroudas 1970), our more recent results obtained on large globular solutes show a relatively small reduction in the ratio $\bar{D}/D$ (Maroudas 1975a; Maroudas 1976b). Thus, for serum albumin the value of $\bar{D}/D$ is the range 0.25–0.3 as compared with 0.45 for urea or proline (Maroudas 1976b). This result clearly does not fit the Faxen equation.

Ogston, Preston and Wells (1973), on the basis of a stochastic model, suggested the following relation between $\bar{D}$ and D for compact molecules in solutions of chain-polymers:

$$\frac{\bar{D}}{D} = A\exp(-B\sqrt{C_x}) \qquad (22)$$

where C_x = concentration of chain polymers,
B = a function of the solute radius r_s.

Although this relation fits the experimental results obtained by the above authors for a range of solutes in hyaluronate solutions, it does not appear to account satisfactorily for our results, particularly with respect to the lack of dependence which we observe between the diffusion coefficients of large solutes and the GAG content (Maroudas 1977, unpublished results). It should be borne in mind, however, that Ogston et al. have used much less concentrated proteoglycan solutions than those corresponding to the cartilage matrix and could therefore assume that solute transport takes place randomly throughout the entire meshwork. Because of the very low partition coefficients of large solutes between the cartilage matrix and external solution, this assumption is probably no longer justified.

4.4. Summary

The values of typical diffusion coefficients for different types of solutes are given in Table 4.3 (p. 245).

The diffusion coefficients of small solutes which do not interact with the matrix lie in the range 0.35–0.45 of their values in free solution. This decrease is consistent with theoretical predictions based on considerations of increased tortuosity.

Using the above values of the diffusion coefficients, one can show that the requirements of the chondrocytes for substances such as glucose, amino-acids or the sulphate ion can be fully met by passive diffusion from the synovial fluid (Chapter 8).

In degenerate cartilage, the diffusion coefficients are higher than in normal tissue because of the increased water content but the effect is of the order of 10% only. However, since solute flux into the tissue depends on both the diffusion and the partition coefficient, the transport of ionic solutes can be considerably affected by a decrease in fixed charge density. As the partition coefficients of anions vary substantially with fixed charge density, the rate of transport of an electrolyte such as Na_2SO_4 will be increased where GAG depletion has occurred.

As far as the penetration of large molecules is concerned, it is again the partition coefficient rather than the diffusivity which is the controlling factor. Because of the very great sensitivity of the partition coefficient of these solutes to the GAG content, a small increase in the water content accompanied by a very limited loss of GAG in the surface zone may lead to a tenfold increase in the penetration of IgG. This phenomenon may explain the presence of immune complexes observed by Cooke *et al.* in the superficial zone of articular cartilage not only in the cases of rheumatoid arthritis but also in a considerable number of cases of osteoarthrosis (Cooke, Richer, Hurd and Jasin 1975; Cooke, Bennett and Ohno 1979).

5. PHYSICOCHEMICAL BASIS FOR TURNOVER STUDIES

Metabolic turnover rates cannot be measured directly but can be deduced from radioactive tracer uptake studies. Quantitative approaches based on tracer kinetics have been developed and applied to the study of metabolic rates in various tissues (e.g. Zilversmit, Entenman and Fischler 1943; Robertson 1957). However, until recently, only qualitative studies have been made of the matrix turnover in cartilage.

In this Section the fundamental concepts underlying the quantitative approaches to metabolic studies are discussed, with special reference to the development of both *in vivo* and *in vitro* methods for cartilage. Some results will be given by way of illustration.

With respect to cartilage, the metabolite whose turnover has been most extensively studied has been the glycosaminoglycan.

The *in vivo* studies of proteoglycan turnover (such as those of Bostrom 1952; Schiller, Matthews, Cifonelli and Dorfman 1956; Gross, Matthews and Dorfman 1960; Davidson and Small 1963; Mankin and Lippiello 1969; Rokosova and Bentley 1973; and Lohmander, Antonopoulos and Friberg 1973) have been carried out on various small animals, the usual procedure being to inject a radioactively labelled precursor (such as (^{35}S) sulphate, which becomes incorporated into the proteoglycan molecule) into a group of animals, to kill the latter at various intervals over a long period of time, and to obtain in this way a time course of radioactive decay for the incorporated (^{35}S) sulphate. If all the proteoglycans were being replaced at the same rate, one could deduce from the rate of disappearance of the tracer the overall rate of turnover of the proteoglycans. However, if several pools of proteoglycans are present, with different turnover rates, the results obtained by the above method become very difficult to interpret quantitatively. Amongst the above authors, only Lohmander *et al.* (1973) made a serious attempt at a quantitative analysis of their results. Unfortunately, they had used young animals only.

Since in normal adult cartilage the level of proteoglycans changes very little with age, the proteoglycans which are being lost must continuously be replaced by those which are being freshly synthesized. Thus, an alternative method for measuring the turnover rate of the proteoglycans is to determine the rate of (^{35}S) sulphate incorporation into the matrix rather than its rate of disappearance. There are two main advantages to this method. First, unlike the (^{35}S) decay, it can yield unambiguous quantitative values for the turnover rates of the proteoglycans, both on an overall basis and with respect to the individual pools if the latter can be isolated. Secondly, with suitable modifications, the method can be employed in the animal *in vivo* as well as on freshly excised pieces of tissue *in vitro*.

The procedure is simple in principle, but in order to obtain from it absolute values for the rates of sulphate uptake, supplementary data are required. These are the actual concentration of the free sulphate ion in the tissue as well as the radioactivity associated with it during the course of the incorporation, whether *in vivo* or *in vitro*. Prior to the work by the present author (Maroudas and Evans 1974; Maroudas 1975a) no attempt had been made to measure the above parameters, which are related to the transport of free sulphate, and therefore all incorporation results were treated in a purely comparative manner.

Thus, for instance, *in vitro* incubations of human articular cartilage in (^{35}S)-containing media were usually aimed at obtaining a comparison between normal and pathological tissue (e.g. Collins and McElligott 1960; Collins and Meachim 1961; Bollet and Nance 1966; Mankin and Lippiello 1971) under a particular set of experimental conditions rather than arriving at general values for the rate of sulphate incorporation. Because of this, it was neither possible to compare values obtained by different workers with one another, nor to test their absolute validity.

Quantitative procedures, based on the knowledge of partition and diffusion of free sulphate in cartilage, were therefore developed by the present writer and used to study sulphate uptake *in vivo* as well as *in vitro* (Maroudas and Evans 1974; Maroudas 1975a, b). The principles underlying these methods are summarized below and the results given.

5.1. Principle of the Method

The principle of the method for determining the rate of sulphate uptake (or that of any other precursor) from tracer incorporation, whether carried out *in vivo* or *in vitro*, is as follows. The radioactive tracer which has been introduced into the incubation medium (in the case of *in vitro* work) or into the animal's blood-stream (in an *in vivo* experiment) diffuses into the aqueous phase of the cartilage and is thence taken up by the cells, incorporated into the newly synthesized structural molecules and becomes fixed within the matrix. In order to obtain the incorporation rate, the mean radioactivity due to the 'free' tracer in the tissue (i.e. the tracer within the aqueous phase of the matrix) must be determined separately from that due to the tracer incorporated into the structural molecules. Provided the concentration of the free sulphate ion in the cartilage matrix is known, it is possible, from a simple mass balance, to calculate the rate, Q, of sulphate uptake into the glycosaminoglycans. Thus, Q is given by

$$Q = \frac{N_{inc} \times \bar{C}_{free}}{N_{free} \times t} \tag{23}$$

where N_{inc} = the detected radioactivity due to (^{35}S) present as incorporated sulphate per gram of wet cartilage,

N_{free} = the detected radioactivity due to (^{35}S) present as free, inorganic sulphate per gram of cartilage (mean value for the duration of the experiment),

$\bar{C}_{free}$ = the concentration of free sulphate in cartilage in mmol/g of tissue.

The concentration of free sulphate cannot be measured directly in cartilage but can readily be calculated from the value in the surrounding fluid (the incubation medium *in vitro* or synovial fluid (or plasma) *in vivo*) once the partition coefficient has been determined.

Thus, $\bar{C}_{\text{free}}$ is calculated from the formula:

$$\bar{C}_{\text{free}} = KC_o \tag{24}$$

where C_o = the molar concentration of inorganic sulphate in plasma,

K = the distribution coefficient for inorganic sulphate between cartilage and blood plasma; for convenience, it is expressed in the following units: mmol solute/g wet tissue divided by mmol solute/cm^3 of medium or plasma.

In an *in vitro* incubation, there is an initial unsteady state period during which the free tracer diffuses into the tissue. For slices less than 2 mm in thickness, this equilibration time is less than 1 hour (Maroudas and Evans 1974). Thereafter, N remains virtually constant since the amount of radioactivity taken up by the cartilage cells is negligible in comparison with the total radioactivity associated with the free sulphate present in the medium. Hence, equations (23) and (24) enable Q to be calculated directly.

In an *in vivo* experiment, since only a pulse of tracer is injected, the radioactivity due to free (^{35}S) in the plasma decays with time as the tracer first distributes itself throughout the body and then becomes gradually eliminated. If the cartilage is very thin (e.g. in the rabbit), the (^{35}S) in the tissue is practically in equilibrium with synovial fluid and the plasma throughout the experiment. In the case of thicker cartilage, a certain time lag will exist. In any case, N will no longer be constant and a mean value has to be obtained (Maroudas 1975a, 1979).

Obviously, it is not possible to measure an average value of N_{free} for a given animal, since N_{free} can only be obtained at the end of an experiment. However, if experiments are carried out on a number of animals for different periods of time, care being taken to inject the same amount of radioactivity per unit body mass and to keep all other experimental conditions constant, the variation of N_{free} with time can be estimated and hence a reasonably accurate mean value of N_{free} over a given period can be obtained for any one animal.

The ratio $N_{\text{free}}/\bar{C}_{\text{free}}$ is the specific activity of the free sulphate in the tissue at a given time. If the specific activity is plotted versus time, as shown in Figure 4.15a, its mean value up to the time, t, will be readily obtainable from the area under the curve; Q can then be calculated from equation (23). The calculating procedure is illustrated by an example in Figure 4.15b.

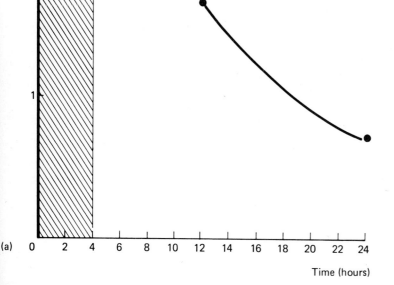

(a) Specific activity of free tracer (c.p.m./mmol) × 10⁻⁹

Time (hours)

Specific activity of free sulphate

in cartilage = $\dfrac{\text{counts (c.p.m.)}}{\text{mmol free sulphate}}$

Figure 4.15 (a) Variation in specific activity of free (³⁵S) sulphate in rabbit articular cartilage as a function of time after intravenous injection of (³⁵S). (b) (*below*) Method of calculating rate of glycosaminoglycan synthesis: a numerical example.

(b)

Mean specific activity up to 4 hours =

$$\frac{\text{shaded area}}{4} = 4 \times 10^9$$

At 4 hours counts of incorporated sulphate

$$1.8 \times 10^5 \quad \text{c.p.m./g}$$

∴ rate of sulphate incorporation per hour =

$$\frac{1.8 \times 10^5}{4 \times 10^9 \times 4} =$$

$$1.1 \times 10^{-5} \quad \text{mmol/g of cartilage}$$

Also, cartilage contains ∿ 0.09 mmol/g sulphate in its CS and KS.

∴ turnover time =

$$\frac{0.09}{24 \times 1.1 \times 10^{-5}} = 341 \text{ days}$$

Once Q has been calculated, the turnover time (defined as the time taken for all the glycosaminoglycans of the matrix to be replaced) can readily be obtained from the following formula:

Turnover time in days

$$= \frac{\text{total glycosaminoglycan sulphate (mmol)}}{\text{mean rate of sulphate uptake} \times 24 \text{ (mmol/h)}} \qquad (25)$$

5.2. Experimental Procedures

5.2.1. In Vivo Procedure. The experimental animals (rabbits and dogs were used by the present writer) are given an intravenous injection containing 1 mCi of carrier-free sodium (^{35}S) sulphate in saline solution per kilogram body mass. The present writer believes that intravenous rather than intra-articular administration of tracer should be used because in this way the concentration of inorganic sulphate in cartilage does not vary too much during an experiment, being in equilibrium with blood practically through-out (Maroudas 1975a; Maroudas 1976, unpublished results). On the other hand, if (^{35}S) were to be injected directly into the articulation, the cartilage would be in contact with a highly radioactive solution for a very short initial period of time. This solution would rapidly become less and less radioactive until a steady-state value equal to about one-thousandth of the initial concentration was reached (Maroudas and Holm 1976, unpublished results). Under such conditions, it would be more difficult to estimate accurately the mean radioactivity due to inorganic (^{35}S) in cartilage during an experiment.

To obtain the data required, the animals are sacrificed at various times up to 24 hours after the injection, blood samples being taken at regular intervals to check the level of radioactivity. After death, several joints are excised as rapidly as possible and frozen immediately. The cartilage is dissected, weighed and the inorganic sulphate desorbed in a known volume of saline. The desorbate is then 'counted' to determine the radioactivity present as inorganic sulphate. The tissue is finally digested and aliquots taken for glycosaminoglycan analyses as well as for the determination of radioactivity due to glycosaminoglycan sulphate.

The rate of sulphate uptake can be calculated from these measurements by means of equation (23).

5.2.2. In Vitro Procedure. The present writer believes that the following technical points are of importance in turnover studies *in vitro*.

(a) *The effect of inorganic sulphate concentration in the incubation medium.* It has been shown (Maroudas and Evans 1974) that the rate of sulphate incorporation is dependent on the concentration of inorganic sulphate in the medium. It is thus essential to maintain the concentration of inorganic sulphate at the physiological level.

(b) *The diffusion of (^{35}S) sulphate.* From a knowledge of the diffusion coefficient of sulphate it is possible to calculate how long it will take for a specimen of cartilage of a given thickness to come close to equilibrium, from the moment it is immersed in a solution containing (^{35}S). A table of such times (Table 4.4) has been compiled for various cartilage thicknesses (Maroudas and Evans 1974). Thus, for a piece of cartilage 2 mm thick, exposed to solution from both sides, the equilibrium time will be approximately 1 hour, while for a thicker specimen (e.g. from the patella) of 4 mm the time would be close to 4 hours. If the specimen is not removed from the bone the above times will be increased by a factor of 4.

Table 4.4   Equilibration times for cartilage of varying thickness

Cartilage thickness (cm)	Diffusion coefficient $10^6 \times D$ (cm²/s)	Time required to achieve 90% of final equilibrium	
		One side exposed to solution	Both sides exposed to solution
0.5	–	18 h 24 min	4 h 36 min
0.3	3.0	6 h 40 min	1 h 40 min
0.25	3.0	4 h 36 min	1 h 9 min
0.20	3.0	2 h 56 min	44 min
0.15	3.0	1 h 40 min	25 min
0.10	3.0	44 min	11 min
0.05	3.0	11 min	3 min

(Reproduced from Maroudas and Evans (1974) by permission.)

If experiments designed to compare rates of sulphate incorporation (to be examined by autoradiography or scintillation counting) are to be carried out on full-depth specimens of differing thickness, the following precautions should be taken; either the non-steady state period should be short as compared with the total incubation time (this can easily be achieved for relatively thin specimens), or the specimens should be allowed to come to equilibrium at 4°C with the radioactive solution before incubation at 37°C.

(c) *The effect of slicing cartilage before incubation.* Although the difficulties mentioned under (b) could be overcome by cutting full-depth specimens into thin slices, this procedure has been shown to cause a considerable decrease in the sulphate incorporation, probably as a result of the damage inflicted on a large proportion of cells during the cutting process (Maroudas 1975c).

5.3. Results

Table 4.5 gives the mean rates of sulphate uptake for articular cartilage, calculated according to the above equations from some *in vivo* as well as *in vitro* results (Maroudas 1975c).

It can be seen that in the case of dog cartilage or the adult rabbit there is no significant difference between the sulphate uptake obtained *in vivo* or *in vitro*. In the case of young rabbit cartilage, the uptake *in vitro* was 30% lower than *in vivo*, most probably because the rabbit cartilage was very thin and difficult to excise without inflicting some damage on the cells.

The good overall correspondence between the *in vitro* and *in vivo* values observed in the case of the larger experimental animals means that it is now possible to obtain a measure of the turnover of

Table 4.5 Sulphate incorporation into articular cartilage

Animal	Conditions of test	$10^5 \times$ rate of sulphate uptake / Mass of tissue (mmol h^{-1}g^{-1})	Proteoglycan sulphate / Mass of wet cartilage (mmol/g)	Approximate mean life of sulphated proteoglycans (days)
Young rabbit (4 weeks)	*in vitro*	18*	0.075	16
Young rabbit (3–5 months)	*in vivo*	2.4†	0.055	90
	in vitro	1.7†		130
Adult rabbit	*in vivo*	1.2*	0.09	340
	in vitro	1.1*	0.09	310
Adult dog (greyhound)	*in vivo*	1.3†	0.085	280
	in vitro	1.2†		300
Human infant	*in vitro*	1.7†	0.10	250
Human adult: Normal cartilage	*in vitro*	0.2–0.6†‡	0.08–0.11	600–1000
Osteoarthrotic cartilage	*in vitro*	0.1–0.6‡	0.05–0.11	

Note that the range of values in the case of human cartilage corresponds to different joints and different sites from the same joint.

* Maroudas 1978.   † Maroudas 1975.   ‡ Byers *et al.* 1977.

the glycosaminoglycans in human cartilage on the basis of *in vitro* experiments alone (Maroudas 1975c; Byers *et al.* 1977), as illustrated in Table 4.5.

Procedures similar to those described above have also been used for the study of collagen turnover (Maroudas 1977).

The rate of hydroxyproline synthesis in normal human femoral head cartilage was found to be 0.005×10^{-5} mmol $h^{-1} g^{-1}$ of cartilage, which corresponds to a turnover time of approximately 400 years.

5.4. Summary

By developing a procedure for the quantitative estimation of sulphate uptake in animals *in vivo*, it has been possible to compare the *in vivo* with the *in vitro* rates of sulphate incorporation and to show that there is a very good correspondence between the two.

It has thus been possible, for the first time, to obtain values for the mean glycosaminoglycan turnover in man. The turnover time for adult human cartilage is in the region of 3 years, compared with 1 year for the adult dog and rabbit. Cartilage from young animals exhibits a much higher turnover of glycosaminoglycans than adult tissue.

Cartilage from osteoarthrosic heads appears to have approximately the same sulphur uptake as normal cartilage.

Although radioactively labelled proline is incorporated into cartilage collagen, the actual rate of collagen synthesis which corresponds to this is extremely low in adult tissue. There is thus no collagen turnover as such; at most, a minute repair process. Even if, as has been recently reported, there is an increase in the rate of hydroxyproline synthesis in cartilage undergoing degenerative changes (Nimni and Deshmukh 1973; Eyre, McDevitt and Muir 1975; Lippiello and Mankin 1976), this would be far too low to be of use in replacing a measurable fraction of damaged collagen.

6. FLUID FLOW

6.1. Cartilage Structure in Relation to Deformation and Fluid Flow

The constituents of cartilage which have so far been identified all consist of molecules which are of constant specific volume, i.e. in themselves they are non-extensible and non-compressible. Thus, when cartilage is subjected to an applied load the deformation which one observes is not due to a change in the volume of its solid constituents but to (a) a molecular rearrangement of the polymer network which leads to a change in the shape of the specimen at constant volume (Poisson ratio ~0.5) and (b) a loss of fluid from the matrix which causes a decrease in the total volume of the tissue and hence a closer packing of the solid constituents.

The former effect is usually referred to as the 'instantaneous deformation' of cartilage and is essentially elastic in nature (see Chapter 6). The latter is the cartilage 'creep' (see Chapter 6, Section 3.8), which in normal cartilage is due entirely to the expression of fluid. This has been shown experimentally by Maroudas and Kempson (Maroudas 1975b) and is illustrated in Figure 4.16. In order to understand the time-dependent mechanical behaviour of cartilage under load (i.e. 'creep') it is thus necessary to know the parameters which control fluid flow, and these are considered below.

It has long been recognized by chemists (e.g. Fessler 1960; Ogston 1970) that the most likely model of cartilage is a relatively coarse network formed by collagen fibrils, capable of resisting

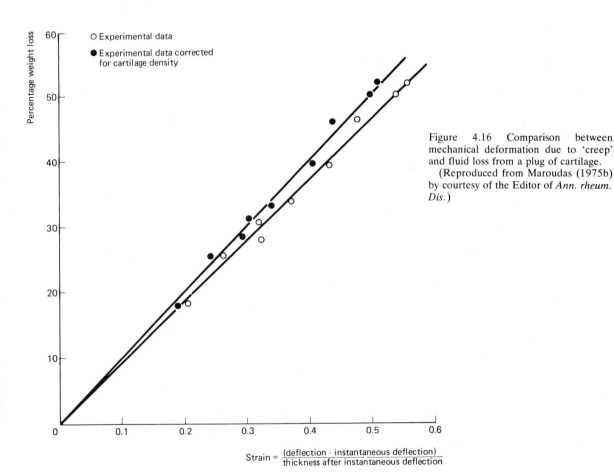

Figure 4.16 Comparison between mechanical deformation due to 'creep' and fluid loss from a plug of cartilage.
(Reproduced from Maroudas (1975b) by courtesy of the Editor of *Ann. rheum. Dis.*)

tension but not compression, filled with a concentrated solution (or a gel) of proteoglycans and non-collagenous proteins, with accompanying ions and other small solutes (see also Chapter 5, Section 3). Because of its high swelling pressure and low hydraulic permeability, this gel forms the compression-resisting element in cartilage.

Both the elastic forces in the collagen network and the swelling pressure of the proteoglycan–water gel are very sensitive to changes in the hydration of the tissue.

In thermodynamic terms, the steep rise in the swelling pressure of a polyelectrolyte solution which occurs as the concentration of solute increases is due to two main factors: (a) a decrease in the entropy caused by an increase in the excluded volume and (b) a higher Gibbs–Donnan potential, resulting in an increasing number of ions in cartilage as compared with external solution. Both these factors apply to the proteoglycan gel in cartilage. The relatively coarse collagen fibres, on the other hand, are too large for significant excluded volume effects and exhibit no Gibbs–Donnan effect as they possess no net charge; hence their contribution to the swelling pressure of the cartilage matrix is negligible. A polymer network has its own configurational entropy, however, and this usually increases when the volume of the tissue is reduced (Flory 1966). Thus—as far as the collagen network is concerned, at physiological hydrations at least—it is a decrease in the volume which is thermodynamically favourable. By contrast, an expansion of the matrix leads to a decreased configurational entropy due to the untwisting of fibres and will thus be resisted by the collagen network.

To summarize, if the volume of the tissue decreases, the proteoglycan–water gel develops a higher swelling pressure, which tends to resist further changes in this direction. On the other hand, collagen fibres do not resist initial compression, but do counteract expansion.

It should be noted in this context that, unlike some connective tissues (e.g. cornea or the intervertebral disc), intact adult articular cartilage can swell very little over and above its normal water content; even when its swelling pressure is more than doubled by equilibration in distilled water, its volume increases by less than 3% (Maroudas 1975, unpublished result). This means that, near the normal hydration value, the stresses in the collagen network must rise very steeply with increase in hydration (i.e. the collagen network is practically inextensible, a fact reflected by the tensile stiffness of the tissue (see Chapter 6, Section 4)). In practical terms, this means that it is unlikely that under physiological conditions there would be any mechanism whereby in the normal tissue the water content, and hence the thickness, could be increased to any measurable extent above the resting value.

6.2. Balance of Forces and Fluid Movement in Cartilage

6.2.1. General Principles and Mechanisms Involved. In this Section the dynamics of fluid flow are examined in relation to the variation in the properties of the cartilage matrix with hydration.

It should be repeated at the outset that it is the osmotic pressure of the fluid within the cartilage which is responsible for the resistance to compression, and not any forces within the solid components of the matrix. In this respect cartilage is different from an inert sponge.

When cartilage is not under external load, the swelling pressure of the interstitial fluid $(p_{swelling})$ is balanced by the hydrostatic pressure $(p_{elastic})$ due to the elastic forces in the collagen network.

$$p_{applied} = 0 \quad \text{and} \quad p_{elastic} = p_{swelling} \qquad (26)$$

As soon as an external load is applied to a specimen which is not laterally confined, there will first be an instantaneous elastic deformation with a change in the shape of the specimen. This may *a priori* be thought to lead to some change in $p_{elastic}$ before any change in the volume due to fluid flow has taken place. However, it has been found experimentally (see Section 6.2.3) that specimens which were not laterally confined showed the same equilibrium water content under a given external pressure whether the latter was mechanically (i.e. uniaxially) applied or whether it was osmotically applied from all directions so that no change in shape occurred prior to a change in volume. It can therefore be concluded that at equilibrium the balance of forces is not significantly affected by the initial elastic change in the shape of the specimen.

When an external compressive load is locally applied to cartilage the sum of the applied hydrostatic pressure $(p_{applied})$, and the hydrostatic pressure produced by the elastic stresses $(p_{elastic})$, exceeds the difference in the osmotic pressure between the inside of the tissue and the outside medium (i.e. the so-called swelling pressure $(p_{swelling})$), with the result that fluid flow takes place away from the loaded region due to a net pressure differential given by

$$\Delta p = p_{applied} + p_{elastic} - p_{swelling} \qquad (27)$$

It should be noted at this point that the total pressure to which fluid is subjected within the cartilage matrix can never exceed the external applied pressure since the elastic stresses in the collagen network are at their maximum when the tissue is fully hydrated and are then only just sufficient to balance the gradient of the osmotic pressure. Thus, once the tissue starts being compressed, the elastic stresses within it are lower than the swelling pressure and flow cannot take place from the interior of the cartilage into the fluid film through which cartilage is being loaded. While load is being applied, fluid must flow away from the loaded to the unloaded region. Authors who postulate that under some circumstances fluid flow occurs from the interior of the matrix into the fluid film through which the cartilage surfaces are loaded (see Chapter 7) make the implicit assumption that, during load carriage, the elastic stresses in the cartilage matrix can exceed the swelling pressure and thus add to the effect of the applied pressure so that $p_{applied} + p_{elastic} - p_{swelling} > p_{applied}$, which, in view of what has been said above, clearly cannot be the case.

As liquid is squeezed gradually out of the matrix, $p_{swelling}$ increases since the concentration of colloids in the tissue becomes greater whilst $p_{elastic}$ decreases. Eventually a stage is reached when $p_{applied} = (p_{swelling} - p_{elastic})$ and a new state of equilibrium is achieved, with $\Delta p = 0$; hence no further flow occurs.

Furthermore, at any stage during the loading process, the rate of fluid expression (Q_1) will be proportional to the net driving potential at that stage, in accordance with the Darcy equation; i.e.

$$Q_1 = B(p_{applied} + p_{elastic} - p_{swelling}) \qquad (28)$$

where B is a proportionality factor dependent on the hydraulic permeability of the specimen, κ, and on its geometry.

If the load is lifted off the specimen, the latter will start imbibing liquid at a rate given by

$$Q_2 = B(p_{swelling} - p_{elastic}) \qquad (29)$$

For a cartilage specimen subjected to a given external load, the parameters B, $p_{elastic}$ and $p_{swelling}$ should vary during load carriage as a function only of the water content of the tissue. Hence during fluid expression at a given water content the above parameters should be constant to a first approximation whatever the value of the applied load. (Although the variation of the applied load will alter the instantaneous deformation and hence will have some effect on the geometry of the specimen and on B, within a two- to threefold range of loads this is a second order effect (see Section 6.2.2).)

In equations (26) to (29) the ionic (Donnan) contribution to the swelling pressure was included in the general term $p_{swelling}$. However, this contribution can be evaluated separately and should therefore be expressed as a separate term. Thus

$$p_{swelling} = p_{Donnan} + p'_{swelling} \qquad (30)$$

where $p'_{swelling}$ = swelling pressure due to effects other than ionic.

If experiments involving fluid expression are carried out *in vitro* and salt solutions of different ionic strengths are used as the equilibrating media, p_{Donnan} can be varied whilst B, $p_{elastic}$ and $p'_{swelling}$ will remain unchanged.

6.2.2. Fluid Expression Experiments. In what follows, the course of typical fluid expression (or creep) experiments will be described in order to illustrate the concepts given above and to show the type of data which can be derived from such experiments (Maroudas 1975a, b).

The experimental procedure used by the writer was as follows. Full depth cylindrical plugs of cartilage, 0.32 cm in diameter, were obtained at post-mortem from human femoral heads. The apparatus used in the compression experiments (designed by Kempson) is shown in Figure 4.17. The cartilage specimens were

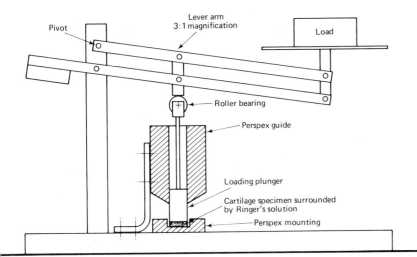

Pivot

Lever arm
3:1 magnification

Load

Roller bearing

Perspex guide

Loading plunger

Cartilage specimen surrounded
by Ringer's solution

Perspex mounting

Figure 4.17 Apparatus for measuring fluid expression.

(Reproduced from Maroudas (1975b) by courtesy of the Editor of *Ann. rheum. Dis.*)

placed in a well, surrounded by NaCl solution of appropriate concentration and a given load was applied. At regular intervals the solution was withdrawn from the well by suction with a cannula and followed by wiping off the remainder of the fluid with a tissue. The load was then removed and the cartilage plug was weighed in a vial which had been pre-equilibrated at 100% humidity to avoid drying out the cartilage specimen. The cartilage was then immediately replaced in the apparatus, the load was reapplied, and finally the well was again filled with solution. This process was repeated until no further fluid loss was observed. Applied loads ranged from 45 to 450 g giving rise to applied pressures from 0.17–1.7 MN/m^2 (1.7–17 atm). The solutions used were 0.15 mol/litre or 1.0 mol/litre NaCl; 1.0 mol/litre NaCl solution was chosen so as to render the ionic contribution to the swelling pressure relatively small.

Figures 4.18 and 4.19 show curves of fluid expression versus time for a number of applied loads, in 1.0 mol/litre and 0.15 mol/litre NaCl solutions, respectively. It can be seen that in order to produce a given reduction in the equilibrium water content of cartilage, higher applied pressures are needed in 0.15 mol/litre than in 1.0 mol/litre NaCl, a finding which confirms the earlier work of Linn and Sokoloff (1955). The difference represents the Donnan (ionic) contribution to the osmotic pressure. It should be noted that in fact even in 1.0 mol/litre (1.0M) NaCl the Donnan contribution to the osmotic pressure is not completely abolished and hence the procedure used in Figure 4.20 is illustrative only. In more recent experiments, 1.5 mol/litre (1.5M) NaCl solutions have been used and calculated corrections for the remaining Donnan contribution made (Urban and Maroudas 1978, in preparation).

The internal cartilage pressure at the final equilibrium is of course equal to the applied pressure. However, most of the curves in Figures 4.18 and 4.19 do not flatten out completely; thus true equilibrium was clearly not attained in these original experiments. Recently, in order to obtain more accurate values for the internal cartilage pressure, compression experiments have been carried out

Figure 4.18 Fluid expression curves. Equilibrating solution: 0.15 mol/litre (0.15M) NaCl.

(Reproduced from Maroudas (1975b) by courtesy of the Editor of *Ann. rheum. Dis.*)

Figure 4.19 Fluid expression curves. Equilibrating solution: 1 mol/litre (1.0M) NaCl.

(Reproduced from Maroudas (1975b) by courtesy of the Editro of *Ann. rheum. Dis.*)

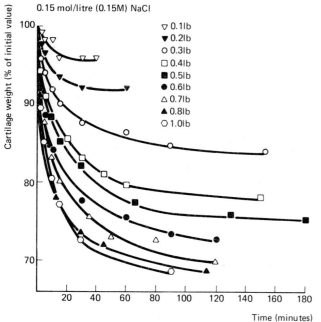

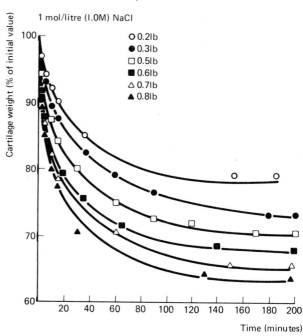

Figure 4.20 Determination of the Donnan contribution to swelling pressure from fluid expression curves.
(Reproduced from Maroudas (1975b) by courtesy of the Editor of *Ann. rheum. Dis.*)

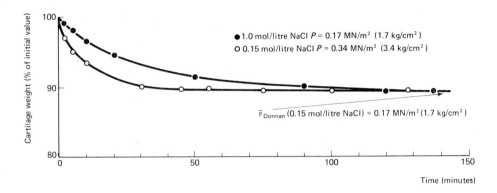

over much longer periods of time—24 hours or more—the apparatus being enclosed in a 100% humidity chamber to prevent evaporation of the solutions. It is from the results of these experiments that a plot of equilibrium applied pressure vs fixed charge density has been obtained (Figure 4.21a).

From the slopes of the fluid expression curves in Figures 4.18 and 4.19 it is possible to calculate the actual rates of fluid expression at a given value of the water content, corresponding to different applied loads, and hence to obtain graphs of the rate of water loss versus applied pressure for different values of the water content. Three typical graphs are shown in Figure 4.22.

In equation (28) the variation of Q with $p_{applied}$ is linear, which means that the internal pressure (i.e. $p_{swelling} - p_{elastic}$) and B are, within the limits of this type of experiment, independent of the applied load and of the possible variations in the instantaneous deformation.

In accordance with equation (28) the intercept on the ordinate gives the term $(p_{swelling} - p_{elastic})$, which is seen to increase as the water content decreases. The difference between the values of the intercept obtained for cartilage in 0.15 mol/litre and 1.0 mol/litre NaCl solutions represents approximately the Donnan contribution to the osmotic pressure, and this too is seen to increase as the water content decreases.

The reciprocal of the slope of the lines in Figure 4.23 gives B, which is proportional to the hydraulic permeability coefficient. Since the lines for salt solutions of different molarity are parallel, the permeability coefficient appears to be independent of the salt concentration. This finding agrees with independent measurements of the effect of salt concentration on permeability

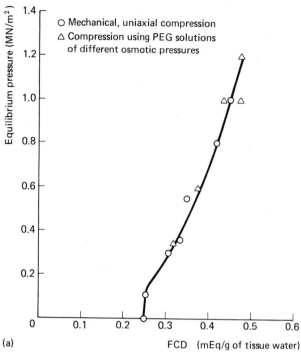

(a)

Figure 4.21 (a) Variation in the equilibrium pressure of femoral head cartilage with fixed charge density. (b) (*below*) Variation in the swelling pressure of proteoglycans extracted from femoral head cartilage with fixed charge density.

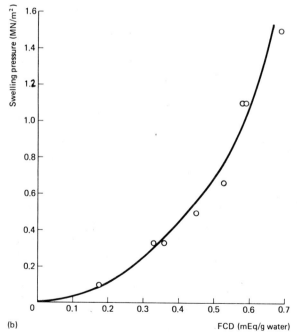

(b)

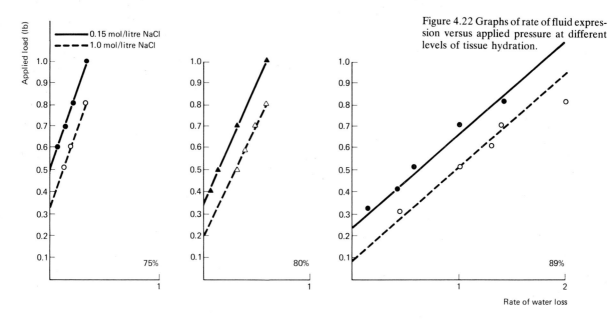

Figure 4.22 Graphs of rate of fluid expression versus applied pressure at different levels of tissue hydration.

(Maroudas 1975, unpublished results) and is consistent with the idea that the proteoglycans in the cartilage occupy, in the natural state, so small a domain that increasing salt concentration does not have much effect on their configuration. On the other hand, the reciprocal of the slope decreases with decreasing water content and this is entirely consistent with the fall in the permeability coefficient with decreasing water content observed in other experiments (see Figure 4.27).

The value of the permeability coefficient can be approximately calculated from graphs such as those in Figure 4.22 using an equation for radial flow given by McCutchen (1962):

$$\frac{dh}{dt} = \kappa \cdot \frac{8Wh}{\pi R^4} \tag{31}$$

where κ = permeability coefficient,
 W = applied load,
 R = radius of specimen,
 h = specimen thickness.

The values lie in the same range as those measured directly. Thus from Figure 4.22, κ was found to be 1.0×10^{-13} cm^3 s^{-1} at 89% of the tissue weight. The corresponding figure from direct measurement for a specimen of somewhat lower glycosaminoglycan content is 1.4×10^{-13} cm^3 s^{-1} (see Figure 4.27 and Section 6.33).

Equation (31) is only valid initially as it is based on the

Figure 4.23 Hydraulic permeability as a function of hydration: comparison between values obtained by the unsteady state method of Fatt and Goldstick (1965) and those obtained by direct measurement.
(Reproduced from Urban (1977) by permission)

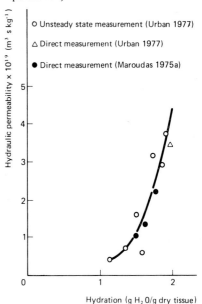

assumption that the hydration is uniform throughout the tissue. A rigorous differential equation for unsteady state conditions, analogous to the diffusion equation, has been derived by Fatt and Goldstick (1965) for fluid expression from the cornea:

$$\frac{\delta M}{\delta t} = \frac{\delta}{\delta z}\left(D(H)\frac{dM}{dz}\right) \tag{32}$$

where M = the hydration expressed as weight of water per weight of dry tissue,

   z = distance based on dry tissue volume, and

$D(H)$ is defined by equation (33):

$$D(H) = \kappa \cdot \frac{\sigma^2}{\sigma + M} \cdot \frac{dP}{dM} \tag{33}$$

where $D(H)$ = the transport coefficient,

   κ = hydraulic permeability,

   σ = the ratio of the specific volume of dry tissue to that of water,

   $\frac{dP}{dM}$ = the rate of change of the internal tissue pressure with hydration.

Equation (32) has recently been used, with suitable boundary conditions, by Urban (1977) as a basis for treatment of fluid flow in the intervertebral disc and cartilage. In order to determine the hydraulic permeability as a function of hydration from fluid expression curves, a knowledge of the relation between the internal tissue pressure and hydration is required. The same treatment enables the course of fluid expression (or resorption) to be predicted if the variation of the hydraulic permeability with hydration is known. Figure 4.23 (Urban 1977) shows a comparison of the hydraulic permeability as a function of hydration determined by the above unsteady-state method with that obtained by direct measurement for a slice of cartilage of low GAG content; the Figure is based on preliminary results and is shown merely to illustrate the method.

6.2.3. Fluid Expression from Cartilage Specimens Immersed in Solutions of High Osmotic Pressure. The above data on swelling pressures and permeability have all been obtained from uniaxial loading experiments on laterally unconfined specimens (Maroudas 1975b). In order to test whether the initial tensile stresses introduced into the tissue in this type of experiment because of the instantaneous lateral expansion influence to any extent subsequent fluid flow and in particular the internal cartilage pressure, a non-mechanical system was developed whereby pressure could be uniformly applied to a specimen from all directions (Urban 1977; Urban and Maroudas, in preparation). Solutions containing different concentrations of polyethylene glycol (PEG) were prepared, with osmotic pressures ranging from 0.05 to 1.0 MN/m² (0.5 to

10 atm). The osmotic pressures of these solutions were calculated by Urban (1977) using the data of Edmonds and Ogston (1968) and Wells (1972). Equilibrating specimens of cartilage in such solutions is tantamount to subjecting them to a range of external pressures uniformly applied from all directions. If the equilibrium water content of the specimen is then measured as a function of the osmotic pressure of the equilibrating PEG solution, a graph can be obtained of the total internal tissue pressure versus the final water content (or the final glycosaminoglycan content).

Such results (Maroudas and Urban, in preparation) are shown in Figure 4.21b, alongside those obtained from uniaxial compression experiments using different applied loads. Both the cartilage specimens used for mechanical testing and those immersed in PEG solutions came from the superior surface of the femoral head and had the same glycosaminoglycan and water contents. It can be seen that the values obtained using PEG solutions fit exactly with those obtained from mechanical tests.

6.2.4. Methods of Determining the Total Osmotic Pressure in Cartilage. Whilst the ionic contribution to the osmotic pressure of cartilage has been estimated in the past by a number of methods (Ogston 1970; Well 1973; Maroudas 1975b), no such estimates have been made for the total osmotic pressure or the elastic stress. These two factors have usually been treated as a lumped sum $(p_{swelling} - p_{elastic})$ in spite of their very different origins. However, because the swelling pressure in cartilage is due primarily to the proteoglycans (whilst the elastic stress is due to the collagen network), it follows that the swelling pressures of isolated proteo-glycan–water gels should be the same as the swelling pressures in cartilage at the corresponding proteoglycan concentrations. The swelling pressures of gels made from proteoglycans extracted from femoral head cartilage have recently been measured by a method of equilibration against PEG solutions of known osmotic pressure (Urban 1977; Urban and Maroudas, in preparation). At a concentration of proteoglycans corresponding to a fixed charge density representative of intact femoral head cartilage (approximately 0.25 mEq/g of tissue water), the total swelling pressure is about 0.2 MN/m^2 (2 atm). Since in unloaded cartilage $p_{elastic} = p_{swelling}$ (see equation (26)), $p_{elastic}$ must also be equal to 0.2 MN/m^2.

The Donnan osmotic pressure as determined both for the proteoglycan–water gel (Urban and Maroudas, in preparation) and for cartilage is around 0.18 MN/m^2 (1.8 atm), so that this constitutes the main contribution to the swelling pressure.

Figure 4.21a shows that, upon application of an external load to cartilage, there is initially a steep rise in the internal cartilage pressure with decreasing hydration (at equilibrium $p_{internal} = p_{applied}$; see p. 264). Thus at a hydration of 2.26 g of water per g of dry tissue as compared with the initial 2.33, the internal cartilage pressure changes from zero to 0.15 MN/m². Since for so small a change in hydration, the increase in fixed charge density is correspondingly small (from 0.250 to 0.258 mEq/g), the swelling pressure of the proteoglycans will have increased very little (Figure 4.21b). Now the internal cartilage pressure is given by the expression $p_{internal} = p_{swelling} - p_{elastic}$; accordingly, in the initial stages of compression the steep increase in the internal cartilage pressure must be due to an equivalent decrease in $p_{elastic}$; i.e. in the tension exerted on the fluid by the collagen fibre network. When the cartilage volume is reduced to about 92% of its 'unloaded' value (corresponding to a hydration of 2.07 and a fixed charge density of 0.275 mEq/g), the internal cartilage pressure becomes equal to the swelling pressure of the proteoglycans alone (Figure 4.21a and b), which means that $p_{elastic}$ is effectively zero. The two curves coincide up to a fixed charge density of about 0.325 mEq/g, corresponding to a hydration of 1.8 g of water per g dry tissue. At lower hydrations the internal cartilage pressure becomes higher than the swelling pressure of the proteoglycans and, as the hydration is further decreased, the difference becomes increasingly larger. There is evidence that this 'extra' resistance to fluid loss at low hydrations is associated with the removal of intrafibrillar water from the collagen (Maroudas, in preparation).

Returning to the situation in unloaded cartilage, it must be pointed out that in calculating the elastic stress in the collagen fibres, it was assumed that the middle and deep zones of cartilage which have a high proteoglycan content are in direct contact with the external solution, which leads to a high osmotic pressure gradient across the interface (0.2 MN/m²). This of course applies only to excised pieces of cartilage. By contrast, in an intact joint it is the surface of cartilage which alone is in contact with solution—and this zone of cartilage has the lowest proteoglycan content. There will thus be a relatively low swelling pressure at the surface (less than 0.05 MN/m², 0.5 atm) and, since the proteoglycan concentration rises *gradually* with depth, the osmotic pressure gradient will remain at this low level throughout the thickness of the tissue although the total osmotic pressure is high. The elastic force in the collagen network, which is needed to balance this gradient, will thus be lower than in excised pieces of tissue (Maroudas 1976a).

It should be noted that, because the collagen network in intact cartilage is virtually inextensible, even excised specimens, with their high osmotic pressure gradients, do not swell by more than about 2% when placed in physiological saline.

The values for the different components of internal pressure given here are typical of normal human adult cartilage from the femoral head of mean fixed charge density around 0.17 mEq/g of tissue. Different values could be expected in other joints since the fixed charge density varies from joint to joint (see Section 2).

6.2.5. The Structural Significance of Increased Hydration in Osteoarthrotic Cartilage. It is appropriate here to recapitulate certain points in order to emphasize the structural implications of the increased hydration observed in osteoarthrotic cartilage.

It is well known that concentrated proteoglycan gels have a tendency to imbibe water. At the concentration present in the surface zone of normal articular cartilage the proteoglycan–water gel has an osmotic pressure which exceeds that of synovial fluid by about 0.05 MN/m^2 (0.5 atm). This swelling pressure is counteracted by the collagen network since no other element in the tissue has tensile strength.

In view of the above facts about normal cartilage, what are the possible explanations for the increased hydration levels in osteoarthrotic cartilage? It is necessary to consider first whether the increased water content in the tissue is in fact accompanied by a volume change in the proteoglycan–water gel or whether the 'extra' water simply replaces the lost proteoglycan. In surface fibrillated osteoarthrotic specimens, the overall proteoglycan content is seldom decreased by more than 20%. Since the proteoglycan concentration in normal tissue is around 10% (weight of proteoglycan/weight of water), and since the density of proteoglycan is about 1.7 if the volume of the proteoglycan–water gel remained unchanged, a 20% loss in the proteoglycan content would be reflected in a gain of less than 2% in the water content. Yet surface fibrillated specimens exhibit an increase of 5–10% in the water content. This must therefore mean that there is an actual increase in the volume of the proteoglycan–water gel, amounting to 3–8% (i.e. the tissue actually swells).

If the tensile stiffness of the collagen network were the same in these mildly degenerate specimens as in normal cartilage, such a considerable increase in the tissue volume could occur only if enormous osmotic pressures developed within the matrix. However, there is no reasonable mechanism which would account for the emergence of such pressures if known facts about the chemical composition of the tissue, its electrolyte content and the state of the proteoglycans in early stages of degeneration are taken into account (Section 2) (Bayliss 1976; Maroudas 1976a; Maroudas and Venn 1977). On the contrary, a decrease in the proteoglycan content will inevitably lead to a decrease in the swelling pressure of the tissue.

Hence the only satisfactory explanation at present for the increased hydration of cartilage observed from the very early stages of degeneration, often in the absence of macroscopic or chemical changes (McDevitt and Muir 1976; Maroudas and Venn 1977; Byers *et al.* 1977), is a decrease in the stiffness of the collagen network. This explanation is also consistent with the fragmented appearance of the collagen network observed by Meachim (Chapter 9) when he examined by electron microscopy specimens of osteoarthrotic cartilage which showed no visible surface alterations and were similar to those studied by Byers *et al.* (1977) and Maroudas and Venn (1977). The pronounced swelling of fibrillated slices of cartilage from the middle zone which occurs upon exposure to salt solutions (Figure 4.24), contrasted with the dimensional stability of normal cartilage slices, is entirely consistent with the above mechanism (Maroudas 1976a).

It therefore seems that it is the collagen network which is the seat of early changes in the degenerative process, leading to increased hydration of the tissue. Proteoglycan loss is often seen as a secondary phenomenon.

Figure 4.24 Swelling of slices of degenerate cartilage exposed to NaCl solutions.

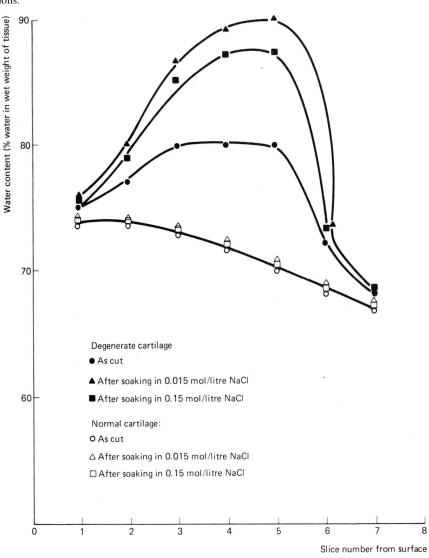

Degenerate cartilage
● As cut
▲ After soaking in 0.015 mol/litre NaCl
■ After soaking in 0.15 mol/litre NaCl

Normal cartilage:
○ As cut
△ After soaking in 0.015 mol/litre NaCl
□ After soaking in 0.15 mol/litre NaCl

Water content (% water in wet weight of tissue)

Slice number from surface

274

6.3. Hydraulic Permeability

In accordance with the Darcy equation, fluid flow through porous media is proportional to the effective pressure gradient and the hydraulic permeability of the material (see Section 6.2.1, equation (28)).

The former has been discussed at length in the previous section. It remains to consider the hydraulic permeability, κ.

The resistance to fluid flow (i.e. the reciprocal of the hydraulic permeability) is dependent on the frictional interactions between the fluid and the solid constituents within the matrix. Since the collagen fibrils are relatively coarse in comparison with the 'branches' of the proteoglycan molecules, it is the latter which are chiefly responsible for frictional interactions with the fluid and hence for the high resistance to flow. However, some of the cartilage water, probably around 15–20%, is actually present inside the collagen fibrils; since the spaces within these fibrils are small—for reconstituted collagen the intermolecular distance is about 6Å (Katz and Li 1973)—the bulk movement of the interfibrillar water will be controlled by interactions with the collagen molecules rather than with the proteoglycans. Since the proportion of proteoglycans, collagen and water varies from joint to joint and, in a given joint, from the surface to the deep zone, corresponding differences in the hydraulic permeability coefficient are to be expected.

6.3.1. The Variation of Hydraulic Permeability with Depth.
The hydraulic permeability of cartilage was first measured by McCutchen (1962) on a cow's 'leg joint'. He obtained an average value of 5.8×10^{-13} cm^3 s g^{-1} for κ normal to the surface and observed that κ decreases with depth. A number of measurements have since been made on human cartilage, as a function of distance from the articular surface and of glycosaminoglycan content (Maroudas 1968; Muir, Bullough and Maroudas, 1970). Typical curves of the hydraulic permeability versus depth for normal articular cartilage from femoral condyles are shown in Figure 4.25.

It can be seen that the permeability either decreases continuously from the surface to the deep zone or shows an initial increase and decreases thereafter. The permeability lies in the range $3–7 \times 10^{-13}$ cm^3 s g^{-1} near the articular surface, decreasing to $1.5–2.5 \times 10^{-13}$ cm^3 s g^{-1} in the deep zone.

Femoral head cartilage, which has a much higher fixed charge density than knee cartilage (Maroudas 1975a), has a much lower hydraulic permeability, the mean value being around $1–2 \times 10^{-13}$ cm^3 s g^{-1}.

On the whole, there is an inverse relationship between permeability and fixed charge density. However, there is sometimes an

275

apparent anomaly in the superficial zone where a decreased permeability has been observed in spite of a low fixed charge density. A number of factors could be responsible for this, such as (a) a somewhat higher collagen content; (b) the presence of finer collagen fibrils; and (c) a higher cell density (Muir *et al.* 1970). Of these, the most likely, in the view of the present writer, is the presence of a fine collagen meshwork, which leads to the fluid–collagen fibril friction being no longer negligible as compared with the fluid–proteoglycan interaction. However, it must be borne in mind that this effect is of a secondary nature and that the proteoglycan content remains by far the most important determinant of hydraulic permeability.

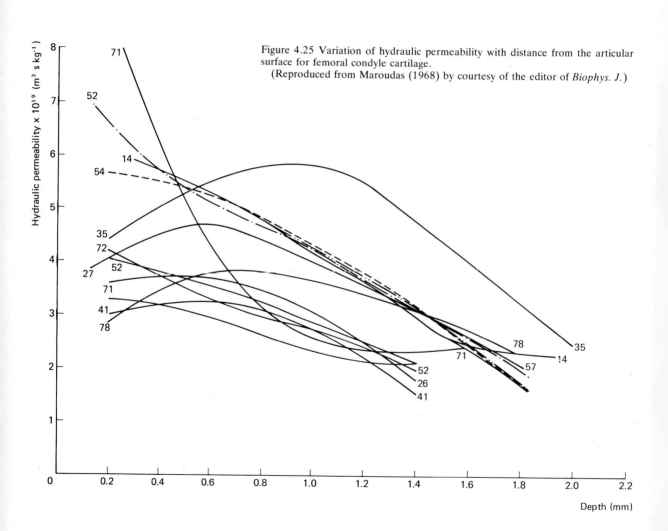

Figure 4.25 Variation of hydraulic permeability with distance from the articular surface for femoral condyle cartilage.
(Reproduced from Maroudas (1968) by courtesy of the editor of *Biophys. J.*)

6.3.2. The Measurement of Tangential Permeability. Since *in vivo* fluid flow is mainly in a direction tangential to the cartilage surface, the tangential permeability is perhaps of more physiological relevance than the permeability normal to the surface. Unfortunately, the former is the more difficult to measure.

McCutchen (1962) was the first to state, on the basis of indirect evidence obtained from a 'squeezing' experiment, that the tangential permeability was approximately equal to the normal. This was confirmed by direct measurement of normal and tangential permeability of adjacent plugs of cartilage (Maroudas 1974). A graph of normal permeability versus distance from the articular surface together with mean values of tangential permeability are shown in Figure 4.26. It can be seen that the values for the mean tangential permeability correspond exactly with the values of normal permeability obtained for the middle zone.

Figure 4.26 Comparison between normal and tangential hydraulic permeability.
(Reproduced from Maroudas (1974) by courtesy of the Institute of Orthopaedics.)

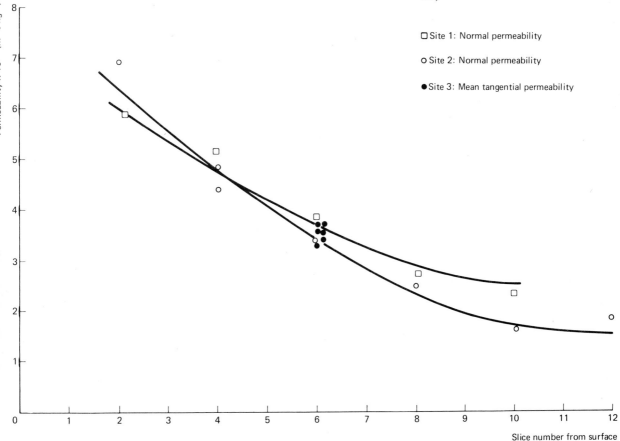

□ Site 1: Normal permeability

o Site 2: Normal permeability

● Site 3: Mean tangential permeability

Slice number from surface

Mulholland, Millington and Manners (1975) measured both the normal and the tangential permeability on full depth plugs of cartilage and reported that the latter was higher than the former. However, they omitted to consider the following factor: in order to compare the normal with the tangential permeability from overall values obtained on full depth specimens, it is necessary to allow for the fact that in the former case one is dealing with the sum of resistances in series whilst in the latter the resistances are in parallel. Hence, even though at any given depth in cartilage the permeabilities in the normal and the tangential directions are identical, the overall permeability as measured on a full depth specimen in the normal direction must of necessity be lower than that measured in the tangential direction. However, if the permeabilities of thin sections cut in the normal direction are summed and then meaned, the true overall permeability can be obtained for lateral flow.

In conclusion, it is completely justifiable to use the values obtained for the hydraulic permeability in the normal direction to describe tangential flow provided due account is taken of the variation of permeability with depth. It should be noted that the finding that at a given depth in the tissue the hydraulic permeability is the same in the normal as in the tangential direction is consistent with the isotropic nature of the proteoglycan–water gel which is responsible for the main resistance to fluid flow.

6.3.3. Variation of Hydraulic Permeability with Hydration. The variation of the hydraulic permeability coefficient, κ, with hydration is shown in Figure 4.22 for a slice of low GAG. The sharp decrease observed with a decrease in the water content (Maroudas 1975b) is consistent with the fact that a decreased water content means a higher effective proteoglycan concentration.

6.3.4. Variation of Hydraulic Permeability with Applied Load at Constant Hydration. The results described in Section 6.2.2 show that the permeability coefficient at steady state is independent of the applied pressure gradient provided the latter is small compared with the swelling pressure of the tissue; i.e. provided the tissue is barely compressible under the given experimental conditions. Fluid flow through cartilage under these conditions thus obeys the basic Darcy law. The same conclusion was reached by Mulholland *et al.* (1975). Mansour and Mow (1976), on the other hand, report a pressure dependence of the permeability coefficient. The present writer has been unable to reproduce their results.

6.3.5. A Calculation of the 'Pore Size' of Cartilage from the Hydraulic Permeability and Diffusivity of Water. The results of permeability measurements provide some information on the basic structure of cartilage. Thus if, as a very simplified model, cartilage

278

is thought of as a network of capillaries of average radius, r, it is possible to apply Poiseuille's law for viscous flow of water, in combination with Fick's law of diffusion, in order to derive an expression for r. A number of closely related expressions have been derived (reviewed by House 1974).

The expression given below has been widely used to characterize synthetic membranes and therefore, for comparative purposes, it is the one which will be considered here (House 1974).

The expression is

$$r^2 = \frac{8\kappa\eta D\bar{V}_w}{RT}\sqrt{(\frac{RT}{V_w\bar{D}} - 1)} \qquad (34)$$

where r = effective pore radius,
$\quad \eta$ = viscosity of water,
$\quad V_w$ = specific volume of water,
$\quad R$ = universal gas constant,
$\quad T$ = absolute temperature,
$\quad D$ = diffusion coefficient of water (or one of its isotopes, in this case ^3HHO) in free solution,
$\quad \bar{D}$ = effective diffusion coefficient of water (i.e. in this case ^3HHO) in the membrane,
$\quad \kappa$ = hydraulic permeability of the membrane.

At a given temperature, the only variables in equation (34) are $\bar{D}$ and κ. $\bar{D}$ varies only slightly with the water content and not at all with the glycosaminoglycan content (Maroudas and Venn 1977) (see also Section 4.3.1). The parameter which thus mainly varies with r (i.e. with effective pore radius) is the hydraulic permeability, κ. If one takes $\kappa = 1.0 \times 10^{-13}\,cm^3\,s\,g^{-1}$, a value characteristic, for instance, of the middle and deep zones of femoral head cartilage and of the deep zone in the femoral condyles, the radius, r, works out to be 4 nm (40Å). For $\kappa = 5 \times 10^{-13}\,cm^3\,s\,g^{-1}$ which would correspond, for instance, to the superficial zone of knee cartilage, the radius, r, would be 9 nm (90Å).

Since the parallel capillary model obviously does not accurately represent physical reality, the physical meaning of r is somewhat dubious; however, it does provide a measure of effective meshwork size, which agrees with independent estimates obtained from the penetration of large molecules (Section 3.3).

6.4. The Effect of Proteoglycan Content and Hydration on Fluid Transport

In order to demonstrate the importance of the proteoglycans in limiting fluid flow, a specimen of cartilage from a normal adult femoral head was treated so as to remove the bulk of the proteoglycans (Maroudas 1974, unpublished). This treatment, relying on the combined action of trypsin, hydrogen peroxide and EDTA (Steven and Thomas 1973), is non-destructive to the collagen network.

An adjacent specimen was cut to the same dimensions (both had a cross-sectional area of 0.2 cm² and thickness 1 mm) and both were tested in the apparatus shown in Figure 4.17 under a pressure of 0.7 MN/m² (7 atm).

The curves of fluid expression versus time for the two specimens are shown in Figure 4.27. Clearly, the initial rate of fluid loss

Figure 4.27 Expression of fluid from an intact and a proteoglycan-free specimen of cartilage.

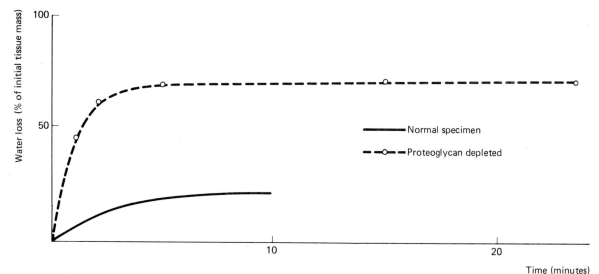

(which is equivalent to the rate of strain) is about ten times as high in the proteoglycan-depleted as in the normal specimen. The amount of water lost at equilibrium in the treated specimen is three and a half times that lost from the normal. In absolute terms, the equilibrium water content of the proteoglycan-depleted cartilage corresponds to less than the dry weight of the tissue, whilst in the normal specimens it is three times that amount. This example shows that it is the water retained by the proteoglycans in cartilage which possesses the capacity to support a compressive load effectively. This is entirely consistent with the discussion of swelling pressures in Section 6.1 and with the considerations of hydraulic permeability mentioned above.

It should be noted, however, that at very low hydrations it becomes increasingly difficult to express water from cartilage even in the absence of proteoglycans. This is clearly due to the fact that under such conditions it is the intrafibrillar water which has to be expelled and this must require pressures which have not been considered in the present treatment.

Figure 4.28 shows the rate of fluid loss in three specimens of cartilage of different origin and different initial fixed charge density: specimen 1 represents cartilage from an intact femoral head; specimen 2 that from an intact femoral condyle; and specimen 3 that from a fibrillated femoral condyle.

The different behaviour of the three specimens shows that as the concentration of proteoglycans increases, both the rate of fluid loss and the total amount of fluid which can be expressed before final equilibrium is reached fall. The former effect is due chiefly to a

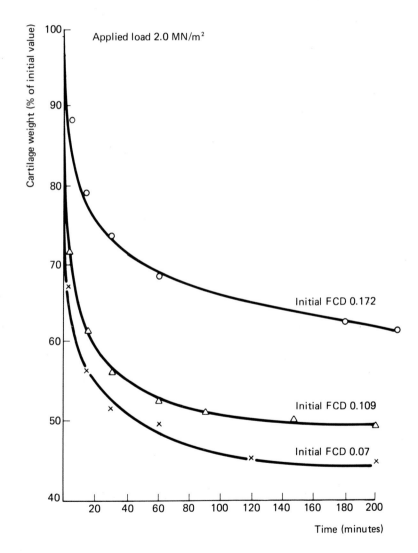

Figure 4.28 Expression of fluid from cartilage specimens of different glycosaminoglycan contents.
(Reproduced from Maroudas (1975b) by permission.)

lower hydraulic permeability and the latter to the higher swelling pressure. It should be noted that since fixed charge density is expressed on a wet basis, a lower fixed charge density (i.e. a reduced concentration of proteoglycan) may be due to a higher hydration, a fall in the absolute amount of proteoglycan present or a combination of the two. In mildly degenerate cartilage it seems likely that the collagen network is no longer intact (see Chapter 9), with the result that the elastic forces are not sufficient to balance the osmotic pressure until the network has been more distended than is normally the case. As a result, swelling occurs (Maroudas *et al.* 1973; Maroudas 1976a). This effect would lead to increased hydration and a consequent decrease in fixed charge density (i.e. proteoglycan concentration) prior to any actual loss of proteoglycans from the tissue (Maroudas and Venn 1977, 1979) (see Chapters 3 and 9).

6.5. Some Physiological Implications of Studies of Fluid Flow in Cartilage

Since the mechanism of fluid flow in cartilage is now understood, and the relevant parameters (i.e. the hydraulic permeability and the various components of internal pressure) have been identified and correlated with the chemical structure, it becomes in principle possible to predict the time-dependent mechanical behaviour in any joint. If the contact areas and the pressure distribution in a given joint could be determined, the continuity and a modified form of the Darcy equation could be used to obtain numerical solutions which will describe accurately fluid flow and hence compressive strain under both static and cyclic loading conditions.

However, even without an exact knowledge of the pressure distribution and without exact mathematical solutions to the strongly non-linear differential equations, it is possible to form an estimate of the amount of fluid loss which is likely under conditions of cyclic loading (e.g. during walking).

Using the same expression as in Section 6.2.2 (i.e. equation (31), which is derived by making a number of simplifying assumptions), it is possible to estimate the initial rate of cartilage deformation due to fluid flow. If a mean value for the hydraulic permeability, κ, of femoral head cartilage is taken as 10^{19} N s kg^{-1} (1×10^{-13} cm^3 sec/g) and the loaded area of cartilage is assumed to be a disc 2.2 cm in radius (Day, Swanson and Freeman 1975) and 0.25 cm in thickness, the initial rate of deformation due to fluid escape works out to be of the order of 0.75×10^{-3} cm/min (or about 0.03% of the total cartilage thickness) for a pressure of 3 MN/m^2 (3×10^7 dyn/cm^2; 30 kg/cm^2). This implies that in a normal walking cycle during which the load is applied for a fraction of a second (Chapter 5) the deformation due to fluid flow is negligible. Thus, if cartilage were to recover completely between each load application, its deformation during walking would be negligible. However, the rate of recovery is determined by the swelling pressure, which for small strains is far lower than the physiological load. Thus recovery from small deformations is far slower than the initial rate of deformation produced by a physiological load. Accordingly, recovery in a cycle is likely to be incomplete unless the 'off-load' intervals are considerably longer than the 'on-load' periods. Hence although the amount of water lost per cycle is extremely small, the total deformation after a period of walking may not always be negligible.

It should be pointed out that the swelling pressure in fully hydrated cartilage is low compared with the average applied pressure under physiological conditions (about 0.2 MN/m²; 2 atm) in the hip compared to a mean applied pressure of some 3 MN/m² (30 atm)). It rises steeply, however, with loss of water. Thus the importance of the swelling pressure of cartilage, as far as cyclic loading is concerned, lies more in controlling the rate of recovery than that of fluid expression. On the other hand, under prolonged loading conditions it serves to limit both the rate and the total amount of fluid lost. The sharp decrease in the permeability coefficient with decrease in the fluid content (see Figure 4.27) reinforces the effect.

6.6. Streaming Potential

Whenever fluid is made to flow through a material containing fixed positive or negative groups, an electrical potential develops which is called the streaming potential. The magnitude of the streaming potential depends on the fixed charge density, hydraulic permeability and electrical conductivity of the material (Helfferich 1962). These variables are related by the equation:

$$\frac{\Delta\psi}{\Delta p} = \frac{F\bar{C}_x\kappa}{\lambda} \qquad (35)$$

where $\Delta\psi$ = streaming potential,
Δp = pressure differential,
$\bar{C}_x$ = concentration of fixed negatively charged groups in cartilage,
F = Faraday's constant,
κ = flow permeability,
λ = specific electrical conductivity.

This relation affords yet another simple physical method for determining the fixed charge density of cartilage specimens since it is easy to measure their streaming potential as well as the hydraulic permeability and electrical conductivity (Maroudas et al. 1969).

The values of the streaming potential for cartilage equilibrated in Ringer's solution lie in the range $4\text{–}6 \times 10^{-9}$ N s kg^{-1} ($4\text{–}6 \times 10^{-4}$ V/atm) pressure gradient (Maroudas 1968). Thus for weight-bearing joints where pressures of the order of 3 MN/m^2 (3×10^7 dyn/cm^2) can be expected, a streaming potential of about 15 mV would develop. The loaded area will always be negatively charged with respect to the non-loaded zone and the potential will be there as long as the pressure gradient exists. It is not known at present whether or not the development of this streaming potential has any physiological significance.

Apart from the streaming potential caused by fluid flow, there are other electrical potentials in cartilage, viz. the Donnan potential due to gradients in fixed charge density and diffusion potentials due to movements of ions. These, however, have not been measured.

7. LUBRICATION

Although the subject of joint lubrication is considered in detail in Chapter 7, in this Section some of the physicochemical data relating to cartilage–synovial fluid interactions are discussed.

7.1. Filtration of Synovial Fluid through Cartilage

It has been shown earlier in this Chapter that cartilage, though permeable to water and small solutes, is impermeable to solutes whose molecular weight exceeds about 70 000. Hyaluronic acid of molecular weight 1 000 000 cannot therefore penetrate into cartilage at all. Thus, if synovial fluid is made to flow through cartilage, the hyaluronic acid in it will be retained at the cartilage surface. The physiological implications of this fact are as follows.

As two opposing joint surfaces are made to approach each other under load, the gap between them gradually decreases. At first synovial fluid can easily be squeezed out sideways through the gap into the unloaded zone. However, as the gap becomes narrower, the resistance to the fluid flowing through the gap increases and some flow must now take place through cartilage as shown in Figure 4.29. As the gap narrows further, the flow through it becomes negligible compared with the flow through cartilage and the latter becomes the major route. There is a basic difference between the two paths: whereas all constituents of synovial fluid pass together when flow is taking place through the gap between the cartilage surfaces, cartilage has pores which are too small to allow the molecules of hyaluronic acid to pass. Thus, when cartilage is the major flow path, calculation shows that the solution in the gap becomes more and more concentrated in hyaluronic

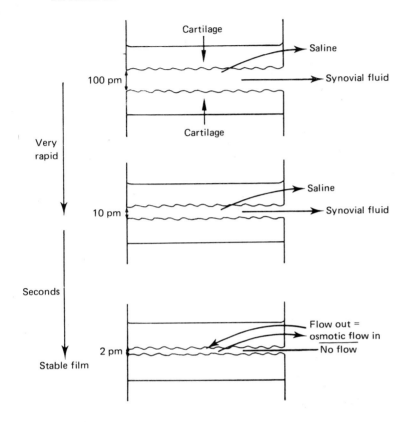

Figure 4.29 Formation of stable hyaluronic acid–water gels on the surface of cartilage.

(Reproduced from Maroudas (1969) by permission of the Editors.)

acid and eventually changes into a gel. The osmotic pressure of the gel gradually increases until it becomes equal to the applied pressure. At this stage all flow of water from the gel ceases and the film remains stable.

Calculations show that the gap width at which the escape of water through cartilage supersedes the sideways flow of synovial fluid in the gap is of the order of 0.5–1.0 μm (Maroudas 1967, 1969, 1972).

From the latter value of the gap and from a knowledge of the osmotic pressure of hyaluronic acid gels of various concentrations, it is possible to predict the final equilibrium film thickness which turns out to be of the order of 0.02–0.03 μm for physiological loads (Maroudas 1967, 1969). It can therefore be stated that when opposing cartilage surfaces are brought together in synovial fluid they can be expected not to come into direct contact but to remain separated by a film 0.02–0.03 μm in thickness consisting of a hyaluronic acid–water gel.

Dowson, Unsworth and Wright (1970) speak of much thicker films of hyaluronic acid: indeed the latest form of their 'boosted lubrication' theory is based on the hypothesis that hyaluronic acid becomes increasingly concentrated in the gap when the latter is in the range 10–1 μm. However, there is no physicochemical basis for assuming any increase in the concentration of hyaluronic acid at such large gap widths since there is no flow through cartilage at this stage and the opening between the two cartilage surfaces is far too wide to act as a filter for hyaluronic acid: it has been shown in experiments with cellulose acetate membranes (millipore filters) of varying pore size (Maroudas 1972, unpublished data) that no hyaluronic acid is retained on filters having a pore size of 0.8 μm. (The latter finding is consistent with the results of McCutchen on the lubricating ability of synovial fluid residue and filtrate after passage through different millipore membranes.)

Furthermore, experiments using an x-ray probe (Maroudas 1972) point to the absence of thick hyaluronic acid films between loaded areas of cartilage. The method is capable of detecting films of 0.5 μm in thickness.

7.2. Adsorption of Hyaluronic Acid to the Surface of Cartilage

Ultrafiltration is one of the possible mechanisms which could lead to the formation of hyaluronic acid–water films between opposing cartilage surfaces. Another mechanism, postulated originally by McCutchen (1966), is that of adsorption. McCutchen found that synovial fluid is a more effective boundary lubricant for cartilage than Ringer's solution. He also found that the protein moiety of the hyaluronic acid–protein complex appears to be essential for the effectiveness of synovial fluid as a boundary lubricant. He explained his results by assuming that the hyaluronic acid–protein complex becomes adsorbed onto the cartilage surface and that it is the protein moiety which promotes adsorption.

In order to study directly the surface interactions between cartilage and the constituents of synovial fluid, the present author used the method of microelectrophoresis (Shaw 1969). The electrophoretic mobilities of finely ground cartilage particles were measured, first on their own and subsequently in the presence of different solutes. When a solute becomes adsorbed onto cartilage particles the electrophoretic velocity of the particles is modified and becomes close to that of the solute (Maroudas 1969).

It was found that both pure hyaluronic acid, without the protein moiety, and the hyaluronic acid–protein complex as present in synovial fluid became adsorbed onto cartilage. This means that, though the protein moiety of the hyaluronate molecule appears to play some part in lubrication (Chapter 7), there is no indication that its role is to promote adsorption between cartilage and hyaluronic acid.

LIST OF SYMBOLS

A	= constant
a	= ionic activity
B	= function of r_s
C	= molar concentration
C_x	= concentration of rod-like macromolecules/chain polymers
d_i	= solute diameter
d_p	= pore diameter
D	= diffusion coefficient
F	= drag factor
h	= cartilage thickness
J	= total solute flux
K	= distribution coefficient
K_B^A	= selectivity coefficient
M	= cartilage hydration
m	= molar concentration of a solute per unit volume of water in a phase
N	= detected radioactivity per g cartilage
Δp	= pressure gradient
dp/dx	= hydrostatic pressure gradient
P	= solute flux
dP/dM	= rate of change of internal tissue pressure
Q	= rate of sulphate uptake into glycosaminoglycans
R	= cartilage radius
r_s	= radius of solute molecule
r_x	= radius of macromolecular rod
T	= absolute temperature
V_w	= specific volume of water
V_s	= volume of fraction of solids in cartilage
W	= applied load to cartilage
y	= 'dry' depth of tissue
z	= ionic valency
γ	= activity coefficient
κ	= hydraulic permeability coefficient
λ	= specific electrical conductivity
π	= Donnan osmotic pressure
φ	= osmotic coefficient
σ	= ratio of specific volume of dry tissue to that of water
η	= viscosity of water
$\Delta\psi$	= streaming potential

Subscripts Na^+, etc., refer to the species named.
Symbols with overbars are used for the interior of cartilage.

287

REFERENCES

Almeida L. (1973) Articular Cartilage. MD Thesis, University of Luanda.

Bayliss M. (1976) Study of the Biochemical Mechanisms involved in Human Osteoarthrotic Cartilage. PhD Thesis, University of London.

Benderly H. and Maroudas A. (1975) Equilibria of calcium and phosphate in human articular cartilage. *Ann. rheum. Dis.* **34**, Suppl. 2, 46.

Bollet A. J. and Nance J. L. (1966) Biochemical findings in normal and osteoarthritic articular cartilage. II: Chondroitin sulfate concentration and chain length, water and ash content. *J. clin. Invest.* **45**, 1170.

Bostrom H. (1952) Chondroitin sulphuric acid. *J. biol. Chem.* **196**, 477.

Byers P. D., Contempomi C. and Farkas T. A. (1970) A post-mortem study of the hip joint. *Ann. rheum. Dis.* **29**, 15.

Byers P. D., Maroudas A., Oztop F., Stockwell R. A. and Venn M. F. (1977) Histological and biochemical studies on cartilage from osteoarthrotic femoral heads with special reference to surface characteristics. *Conn. Tiss. Res.* **5**, 41.

Collins D. H. and McElligott T. F. (1960) Sulphate ($^{35}SO_4$) uptake by chondrocytes in relation to histological changes in osteoarthritic human articular cartilage. *Ann. rheum. Dis.* **19**, 318.

Collins D. H. and Meachim G. (1961) Sulphate ($^{35}SO_4$) fixation by human articular cartilage compared in the knee and shoulder joints. *Ann. rheum. Dis.* **20**, 117.

Cooke T. D. V., Bennett E. and Ohno O. (1979) Identification of immunoglobulins and complement components in articular collagenous tissues of patients with idiopathic osteoarthrosis. *Aetiopathogenesis of Osteoarthrosis,* Ed. by G. Nuki, Pitman Medical, Tunbridge Wells, in press.

Cooke T. D., Richer R. S., Hurd E. and Jasin H. E. (1975) Localization of antigen–antibody complexes in intra-articular collagenous tissues. *Ann. N.Y. Acad. Sci.* **256**, 10.

Crank J. (1975) *The Mathematics of Diffusion.* Clarendon Press, Oxford.

Davidson E. A. and Small W. (1963) Metabolism *in vivo* of connective tissue mucopolysaccharides. *Biochim. biophys. Acta* **69**, 445.

Day W., Swanson S. A. V. and Freeman M. A. R. (1975) Contact pressures in the loaded cadaver hip. *J. Bone Jt Surg.* **57B**, 302.

Dowson D., Unsworth A. and Wright V. (1970) Analysis of boosted lubrication in human joints. *J. Mech. Engg Sci.* **12**, 384.

Edmonds E. and Ogston A. G. (1968) Phase separation in ternary aqueous systems. *Biochem. J.* **109**, 569.

Eichelberger L., Akeson W. H. and Roma M. (1958) Biochemical studies of articular cartilage. I: Normal values. *J. Bone Jt Surg.* **40A**, 142.

Eyre D. R., McDevitt C. A. and Muir H. (1975) Experimentally induced osteoarthritis in the dog. Collagen biosynthesis in control and fibrillated articular cartilage. *Ann. rheum. Dis.* **34**, Suppl. 2, 138.

Fatt I. and Goldstick T. K. (1965) Dynamics of water transport in swelling membranes. *J. Colloid Sci.* **20**, 962.

Faxen H. (1922) Der widerstand gegen die Bewegung einer starren Kugel in einer zähen Flüssigkeit, die zwischen zwei parallelen ebenen Wänden eingeschlossen ist. *Ann. Physik.* **68**, 69.

Fessler J. H. (1960) A structural function of mucopolysaccharide in connective tissue. *Biochem. J.* **76**, 124.

Ficat C. and Maroudas A. (1975) Cartilage of the patella. *Ann. rheum. Dis.* **34**, 515.

Flory P. J. (1966) *Principles of Polymer Chemistry.* Cornell University Press, Ithaca.

Freeman W. D. S. C. and Maroudas A. (1975) Charged group behaviour in cartilage proteoglycans in relation to pH. *Ann. rheum. Dis.* **34**, Suppl. 2, 44.

Gross I. G., Matthews M. B. and Dorfman A. (1960) Sodium chondroitin sulphate-protein complexes of cartilage. *J. biol. Chem.* **235**, 2889.

Guyton A. C. (1966) *Textbook of Medical Physiology.* W. B. Saunders, Philadelphia.

Helfferich F. (1962) *Ion Exchange.* McGraw-Hill, New York.

Herbai G. (1970) A double isotope method for determination of the miscible inorganic sulphate pool of the mouse applied to *in vivo* studies of sulphate incorporation into costal cartilage. *Acta physiol. scand.* **80**, 470.

Hirsch C. (1944) A contribution to the pathogenesis of chondromalacia of the patella. *Acta chir. scand.* **90**, Suppl. 83, 1.

Hjertquist S. O. and Lemperg R. C. (1972) Identification and concentration of the glycosaminoglycans of human articular cartilage in relation to age and osteoarthritis. *Calc. Tiss. Res.* **10**, 223.

House C. R. (1974) *Water Transport in Cells and Tissues.* Edward Arnold, London.

Iwasa K. and Kwak J. C. T. (1976) On the correction

term for interactions between small ions in the interpretation of activity data in polyelectrolyte—simple electrolyte mixtures. *J. phys. Chem.* **80,** 215.

Katz E. P. and Li S. T. (1973) The intermolecular space of reconstituted collagen fibrils. *J. Molec. Biol.* **73,** 351.

Kwak J. C. T. (1973) Mean activity coefficients for the simple electrolyte in aqueous mixtures of polyelectrolytes and simple electrolytes. *J. phys. Chem.* **77,** 2790.

Li S. T. and Katz E. P. (1976) An electrostatic model for collagen fibrils. *Biopolymers* **15,** 1439.

Linn F. C. and Sokoloff L. (1965) Movement and composition of interstitial fluid of cartilage. *Arthritis Rheum.* **8,** 481.

Lippiello L. and Mankin H. (1976) Collagen Turnover in Osteoarthritis. *Trans. 22nd Annual Meeting of the Amer. Orthop. Res. Soc.* **1,** 94.

Lohmander S., Antonopoulos C. A. and Friberg U. (1973) Chemical and metabolic heterogeneity of chondroitin sulphate and keratan sulphate in guinea pig cartilage and nucleus pulposus. *Biochim. biophys. Acta* **304,** 430.

McCutchen C. W. (1962) The frictional properties of animal joints. *Wear* **5,** 1.

McCutchen C. W. (1966) Boundary lubrication by synovial fluid: demonstration and possible osmotic explanation. *Fed. Proc.* **25,** 1061.

McDevitt C. A. and Muir H. (1976) Biochemical changes in the cartilage of the knee in experimental and natural osteoarthrosis in the dog. *J. Bone Jt Surg.* **58B,** 94.

Mackie J. S. and Meares P. (1955) Diffusion of electrolytes in a cation exchange resin. *Proc. R. Soc. A* **232,** 498.

Mankin H. J. and Lippiello L. (1969) The turnover of adult rabbit articular cartilage. *J. Bone Jt Surg.* **51A,** 1591.

Mankin H. and Lippiello L. (1971) The glycosaminoglycans of normal and arthritic cartilage. *J. clin. Invest.* **50,** 1712.

Mankin H. and Zarins-Thrasher A. (1975) Water content and binding in normal and osteoarthritic human articular cartilage. *J. Bone Jt Surg.* **57A,** 76.

Manning G. S. (1969) Limiting laws and counterion condensation in polyelectrolyte solutions. *J. Chem. Physics* **51,** 924.

Mansour J. M. and Mow V. C. (1976) Permeability of articular cartilage under compressive strain at high pressures. *J. Bone Jt Surg.* **58A,** 509.

Marinsky J. A. (1966) *Ion Exchange.* Edward Arnold, London.

Maroudas A. (1967) Hyaluronic acid films. *Proc. Instn mech. Engrs* **181,** 122.

Maroudas A. (1968) Physicochemical properties of cartilage in the light of ion-exchange theory. *Biophys. J.* **8,** 575.

Maroudas A. (1969). Studies on the formation of hyaluronic acid films. *Lubrication and Wear in Joints,* Ed. by V. Wright, p. 124. Sector, London.

Maroudas A. (1970) Distribution and diffusion of solutes in articular cartilage. *Biophys. J.* **10,** 365.

Maroudas A. (1972) X-ray microprobe analysis of articular cartilage. *Conn. Tiss. Res.* **1,** 153.

Maroudas A. (1974) Transport through articular cartilage and some physiological implications. *Normal and Osteoarthrotic Articular Cartilage.* Ed. by S. Y. Ali, M. W. Elves and D. H. Leaback. Institute of Orthopaedics, London.

Maroudas A. (1975a) Biophysical properties of collagenous tissues. *Biorheology* **12,** 233.

Maroudas A. (1975b) Fluid transport in cartilage. *Ann. rheum. Dis.* **34,** Suppl. 2, 77.

Maroudas A. (1975c) Glycosaminoglycan turnover in articular cartilage. *Phil. Trans. R. Soc. Lond. B* **271,** 293.

Maroudas A. (1976a) Transport of solutes in cartilage. *J. Anat.* **122,** 113.

Maroudas A. (1976b) Swelling pressure versus collagen tension in normal and degenerate articular cartilage. *Nature (Lond.)* **260,** 808.

Maroudas A. (1979) In vivo and in vitro studies of the matrix turnover in articular cartilage: a quantitative approach. *Models of Osteoarthrosis,* Ed. by G. Nuki. Pitman Medical, Tunbridge Wells, in press.

Maroudas A. and Evans H. (1972) A study of ionic equilibria in cartilage. *Conn. Tiss. Res.* **1,** 69.

Maroudas A. and Evans H. (1974) Sulphate diffusion and incorporation into articular cartilage. *Biochim. biophys. Acta* **338,** 265.

Maroudas A. and Thomas H. (1970) A simple physicochemical micromethod for determining fixed anionic groups in connective tissue. *Biochim. biophys. Acta* **215,** 214.

Maroudas A. and Venn M. F. (1977) Chemical composition and swelling of normal and osteoarthrotic femoral head cartilage. II: Swelling. *Ann. rheum. Dis.,* **36,** 399.

Maroudas A. and Venn M. F. (1979) Biochemical and physico-chemical studies on osteoarthritic cartilage from the human femoral head. *Aetiopathogenesis of Osteoarthrosis.* Ed. by G. Nuki. Pitman Medical, Tunbridge Wells, in press.

Maroudas A., Evans H. and Almeida L. (1973) Cartilage of the hip joint: topographical variation of glycosaminoglycan content in normal and fibrillated tissue. *Ann. rheum. Dis.* **32,** 1.

Maroudas A., Muir H. and Wingham J. (1969) The correlation of fixed negative charge with glycosaminoglycan content of human articular cartilage. *Biochim. biophys. Acta* **177,** 492.

Matthews B. F. (1953) Composition of articular cartilage in osteoarthritis. Changes in collagen/chondroitin sulphate ratio. *Brit. med. J.* **2,** 660.

Meachim G. (1972) Light microscopy of Indian ink preparations of fibrillated cartilage. *Ann. rheum. Dis.* **31,** 457.

Miles J. S. and Eichelberger L. (1964) Biochemical studies of human cartilage during the ageing process. *J. Amer. Geriat. Soc.* **12,** 1.

Muir H., Bullough P. and Maroudas A. (1970) The distribution of collagen in human articular cartilage with some of its physiological implications. *J. Bone Jt Surg.* **52B,** 554.

Mulholland R., Millington P. F. and Manners J. (1975) Some aspects of the mechanical behaviour of articular cartilage. *Ann. rheum. Dis.* **34,** Suppl. 2, 104.

Nimni M. and Deshmukh K. (1973) Differences in collagen metabolism between normal and osteoarthritic human articular cartilage. *Science* **181,** 751.

Ogston A. G. (1958) The spaces in a uniform random suspension of fibres. *Trans. Faraday Soc.* **54,** 1754.

Ogston A. G. (1970) The biological functions of the glycosaminoglycans. *Chemistry and Molecular Biology of the Intracellular Matrix,* Vol. 3. Academic Press, London.

Ogston A. G., Preston B. N. and Wells J. D. (1973) On the transport of compact particles through solutions of chain polymers. *Proc. R. Soc. Lond. A* **333,** 297.

Preston B. N., Snowden J. McK. and Houghton K. T. (1972) Model connective tissue systems: the effect of proteoglycans on the distribution of small non-electrolytes and micro-ions. *Biopolymers* **11,** 1645.

Robertson J. S. (1957) Theory and use of tracers in determining transfer rates in biological systems. *Physiol. Rev.* **37,** 133.

Robinson R. A. and Stokes R. H. (1968) *Electrolyte Solutions.* Butterworths, London.

Rokosova R. and Bentley J. P. (1973) The uptake of glucose (^{14}C) into rabbit ear cartilage proteoglycans. *Biochim. biophys. Acta* **297,** 473.

Schiller S., Matthews M. B., Cifonelli J. A. and Dorfman A. (1956) Metabolism of mucopolysaccharides in animals. *J. biol. Chem.* **218,** 139.

Shaw D. J. (1969) *Electrophoresis.* Academic Press, London.

Snowden J. and Maroudas A. (1976) The distribution of serum albumin in human normal and degenerate cartilage. *Biochim. biophys. Acta* **428,** 726.

Steven F. and Thomas H. (1973) Preparation of insoluble collagen from human cartilage. *Biochem. J.* **135,** 245.

Szirmai J. A. (1969) Structure of cartilage. *The Thule International Symposium; Ageing of Connective and Skeletal Tissue.* Nordiska Bok Handelns Forlag, Stockholm.

Torzilli P. A. and Mow V. C. (1976) On the fundamental fluid transport mechanism through normal and pathological articular cartilage during function. *J. Biomechanics* **9,** 541.

Urban J. (1977) Solute and Fluid Transport in the Intervertebral Disc. PhD Thesis, University of London.

Venn M. F. (1977) Variation of chemical composition with age in human femoral head cartilage. *Ann. rheum. Dis.* **37,** 168.

Venn M. F. and Maroudas A. (1977) Chemical composition and swelling of normal and osteoarthrotic femoral head cartilage. I: Chemical composition. *Ann. rheum. Dis.* **36,** 399.

Wells J. D. (1972) PhD Thesis, Australian National University.

Wells J. D. (1973) Salt activity and osmotic pressure in connective tissue. *Proc. R. Soc. Lond. B* **183,** 399.

Zilversmit D. B., Entenman C. and Fischler M. C. (1943) Calculation of turnover time and turnover rate from experiments involving the use of labelling agents. *J. gen. Physiol.* **26,** 325.

5. Load Carriage

B. Weightman and G. E. Kempson

1. INTRODUCTION

A synovial joint is a mechanical system: it allows the relative motion of two body segments under load. It follows that articular cartilage is subjected to mechanical stress and that there is a need to study the tissue from a mechanical engineering/materials science point of view. In addition, the tissue occasionally breaks down and the possibility that this is the result, at least in part, of a mechanical failure requires investigation.

The study of articular cartilage from a mechanical point of view should aim to answer the following questions:

(a) What are the mechanical functions, if any, of the tissue?
(b) To what loads is the tissue subjected?
(c) How do the various structural elements of the tissue interact to support these loads?
(d) What stresses do each of the structural elements of the tissue experience?
(e) What is the capability of each element to withstand these stresses?
(f) What are the possible mechanisms of mechanical failure?

These questions are discussed in this and the following two Chapters. Although there is some unavoidable overlap between the three Chapters, in general the present Chapter discusses the load-carrying ability of the tissue, whilst Chapter 6 is concerned with its mechanical properties and Chapter 7 with its lubrication.

2. MECHANICAL FUNCTIONS OF CARTILAGE

2.1. Possible Mechanical Functions

Large forces are transmitted from one body segment to another across synovial joints. Peak resultant forces across human hip, knee and ankle joints, for example, have been shown to reach seven, four and six times body weight respectively during normal walking (Paul 1967; Morrison 1970; Brewster, Chao and Stauffer 1974, respectively). This suggests that the mechanical functions of articular cartilage might be to (a) protect the bone from high stresses, and (b) provide a pair of low friction bearing surfaces. The second of these possible functions is discussed in Chapter 7.

The bony anatomy of synovial joints is such that, first, the subchondral bone surfaces are incongruous, and secondly, there are small asperities on the surfaces of the bones. Thus both on the gross and on the minute scale the bone surfaces do not mate perfectly, and as a consequence of this and the hardness of bone, extremely high local stresses would be produced if the bones made direct contact under load. In principle, therefore, one important function of cartilage might be to compensate for these bony incongruities by deforming under load in such a way as to (a) increase the area of contact at the articulating surfaces, thereby reducing the nominal contact pressure (the nominal contact pressure, or nominal stress, being equal to the load applied to the joint divided by the projected contact area), and (b) spread the applied load evenly over the bone surface. If cartilage is to fulfil this protective function during an activity in which the load is repeatedly applied and removed, such as normal walking, it would clearly be advantageous for the cartilage to recover a significant proportion of its deformation during the unloaded phase, i.e. to deform almost elastically, so as to retain its thickness throughout a period of repetitive loading.

Most joints in the body are subjected to loads which are applied rapidly and which could therefore expose the bones of the joint to high loads of short duration. Cartilage might protect the bones from these impacts if it attenuated dynamic loads.

Thus casual inspection of the general anatomy and function of synovial joints suggests that one of the primary functions of cartilage is to protect bone from high stresses, and that to fulfil this function cartilage should, ideally,

(a) be more deformable than bone so as to provide a larger area of contact under load;
(b) have the ability to even out any variations in stress applied to it;
(c) deform elastically so as to function under fluctuating loads; and
(d) attenuate dynamic loads.

2.2. Does Cartilage Reduce Static Contact Stresses?

Cartilage deforms much more than bone, its modulus of elasticity in compression being approximately 20 times less than that of cancellous bone. Thus, except in the unreal case of completely smooth congruous bone surfaces, it might be expected that the presence of cartilage would increase the loaded contact area in a joint. If this happens in practice, the contact stresses, and hence the stresses on the subchondral bone, would be reduced. The fact that cartilage does function to a useful extent in this way can be illustrated by considering the contact stresses in the human hip joint in the presence and then in the absence of cartilage.

In a study of the contact pressures in loaded human cadaver hips, Day, Swanson and Freeman (1975) found that the maximum contact pressures in three normal hips under loads of 1.7, 1.8 and 1.5 kN (three times the body weight of the cadaver from which the joints had been taken) were 2.9, 2.0 and 3.0 MN/m² (420, 290 and 435 lbf/in²)* respectively.

In the case of the absence of cartilage and hence direct bone-to-bone contact, the Hertzian solution for a sphere in a spherical seat may be used to calculate the approximate maximum contact pressure from equation (1):

$$\sigma = 0.616\left[PE^2\left(\frac{D_1 - D_2}{D_1 D_2}\right)^2\right]^{\frac{1}{3}} \qquad (1)$$

where σ = the maximum contact stress,
P = the load,
E = Young's modulus of the surfaces,
D_1 = the diameter of the seat,
D_2 = the diameter of the sphere.

Considering a hip with only slight incongruity between the acetabulum and the femoral head, the following values of D_1 and D_2 may be used:

$D_1 = 50$ mm
$D_2 = 45$ mm.

Taking the Young's modulus of cancellous bone to be 300 MN/m² (43×10^3 lbf/in²) (Evans 1961) and considering the maximum load used by Day *et al.* of 1.8 kN (400 lbf) equation (1) gives

Max. contact stress = 5.72 MN/m² (830 lbf/in²).

These experiments and calculations therefore suggest that, in the hip, the absence of cartilage would probably lead to a two- to threefold increase in contact stress, a conclusion illustrated by a photoelastic model in Figure 5.1.

Evans (1961) listed the value of the ultimate compressive strength of the cancellous bone of the femoral head as 3.76 MN/m² (545 lbf/in²). Thus, if the cartilage were lost from the joint so that bone-to-bone contact occurred, the above calculation suggests that the contact stress would be considerably higher than the ultimate compressive strength of the bone.

* A conversion table from Système International (SI) units is given on p. 545.

(a)

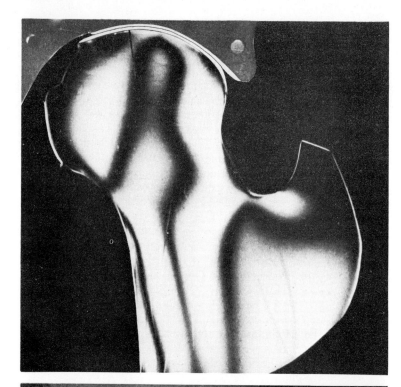

Figure 5.1 Photographs of a photoelastic model of the femoral head transilluminated with polarized light. (a) The femoral head is separated from the acetabulum by rubber simulating cartilage of full thickness. Note that the stress is evenly distributed over the surface of the femoral head and that the stress levels are relatively low. (b) The rubber has been removed. Note now that the stress is sharply concentrated at the contact area and that the stress level has risen substantially. Compare the change in this photoelastic model with that shown in the radiographs of the hip in Figure 5.2.

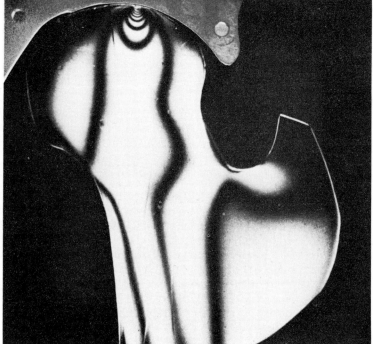

(b)

It is interesting to note that even in the presence of cartilage the maximum contact pressure in normal hips under a load of three times body weight approaches the ultimate compressive strength of cancellous bone. This suggests that the successful functioning of synovial joints depends not only on the ability of cartilage to provide an increased area of contact but also on its ability to even out variations in contact pressure so as further to reduce the maximum stress applied to the subchondral bone. The necessity for cartilage to have this second ability is even more apparent when the fatigue life of bone is considered. Swanson, Freeman and Day (1971) have shown that the stress required to cause failure of cortical bone after a median life of 10^6 load cycles is approximately 0.6 times the static failure stress. In the same investigation it was stated that man subjects the hip joint to approximately 10^6 load cycles per annum. Applying this information to the previously quoted ultimate compressive strength of cancellous bone suggests that if the maximum stress applied to subchondral bone were not lower than the maximum cartilage-to-cartilage contact stress, fatigue failure of the cancellous bone of the human femoral head and acetabulum would be a normal occurrence.

Freeman, Swanson and Manley (1975) have demonstrated experimentally that cartilage does in fact protect the subchondral bone from fracture. Nine cadaveric human hips were subjected to a compressive load which increased from zero to three times body weight and back to zero again at a frequency of 20 cycles per minute. Of the nine hips tested, five possessed normal or nearly normal cartilage and after recovery following 2000 load cycles these five hips displayed no permanent deformation in either the cartilage or the bone. In contrast, when the same five hips were subjected to an identical sequence of loading after the cartilage had been removed from the femoral head and acetabulum, permanent non-recoverable deformation was recorded due to fractures of the trabeculae within the femoral head (and possibly in the acetabulum as well). Thus in these hips the cartilage protected the bone from fracture after 2000 cycles of a load of physiological magnitude.

In summary, the above discussion indicates that normal cartilage protects subchondral bone from both static and fatigue failure by producing (a) a large contact area, and (b) a more even distribution of stress at the subchondral bone surface than at the articular surface. *In vivo* if the cartilage is either degenerate or lost completely, or if the bone becomes porotic, it would be expected that the stresses within the bone would increase and so also would the likelihood of fatigue fracture.

If the rate of production of such fractures eventually outstripped the rate at which healing occurred, such changes could lead to collapse of the bone or fracture formation on the gross scale. These conclusions are supported by studies of the trabeculae in the human femoral head (Todd, Freeman and Pirie 1972; Freeman, Todd and Pirie 1975). In the first of these studies aggregates of woven bone on trabeculae, considered to represent callus around fatigue fractures, were found in osteoarthrosis, rheumatoid arthritis and subcapital fracture, and in cadaveric specimens in which the articular cartilage showed degenerative changes and the bone was porotic. Aggregates of woven bone were not found in the absence of other pathological finding. In the second study, senile femoral neck fractures in osteoporotic patients were shown to be the end result of progressive fatigue failure of individual trabeculae.

2.3. Does Cartilage Reduce Peak Dynamic Stresses?

Forces of about four to seven times body weight are transmitted across the synovial joints of the human lower limb during the loading phase of normal walking. Since each loading phase, from heel-strike to toe-off, takes only approximately 0.5 s (Contini, Gage and Drillis 1965), these loads are applied at high loading rates. Such rapidly applied loads might produce high transient stresses in the supporting bone of the joints if cartilage did not attenuate dynamic loads.

A simple model can be used to illustrate the important factors influencing dynamic force attenuation. Consider a weight being dropped a certain distance onto a spring. If no energy is dissipated in the impact, the spring will compress until the energy of the falling weight is stored in it. The energy of the falling weight is given by its initial potential energy. That is

$$\text{Energy of falling weight} = m.g.h.$$

where m = the mass of the weight,
h = the distance dropped.

The energy stored in an elastic spring is given by

$$\text{Energy in spring} = \frac{kx^2}{2}$$

where k = the spring stiffness,
x = the compression of the spring.

Assuming that x is much smaller than h, the spring will compress until

$$m.g.h = \frac{kx^2}{2}$$

i.e. until

$$x = \left(\frac{2\,m.g.h}{k}\right)^{\frac{1}{2}}$$

296

The maximum force experienced by the spring will be equal to the product of the spring stiffness and the compression; i.e.

$$F_{max} = kx$$

so that

$$F_{max} = (2\ m.g.h.k)^{\frac{1}{2}}$$

Thus for a given impact energy ($m.g.h$) the maximum force produced depends on the stiffness of the spring; the stiffer the spring the greater the peak force.

All materials which deform in a linear elastic fashion behave like a spring with stiffness given by

$$k = \frac{EA}{t}$$

where E = the Young's modulus of the material,
  A = the area of the material,
  t = the thickness of the material.

Thus the maximum force experienced by a specimen of material is given by

$$F_{max} = \left(2\ m.g.h.\ \frac{E.A}{t}\right)^{\frac{1}{2}} \tag{2}$$

This equation indicates that in order to be an effective dynamic force attenuator a material needs to be both thick and soft (i.e. large t, small E).

Equation (2) suggests that because the articular cartilage of synovial joints is thin it is likely to be a relatively poor dynamic force attenuator. Although it has a higher modulus of elasticity than cartilage, the supporting bone of a synovial joint is much thicker and might therefore be a much better force attenuator.

If equation (2) is divided by the area of the loaded specimen, it gives an expression for the maximum stress produced by the dynamic load:

$$\text{Maximum stress} = \left(\frac{2\ m.g.h.E}{A.t}\right)^{\frac{1}{2}}$$

This equation indicates that the maximum stress produced will be relatively low if the loaded material is thick and the load acts on a large area.

Without cartilage the bones of a synovial joint would make contact over a relatively small area. The above simple analysis therefore suggests that even though the bones are thick, high peak dynamic stresses would be produced in the absence of cartilage. Thus the protection of bone from high transient stresses appears to depend on the thickness of the bone and the load-spreading ability of the cartilage; that is, the ability of the cartilage to ensure that the bone is loaded over a large area allows the bone to attenuate the dynamic loads and hence protect itself.

The above simple analysis ignores the viscoelastic nature of articular cartilage, i.e. it ignores the effect of damping within the cartilage. Damping, in so far as it exists, would be expected to dissipate some of the input energy and so reduce the force transmitted to the bone. However, since damping depends on the viscous deformation of the loaded material and it seems unlikely that significant viscous deformation occurs when cartilage is loaded for a short time in life (see Sections 3.2.2 and 3.2.4), the tissue probably provides little damping.

Radin and Paul (1971) confirmed experimentally that the bone supporting a synovial joint will attenuate dynamic forces more effectively than will the cartilage. Bovine middle phalanges, with their distal articular ends intact and their proximal articular ends removed, were mounted in holders and subjected to impact loading in a specially designed rig. In this rig weights were dropped onto the joints and the forces produced were measured with a force transducer. The overall length of the specimens was approximately 50 mm and the cartilage was approximately 0.6 mm thick.

Results of tests with three different specimens showed that when the cartilage was removed, the peak force produced by dropping a mass of 1 kg a distance of 1.6 mm onto the joints increased by an average of 4%, and the peak force produced by dropping the same mass a distance of 3.2 mm increased by an average of 9%. After these tests half the bony shafts were removed and the joints were retested. In contrast to the relatively small effect of removing the cartilage, removing half the bone produced a further increase in peak force of 49% when the 1 kg mass was dropped 1.6 mm and 28% when the mass was dropped 32 mm. Radin and Paul concluded that the cartilage is so thin compared to the bone comprising the joint that its capacity to reduce peak transient stresses is small compared with the total attenuation contributed by the bone, i.e. that rather than the cartilage protecting the bone from dynamic loads, the bone probably protects the cartilage.

2.4. Is the Bone-protecting Function of Cartilage Critically Dependent on its Stiffness and Thickness?

2.4.1. The Effect of Physiological Variation.
In order to fulfil the function of reducing the static contact stresses in a loaded joint, cartilage must, self-evidently, possess a stiffness intermediate between zero and a value equal to that of bone since at either of these extremes the presence of the tissue would have no special effect.

There is a considerable topographical variation in the compressive stiffness of the cartilage on the normal femoral head (see Chapter 6, Section 3.5), and there is even variation within the band of stiff cartilage which has been identified over the zenith of the head (Kempson *et al.* 1971). Such variations in the stiffness of cartilage would not, however, be expected to affect significantly the ability of the tissue to reduce the contact stresses because these variations are small in relation to the difference in stiffness between cartilage and bone. Thus, within the physiological range, the exact stiffness of cartilage does not appear to be critical.

Mechanical considerations indicate that there is a minimum value for the thickness of cartilage below which its bone-protecting function would be impaired regardless of its stiffness. Thus if the thickness of cartilage were of the same order as the height of the asperities on the subchondral bone, a situation which does not normally occur except perhaps at the extreme periphery of an articular surface, the stresses within the cartilage over these asperities would be expected to be much higher than those in the rest of the cartilage. This would mean (a) that the stresses produced in the bone asperities would be much higher than those in the rest of the bone surface (i.e. the cartilage would not be producing an even distribution of stress at the bone surface), and (b) the high stresses in the cartilage over the bone asperities might be so high as to damage the cartilage itself. Thus in order to distribute stresses evenly over the bone surface, without the production of dangerously high local stresses in both the bone and cartilage, the latter must be considerably thicker than the peak-to-valley heights of the asperities on the bone. From the stand-point of bone protection there is no maximum thickness beyond which cartilage would cease to function usefully, but such a limit is obviously imposed anatomically.

Similar arguments indicate that physiological variations in cartilage stiffness and thickness would not materially affect the slight contribution which the tissue may make to the attenuation of peak dynamic stresses in the joint.

In summary, physiological variations in the stiffness and thickness of cartilage would not be expected materially to affect the ability of the tissue to protect bone from high static and dynamic stresses.

2.4.2. The Effect of Pathological Variation. The total absence of cartilage has been shown, theoretically and experimentally, to lead to a dangerous increase in static bone stresses in the hip (Section 2.2). However, total loss, although it occurs pathologically, is obviously an extreme case. Before undergoing total loss, cartilage becomes softer and thinner, so that the question arises: do these changes also affect bone stresses?

In the study by Freeman, Swanson and Manley (1975) described in Section 2.2, four of the nine hips studied displayed severe cartilage fibrillation and ulceration. Permanent residual deformation was recorded after 2000 load cycles with the cartilage surfaces present in three of these four hips. This irrecoverable deformation occurred in both the cartilage and the subchondral bone. Whether or not the cartilage would have failed had the subchondral bone remained intact is a matter for speculation since the investigation did not show whether the bone or the cartilage failed first. When the cartilage was removed and the three hips were subjected to the same loading sequence as before, the bone failed even more extensively.

The normal contact pressures in the hips in which permanent deformation occurred in the presence of cartilage were in the same range as the other hips which possessed normal or near normal cartilage and which did not display permanent deformation, and therefore this difference in the behaviour of the hip in the presence of cartilage degeneration could not be attributed to dissimilar cartilage-to-cartilage contact pressures. By inference the authors concluded that the degenerate cartilage was as effective in providing a large contact area as was normal cartilage, but that the distribution of stress at the subchondral bone surface was more uneven than with normal cartilage. These experiments fully support the speculation advanced in Section 2.2 that normal cartilage protects the underlying bone not only by providing a large area of contact but also by producing an even distribution of stress at the subchondral bone surface.

The effect of thinning of cartilage on gross congruence has been studied by examining photoelastic models of the hip in which cartilage of constant stiffness was simulated by rubber (Freeman 1972). It was found that a reduction in 'cartilage' thickness to 50% of normal had little effect on the stress pattern within a simulated hip joint but that when the 'cartilage' thickness was reduced to 25%, the stress distribution in a photoelastic model of the femoral head was noticeably changed (Figure 5.1).

When cartilage fibrillates it becomes not only thin but also soft, and the softer it is, the thinner it will be when loaded. Thus loaded fibrillated cartilage will be abnormally thin even though the unloaded tissue is of normal thickness. Thus a reduction in the thickness, or stiffness, of cartilage to 25% of normal values probably leads to increased bone stresses (at least in the hip). Lesser abnormalities probably have little or no effect on the bone stresses. This conclusion is in line with clinical observation since radiological bone changes may be absent in the hip even though the joint space is much diminished, but they appear as soon as it is lost (Figure 5.2) and their distribution is reminiscent of that of the interference fringes in a photoelastic model of the femoral head loaded in the absence of simulated cartilage (Figure 5.1).

A reduction in the thickness of cartilage would not be expected to have a significant effect upon its ability to compensate for bony asperities until the thickness was of the same order as the peak-to-valley heights of these asperities. By the time that cartilage had been reduced in thickness to this extent it could be regarded as being anatomically absent.

In Section 2.3 it was concluded that cartilage is a relatively poor attenuator of dynamic loads and that the supporting bone of synovial joints protects itself (and the cartilage) from high transient dynamic stresses if the cartilage ensures that the bone is loaded over a large area. It follows from this and the above discussion that a reduction in cartilage thickness of less than 75% is likely to have little effect on the dynamic stresses produced in the bone. A decrease in the stiffness of cartilage would tend to increase its ability to attenuate dynamic loads but the overall effect would be slight.

In summary, it may be concluded that even pathologically observed degrees of softening and thinning will not materially affect the bone-protecting function of cartilage until they amount to severe fibrillation or near-total loss of the tissue. Put another way, cartilage appears to possess a very large functional reserve, in which respect it resembles most other tissues of the body.

Figure 5.2 Anteroposterior radiographs of the hip of a patient with rheumatoid arthritis. In September 1970 (a) there was a small radiological joint space probably denoting the presence of a thin residual layer of cartilage in the joint. At this time the bone of the femoral head and acetabulum were porotic but showed no focal abnormalities. The hip was not painful. Eleven months later (b) the radiological joint space had disappeared at the zenith of the femoral head, denoting the loss of the residual cartilage. Coincident with the loss of cartilage the contacting bone had become sclerotic and the hip painful.

(a) 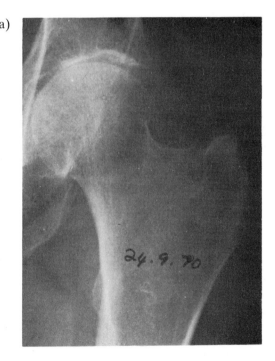 (b)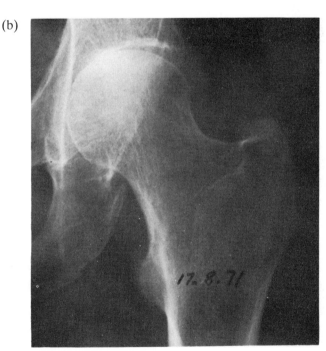

3. HOW DOES CARTILAGE CARRY LOAD?

In Section 2 it was concluded that the severe fibrillation or total loss of cartilage leads to dangerously high stresses in the supporting bone of synovial joints. Severe fibrillation and loss of cartilage occur pathologically and the causes of these changes are therefore of importance. In the absence of any obvious predisposing disease or abnormality, such changes might be due to the tissue having been subjected to stresses in excess of its strength. It is therefore important to consider how cartilage acquires its normal strength (i.e. how it carries the loads which are applied to it) and hence how it might fail mechanically. (The mechanism of load carriage is also important in any discussion of liquid transport in, and the lubricating ability of, the tissue—see Chapters 4 and 7 respectively.)

Cartilage is a complex composite material which is extremely difficult to study directly. Although it is possible to measure the gross mechanical behaviour of isolated specimens of cartilage in simple laboratory tests (see Chapter 6) it is impossible to measure (a) the tissue's gross behaviour in whole joints under completely physiological conditions (because the conditions are so complex) or (b) the detailed behaviour of its individual structural components (collagen fibres, proteoglycans and water) under load (because the components are inaccessible to currently available measuring devices). The engineer is therefore driven back on an indirect approach. In this he makes use of what is known of the composition and structure of cartilage, of the mechanical and chemical properties of its individual components, and of its gross mechanical behaviour under simple loading, to construct a 'model' of the tissue. Such a model may be expressed verbally, pictorially or mathematically. The engineer then attempts to deduce information about cartilage, such as its general response to physiological loading, or the way in which its structural elements interact to carry load, from the behaviour of the model.

Although modelling is essential to the study of cartilage, it is important to appreciate that the information which is obtained from a model is only of value if the model is valid; if the model is invalid then the information obtained from it relates to the model but not to the real tissue. Ideally the engineer should construct a mathematically expressed model of cartilage which accurately reflects the complex structure of the tissue, and in which the behaviour of the individual structural components is based on their known physical and chemical properties and on fundamental physical and chemical laws. Such a model would be valid for the study of all aspects of the behaviour of cartilage and would yield (probably with the aid of a computer since the number of variables would be so large) quantitative results.

To date it has proved impossible to construct such an all-embracing model, and a number of different models have therefore been developed to study specific aspects of cartilage behaviour. All of these models have limitations. For example, modelling cartilage as a single-phase polymer may provide a useful description of the deformation versus time characteristics of cartilage under load but is clearly of no value to the study of fluid flow in the tissue. In general, the simpler models, in which cartilage is treated as a one- or two-phase material, can be expressed mathematically and can therefore yield quantitative results but are of limited value, while the more complex three-component models are more widely applicable but cannot be expressed mathematically and can therefore yield only qualitative results.

Since the primary aim of this section is to analyse the way in which the three structural elements of cartilage interact to carry load, a three-component model will be described and used to predict the behaviour of the real tissue. This model has the disadvantage of giving only qualitative results but the advantage of being widely applicable to other aspects of cartilage behaviour such as fluid transport through the tissue. For the sake of completeness the description of this model is preceded by a critical review of other cartilage models.

3.1. A Critical Review of Previous Cartilage Models

It is well known to engineers that a soil under load does not assume an instantaneous deflection but settles gradually at a variable rate. The process is known as soil consolidation. Terzaghi (1943) developed a theory of soil consolidation to explain this phenomenon by modelling soil as a linearly elastic porous material with the voids filled with water; that is, a sponge saturated with water. A number of workers have applied the theory of consolidation to loaded cartilage.

Figure 5.3 shows the consolidation model for a soil in its simplest form. A saturated soil in a rigid impervious cylindrical container is being loaded through a highly porous close-fitting piston. The soil itself is modelled by a close-fitting frictionless low-porosity piston, springs and water. The pores in the piston represent the voids in the soil which offer resistance to liquid flow and the springs represent the linearly elastic solid component. The load being applied to the soil is carried partly by the springs and partly by hydrostatic pressure produced in the water so that

$$F = F_s + p.a$$

where F = the applied load,
$\quad F_s$ = the force in the springs,
$\quad p$ = the hydrostatic pressure,
$\quad a$ = the area of the piston over which the pressure is acting.

When the load is first applied it is carried entirely by hydrostatic pressure in the water. The initial hydrostatic pressure is therefore equal to F/a. The pressure difference across the surface of the soil produces a gradual escape of water from the soil. As this occurs

303

Figure 5.3. Simple model of a consolidating soil.

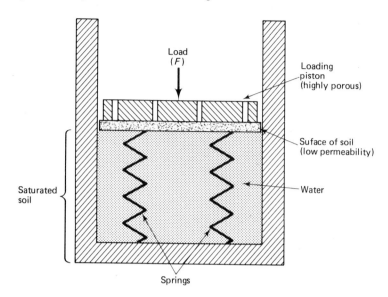

the springs compress and carry load. Gradually the load in the springs increases and the hydrostatic pressure in the water decreases until eventually an equilibrium is reached when the springs carry the entire load and the hydrostatic pressure in the water is zero. There is no further water flow and therefore no further deformation (consolidation) of the soil. Since the hydrostatic pressure in the water decreases with time the rate of escape of water from the soil, and hence the soil's rate of compression, decreases with time, giving a deformation/time curve as shown in Figure 5.4.

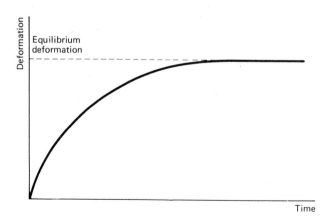

Figure 5.4 Deformation/time curve for a consolidating soil.

304

Biot (1941) extended this one-dimensional treatment to include the analysis of soil consolidation when a load is applied through a highly porous, infinitely long strip over only part of the soil surface. The load distribution across the width of the strip was assumed to be rectangular. Biot found that there were three phases in the settlement. The first phase was due largely to water flowing out of the soil directly beneath the load (i.e. through the porous loading strip); the second phase was due largely to water flowing from the loaded region to the unloaded region of the soil; and the third phase was due to the restraining effect of the unloaded region on the loaded region.

McCutchen and Lewis (McCutchen 1959; Lewis and McCutchen 1959, 1960; McCutchen, 1962) postulated that structurally cartilage resembles a rather stiff sponge through which fluid can move far more easily in a direction normal to the surface than in a direction parallel to the surface. These authors suggested that in a synovial joint the fluid between the loaded cartilage surfaces is supplied from within the cartilages by a mechanism which was termed 'weeping lubrication'. According to this theory the two cartilage surfaces are separated by synovial fluid at high pressure but make contact at a few high spots; at these high spots the two cartilages are pushed back into the fluid in which they are soaked; this pressurizes the fluid in the cartilages to a higher pressure than that in the fluid between the surfaces, and as a consequence of this (and the difficulty of lateral flow) fluid flows from within the cartilages to the loaded joint space.

In his later paper, McCutchen (1962) described a 'weeping bearing' as one in which: (a) the solid matrix is porous, deformable and soaked in liquid; (b) the liquid carries most of the load (because the solid matrix is deformable); and (c) the matrix prevents the liquid from flowing parallel to the bearing surfaces. McCutchen (1962) also expressed his model mathematically for the case of a cylindrical disc of cartilage squeezed between flat impermeable sheets. The total applid force (F) was assumed to be resisted by a force, F_p, generated by fluid pressure within the matrix and a force, F_y, generated by the stiffness of the (assumed) linearly elastic matrix, according to the equation:

$$F = F_p + F_y = \pi R^2 \left[-\frac{\dot{h}}{h} \frac{R^2}{8k_t} + \left(1 - \frac{h}{h_o} \right) Y \right]$$

where R = outer radius of the cartilage disc,
    h = thickness of the cartilage disc at time, t, after the application of the load,
    $\dot{h}$ = rate of compression,
    h_o = original thickness of the cartilage disc,
    k_t = tangential permeability,
    Y = Young's modulus of the solid matrix.

305

At $t = 0$ this equation reduces to

$$\dot{h} = - \frac{8h_o F k_t}{\pi R^4}$$

which is independent of the Young's modulus of the solid matrix since no deformation has taken place and consequently F_y is zero. McCutchen used this expression to calculate the tangential permeability of cartilage from experimental measurements. He found that the tangential permeability was essentially the same as the permeability normal to the articular surface. This result, which was later confirmed by Maroudas (1973) using a different technique (see Chapter 4, Section 6.3.2), suggests that cartilage does not possess one of the properties which McCutchen thought necessary for a weeping bearing—namely a higher resistance to lateral flow than to flow normal to its surface.

A second criticism of McCutchen's weeping lubrication theory is that cartilage-to-cartilage contact may not occur *in vivo*. Calculations (Fein 1967) (see Section 3.2.3) indicate that the time required to squeeze out a film of synovial fluid from between the opposing cartilage surfaces of a loaded synovial joint is much longer than the load phase of a walking cycle. Even if the surfaces did eventually make contact at a few high spots, it is difficult to imagine fluid flowing out of the cartilage into the high pressure synovial fluid since, in order for fluid to flow in this direction, a pressure higher than that in the synoval fluid would have to be produced within the cartilages. This would be conceivable only if a significant proportion of the load being transmitted across the joint were applied to the solid matrix of each 'sponge' at the points of contact. However, if this situation were ever to arise, it (a) would be unlikely to persist, since the suface asperities might be expected quickly to flatten out, and (b) would, by definition, represent a breakdown in lubrication, since high loads would be being transmitted via solid-to-solid contact.

Zarek and Edwards (1964) considered cartilage to consist of a porous elastic matrix, made up of collagen fibres, ground substance and cells, saturated by a 'pore liquid'. Any load applied to the tissue was thought to be carried partly by pressure in the liquid and partly by compressive stresses in the solid matrix. After describing the classical theory of consolidation, these authors discussed its application to cartilage loaded as in an animal joint. They concluded that:

(a) the highest pore pressures are generated at the area of contact and that consequently liquid flows away from this area, through the cartilage and out into the joint space at the unloaded articular surface;
(b) at the instant when load is applied most of the load is

carried by the liquid and hence the stresses developed in the solid matrix are small; and

(c) if a static load were applied for a sufficient length of time, an equilibrium would be reached when the pore pressure throughout the cartilage was the same as that in the joint space and the applied load was being carried entirely by the solid matrix.

There are a number of criticisms of the basic sponge model of cartilage as described by McCutchen and Lewis, and Zarek and Edwards. First, the model assumes a mechanism of load carriage which ignores the physical chemistry (i.e. the osmotic pressure) of the tissue. Secondly, the models predict low stresses in the solid matrix when load is first applied and this gives the impression that the stresses in the collagen fibres are initially low. Thirdly, and perhaps most important, cartilage does not resemble a saturated porous sponge structurally. Between them the collagen fibres, proteoglycan gel and cells 'contain' all the water in the tissue (see Chapter 4, Section 2). Thus if these components are combined into one solid phase, such a phase would represent the whole tissue; there would be no additional 'pore liquid'. Conversely, if the collagen fibres, proteoglycan *molecules* and cells are considered as one solid phase, leaving the water of the proteoglycan gel as the liquid phase, then it is difficult to see how the matrix could support compressive loads.

In a later paper, Edwards (1967) answered some of these criticisms by stating:

(a) that the stress in the solid matrix of the sponge model (now called effective stress) represents the swelling pressure of the tissue;

(b) that this is zero in the unloaded state because of a balance between tensile forces in the fibrous (collagen) network and compressive forces in the swelling substance (the protoglycans; and

(c) that the hydrostatic pressure in the liquid phase (now called fluidic stress) represents the stress which causes liquid flow.

Expressed another way, the sponge model is a conceptual model and not a structural model. As such, if the behaviour of the imaginary solid phase is made to reflect both the osmotic properties of the proteoglycan gel and the mechanical properties of the collagen fibres, it appears to be valid. Clearly, however, the model cannot be used to estimate the magnitude of the stresses produced in the collagen fibres of the real tissue.

Edwards (1967) showed experimentally that the imaginary solid phase cannot be modelled as being linearly elastic. Cylindrical specimens of cartilage from the femoral head of a dog were placed in a confining impermeable cylinder and loaded through a porous piston (i.e. the basic consolidation experiment illustrated in Figure

5.3). When a load was applied, the cartilage specimens compressed quickly at first and then more slowly until eventually the deformation reached an equilibrium value. Loads of different magnitudes produced different equilibrium thicknesses (i.e. different equilibrium strains). At equilibrium there was no liquid flow from the cartilage through the porous piston. Hence by definition, the 'fluidic stress' was zero and the 'effective stress' (i.e. the 'compressive stress' on the imaginary solid matrix—in fact the swelling pressure of the tissue) was equal to the applied pressure. The results of these experiments, which were originally plotted on a graph of equilibrium thickness versus applied pressure, can therefore be replotted on a graph of effective stress (or 'compressive stress' or swelling pressure) versus strain, as shown in Figure 5.5. Clearly, the behaviour is grossly non-linear.

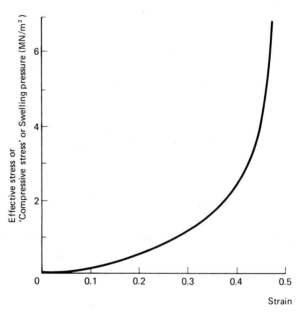

Figure 5.5 'Effective stress'/strain curve for cartilage (results replotted from Edwards (1967)).

Higginson and Norman (1974a, b) studied the effect of cartilage permeability on the rate at which the two surfaces of a human joint approach each other under load, both analytically and experimentally. The geometry of the admittedly simple model was a spherical surface falling through a viscous fluid onto a flat surface. In the particular cases studied the spherical surface was rigid while the lower surface was:

(a) a rigid plate,

(b) a thin, linearly elastic impermeable layer on a rigid backing;

(c) a thin, linearly elastic permeable layer on a rigid backing, in which the permeability of the layer was the same in all directions; and

(d) a thin, linearly elastic permeable layer on a rigid backing, in which the permeability of the layer normal to the surface was much greater than the permeability parallel to the surface.

In the computer-aided theoretical analysis of this model a simplifying assumption—that the local deformation of the soft layers was proportional to the local pressure in the fluid above the surface—was made in order to avoid impractically large computational work. The results of the theoretical analysis showed that:

(i) The rate at which the two surfaces approached each other was much lower with the soft impermeable layer (case (b) above) than with the rigid surface (case (a) above). One of the reasons for this was that the deformation of the soft layer reduced the peak pressure in the squeeze film by spreading the load over a larger area.

(ii) In general, with the isopermeable layers (case (c) above) the thickness of the squeeze film decreased more rapidly than with an impermeable layer of the same stiffness. This was because the porosity of the layers offered additional escape routes for the fluid. There was one exception to this general finding: with a very low permeability layer the surfaces approached each other slightly more slowly than with an impermeable layer of the same stiffness.

(iii) A layer with zero permeability parallel to the surface and infinite permeability normal to the surface performed only marginally better than the low isopermeable layer.

The experimental studies with silicone rubbers and porous plastics showed good agreement with the theoretical analysis, with the one exception that experimentally the soft impermeable layer performed significantly better than theoretically predicted. This was thought to be because in practice (but not in the computer model) the soft layer deformed in such a way as to trap fluid between the approaching surfaces. Higginson and Norman concluded that while there is some theoretical evidence of weeping, this appears to have negligible effect on film thickness. Even the most favourable case for weeping, namely zero permeability parallel to the articular surface, was only marginally better than an impermeable layer theoretically, and might be worse in practice because of the beneficial effect of fluid entrapment with the impermeable layer.

Although Higginson and Norman concluded that the effect of weeping is negligible, their theoretical finding that weeping can occur requires comment. In their second paper, Higginson and Norman (1974b) state: in order that a soft porous layer may deform some fluid must be expelled from the layer and if this fluid is expelled from the layer into the centre film then the film thickness will benefit. The first part of this statement is true only if the deformation of the layer involves a reduction in volume (i.e. it ignores the possibility of a deformation produced by a change in shape but not in volume). Taken together with the previously mentioned assumption, that the local deformation of the layers was proportional to the local pressure generated in the fluid film, the statement implies that in the computer model the pressures generated in the film produced local deformations (i.e. reductions in volume) of the porous layer and that these deformations 'produced' a flow of liquid out of the layer. In the opinion of the present authors such a mechanism of fluid flow is fallacious. In their view, soft porous materials can deform in two ways:

(a) due to a change in shape, and
(b) due to a change in volume.

The first of these mechanisms does not involve a loss of liquid. In the second mechanism the material deforms *because of a loss of liquid*; the liquid does not flow out of the material *because of a deformation*. Expressed another way, while the deformation of the material (after any initial change in shape) clearly depends on its stiffness, the stiffness depends on fluid flow, and it is therefore erroneous to assume a certain stiffness and to predict fluid flow from the resulting deformations. In the case of the layer with zero permeability parallel to the surface and infinite permeability normal to the surface, for example, assuming liquid flow to be produced by deformation (i.e. reduction in volume) must lead to the prediction of 'weeping', since the liquid can flow in only one direction. In reality, however, the liquid in the layer could not flow into the high pressure film of liquid above it; there would be no reduction in volume and therefore no 'weeping'.

Higginson, Litchfield and Snaith (1976) developed a saturated sponge model of cartilage which took into account the chemistry of the tissue. That is, the following expression, derived from the results of Edwards' (1967) consolidation experiments (i.e. Figure 5.5), was used to describe the behaviour of the 'solid' matrix of the sponge:

$$\sigma_s = \frac{1.66e}{1 - 1.83e} \text{ MN/m}^2$$

where σ_s = the effective stress in the 'solid' matrix,
$\quad\quad e$ = cartilage strain.

Other expressions relating the permeability of the tissue to strain were derived from experiments with a porous polymeric filter. When the resulting computer model was loaded as in the simple consolidation experiment (i.e. in a confining cylinder with a constant load applied through a porous piston) the predicted deformation versus time response showed good agreement with experimental results. The assumed variation of permeability with strain, however, was found to have a critical effect on the theoretical model.

Mow and Torzilli (1975) and Torzilli and Mow (1976a, b) treated cartilage as a saturated linearly elastic sponge; i.e. a solid phase composed of collagen fibres, proteoglycans and cells, and a liquid phase composed mainly of water. Fluid transport through the tissue during normal functioning was considered to be the net result of two superimposed effects. First, fluid flow was thought to be produced by directly generated pressure gradients, e.g. as a result of the generation of pressure in the synovial fluid by the squeeze-film action of the two approaching cartilage surfaces. This mechanism is analogous to the one operating in the typical permeability experiment where a pressure differential is applied across a specimen of cartilage in the absence of tissue deformation. Secondly, fluid flow was thought to be produced by consolidation of the solid matrix, e.g. as a result of compression of the solid matrix due to cartilage-on-cartilage contact. This mechanism was considered to be analogous to the one operating in Biot's (1941) consolidation model where a porous specimen is compressed by a rigid porous block and the interstitial fluid is free to escape at the surface. After including the interaction which occurs between the solid and liquid phases because of their relative motion (i.e. the frictional drag force), Torzilli and Mow derived the stress equations of motion of the solid and liquid phases.

Perhaps the most significant result coming from the analysis of these equations of motion was the prediction that when a load is applied to normal healthy articular cartilage in a synovial joint, liquid will be excluded from the tissue directly under the load. Torzilli and Mow considered that this predicted flow represents the unique capability of the tissue to generate its own lubricant during function.

However, the work can be questioned on a number of grounds. As previously discussed in connection with the McCutchen model, it would appear to be erroneous to model cartilage as a water-saturated porous sponge in which the solid phase carries real compressive loads. Torzilli and Mow assumed that applied load is shared between the solid and liquid phases at the surface of their model in proportion to the area of the surface occupied by each. The pressure in the liquid at the surface produced the directly generated pressure gradients which, it was found, led to flow into the loaded area of the cartilage from the synovial fluid. The load carried by the solid, on the other hand, produced consolidation of the solid matrix which 'pumped' liquid out through the loaded surface of the tissue. In their model of normal healthy cartilage the flow out of the tissue due to the pumping mechanism was found to be much greater than the flow into the tissue due to the directly generated pressure gradients, and hence the net flow was predicted to be out of the tissue.

In computing the magnitude of the flow produced by the pumping mechanism, Torzilli and Mow calculated the deformation of the solid matrix from the published mechanical properties of the tissue as measured in laboratory indentation tests, and apparently then assumed that this deformation 'produces' fluid flow. For example, they state:

(a) pressures are generated indirectly, e.g. as a result of the consolidation of the solid matrix due to tissue deformation;

(b) that the primary cause of fluid flow in consolidation is the dilatation field of the solid matrix;

(c) fluid flow (in consolidation) occurs due to the volume changes in the solid matrix which produce a pressure gradient field within the interstitial fluid; and

(d) the interstitial fluid, being nearly incompressible, can develop high fluid pressures as the matrix is deformed.

In the opinion of the present authors this is erroneous. The compressive behaviour of cartilage can be considered to consist of an instantaneous, essentially constant volume, deformation, followed by creep as liquid is exuded from the tissue. The magnitude of the instantaneous deformation depends upon the degree of confinement of the tissue and the rate of deformation during the creep phase depends upon the ease with which liquid can escape from the tissue. It is therefore erroneous to predict fluid flow in a given situation (e.g. a synovial joint) from the mechanical behaviour of the tissue in a different situation (e.g. a laboratory indentation test). Put another way, after any instantaneous response which involves no fluid flow, fluid loss produces consolidation; consolidation does not 'produce' fluid flow. When the model of a saturated soil in an impervious cylindrical container is loaded through a highly porous piston (i.e. the simple consolidation model in Figure 5.3) there will be no instantaneous deformation if the water is assumed to be incompressible and the container is assumed to be rigid (i.e. the soil is fully confined). During consolidation the compression of the springs (i.e. the solid phase) does not push the water out through the piston (in fact, the load carried by the springs is initially zero); the water flows out through the piston because (a) it initially carries all of the applied load and is therefore highly pressurized, (b) the pressure on the other side of the piston is zero, and (c) there is nowhere else for it to go. The soil consolidates *because* the water leaves the container, and, as it does, the solid phase carries an increasing fraction of the applied load.

Although it must be true that if load is applied to only the solid part of a saturated sponge, water will be squeezed out of the sponge, in our view cartilage does not resemble a saturated sponge and does not, therefore, behave in this way. Since, in our view, the solid and liquid components of cartilage do not exist as separate phases, the tissue can be modelled as a saturated sponge only if the behaviour of the imaginary solid phase is made to reflect the osmotic properties of the proteoglycan gel and the mechanical properties of the collagen fibres. In this case the imaginary compressive loads carried by the solid phase will be a function of the deformation of the tissue, in the same way that the forces in the springs in the simple model of consolidation gradually increase from zero as consolidation proceeds, and no pumping will occur.

A less important criticism of this work concerns the distribution of load between the liquid and the solid phases of the sponge model. On the basis of scanning electron microscope studies of normal healthy cartilage (Redler and Mow 1974), 80% of the applied load was assumed to be carried by the solid phase at the articular surface. However, the observation that 80% of the surface of dehydrated specimens appears to be solid in a scanning electron microscope seems unlikely to apply to the hydrated tissue, over 70% of which is water. Clearly, if the proportion of solid at the surface is less than 80%, the fraction of the applied load carried by the solid matrix (assuming for the moment that it can carry load) would be less and the model would predict a reduced flow out of the tissue due to pumping.

3.2. A Three-phase Model of Cartilage

3.2.1. Fluid Pressures and their Associated Stresses in Unloaded Cartilage. Structurally, articular cartilage consists of a relatively coarse collagen fibre network, a much finer, molecular, network of proteoglycan 'fibres', and water. The collagen, proteoglycans and water make up approximately 15–20%, 2–10% and 70–75% of the weight of the tissue respectively (Chapter 3).

Cartilage is bonded to subchondral bone via its calcified zone. Within the matrix of cartilage itself the close meshwork of collagen fibres in some way immobilizes the proteoglycan moiety. Although the exact relationship between collagen and proteoglycans is not fully understood, it appears probable that physical entanglement of the proteoglycan molecules with the collagen, rather than a chemical bond between the two components, is responsible for immobilizing most of the proteoglycans. Whatever the mechanism by which collagen immobilizes the proteoglycans, without collagen the proteoglycan moiety would not be retained over the bone extremities to form a coherent, functionally useful layer.

Proteoglycans are hydrophilic molecules which swell in the presence of water to form gels. Gels possess an elastic resistance to expansion (Ogston 1966) so that a particle of a gel in water will swell until the swelling tendency (which decreases as swelling proceeds) is balanced by elastic forces in the molecular chains. Thus a particle of a gel in water can be thought of as a balloon inflating itself with water. In water the ballon inflates until the tensile forces in its skin 'produce' an internal hydrostatic pressure of such a magnitude that the rate of flow of water out of the balloon, due to the hydrostatic pressure difference between the inside and outside, equals the rate of flow of water into the balloon due to self-inflation.

Essentially, cartilage consists of a large number of these proteoglycan 'balloons' entangled in a meshwork of collagen fibres. In the tissue the balloons are only slightly inflated so that the swelling tendency is large, the elastic forces in the skins are small, and there is a net tendency for the balloons to inflate further. This net tendency to swell is the osmotic pressure of the proteoglycan gel (Ogston 1966) and its realization (i.e. actual swelling) is prevented by the surrounding collagen fibres (Harkness 1968). This situation implies that in unloaded cartilage tensile forces in the collagen fibres produce an internal hydrostatic pressure equal to the osmotic pressure of the proteoglycan gel such that flow of water into the tissue due to osmotic forces is equal to the flow out due to the hydrostatic pressure difference between the inside and outside. As Wainwright *et al.* (1975) point out, it is the swelling tendency of the proteoglycan gel against the constraints imposed by the collagen fibre network which gives articular cartilage its rigidity.

The osmotic pressure of the proteoglycan gel in normal human femoral head cartilage has been found to be approximately 0.2 MN/m^2 (30 lbf/in^2) (see Chapter 4, Section 6). Although the concomitant tensile stresses in individual collagen fibres cannot be measured with presently available techniques, the existence of 'interlocked' tensile stresses can be demonstrated by the distortion of cartilage which occurs when it is removed from subchondral bone (Fry 1974).

3.2.2. The Response of Cartilage to the Single Application of a Load of Short Duration. *In vivo* it seems that cartilage is predominantly loaded perpendicular to its surface and only the carriage of loads applied in this direction will be considered.

If, when load is first applied to a synovial joint, the two cartilage surfaces are separated by synovial fluid, the load will be transmitted from one cartilage surface to the other via pressure in the fluid. The pressure will vary throughout the fluid but the following discussion will be simplified by considering a region of high pressure, the loaded region, and a region of low pressure, the unloaded region, as shown in Figure 5.6.

When load is first applied to the joint, synovial fluid will flow laterally from the high pressure region to the low pressure regions

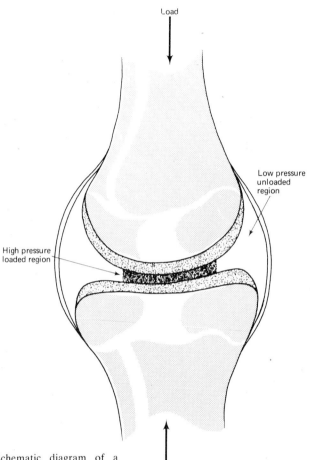

Figure 5.6. Schematic diagram of a loaded synovial joint.

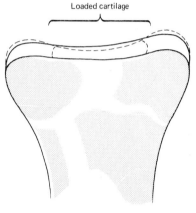

Figure 5.7 The initial deformation of cartilage.

through the gap between the two cartilage surfaces and consequently the two surfaces will begin to approach each other. The loaded regions of the cartilages will be compressed in a direction normal to their surfaces and this will produce a lateral expansion of the loaded cartilage and an increase in the internal hydrostatic pressure. The lateral expansion of the loaded cartilage effectively compresses the surrounding 'unloaded' cartilage in a direction parallel to the articular surface and this in turn will produce an expansion of the 'unloaded' cartilage normal to the articular surface and an increase in its internal hydrostatic pressure. The resulting cartilage deformation is shown in an exaggerated form for one cartilage in Figure 5.7.

The increased pressure within the 'unloaded' cartilage disturbs the flow equilibrium between it and the low pressure synovial fluid above it so that water, but not proteoglycan (Linn and Sokoloff,

1965), will flow from the 'unloaded' cartilage to the low pressure synovial fluid across the articular surface. The effect of this expression of water on the flow within the cartilage and on the further deformation of the cartilage is difficult to analyse. Water will flow from the loaded cartilage to the unloaded cartilage but whether this produces (a) further deformation of the cartilage, or (b) flow from the high pressure synovial fluid into the cartilage, or (c) a combination of both, is not immediately obvious. However, the situation appears to be essentially the same as that shown in Figure 5.8. That is, the cartilage is a hydrostatic system with a

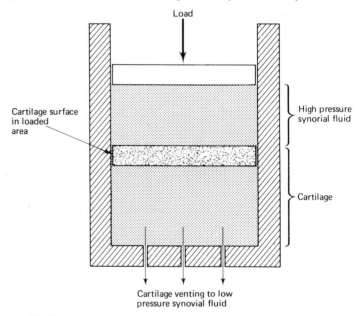

Figure 5.8 Simple model for fluid flow in a loaded joint.

porous surface, loaded hydrostatically, with the water in the tissue venting to lower pressure. If the piston which represents the loaded surface of the cartilage were impervious, there could be no flow through it as water flowed out of the 'cartilage' beneath it. Hence the expression of water from the tissue would produce deformation only. At the other extreme, if the surface piston had a porosity of 100%, and therefore offered no resistance to flow, it would not move as water flowed out of the 'cartilage' beneath it. The loss of water from the cartilage to the low pressure synovial fluid would be exactly equal to the flow of liquid into the cartilage from the high pressure synovial fluid, and consequently the cartilage would not deform. Since the loaded surface of articular cartilage has a porosity between zero and 100%, this simple model predicts that there will be a flow of liquid into the cartilage from the high pressure synovial fluid, that this flow will be less than the flow of water out of the tissue to the low pressure synovial fluid, and that, consequently, the tissue will deform due to a net decrease in volume.

The rate of flow into the cartilage and the rate of flow out, however, both depend on the permeability of the tissue and since this is low (see Chapter 4, Section 6.3), loads which are applied for a very brief time can be expected to produce a very small flow of water out of the cartilage, an even smaller flow into the cartilage, and hence a negligible change in volume of the tissue. If loads of brief duration do in fact produce only a small decrease in volume, it follows that the cartilage will behave in an essentially elastic fashion; that is, its instantaneous deformation will be instantaneously recoverable on removal of the load.

The instantaneous deformations of the cartilage which occur when the load is first applied (Figure 5.7) are a reflection of the tendency for the proteoglycan gel to flow (i.e. be displaced) under the action of the pressure gradients established within the cartilages, and it seems clear that it is only the collagen meshwork which restricts this flow. In fulfilling this function the collagen fibres must experience increased tensile stresses. Expressed another way, the increased tensile stresses in the collagen meshwork 'produce' the increased pressure in the proteoglycan gel which supports the applied load.

3.2.3. The Response of Cartilage to the Single Application of a Load of Long Duration.
Initially, the cartilages of a loaded synovial joint will respond to a load of long duration as they do for a load of short duration. That is, they will deform instantaneously due to bulk movement of proteoglycan and water. If the load is then maintained, significant volumes of liquid will begin to flow (a) between the cartilage surfaces, from the high pressure synovial fluid to the low pressure synovial fluid, (b) into the loaded cartilage from the high pressure synovial fluid, (c) through the cartilage from the loaded to the unloaded regions, and (d) out of the unloaded cartilage into the low pressure synovial fluid. The deformation of the cartilage will also start to increase due to a net expression of liquid.

For a number of reasons, the above series of events will not continue indefinitely. First, the resistance to the lateral flow of synovial fluid between the cartilage surfaces gradually increases as the surfaces approach each other and the gap between them narrows. Thus the flow of synovial fluid along this path gradually decreases. This is 'squeeze-film lubrication' (see Chapter 7, Sections 6.1.3 and 6.8), and Fein (1967) has calculated that it will result in a film of synovial fluid 3.5 μm thick existing in the human hip joint 1 s after the application of a 300 N (67.5 lbf) load. Fein's calculation ignored the flow of liquid into the cartilage but this is unlikely to be a serious criticism since this flow is significantly less than that between the cartilage surfaces until the gap is of the order of $1.0\,\mu$m (see Chapter 4).

Secondly, as the flow from the high pressure synovial fluid into the cartilage proceeds, the remaining synovial fluid becomes more and more concentrated in protein–hyaluronate molecules since these molecules are too large to pass into the tissue (see Chapter 4). For reasons discussed in Chapter 4, it would seem that the synovial fluid in the loaded region must eventually change into a gel, the osmotic pressure of which increases as the gel becomes more and more concentrated. The osmotic pressure (self-inflating tendency) of the gel increases until the flow out of it, due to hydrostatic pressure gradients, equals the flow into it due to self-inflation. That is, an equilibrium is eventually reached such that the flow of water (and small solutes) into the cartilages ceases. Maroudas (1967, 1969; and see Chapter 4) has estimated that this situation will be produced under physiological loads when the two cartilages are approximately 0.02–$0.03\,\mu$m apart. Since this is a factor of 100 less than the previously quoted film thickness 1 s after the application of load, it will clearly take considerably longer than 1 s to form the equilibrated protein–hyaluronate gel between the cartilage surfaces.

Thirdly, as the deformation of the cartilage increases, three things will happen: (a) the permeability of the tissue decreases, (b) the loaded area is likely to increase (because of the shape of most articular surfaces) so that the area of surface available for the expression of water (the unloaded surface) decreases and the length of the flow path from the centre of the loaded area to the unloaded area increases, and (c) the osmotic pressure of the hydrated proteoglycan gel increases. For all the of these reasons the rate at which water is expressed from the tissue can be expected to decrease as time elapses under load until finally the rate of loss reaches zero. After this time no further deformation of the cartilage will occur.

The changes which occur in the collagen fibre stresses after the initial instantaneous deformation are difficult to predict. The decreasing volume of the loaded regions of the cartilages probably allows the collagen in these regions to relax. (Although the swelling tendency of the proteoglycan 'balloons' in the loaded regions gradually increases, this tendency is now opposed by the externally applied load instead of by the surrounding collagen fibres.) However, when the highly pressurized synovial fluid eventually changes into an equilibrated gel the loaded cartilage will be compressed by what is effectively a solid, and this will tend to 'squeeze' the proteoglycan gel itself laterally (i.e. the proteoglycan gel will be loaded directly and will therefore be deformed rather than displaced). Only the collagen fibres oppose this deformation so that, again, additional tensile stresses will be produced in them.

In the unloaded regions the volume of the tissue decreases after the initial deformation but the increasing swelling tendency of the proteoglycan 'balloons' is still opposed by the collagen fibres. The net result of these two effects is probably a gradual reduction in the tensile stresses in the collagen fibres in the unloaded cartilage.

On removal of the load the hydrostatic pressure in the cartilages will fall. Relieved of the stresses which were generated by the applied load, the cartilage will instantaneously recover part of the total deformation. This partial recovery will be due primarily to a change in shape, but not in volume, of the tissue. The osmotic pressure will then cause a gradual imbibition of water until complete recovery of the original thickness of the tissue is achieved. The internal hydrostatic pressure and collagen stresses will finally be equal to those present in the unloaded matrix.

3.2.4. The Response of Cartilage to Cyclical Loading. The two previous Sections have shown that when a constant load is applied to a synovial joint, (a) the film of synovial fluid between the two cartilage surfaces gradually becomes thinner and eventually changes into a equilibrated gel, and (b) the cartilages deform instantaneously and the deformation then gradually increases to an equilibrium value. It follows that since the response of a joint to a constant load is time-dependent, the response of a joint to a cyclic load will depend on the frequency of the loading cycle.

In a single step of a walking cycle, load is applied to a joint for approximately 0.2 s (Paul 1965). The previously referred to calculations of Fein (1967) and Maroudas (1967, 1969) indicate that it will take considerably longer than 1 s to produce a protein–hyaluronate gel between the cartilage surfaces. Since Fein also showed that the synovial fluid film could be replenished by the relative sliding motion of the two joint components, the possibility exists that an equilibrated gel is not produced during normal activity. If, however, the synovial fluid is not replenished during each load cycle, the thickness of the layer will gradually decrease over a number of cycles until the equilibrium thickness of pro-tein–hyaluronate gel is produced.

The response of the cartilages to a cyclically applied load will depend on the net volume of water lost from the tissue during the loading phase and the degree of reimbibition during the unloaded phase. Maroudas has estimated that in a loaded hip joint the initial rate of cartilage deformation due to fluid loss will be of the order of 0.03% per minute (Chapter 4, Section 6.5). Although the calculation involved a large number of simplifying assumptions it is clear that only a minute quantity of water will be lost from the cartilages during each loading phase of a walking cycle. However, the reimbibition of this water will take a finite time and conse-quently, if a second load is applied before the cartilage has fully reimbibed the water lost in the first loading period, incomplete recovery will have occurred at the end of the first cycle. (It should be noted that the force driving water out of the matrix during the loaded phase (essentially the applied load) is greater than the force driving water into the matrix during the unloaded phase (essentially the osmotic pressure). Although the area of surface through which water can flow out of the tissue during the loaded phase (i.e. the unloaded surface) will be smaller than the surface area available for imbibition during the unloaded phase (i.e. the entire surface), on balance it seems likely that slightly more water will be lost during the loaded phase than is regained during the unloaded phase.) If this process is repeated, the unrecovered deformations occurring during each loading cycle (i.e. the increments of water lost from the matrix) will summate so that the total unrecovered deformation will steadily increase as cyclic loading is continued. This process will not continue indefinitely, however, since, as with the application of a single load of long duration (Section 3.2.3), an increasing deformation will result in an increasing resistance to flow out of the tissue and an increasing tendency for water to be held in the matrix by physicochemical forces (i.e. osmotic pressures). Thus eventually the matrix will take up a steady unrecovering deformation (the magnitude of which will depend on the magnitude of the applied load and on the frequency and duration of the loading cycle) with an elastically recoverable deformation superimposed at each load application.

For the reasons already given, the volume of water eventually lost from the tissue in life seems unlikely to be large, so that the osmotic changes in the matrix and the magnitude of the unrecovering deformation are probably small. This fact is not surprising when it is considered that large changes in the osmotic pressure of the matrix might conceivably damage chondrocytes in the loaded areas.

To date, the question of whether or not cartilage experiences an unrecovering deformation in life has not been satisfactorily studied in the laboratory. Although Linn (1967) has shown unrecovering deformation in the cartilage of dog ankles articulating in his 'arthrotripsometer', these experiments were performed under a static load with saline instead of synovial fluid. An interesting result from Linn's work was the finding that the equilibrium deformation of the cartilage in an oscillated joint was significantly lower than that in a non-oscillated joint. Freeman, Swanson and Manley (1975) have shown unrecovering deformations in cartilage of cyclically loaded human hip joints but in the absence of sliding motion between the surfaces.

3.2.5. Summary. We now propose that cartilage functions as follows.

Both the proteoglycans and the collagen contribute to load carriage by cartilage: the former by retaining water in the matrix osmotically and impeding the loss of water from the loaded matrix both osmotically and by reducing the permeability of the tissue, the latter by retaining the proteoglycans in place. The carriage of any load, whether the load be applied once briefly, once for a long period of time, or repetitively, involves both of these tissue elements simultaneously and thus they are functionally inter-dependent.

In the cartilage of an unloaded synovial joint the osmotic pressure of the proteoglycan gel produces an internal hydrostatic pressure and tensile stresses in the collagen fibres.

When load is first applied to the joint the internal pressure increases, pressure gradients are produced and the cartilages deform due to the displacement of the proteoglycan gel. In limiting this displacement the collagen fibres experience increased tensile stress. If the load is removed after only a short time the cartilages rapidly return to their unloaded state.

Under a prolonged load the cartilages will gradually decrease in volume due to a net loss of water. During this time the tensile stresses in the collagen fibres probably fall. However, if the load is maintained for sufficient time for the highly pressurized synovial fluid to change into an equilibrated gel then the tensile stresses probably increase again due to the direct loading of the proteo-glycan gel. Complete recovery after prolonged loading will take a finite time.

Under cyclically applied loads the behaviour of the tissue will depend to a large extent on the frequency of loading and the number of load cycles. If the frequency is low and/or the number of cycles is large, the cartilage may take up a steady state deformation with a fully recovering deformation superimposed during each load cycle.

3.3. Is the Distribution of Collagen in Cartilage Dependent on the Tensile Stresses in the Tissue?

In Section 3.2 it has been argued that tensile stresses are produced in the collagen fibres of cartilage. The question now arises: can the spatial distribution of collagen in cartilage be accounted for mechanically?

Although it is tempting to interpret the distribution of the collagen in cartilage in terms of its possible mechanical function, sight must not be lost of the fact that its distribution is dependent on the activity of the cells and as such is presumably genetically controlled and subject to the same environmental influences as are other cellular systems. Thus, for example, although it is tempting to regard the orientation of collagen fibres close to the surface as being an attempt to withstand tensile stresses developed within the surface, it is at the same time hard to imagine that the cells adjacent to the surface deposit collagen in any other orientation.

3.3.1. The Distribution of Collagen in Articular Cartilage.

It is now well recognized that the arrangement of the collagen fibres in articular cartilage varies with depth from the articular surface; Figure 5.9 is a composite photograph, showing the collagen fibres in different zones of cartilage.

The fibres in the superficial zone, which may extend to a depth of 200 μm or more (Weiss, Rosenberg and Helfet 1968), are arranged in bundles or sheets which lie essentially parallel to the articular surface. These fibre bundles, or sheets, appear to be arranged mainly in two directions which are perpendicular to each other. However, as the studies of Bullough and Goodfellow (1968) and Meachim, Denham, Emery and Wilkinson (1974) have shown, there does appear to be a preferred direction in which most of the fibres of the superficial zone are aligned.

In the intermediate zone of cartilage the collagen fibres are arranged in a more random, three-dimensional network, although (Clarke (1971) and Cameron, Pillar and MacNab (1975) have observed what appears to be a superimposed non-random organization.

In the deepest zone of cartilage the collagen fibres show a slight tendency to be aligned perpendicular to the subchondral bone/cartilage interface (Chapter 1, Section 2.5.2).

3.3.2. The Function of Collagen in the Intermediate and Deep Zones.

As discussed in Section 3.2. the rigidity of cartilage depends on the collagen fibres preventing the proteoglycan molecules from swelling. This function of collagen will be best performed by a random three-dimensional network of fibres.

In Section 3.2 it was also argued that, when a synovial joint is loaded, additional tensile stresses are produced within the collagen meshworks of the opposing cartilages. The argument was based on the concept of articular cartilage functioning as a hydrostatic system, with the hydrated proteoglycan gel acting as the fluid element and the collagen fibre meshwork acting as the container (Wainwright *et al.* 1975). If this concept is correct then the need for the fluid element of a hydrostatic system to be completely enclosed by a container indicates the need for a random three-dimensional network of collagen fibres in the tissue.

In the deepest zone of cartilage the collagen fibres show a slight tendency to be aligned perpendicular to the subchondral bone/cartilage interface. It may be presumed that in this zone collagen has the additional function of tethering the matrix to the subchondral bone.

3.3.3. The Function of Collagen in the Superficial Zone.

The suggestion that the collagen fibres in the superficial zone of cartilage might display a predominant alignment was first made by Hultkrantz (1898). Using a sharp-pointed awl of circular cross-

322

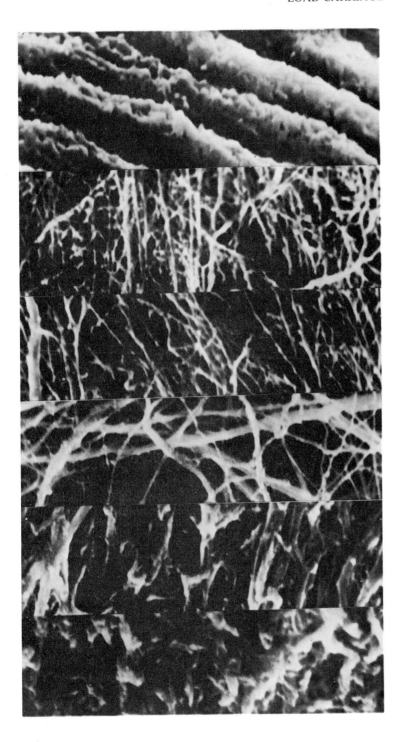

Figure 5.9 Composite photograph showing the collagen fibre distribution in articular cartilage.
(Reproduced by kind permission of I. Redler MD, New Orleans, Louisiana, USA.)

section, Hultkrantz punctured the surface of cartilage in many sites and then stained the punctures with Indian ink. He observed that the punctures were elongated instead of circular and that, when sufficient of them were made, the orientation of the punctures, or cleavage lines, formed a pattern which was unique to a particular joint but essentially repeatable for that joint from person to person. This pattern is commonly referred to as the prick pattern or cleavage pattern. Figure 5.10 shows the results of applying the method of Hultkrantz to the femoral condyles of the knee joint.

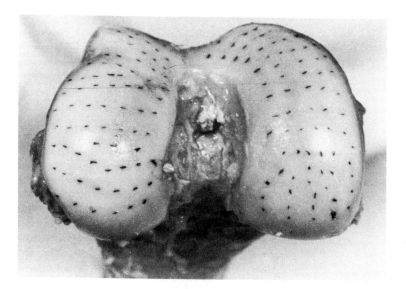

Figure 5.10 Prick pattern on the femoral condyles of a human knee joint.

In an attempt to interpret the prick patterns, Hultkrantz assumed that they represented the predominant alignment of the collagen fibres in the superficial zone and, since collagen fibres were the main tension-resistant filaments in other tissues, he argued that the prick patterns followed the direction of the maximum tensile stresses produced by both compression and friction. Commenting on the conclusion of Hultkrantz, Fick (1904) pointed out that the tensile stresses produced by friction were unlikely to be significant because the coefficient of friction between cartilage surfaces is extremely low. Therefore, he argued, tensile stresses parallel to the articular surface were most likely to be produced as a secondary effect to the normal compressive loading of cartilage in synovial joints. This argument is supported in part by more recent data. Little, Freeman and Swanson (1969) (and see Chapter 7, Section 2.2.1) obtained values for the coefficient of friction in the human hip joint of between 0.003 and 0.015, and with a typical maximum load of 1.8 kN (three times body weight) this implies a frictional shear force of between 5.4 and 27 N (1.2–6 lbf). Freeman, Swanson and Manley (1975) measured contact areas in the loaded human hip joint of the order of 1500 mm^2, so that the largest average shear stress can be estimated to be approximately 0.018 MN/m^2 (2.6 lbf/in^2). Such a small shear stress would hardly need a substantial array of collagen to resist it.

Benninghoff (1924, 1925a, b, 1939) did not agree with the conclusions of Hultkrantz. He suggested that the prick pattern depended on the variation of curvature of the cartilage surface and that any relationship between its direction and the tensile stress in the superficial zone was only very approximate.

The most extensive study of the prick patterns in cartilage was performed by Pauwels (1959). Using a gelatin model of the glenoid cavity in the human shoulder joint and employing the engineering technique of photoelastic stress analysis, Pauwels concluded that the predominant alignment of the superficial collagen fibres, as manifested by the prick pattern, coincided with the maximum tensile stresses produced by the compression of cartilage. This result was consistent with the hypothesis of Hultkrantz. Pauwels was also able to explain an observation made by Benninghoff—namely, that in a few cases, the prick lines deviated markedly from the tensile stress trajectory—by showing that the subchondral bone exhibited some anatomical abnormality in those specimens which, he suggested, caused the collagen fibres to adopt a local atypical configuration.

Zarek and Edwards (1963) applied the now classical Hertzian solution for the problem of two elastic spheres in contact (Hertz 1881) to articular cartilage. The Hertzian solution shows that the stresses parallel to the surface, at the surface, become tensile immediately outside the area of contact if the radius of the area of contact is small compared to the radii of curvature of the two bodies. The maximum tensile stress is produced at the edge of the contact area and has a value given by

$$\text{Maximum surface tensile stress} = \frac{(1 - 2v)}{3} \cdot P_{max}$$

where v = Poisson's ratio (see Chapter 6),
P_{max} = maximum contact pressure.

Zarek and Edwards used a value of 0.3 for the Poisson ratio of the tissue and concluded that the maximum tensile stress in the surface of loaded cartilage was 0.133 P_{max}. In the case of the hip this calculation would imply that, with a maximum contact pressure of 3.0 MN/m^2 (435 lbf/in^2) (Day, Swanson and Freeman 1975; and see Section 2.2), the maximum tensile stress would be equal to 0.4 MN/m^2 (58 lbf/in^2).

Zarek and Edwards concluded that the superficial fibres are

orientated in the direction of the principal tensile stresses in the surface.

There are a number of criticisms of this work. First, the value of Poisson's ratio used by Zarek and Edwards is too low and consequently the calculated value of maximum tensile stress is too large. If a value of 0.45 is taken for the Poisson ratio (see Chapter 6, Section 5), the Hertzian solution predicts a maximum tensile stress of only 0.15 MN/m^2 (22 lbf/in^2). Secondly, cartilage is relatively thin and is bonded to bone which has different physical properties, and this means that the Hertzian solution is not strictly applicable. Thirdly, cartilage is a multiphase, non-homogeneous and anisotropic material: again the Hertzian solution is not applicable.

More recently, Askew and Mow (1976) have taken the non-homogeneous anisotropic nature of cartilage into account. Their model consisted of a transversely isotropic layer (representing the superficial zone) bonded to an isotropic layer (representing the intermediate and deep zones) bonded in turn to an isotropic elastic half-space (representing the subchondral bone). The relevant mechanical properties of the different layers were taken from the literature. The results of the stress analysis of this model showed that when the ratio of the radius of the contact area to the cartilage depth was greater than three, areas of surface tensile stress were well outside the loaded region.

The main criticism of the work of Pauwels, Zarek and Edwards, and Askew and Mow is that cartilage is treated as a single-phase material. This treatment completely ignores the unique way in which the three structural components of the tissue interact to carry load. When a single-phase material is subjected to a compressive load, relatively small tensile stresses are produced. The above-named authors have attempted to correlate the magnitude and direction of these tensile stresses with the density and orientation of the collagen fibres. Articular cartilage, however, does not support load in the same way as a single-phase material; it is a hydrostatic system. As Serafini-Fracassini and Smith (1974) point out, 'the purpose of collagen in cartilage is not the direct resistance of tensile stresses arising in a homogeneous body but the fixation of the elastic domains of proteoglycan molecules when these experience deforming and displacing stresses'.

It follows that since consideration of the multiphase nature of articular cartilage suggests the need for a random three-dimensional network of collagen, the spatial distribution of collagen in the superficial zone of the tissue cannot be accounted for in terms of mechanical stress.

3.3.4. Summary. The strength of articular cartilage depends upon the collagen (a) preventing the proteglycan gel from swelling, and (b) immobilizing the proteoglycan gel when the tissue is subject to compressive loads. These functions of collagen require a random three-dimensional network of fibres. Collagen also has the function of bonding cartilage to the bone. These considerations explain the spatial distribution of collagen in the intermediate and deep zones of articular cartilage. At present there is no satisfactory mechanical explanation of the spatial distribution of collagen in the superficial zone, and indeed there may not be one: it is not easy to see how surface chondrocytes could lay down collagen in any orientation other than parallel to the surface whilst within the plane of the surface prick lines (and the preferred alignment which they reflect) are reminiscent of the equally inexplicable Langers lines in skin. Perhaps both, like finger-prints, are genetically determined.

4. MECHANICAL FAILURE IN CARTILAGE

In general the strength of a material is defined as the minimum stress at which fracture occurs. The strength of a material may vary depending upon whether it is subjected to tensile, compressive or shear stresses, or a combination of these. It also depends upon whether a load is applied once or repeatedly. In the case of a cyclically applied load, fracture can occur at a load value which is lower than the static load required to cause fracture. This kind of behaviour is known as fatigue, and a fatigue-prone material may be considered as being 'weaker' when subjected to a cyclically applied load than when it is subjected to a load which is applied only once.

In the previous Sections of this Chapter it has been argued that the strength of cartilage depends on the retention of an aqueous proteoglycan gel within the loaded matrix and on the tensile strength of the collagen network which acts to immobilize the gel. If this postulated mechanism of load carriage is valid, mechanical failure seems unlikely in the proteoglycan gel since this component of the matrix functions from the mechanical viewpoint as a fluid. Although at least in theory the gel could be expressed from the matrix, it could not be fractured. The precise mechanism by which the proteoglycans are retained in the matrix of cartilage is not understood, but it seems certain that proteoglycan complexes are too large to move through the collagen meshwork (i.e. they are physically trapped) and they may, in addition, be bonded chemically to collagen (see Chapter 3). Thus, provided the collagen network remains intact, the expression of proteoglycans from the matrix by compression appears to be impossible. The expression of water alone from the matrix, on the other hand, occurs normally but would not of itself constitute mechanical failure provided that the mechanism for its reimbibition remained intact, i.e. provided that the proteoglycans remained within the matrix. It may therefore be concluded that irreversible structural failure in cartilage is less likely to occur initially in the proteo-glycan gel than in the collagen fibre mesh.

Structural failure affecting primarily the collagen network would, on the other hand, appear to be perfectly possible since collagen fibres, or the bonds between them, might be overstressed in tension. In Section 3.2.2 it was argued that a single load of brief duration would produce additional tensile stresses in the collagen fibres in cartilage. If such a load were of great magnitude (e.g. if the cartilage were to be subjected to externally applied, violent impact), the tensile stresses might be sufficiently large to fracture the network; that is to say, the resulting pressure in the aqueous proteoglycan gel could burst the tissue. It is of course known that this mechanism can occur since compression injuries to human joints can produce splits in cartilage.

The continuous application of a very high load would eventually cause a considerable loss of water from the tissue and conse-quently a large compressive deformation. Whatever the result of such a large deformation of the collagen fibres would be, it is an established fact that prolonged pressure applied experimentally to a joint causes degeneration of the cartilage together with damage to the chondrocytes (Salter and Field 1960; Trias 1961). It seems unlikely, however, that a load of sufficient magnitude would ever be applied for long enough in life to express even 50% of the water from the matrix. Thus, mechanical failure in normal cartilage in life as a consequence of this mechanism can probably be dis-counted.

The collagen network in cartilage might fracture in the face of a cyclically applied load (Section 3.2.4) if the fluctuating tensile stresses produced by such a mode of loading were sufficient to cause fatigue failure in the collagen network. Alternatively, cyc-lically applied loads of great magnitude acting over a long period of time might eventually cause the expression of enough water, and hence a sufficiently large deformation, to produce irreversible damage of the cartilage, for the same reasons as those which apply to large, statically applied loads of long duration. However, this latter form of failure seems unlikely to occur in normal cartilage in life and it is clear from everyday experience that the mechanism by which water is retained in normal cartilage is sufficient to prevent failure in this way in the face of the loads applied, for example, by such activities as walking.

In summary, the mechanism of load carriage postulated in this Chapter suggests than any mechanical failure of articular cartilage is likely to be a tensile failure of the collagen meshwork, either as a result of a single application of a load of great magnitude or as a result of a cyclic application of load. Further speculation on both the mechanism of load carriage and the possibility of mechanical failures occurring in life clearly requires quantitative data on the behaviour and strength of the tissue under different types of loading. It is equally clear that the relevant types of loading are (a) static compression, (b) static tension, (c) cyclic compression and (d) cyclic tension. Such studies are described in detail in the following Chapter.

REFERENCES

Askew M. J. and Mow V. C. (1976) Stress analysis of a nonhomogeneous, anisotropic model of articular cartilage. 22nd Annual Orthopedic Research Society Meeting, New Orleans.

Benninghoff A. (1924) Experimentells untersuchungen über den Einfluss verschiedenartiges mechanischer Beanspruchung auf den Knorpel. *Verh. anat. Ges. (Jena)* **33,** 194.

Benninghoff A. (1925a) Die modellierenden und former haltenden Faktoren des Knorpelreliefs. *Z. Anat. Entwickl.-Gesch.* **76,** 43.

Benninghoff A. (1925b) Form und Bau der Gelenkknorpel in ihren Beziehungen zu Funktion. II: Der Aufbau des Gelenkknorpel in seinen Beziehungen zu Funktion. *Z. Zellforsch.* **2,** 783.

Benninghoff A. (1939) *Lehrbuch der Anatomie des Menschen,* Vol. 1. Lehmann, Munich.

Biot M. A. (1941) General theory of three-dimensional consolidation. *J. appl. Physiol.* **12,** 155.

Brewster R. C., Chao E. Y. and Stauffer R. N. (1974) Force analysis of the ankle joint during the stance phase of gait. Abstract of Communication at the 27th ACEMB, Philadelphia, USA.

Bullough P. G. and Goodfellow J. (1968) The significance of the fine structure of articular cartilage. *J. Bone Jt Surg.* **50B,** 852.

Cameron H. U., Pillar R. M. and MacNab I. (1975) The microhardness of articular cartilage. *Clin. Orthop.* **108,** 275.

Clarke I. C. (1971) Articular cartilage: a review and scanning electron microscope study. *J. Bone Jt Surg.* **53B,** 732.

Contini R., Gage H. and Drillis R. (1965) Human gait characteristics. *Biomechanics and Related Bioengineering Topics,* Ed. by R. M. Kenedi, p. 413. Pergamon Press, Oxford.

Day W. H., Swanson S. A. V. and Freeman M. A. R. (1975) Contact pressures in the loaded human cadaver hip. *J. Bone Jt Surg.* **51B,** 302.

Edwards J. (1967) Physical characteristics of articular cartilage. *Proc. Instn mech. Engrs* **181,** 16.

Evans F. Gaynor (1961) *Biochemical Studies of the Musculoskeletal System.* Thomas, Springfield, Ill.

Fein R. S. (1967) Are synovial joints squeeze-film lubricated. *Proc. Instn mech. Engrs* **181,** 125.

Fick R. (1904–1911) *Handbuch der Anatomie und Mechanik der Gelenke,* Vols I—III. Fischer, Jena.

Freeman M. A. R. (1972) The pathogenesis of primary osteoarthrosis: an hypothesis. *Modern Trends in Orthopaedics—6,* Ed. by A. G. Apley. Butterworths, London.

Freeman M. A. R., Swanson S. A. V. and Manley P. T. (1975) Stress-lowering function of articular cartilage. *Med. Biol. Engg* **13,** 245.

Freeman M. A. R., Todd R. C. and Pirie C. J. (1975) The role of fatigue in the pathogenesis of senile femoral neck fractures. *J. Bone Jt Surg.* **56B,** 698.

Fry H. J. H. (1974) The interlocked stresses of articular cartilage. *Brit. J. Plast. Surg.* **27,** 363.

Harkness R. D. (1968) Mechanical properties of collagenous tissues. *Treatise on Collagn* Part A, Ed. by B. S. Gould. Academic Press, London and New York.

Hertz H. R. (1881) On the contacts of elastic solids. *J. reine angens. Math.* **92,** 156.

Higginson G. R. and Norman R. (1974a) A model investigation of squeeze-film lubrication in animal joints. *Phys. Med. Biol.* **19,** 785.

Higginson G. R. and Norman R. (1974b) The lubrication of porous elastic solids with reference to the functioning of human joints. *J. Mech. Engg Sci.* **16,** 250.

Higginson G. R., Litchfield M. R. and Snaith J. (1976) Load/deformation/time characteristics of articular cartilage. *Int. J. Mech. Sci.* **18,** 481.

Hultkrantz J. W. (1898) Über die Spaltrichtungen der Gelenkknorpel. *Verh. anat. Ges. (Kiel)*

Kempson G. E., Spivey C. J., Swanson S. A. V. and Freeman M. A. R. (1971) Patterns of cartilage stiffness on normal and degenerate human femoral heads. *J. Biomechanics* **4,** 597.

Lewis P. R. and McCutchen C. W. (1959) Experimental evidence for weeping lubrication in mammalian joints. *Nature (Lond.)* **184,** 1285.

Lewis P. R. and McCutchen C. W. (1960) Reply to letter from M. A. MacConaill entitled 'Lubrication of mammalian joints'. *Nature (Lond.)* **185,** 920.

Linn F. D. (1967) Lubrication of animal joints. I: The arthrotripsometer. *J. Bone Jt Surg.* **49A,** 1079.

Linn F. C. and Sokoloff L. (1965) Movement and composition of interstitial fluid of cartilage. *Arthritis Rheum.* **8,** 481.

Little T., Freeman M. A. R. and Swanson S. A. V. (1969) Experiments on friction in the human hip joint. *Lubrication and Wear in Joints,* Ed. by V. Wright, p. 110. Sector, London.

McCutchen C. W. (1959) Mechanism of animal joints. Sponge-hydrostatic and weeping bearings. *Nature (Lond.)* **184,** 1284.

McCutchen C. W. (1962) The frictional properties of animal joints. *Wear* **5,** 1.

Maroudas A. (1967) Hyaluronic acid films. *Proc. Instn mech. Engrs* **181,** 122.

Maroudas A. (1969) Studies on the formation of hyaluronic acid films. *Lubrication and Wear in Joints,* Ed. by V. Wright, p. 124. Sector, London.

Maroudas A. (1973) Transport through articular cartilage and some physiological implications. *Proceedings of Symposium on Normal and Osteoarthrotic Articular Cartilage.* Institute of Orthopaedics, London.

Meachim G., Denham D., Emery I. H. and Wilkinson P. H. (1974) Collagen alignments and artificial splits at the surface of human articular cartilage. *J. Anat. (Lond.)* **118,** 101.

Morrison J. B. (1970) The mechanics of the knee joint in relation to normal walking. *J. Biomechanics* **3,** 51.

Mow V. C. and Torzilli P. A. (1975) Fundamental fluid transport mechanisms through articular cartilage. *Ann. rheum. Dis.* **34,** Suppl. 2, 82.

Ogston A. G. (1966) When is pressure osmotic? *Fed. Proc.* **25,** 1112.

Paul J. P. (1965) Bio-engineering studies of the forces transmitted by joints. III: Engineering analysis. *Biomechanics and Related Bio-engineering Topics,* Ed. by R. M. Kenedi, p. 369. Pergamon Press, Oxford.

Paul J. P. (1967) Forces transmitted by joints in the human body. *Proc. Instn mech. Engrs* **181,** 8.

Pauwels F. (1959) Structure of the tangential fibrous layer of the articular cartilage in the scapular glenoid cavity and an example of an unsubstantiated strain field. *Z. Anat. Entwickl.-Gesch.* **121,** 188.

Radin E. L. and Paul I. L. (1971) Importance of bone in sparing articular cartilage from impact. *Clin. Orthop.* **78,** 342.

Redler I. and Mow V. C. (1974) Biomechanical theories of ultrastructural alterations of articular surfaces of the femoral head. *Proceedings of Symposium on Bioengineering and Arthritis of the Hip,* Ed. by William Harris, pp. 23–59. Mosby, St Louis.

Salter R. B. and Field P. (1960) The effects of continuous compression on living articular cartilage. *J. Bone Jt Surg.* **42A,** 31.

Serafini-Fracassini A. and Smith J. W. (1974) *The Structure and Biochemistry of Cartilage.* Churchill Livingstone, Edinburgh and London.

Swanson S. A. V., Freeman M. A. R. and Day W. H. (1971) The fatigue properties of human cortical bone. *Med. Biol. Engg* **9,** 23.

Terzaghi K. (1943) *Theoretical Soil Mechanics.* Chapman and Hall, London.

Todd R. C., Freeman M. A. R. and Pirie C. (1972) Isolated trabecular fatigue fractures in the femoral head. *J. Bone Jt Surg.* **54B,** 723.

Torizilli P. A. and Mow V. C. (1976a) On the fundamental fluid transport mechanisms through normal and pathological articular cartilage during function. I: The formulation. *J. Biomechanics* **9,** 541.

Torizilli P. A. and Mow V. C. (1976b) On the fundamental fluid transport mechanisms through normal and pathological articular cartilage during function. II. The analysis, solution and conclusions. *J. Biomechanics* **9,** 587.

Trias A. (1961) Effect of persistent pressure on the articular cartilage. *J. Bone Jt Surg.* **43B,** 376.

Wainwright S. A., Biggs W. D., Currey J. D. and Gosline J. M. (1975) *Mechanical Design in Organisms.* Edward Arnold, London.

Weiss C., Rosenberg L. and Helfet A. (1968) An ultrastructural study of normal young adult human articular cartilage. *J. Bone Jt Surg.* **50A,** 663.

Zarek J. M. and Edwards J. (1963) The stress–structure relationship in articular cartilage. *Med. Electron. Biol. Engg* **1,** 497.

Zarek J. M. and Edwards J. (1964) Dynamic considerations of the human skeletal system. *Biomechanics and Related Bio-engineering Topics,* Ed. by R. M. Kenedi, p. 187. Pergamon Press, Oxford.

6. Mechanical Properties of Articular Cartilage

G. E. Kempson

1. INTRODUCTION

Normal articular cartilage possesses certain mechanical properties which enable it to fulfil three main functions within synovial joints: namely, to reduce the stresses applied to the subchondral bone; to prevent abrasion between the articulating bone extremities; and to provide low friction bearing surfaces which do not themselves suffer from severe abrasive wear. These functions are considered in detail in Chapters 5 and 7. This Chapter is concerned with the fundamental mechanical properties of cartilage without reference to any particular functional requirement, in the same way that the mechanical properties of steel, for example, could be described without reference to any particular application.

Knowledge of the stresses which cartilage experiences *in vivo* is likely to indicate those mechanical properties which are of the greatest functional importance to the tissue. Therefore, the stress environment of cartilage, as far as it is known, is discussed in Chapter 5 whilst the fundamental mechanical properties are described in this Chapter.

2. ENGINEERING CONSIDERATIONS

2.1. Terminology

Force—That interaction between two or more bodies which tends to change their state of motion or to deform them.
Stress, pressure—force per unit area.
  Direct stress—that component of the total stress which acts *perpendicularly* to the area under consideration and tends to change the *volume* of the body, e.g. tension and compression.

Shear stress—that component of the total stress which acts parallel to the area under consideration and tends to change the *shape* of the body, rather than the volume.

Fracture stress or *Ultimate stress*—the stress at which the material fractures. 'Fracture stress' and 'strength' are synonymous in this Chapter.

Strain—the change in a particular dimension of a body as a proportion of the original dimension.

Direct strain—tensile or compressive, is either the increase or the decrease of a particular dimension as a proportion of its original value, measured in the direction of the applied stress.

Shear strain—relative displacement of two points in the direction perpendicular to the line joining them, as a proportion of the length of that line.

Poisson's ratio—in a particular direction, is the ratio between the strain in that direction and the strain in the direction parallel to the applied stress.

Stress/strain curve—the graphical representation between the applied stress on a body and the resulting strain.

Elastic region—that region of the stress/strain curve where the strain returns to zero on removal of the applied stress.

Elastic modulus or *Young's modulus*—the measure of resistance to deformation. It is usually obtained from the gradient of the elastic region of the stress/strain curve.

Strain energy—that energy which is stored within a body when it is distorted by stress. If the body distorts elastically then the strain energy is recoverable and is termed elastic strain energy.

Creep—the progressive deformation of a material with time when the applied stress is constant. (Cartilage displays creep.)

Creep curve—graphical representation of the increase in deformation with time for a constant stress.

Creep modulus—the elastic modulus calculated at a particular point on the creep curve.

Viscoelastic material—the term applied to a material which displays the physical characteristics of both a fluid and a solid. (Cartilage is an example.)

Compliance—for a linear viscoelastic material, the strain per unit of stress.

2.2. Units

The Système International (SI) system of units is used, in which:

Force is expressed in newtons (N).

Length is expressed in metres (m).

Stress is expressed in newtons per square metre (N/m^2).

Creep modulus is expressed in newtons per square metre (N/m^2).

The following multiples of the above units are also used:

10^{-6} is expressed by the prefix 'micro', for which the symbol is μ.

10^{-3} is expressed by the prefix 'milli', for which the symbol is 'm'.

10^3 is expressed by the prefix 'kilo', for which the symbol is 'k'. (Thus 1 kN is 1000 newtons or 1 kilo-newton)

10^6 is expressed by the prefix 'mega', for which the symbol is 'M'.

Other unit systems: the following relationships may be useful:

1 lbf = 4.448 N

1 kgf = 9.807 N

1 lbf/in^2 = 6895 N/m^2 or 6.895 kN/m^2

1 kgf/cm^2 = 0.09807 MN/m^2

2.3. General Engineering Considerations

When examining the mechanical properties of a material, an engineer attempts to perform tests which reveal fundamental behaviour patterns and which yield information in the form of useful mechanical constants. Examples would be uniaxial tension and compression tests, torsion and creep tests. It is important that the information obtained should enable the engineer to assess the suitability of the material in different applications. In the case of articular cartilage the functions of the tissue are already specified by natural methods and it must be the objective of the engineer to determine the stresses which cartilage is likely to experience *in vivo* and to test the tissue in accordance with his conclusions. From the results of the tests the relevant fundamental mechanical properties of cartilage will be determined. Such tests may also reveal the differences in the mechanical properties of normal and degenerate cartilage and thereby indicate the extent to which a particular function may be impaired. The results of such studies are described in this Chapter.

3. STATIC MECHANICAL PROPERTIES OF CARTILAGE IN COMPRESSION

3.1. Compression versus Time under Load

A convenient method for determining the response of cartilage to a compressive force is by use of the indentation test, in which the response of cartilage to a loaded indenter is measured while the tissue remains intact on the joint surface.

335

The earliest recorded indentation tests on cartilage were those of Bär (1926) and Göcke (1927), in which both authors used a modified form of an apparatus which was originally designed by Schäde (1912). Some typical indentation versus time curves for cartilage obtained by Göcke are shown in Figure 6.1. It can be seen that when a constant load was applied suddenly to the

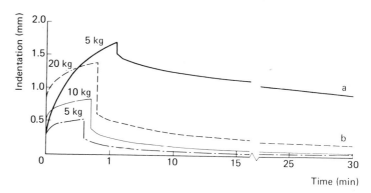

Figure 6.1 Indentation/time curves for human knee joint cartilage (Göcke 1927)

cartilage surface via an indenter the tissue deformed almost instantaneously, after which the indentation increased with further lapse of time after load application. This time-dependent part of the indentation curve is usually termed 'creep', and in the case of cartilage the rate of creep gradually decreased with increasing time. When the load was removed, cartilage displayed an 'instantaneous' recovery followed by a time-dependent recovery which was usually incomplete.

The corresponding indentation/time curves of Bär, which are not shown here, displayed a step-wise progression, thereby revealing a serious problem encountered in such tests on cartilage where the indentations are small and they occur slowly, namely that of dry friction in the moving parts of the indentation apparatus.

The recovery phase of the curves of Bär, like those of Göcke, were also incomplete because both authors performed their tests in air. Under this condition the cartilage surface dries so that the tissue can not imbibe sufficient water in the recovery phase to allow complete recovery. Both authors used the final residual indentation as a measure of the elasticity of cartilage, which they then used (erroneously) to judge whether the tissue was normal or degenerate.

Interest in the use of the indentation technique to determine the pathological state of cartilage was revived when Hirsch (1944) used it to study the condition known as 'chondromalacia patella'. Hirsch refined the apparatus used in the early tests and attempted to correlate the results of his mechanical tests with the histological appearance of cartilage and, to a limited extent, with the chemical composition of the tissue. It was shown that the magnitude of the indentation varied with position on the patellar surface and that indentations on areas of fibrillated cartilage were much larger than those on visually normal areas. Areas of fibrillated cartilage also possessed a lower content of 'chondroitin sulphuric acid' (chondroitin sulphate) than apparently normal tissue. Unfortunately Hirsch, like Bär and Göcke, also performed his tests in air, which casts some doubt on the validity of some of his measurements.

The incomplete recovery of cartilage after removal of the load was later investigated by Elmore, Sokoloff, Norris and Carmeci (1963). These authors argued that, if the early hypothesis of Benninghoff (1924, 1925a, b, 1939) was correct—namely, that the response to, and recovery from, a compressive force is largely governed by the expression and subsequent imbibition of interstitial water—then cartilage should recover completely after removal of the applied force by imbibing the surrounding fluid, provided that it is immersed in physiological saline during the test procedure.

Using a more rigorously designed apparatus, in which dry friction was considerably reduced compared to previous techniques, the authors performed indentation tests on human and animal patellar cartilage which was immersed in Hank's isotonic saline.

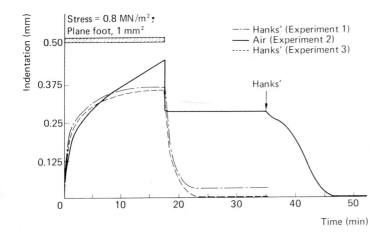

Figure 6.2 Indentation/time curves for cartilage from calf patellae. Plane-ended, cylindrical indenter, 1 mm^2 cross-sectional area. Applied stress = 0.8 MN/m^2 (1.17 × 10^2 lbf/in^2). (Elmore et al. 1963.)

Typical curves of indentation versus time obtained by Elmore et al. are shown in Figure 6.2. Recovery of the indentation produced by a nominal contact stress of 0.8 MN/m^2 (1.17 × 10^2 lbf/in^2) applied for approximately 20 min was usually complete, provided that sufficient time was allowed after removal of the applied load. It should be noted that the stress of 0.8 MN/m^2 (1.17 × 10^2 lbf/in^2) used by Elmore et al. is at the lower end of the range of physiological stresses which have been measured or calculated by other workers for human joints and that a permanent residual deformation, if it were to occur at all *in vivo*, is most likely to occur at the upper end of the stress range. However, for the stresses applicable to their tests, the results of Elmore *et al.* tended to support the earlier hypothesis of Benninghoff concerning the rôle of water transport in the response of cartilage to an applied force.

In the same investigation it was also shown that large regional variations in the magnitude of the indentations occurred on the patella. However, no systematic topographical variation of indentation between patellae from different knee joints was reported.

Changes in the pH level of the surrounding saline solution between 3.5 and 8.3 pH units had an insignificant effect on the depth of the indentation, as did a variation in temperature between 13 and 50°C. It was also found that the mechanical properties of cartilage were not altered by deep freezing it at −70°C for a period of 48 h.

Sokoloff (1966) investigated the relationship between the magnitude of indentations on the human patella and the age of the individual from whom the patella was obtained. Using the same apparatus as that of Elmore *et al.* (1963), he was unable to demonstrate any systematic correlation between the depth of indentation and the age of the specimen. Indentations were shown to vary considerably with the location of the test site but, like the earlier studies of Hirsch and Elmore *et al.*, Sokoloff was unable to demonstrate any systematic topographical variation of indentation over the patellar surface.

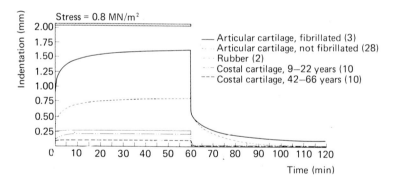

Figure 6.3 Indentation/time curves for cartilage and rubber. Plane-ended, cylindrical indenter, 1 mm² cross-sectional area. Applied stress = 0.8 MN/m² (1.17 × 10² lbf/in²). (Sokoloff 1966.)

Typical indentation/time curves produced by Sokoloff (1966) are shown in Figure 6.3. It was shown that, with increasing time under a constant nominal applied stress of approximately 0.8 MN/m² (1.17 × 10² lbf/in²) the indentation of cartilage tended towards a final equilibrium value. This value was reached within approximately 1 h of load application. At this time the creep part of the curve accounted for some 68% of the total indentation, the

338

remainder being the 'instantaneous' elastic indentation which occurred immediately after the load was applied. After removal of the load the cartilage recovered to its original thickness after a further period of 1 h. The recovery was usually complete to within ± 2% of the equilibrium indentation. There was no significant correlation between either the rate of recovery or the final extent of recovery and the age of the specimen. As Figure 6.3 shows, the depth of indentation in fibrillated cartilage was considerably greater than that in visually normal tissue.

Much important information has been gained from the investigations which have been described so far. However, several questions remained unanswered. First, could a reliable measurement of the resistance of cartilage to compression, independent of the geometry, be obtained from indentation tests? Secondly, did this quantity vary in a systematic manner over a joint surface which was known to be commonly affected by osteoarthrosis? Thirdly, could such measurements reveal degenerative changes in the cartilage which were not apparent to the naked eye? Finally, how did the mechanical measurements correlate with the chemical composition of cartilage?

In an attempt to answer these questions, as they related to the human hip joint, several investigations were performed by Kempson and colleagues (Kempson 1970; Kempson *et al.* 1970, 1971; Kempson, Freeman and Swanson 1971). The apparatus which was used is shown diagrammatically in Figure 6.4. It differed from previous designs in having a lubricated vertical sliding bearing so

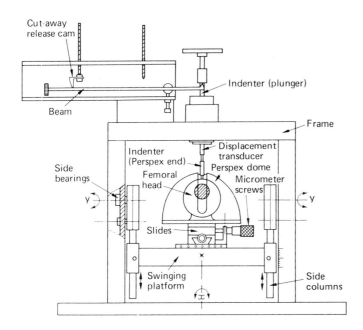

Figure 6.4 Diagram of apparatus used for performing indentation tests on cartilage *in situ* on the human femoral head. (Kempson, Freeman and Swanson 1971.)

that the indenter moved essentially without dry friction. Multiple controls enabled the femoral head to be positioned in 81 positions in which the axis of the indenter was perpendicular to the cartilage surface, although in practice only 30–40 areas were indented on each joint surface because of the rate of autolytic degradation of cartilage under these conditions. The femoral head was immersed in normal Ringer's saline solution at pH 7 and 37°C during the test procedure. Full details of the apparatus and the experimental procedure have been reported in the literature (Kempson *et al.* 1971).

Sixteen femoral heads were tested. Of these, ten were indented using a plane-ended cylindrical indenter 3.18 mm in diameter and six were indented using a hemispherically ended, cylindrical indenter, also 3.18 mm in diameter. The applied force was 8.9 N (2 lbf) in both cases which yielded a nominal compressive contact stress under the plane-ended indenter of 2.76 MN/m^2 (4×10^2 lbf/in^2) well within the physiological stress range. The results obtained from both indenters were compared and shown to be consistent.

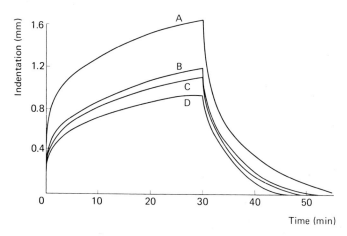

Figure 6.5 Indentation/time curves for four areas of cartilage on the human femoral head. Male aged 68 y, plane-ended, cylindrical indenter, 3.18 mm diameter. Applied force = 22.2 N (5 lbf). The cartilage was immersed in normal Ringer's solution at 37°C and pH 7. (Kempson, Freeman and Swanson 1971.)

Figure 6.5 shows some typical indentation/time curves. The main characteristics are consistent with the results of earlier studies already described. Using a low-inertia recording system which consisted of a linear displacement transducer coupled to an oscillator/amplifier and thence to an ultraviolet light spot recorder, it was observed that the 'instantaneous' elastic indentation of cartilage occurred within 10–20 ms after the load was applied. The final equilibrium indentation, which terminated the creep phase of the response curve, was not reached until 2–3 h after application of the load. However, the increase in indentation which occurred between 30 min after load application and true equilibrium usually constituted less than 10% of the final indentation, and therefore, for practical purposes, the indentation at 30 min could be taken to be the equilibrium value. When the load was removed there was an 'instantaneous' elastic recovery of the indentation followed by a time-dependent phase until the cartilage regained its original thickness, which usually occurred 30 min after removal of the load.

3.2. Constitutive Equations for Articular Cartilage

The response of cartilage to a constant compressive force, as shown in Figures 6.1 to 6.3 and 6.5, is characteristic of a group of materials which are termed viscoelastic. Natural rubber and many polymers fall within this classification. Their behaviour is more complex than that of metals because they display both elastic and time-dependent properties. To promote their understanding of the mechanical properties of such materials engineers frequently construct analogues which comprise idealized elements such as friction elements, springs and viscous dashpots. Each element is assumed to have a known and specified response to a given mechanical disturbance and different combinations of the elements yield a behaviour pattern which can be matched, more or less exactly, to the observed behaviour of the material under examination. The resulting mathematical relations between stress and strain for the analogue are usually termed the viscoelastic constitutive relations for the material.

Articular cartilage is a particularly complex viscoelastic material because the flux of the interstitial water superimposes an additional viscous characteristic. Some attempts have been made, however, to formulate an analogue for cartilage. Fantuzzo and Graziatti (1967) suggested that one Maxwell element and one Voigt element in series was a good approximation to the behaviour of cartilage. Coletti, Akeson and Woo (1972) suggested that a spring and Voigt element in series represented cartilage sufficiently closely for it to be a useful working model. They formulated the following equation to represent the time-dependent, or creep, behaviour of cartilage:

$$ e = \frac{F}{E_1} + \frac{F}{E_2} \left[1 - \exp\left(- \frac{\bar{E}_2}{\bar{N}_2} \cdot t \right) \right] \qquad (1) $$

where
$\quad e$ = creep strain,
$\quad F$ = applied force,
E_1 and E_2 = stiffness of the springs in the two elements, respectively,
$\quad \bar{E}_2$ = the product of the spring stiffness and the resting thickness of cartilage for the Voigt element,

$\bar{N}_2$ = the product of the viscous modulus of the dashpot and the resting thickness of cartilage for the Voigt element.

The most rigorous formulation of the constitutive equations for cartilage was performed by Hayes (1970) who modelled the tissue with a generalized Kelvin solid consisting of one spring element and a finite number of parallel spring and dashpot elements all connected in series. Such a model yields an analytical expression of the form.

$$F(t) = F_o + \sum_{i=1}^{K} F_i [1 - \exp(- \lambda_i \cdot t)] \qquad (2)$$

where $F(t)$ =   the creep compliance of the material at time t after application of the applied force,

$F_o = 1/E_o$ where E_o is the elastic modulus of the initial spring element,

$F_i = 1/E_i$ where E_i is the elastic modulus for the spring element of the ith parallel-connected spring and dashpot,

$\lambda_i = E_i/\eta_i$ where η_i is the viscous modulus of the ith element.

$$F_{\infty} = F_o + \sum_{i=1}^{K} F_i$$

The retardation constants λ_i determine the rate of approach to the final equilibrium value of compliance. Numerical techniques were used to fit the exponential series of equation (2).

Two independent creep tests were performed on cartilage by Hayes to determine the creep compliance in shear and dilatation. In the first test a small cylinder of cartilage was bonded securely to flat parallel surfaces at each end. One end was fixed whilst a constant torque, or twisting moment, was applied at the other end. The resulting creep in torsion was then recorded as a function of time and used to obtain the shear creep compliance of cartilage. In the other test a full-thickness cylinder of cartilage was bonded to a rigid base and restricted in the radial direction by a rigid cylindrical container, whilst a uniform pressure was applied to the upper surface by a movable plunger. In this way the dilatational creep compliance was measured. Thus, experimental data were obtained which were used in conjunction with equation (2) to determine the form of the exponential series, or in other words to determine how many elements were necessary in the analogue to obtain an acceptable fit to the observed behaviour.

The information obtained from equation (2) applies only to the test conditions which are specified, in this case simple shear and dilatation, in which the stresses are carefully controlled. It does not apply automatically to indentation tests on cartilage where the stress conditions are more complex. Furthermore, it is not usually possible to identify components of the real material with discrete elements within the analogue. In other words, the analogue is a phenomenological representation of the real material. Progression from simple tests to a description of the indentation behaviour of cartilage and the relationship between variations in the indentation response and differences in the chemical composition of cartilage required further study.

3.3. The Equation of an Indentation versus Time Curve

The potential usefulness of an equation which describes the indentation/time curve for cartilage is that it might yield a simple method for determining the physical state of the tissue. A precise but complex mathematical analysis of the indentation response of cartilage which correlates the observed experimental response with that predicted from constitutive relationships, whilst being highly desirable, may require certain assumptions to be made. For example, it may be necessary to assume that cartilage displays elastic or linear viscoelastic behaviour which may only be valid, if at all, for a part of the total response of the normal tissue. Degenerate tissue is physically and chemically different from normal cartilage so that, even if the degeneration is only slight, assumptions made for normal cartilage may no longer be valid for the degenerate tissue.

Kempson (1970) chose to fit his indentation/time curves by a simple polynomial expression without recourse to constitutive equations. Curves such as those shown in Figure 6.5 were plotted logarithmically, as shown in Figure 6.6. In addition, two logarithmic curves for indentation data presented by Sokoloff (1966) are shown in Figure 6.7. All the logarithmic plots displayed good linearity in the time range from 2 s to 30 min after load application.

A simple linear relationship of kind shown in Figures 6.6 and 6.7 yields the following expression:

$$\log_{10} Y = \log_{10} k + n \log_{10} t \qquad (3)$$

where $\quad y$ = depth of indentation,
$\quad t$ = time after application of the force,
k and n = constants.

Equation (3) can then be rewritten as:

$$y = kt^n \qquad (4)$$

343

Equation (4) was found to fit indentation/time curves produced by Kempson using both shapes of indenter and curves produced by Sokoloff (1966).

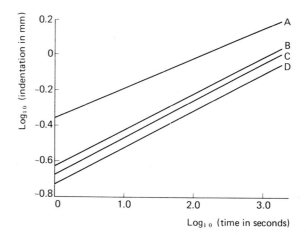

Figure 6.6 Logarithmic plots of indentation/time curves shown in Figure 6.5. (Kempson, Freeman and Swanson 1971.)

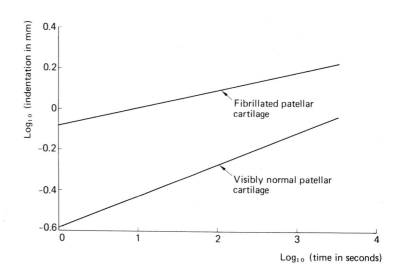

Figure 6.7 Logarithmic plots of indentation/time curves for cartilage as shown in Figure 6.3.

The value of the constant k was found to vary between 0.44 and 0.66 for visually normal cartilage on the human femoral head. The value of k for visually normal patellar cartilage was found to be within the range of values for normal femoral head tissue but for fibrillated patellar cartilage the value was 0.79.

The value of n in equations (3) and (4) may be determined from the gradient of the straight lines in the logarithmic plots. For normal femoral head cartilage n was found to vary between 0.15 and 0.21, the higher value corresponding to a greater depth of indentation or softer cartilage. The value of n for visually normal patellar cartilage, as tested by Sokoloff, was 0.15 which is within the range for femoral head cartilage, but the value for fibrillated patellar cartilage was 0.06 which is lower than that of the tissue.

These results suggest that the values of k and n in equation (4) might be used as simple indicators of the pathological condition of cartilage. Hayes (1970) and Hayes *et al.* (1972), on the other hand, performed a rigorous mathematical analysis of indentation tests on cartilage, treating the tissue as an elastic material.

Referring to the earlier work of Lebedev and Ufliand (1958), Hayes formulated a general equation for the total applied force applied by an indenter over an infinite elastic layer resting on an immovable rigid half space. The form of this equation was:

$$P = 2\pi \int_o^a \varphi(t)\mathrm{d}k \tag{5}$$

where P = total applied force,
a = area of the contact zone,
$\varphi(t)$ = auxiliary function derived in the analysis.

The boundary conditions relating specifically to a plane-ended cylindrical indenter and to a spherical indenter were then invoked to produce two separate expressions for each shape of indenter.

For the plane-ended indenter the expression was:

$$K = \frac{P(1-v)}{4aG\omega_0} = \int_0^1 \omega_1(\tau)\mathrm{d}\tau \tag{6}$$

Numerical values for $\omega_1(\tau)$ allowed computation of K for given values of the ratio a/h (the ratio of the contact area to the thickness of the elastic layer) and v, the Poisson ratio for the material. The values of K were used to calculate relationships between the load, P, and the indenter displacement, ω_0, for an indenter of radius a on a layer of thickness h, elastic shear modulus G and Poisson's ratio v.

For the spherical indenter two expressions were formulated:

$$X = \frac{a^2}{\omega_0 R} = \frac{-\omega_1(1)}{\omega_2(1)} \tag{7}$$

and

$$K = \frac{P(1-v)}{4aG\omega_0}\int_0^1 \omega(\tau)\mathrm{d}\tau \tag{8}$$

Values of X and K were computed for a range of values of a/h and these values were then used to calculate the relationships between P and ω_0, as before. The authors stated that their analysis was restricted to small strains in addition to the other assumptions which they had to make. It is likely, nevertheless, that their analysis would be representative of the mechanics of load carriage in cartilage during normal walking, in which the compressive strain in the cartilage is likely to be only 10% of the thickness or less, according to dynamic experiments on the human hip joint.

3.4. Calculation of the Resistance of Cartilage to Deformation

3.4.1. Indentation Tests. It has already been emphasized in an earlier section of this Chapter that, by using simple mechanical tests, engineers are able to specify the mechanical properties of a material, in the form of Young's modulus, or elastic modulus, in either tension or compression or in the form of the elastic shear modulus or the bulk dilatation modulus. The values obtained, which are independent of the dimensions of the specimens, would reflect the physical state of the material. Such knowledge would be useful for a determination of the pathological condition of articular cartilage. However, as has already been pointed out, cartilage is a more complex material than a metal, possessing viscous as well as elastic properties. The moduli listed above are therefore not single-valued for cartilage. In addition, the maximum thickness of cartilage in human joints is only approximately 5 mm and tests on such thin sheets of material are complicated by the restrictive effects of the boundaries. Finally, it is very convenient to test cartilage using an indentation technique but such a technique, unlike the standard tests, produces a complex stress pattern within the material, which further complicates the analysis to determine its mechanical properties.

It is important to emphasize at this stage that indentation values alone are not a reliable measurement of the mechanical properties of cartilage. The reason for this is that the depth of indentation is influenced not only by the properties of the material but also by the restriction of the boundaries. The thinner is the sheet of cartilage the greater is the restriction of the boundaries and the greater is the effect on the depth of the indentation. Since the thickness of cartilage varies considerably over any one joint surface it would be expected that, other things being equal, the depth of indentation would also vary topographically. Thus, to interpret variations in the depth of indentation alone as a measure of the relative material properties of different areas would be erroneous.

It is also not valid to divide the nominal contact stress under an indenter by the strain which it produces to determine the Young's modulus of cartilage. Such a calculation assumes a uniform state of stress and strain in the material and this does not exist under an indenter in thin sheets of material such as articular cartilage.

The first attempt to calculate the Young's modulus for cartilage from indentation tests was made by Hirsch (1944). By assuming that cartilage was linearly elastic (stress is linearly proportional to strain) and that the solution of Hertz (1881, 1895, 1896) to the problem of contact between elastic bodies was valid for cartilage-to-cartilage contact in synovial joints, Hirsch calculated relative values of Young's modulus for cartilage.

The Young's modulus which corresponded to the minimum indentation force in his tests was considered to be unity and all other values at higher forces were expressed as a ratio of it. Within the limitations which have been described in this Chapter, Hirsch found that the Young's modulus increased as the applied force was increased, but he did not record any absolute values for the modulus.

Sokoloff (1966) pointed out that a Young's modulus for cartilage, when calculated from an indentation test, depended on the geometry of the indenter. Using a plane ended cylindrical indenter, as described earlier in this Chapter, Sokoloff obtained the following expression for the Young's modulus of patellar cartilage from measurements of the 'instantaneous' depth of the indentation:

$$E = \frac{F}{2.67\, P \cdot R} \qquad (9)$$

where E = Young's modulus of cartilage,
F = applied force,
P = depth of the 'instantaneous' indentation,
R = radius of indenter.

A typical value obtained by Sokoloff was $E = 2.28$ MN/m^2 (331 lbf/in^2).

Sokoloff pointed out two possible sources of inaccuracy in his measurements. First, he observed that the articular surface and the subchondral bone/cartilage interface were not always parallel and that when they were not, some of the resulting indentation could be attributed to shear deformation of the cartilage relative to the bone rather than to compression. The effect of this would be to increase the indentation and, therefore, to decrease the apparent value of Young's modulus. Secondly, the possibility that some autolytic degradation might have occurred in his specimens could not be excluded and this also would tend to make the cartilage appear softer than it really was. In summary, therefore, it is possible that the Young's modulus values calculated by Sokoloff were lower than they should have been.

Concerning the limited thickness of cartilage, Sokoloff argued that the cartilage on the patella is usually more than 2 mm thick, at which value the indentation produced by the low stress of 0.8 MN/m^2 (1.17×10^2 lbf/in^2) would not be significantly restricted by the boundary constraints. This argument, however, is not valid for the hip or knee joints where the cartilage is frequently less than 2 mm in thickness. The validity of the statement also decreases as the applied stress, and hence the indentation, increases.

The rigorous analysis of indentation tests on cartilage performed by Hayes (1970) and Hayes *et al.* (1972), allowed the shear modulus (G) for cartilage to be calculated. Values so obtained could be checked against the results obtained from the torsion tests which were performed independently (Hayes 1970; Hayes and Mockross 1971). In this way the authors could check the validity of their derived expression for the indentation tests on cartilage. Only two values for G were quoted by these workers:

$G = 4.1$ MN/m^2 (595 lb/in^2) for healthy cartilage, and

$G = 0.58$ MN/m^2 (84 lb/in^2) for 'somewhat degenerated' cartilage.

The authors do not appear to have extended their work to obtain a range of values of G for cartilage from different sites in one joint or to compare values between different joints.

More recently, Hori and Mockros (1976) have used the theoretical analysis of indentation tests formulated by Hayes *et al.* (1972) to calculate values of the short-term shear and dilatation moduli for both articular cartilage and polyurethane rubber. The calculated values were then compared to values which were obtained from torsional shear tests and confined uniaxial compression tests respectively as used by Hayes *et al.* (1972). It was found that good agreement between the two sets of values was obtained for polyurethane rubber but the agreement for cartilage was only moderate and variable. The authors did not present absolute values of the shear and dilatation moduli calculated from indentation tests but instead they presented the correlation coefficients which were found to exist between the values predicted from indentation tests and those measured directly from shear and dilatation tests. For human articular cartilage these correlation coefficients ranged between 0.522 and 0.914 with levels of significance between $p < 0.01$ and $p < 0.001$.

Kempson and colleagues (Kempson, Freeman and Swanson 1971; Kempson *et al.* 1971) calculated the resistance of cartilage to indentation in the form of a creep modulus, the derivation of which was based on indentation studies of thin sheets of natural rubber by Waters (1965a, b). The resulting expressions took into account the limited and variable thickness of cartilage on the human femoral head.

Because of the time-dependent behaviour of cartilage, indentations were compared at the common time of 2 s after application of the applied load. This time was selected for three reasons. First, the curves of indentation versus time were fully developed after 2 s up to at least 30 min after load application, as indicated in Figure 6.6. That is to say that, with the technique used by the authors, the indentation of cartilage at times shorter than 2 s showed a transient, unsteady response but after that time the indentation assumed a non-fluctuating, increasing value. Secondly, at the time of 2 s after load application approximately 90% of the indentation was 'instantaneously' recoverable, so that it could be considered to be elastic and reversible. The importance of this was clarified in the derivation of the expression for the creep modulus. Finally, it was considered desirable to compare indentations at a time which was physiologically significant. The results of Contini, Gage and Drillis (1965), Paul (1965), Rydell (1965) and Murray, Gore and Clarkson (1971) all show that the duration of the applied load during the walking cycle is between 0.5 and 1 s following heel-strike. Peak loads are applied for less than 0.5 s. In their indentation study, Kempson *et al.* concluded that 2 s was the shortest time, and therefore the closest to the physiological values recorded for normal walking, at which indentations could be reliably compared.

The expressions obtained by Kempson *et al.* for the creep modulus at 2 s after load application for cartilage on the human femoral head *in vitro* were:

$$E = \frac{5.37 \, \varphi \, (t/R)}{d_t} \quad \text{for the plane-ended cylindrical indenter} \quad (10)$$

and

$$E = 1.28 \left[\frac{1 - \exp(-0.42 \, t/a_t)}{d_t} \right]^{3/2} \quad \begin{array}{c} \text{for the hemispherically} \\ \text{ended} \\ \text{cylindrical indenter} \end{array} \quad (11)$$

where E = creep modulus at 2 s,
t = cartilage thickness at zero load,
a_t = radius of the area of contact between the indenter and the cartilage,
d_t = depth of indentation,
R = radius of the indenter,
$\varphi(t/R)$ = a function of the ratio between the cartilage thickness and the indenter radius as formulated by Waters (1965b).

Both expressions allowed the resistance of cartilage to indentation to be calculated in the form of a reliable creep modulus and they took into account the limited and variable thickness of the tissue.

It was shown, using equations (10) and (11), that the creep modulus for visually normal cartilage on the femoral head ranged between 1.9 and 14.4 MN/m^2 (278 and 2090 lb/in^2). The higher the creep modulus the greater was the resistance of the cartilage to indentation.

The lower value obtained by Kempson *et al.* is consistent with the results obtained by Sokoloff, but the upper value is considerably higher. This is perhaps not suprising in view of the comments made previously concerning Sokoloff's experimental conditions and the fact that Sokoloff and Kempson investigated different joint surfaces.

W. H. Simon (1971) concluded that the resistance of cartilage to compression could not be expressed in the form of a modulus, and he simply compared the depth of indentations between different areas. He did show, however, that the thickness of cartilage varies topographically over a joint surface.

More recently, Cameron, Pillar and MacNab (1975) also measured the variation of indentation of cartilage on the human femoral head. Their measurements were made in the directions both parallel to and perpendicular to the articular surface and at increasing depth below the articular surface. The cartilage surface was initially coated with a thin film of brittle lacquer and indentations were made with a diamond pyramid microhardness tester. The applied load (and therefore the resulting indentation) was small so that boundary restrictions were considered to be negligible. The depth of indentation was calculated from the dimensions of the splits produced in the brittle lacquer, knowing the geometry of the indenter. The resistance to indentation was expressed simply by the depth of indentation. The results of this investigation are described in Section 3.5.

3.4.2. Uniaxial Compression Tests. The inherent complexity involved in calculating a Young's modulus or creep modulus from indentation tests on cartilage has led some workers to perform simpler uniaxial compression tests instead.

McCutchen (1962) calculated the Young's modulus for cartilage from tests in which isolated cylinders of the tissue were compressed between porous glass plattens. A series of increasing loads was used and the compression of the cartilage was measured after the load had been applied for 30 min, that is, when the compression had effectively reached its 'equilibrium' value. Values of the Young's modulus for bovine 'leg joint' cartilage, calculated from the first 0.28 mm compression were:

$E = 0.58$ MN/m^2 (84 lb/in^2)   for water-soaked cartilage, and

$E = 0.32$ MN/m^2 (46.4 lb/in^2)   for cartilage soaked in physiological saline.

The Young's modulus calculated from the compression which occurred immediately after the load had been applied was:

$$E = 11.1 \text{ MN/m}^2 \ (1610 \text{ lb/in}^2)$$

From his results, McCutchen concluded that the compressive stiffness of cartilage was largely dependent on the presence of interstitial water within the matrix.

350

In the tests conducted by McCutchen the load which corresponded to the compression of 0.28 mm, at which measurements of the Young's modulus were made, was approximately 4.5 N (1 lbf) and the area of contact between the glass plattens and the specimen was 23.3 mm². These values yield a nominal compressive contact stress of 0.21 MN/m² (30 lbf/in²), which appears to be lower than the physiological range of stresses encountered in the hip joint, for example. At stresses which approached those within the physiological range, it was observed that the load/compression curves were markedly non-linear, indicating that the Young's modulus increased as the applied stress increased. It is likely that at least part of the non-linearity at higher stresses could be attributed to the restrictive effects of the boundaries.

Hayes (1970), as has been described previously, performed a dilatational compression test on small cylinders of cartilage. By using this technique the bulk creep compliance of the tissue was determined. Values are quoted for both an impervious and a pervious load platten and they range between 0.012 m²/MN and 0.044 m²/MN for normal cartilage and between 0.12 m²/MN and 0.6 m²/MN for degenerate cartilage. Values obtained with the impervious platten tended to be generally slightly lower than those obtained with the pervious platten, as would be expected in cartilage where water efflux accounts for a large part of the creep behaviour.

It was stated earlier in this Chapter that Hori and Mockros (1976) used the simple shear and confined compression dilatation tests suggested by Hayes *et al.* (1972) to determine the short-term shear and dilatation moduli for human articular cartilage. These authors found that the shear modulus values ranged between 1.66 and 3.47 MN/m² (241 and 503 lbf/in²) for normal cartilage and between 0.46 and 3.29 MN/m² (66.7 and 477 lbf/in²) for degenerate cartilage. The corresponding values for the bulk dilatation modulus ranged between 24.9 and 71.4 MN/m² (3610 and 10 353 lbf/in²) for normal cartilage and between 9.46 and 167.3 MN/m² (1372 and 24 259 lbf/in²) for degenerate cartilage.

Uniaxial compression tests were also performed by Johnson, Dowson and Wright (1975) in which small cylinders of cartilage were subjected to a sinusoidally varying compressive stress at a frequency of 1 Hz superimposed on a static preload. It was shown that the amplitude of the sine wave decreased as the creep strain increased. A value for the elastic modulus of cartilage was calculated in the form

$$E = \frac{\text{sinusoidal stress amplitude}}{\text{sinusoidal strain amplitude}}$$

The results showed that the elastic modulus in uniaxial compression increased with increasing creep strain from 12 to 45 MN/m²

(1740 to 6525 lbf/in²) at 0.6 creep strain. Comparison of results between tests conducted in Ringer's saline and synovial fluid revealed little effect on the elastic modulus. A variation in frequency from 0.8 to 2.5 Hz also had little effect.

Uniaxial compression tests have also been used by Kempson (1975 and 1976 unpublished data) to calculate the Young's modulus for cartilage. The method sought to avoid measuring the absolute thickness of cartilage, which can vary considerably within even small areas of the joint surface. Isolated, full-thickness cylinders of cartilage were serially sectioned parallel to the articular surface so that the thickness decreased by predetermined amounts. At each value of thickness a uniaxial compression test was performed on the specimen.

Initially it was shown that, provided the compressive strain is 6% or less, the variation of strain with stress is linear when the stress is applied suddenly and the strain is measured at 0.2 s after load application. Under these conditions the relationship between stress and strain may be written as:

$$\sigma = E \cdot e \tag{12}$$

where σ = applied compressive contact stress,
  E = Young's, or elastic, modulus in compression,
  e = compressive strain.

If a compressive stress, σ, is applied to a cylinder of cartilage of thickness, t_1, then for uniaxial and uniform compressive strain:

$$\sigma = E_1 \cdot \frac{\delta_1}{t_1} \tag{13}$$

where δ_1 = resulting compressive deformation.

Equation (13) can be rewritten as:

$$t_1 = E_1 \cdot \frac{\delta_1}{\sigma} \tag{14}$$

When the cartilage thickness is reduced to a new value of t_2 and the test is repeated at the same stress, a similar expression may be written as:

$$t_2 = E_2 \cdot \frac{\delta_2}{\sigma} \tag{15}$$

But if the cartilage is linearly elastic then $E_1 = E_2 = E$, and equations (14) and (15) can be combined to give the difference equation:

$$t_1 - t_2 = \frac{E}{\sigma}(\delta_1 - \delta_2) \tag{16}$$

or, using the difference operator Δ,

$$\Delta t = \frac{E}{\sigma} \cdot \Delta\delta \tag{17}$$

Since the difference in thickness is known accurately from the amount of cartilage removed and the difference between the compressive deformations is also known then, since σ is a known constant, E can be determined.

The method was verified for specimens of natural rubber using indentation tests to obtain independent values for E. Agreement between the two techniques was acceptable.

Results obtained to date for the Young's modulus of human cartilage using the above technique range between $E = 8.4 \, \text{MN/m}^2$ (1218 lbf/in^2) and $E = 15.3 \, \text{MN/m}^2$ (2219 lbf/in^2) for tissue from both the tibial and femoral condyles of the knee joint and from the acetabulum and the femoral head of the hip joints. The value for the femoral head was $11.5 \, \text{MN/m}^2$ (1668 lbf/in^2) which is within the range obtained by indentation tests.

The advantages of the uniaxial compression test are: first, the ease of interpretation; secondly, the absolute value of the cartilage thickness need not be known; and finally, it serves as an independent method for calculating the Young's modulus of cartilage in compression with which the results of indentation tests can be compared.

3.5. The Topographical Variation of the Resistance of Cartilage to Indentation

Two systematic investigations of the topographical variation of the resistance of articular cartilage to indentation have been recorded: namely, those of Kempson *et al.* (1971) and Cameron *et al.* (1975). Both of these studies were made on the human femoral head *in vitro*. Previously the largest number of areas studied on any one joint surface was eight on the human patella. This study was performed by Sokoloff (1966), who was unable to demonstrate any systematic pattern of variation of indentation.

Kempson *et al.* used equations (10) and (11), given in Section 3.4.1., to calculate the creep modulus of cartilage at 2 s after application of the load. Between 30 and 40 areas of cartilage were tested on each of 16 femoral heads from hip joints within the age range 19–82 years. Of these, 10 femoral heads were tested using the plane-ended cylindrical indenter and 6 were tested using the hemispherically ended cylindrical indenter. In both groups the diameter of the indenter was 3.18 mm.

The total range of creep modulus values for all the tested areas in each of the two groups of femoral heads was subdivided into four smaller ranges (shown in Figures 6.8 and 6.9 for the plane-ended indenter and the hemispherically ended indenter, respectively) and the value of the creep modulus for each tested area was allocated to its appropriate range. To display the results, a

Figure 6.8 Two-dimensional layered maps of ten right femoral heads, viewed from the fovea along the neck of the femur, showing the topographical variation of the 2 s creep modulus. Series 1: Plane-ended, cylindrical indenter, 3.18 mm diameter. Applied force = 22.2 N (5 lbf). The femoral heads were immersed in normal Ringer's solution at 37°C and pH 7. Each femoral head was graded according to the severity of areas of overt cartilage degeneration: N = normal; Grade 1 = matt surface texture; Grade 2 = fibrillation and partial thickness tissue loss; Grade 3 = ulceration with full-thickness tissue loss. (Kempson *et al.* 1971.)

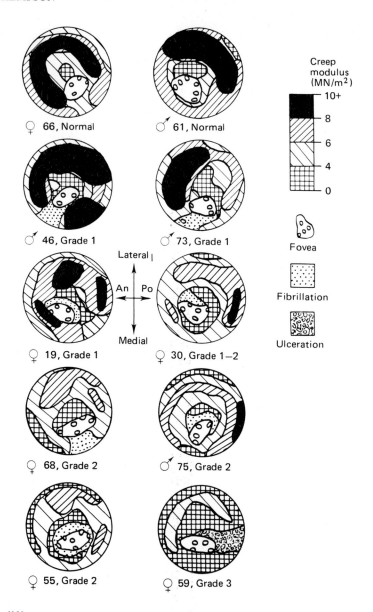

different shading was used to denote each range and areas with the same shading were joined to produce two-dimensional layered maps of the variation in creep modulus over the femoral head. In addition, histograms were constructed for every femoral head which showed the number of areas which fell within each of the ranges of value of creep modulus. The mean value of the creep modulus for each femoral head was also included in the histograms. Figures 6.8 and 6.9 show the two-dimensional layered maps

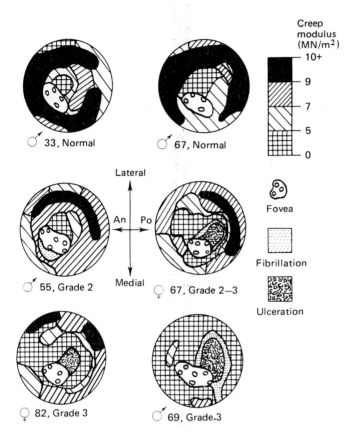

Creep modulus (MN/m²)

Fovea

Fibrillation

Ulceration

Lateral

An | Po

Medial

○ 33, Normal

♂ 67, Normal

♂ 55, Grade 2

♀ 67, Grade 2—3

♀ 82, Grade 3

♂ 69, Grade.3

Figure 6.9 Layered maps of the 2 s creep modulus corresponding to those shown in Figure 6.8, except in this series (Series 2) a hemispherically ended indenter, 3.18 mm diameter, was used with an applied force of 8.9 N (2 lbf).

of creep modulus for each group of femoral heads. All the values relate to cartilage which appeared normal to the naked eye. Areas of visibly degenerate cartilage were not tested but they are shown as appropriately shaded areas on the maps.

The results show that a considerable variation in the creep modulus of cartilage was recorded on all the femoral heads. The values ranged between 1.9 MN/m² (276 lbf/in²) for the softest cartilage up to 14.4 MN/m² (2090 lbf/in²) for the stiffest areas. Creep modulus values of cartilage in the maximum range were typically four times greater than those in the minimum range.

It was observed that the topographical variation of creep modulus over the femoral heads displayed a systematic pattern in which the area of maximum stiffness was located in a band, somewhat variable in shape and area, which extended from the posterior aspect to the anterior aspect of the femoral head via the superior surface. This band corresponded approximately to the cartilaginous area on the acetabulum and to the area of contact between the acetabulum and the femoral head as shown by

Greenwald (1970). The areas of cartilage of minimum stiffness were usually located in the inferofoveal region of the femoral head and at the articular margins, especially that of the fovea. It is interesting to note that, according to Byers, Contempomi and Farkas (1970), these are the areas on the femoral head which frequently show signs of cartilage degeneration which do not usually progress to clinical osteoarthrosis.

It was also found that the topographical variation of the depth of indentation over the femoral head displayed a similar pattern to that of the 2 s creep modulus.

From these results it is tempting to speculate that the compressive stiffness of cartilage on the femoral head is a maximum in the region where the greatest loads are imposed, namely on the superior surface. If this hypothesis were to be valid then the compressive strains in cartilage on the femoral head would tend towards a uniform value even though the stress distribution might be non-uniform. Thus shear strains arising from the difference in direct compressive strain between two adjacent areas would be minimized with possible benefits to the structure of cartilage.

Using a technique which has been described in Section 3.4.1, Cameron *et al.* (1975) confirmed that the topographical variation of indentation hardness of the cartilage on the human femoral head displayed a similar pattern to that described by Kempson *et al.* (1971).

In this study it was also shown that the indentation hardness of the cartilage, measured both perpendicular to and parallel to the articular surface, was a maximum in the superficial zone and that the hardness was approximately constant in the other regions of the tissue.

The indentation hardness, measured parallel to the articular surface, was found to be greater in the direction perpendicular to the local motion vector between the femoral head and acetabulum, as determined by Graham and Walker (1973), than parallel to it. This result was found to be valid at all depths from the cartilage surface to the calcified zone and it led the authors to conclude that, even in the deeper zones, cartilage possesses a structure with directional properties which is superimposed on the apparently random collagen fibre network. This conclusion is consistent with the observation of Clarke (1971) and with the results of tension tests on cartilage by Kempson and colleagues (Kempson, Freeman and Swanson 1968; Kempson 1972; Kempson *et al.* 1972), which are described in Section 4.3.

3.6. The Relationship between the Mechanical Properties in Compression and the Chemical Constituents of Cartilage

The mechanical properties of cartilage clearly depend on the interaction between the different constituents of the matrix and it is therefore important that the relative contributions made by each constituent should be determined.

The earliest recorded attempt to relate the depth of indentation to the chemical constituents of cartilage was made by Hirsch (1944), who found that the greater the depth of indentation the lower was the content of chondroitin sulphate in the tissue. He confirmed this observation qualitatively by examining the tissue histologically. Unfortunately, Hirsch did not express his results quantitatively and it is not possible, therefore, to determine the level of significance of the correlation.

A more recent attempt to correlate the results of indentation tests on cartilage with the results of chemical analyses was performed by Kempson *et al.* (1970). In this investigation areas of cartilage were indented on the human femoral head *in vitro* and the value of the creep modulus at 2 s was calculated for each area using the method described in Section 3.4. Each area of cartilage was then extracted from the femoral head using a trepanning technique and analysed chemically for its chondroitin sulphate, keratan sulphate and collagen contents respectively. The values of chondroitin sulphate and keratan sulphate content were then added to give the total glycosaminoglycan content of the tissue. The results are presented in Figures 6.10 and 6.11 in the form of graphs of creep modulus versus the total glycosaminoglycan and collagen contents respectively. The experimental points were fitted by the best straight line using the least squares analysis and the partial correlation coefficients for each set of results, together with the statistical significance, were calculated and are tabulated in Table 6.1.

Table 6.1 Partial correlations between the 2 s creep modulus and the chemical constituents of cartilage. (Kempson *et al.* 1970)

Creep modulus correlated with percentage dry weight of	Partial correlation coefficient	Level of significance
Total glycosaminoglycans	0.854	$p < 0.001$
Chondroitin sulphate	0.810	$p < 0.001$
Keratan sulphate	0.800	$p < 0.001$
Collagen	0.233	$p > 0.1$

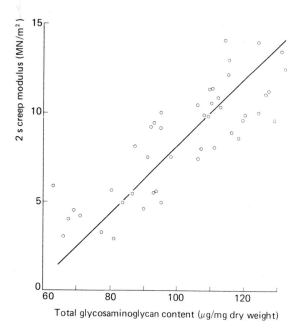

Figure 6.10 Creep modulus at 2 s versus total glycosamino-glycan content for cartilage on the human femoral head. (Author's material: Kempson *et al.* 1970.)

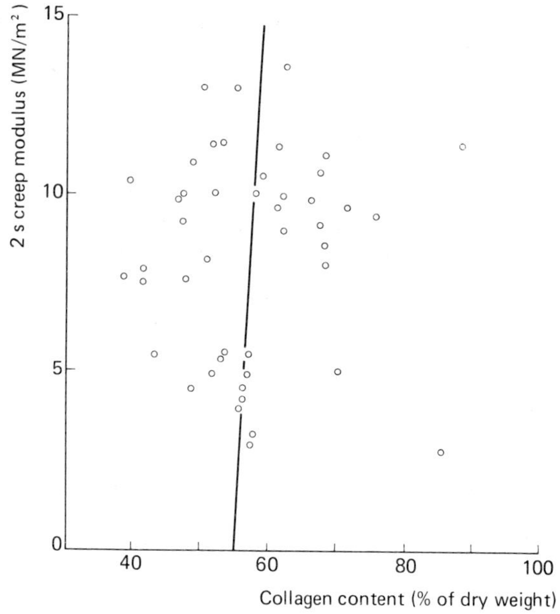

Figure 6.11 Creep modulus at 2 s versus collagen content on the human femoral head. (Author's material: Kempson *et al.* 1970.)

Figure 6.10 shows values of the 2 s creep modulus for cartilage from human femoral heads plotted against the variation in the total glycosaminoglycan content, expressed as a percentage of the dry weight of the tissue. The partial correlation coefficient, which is given in Table 6.1, was $r = 0.854$ with $p < 0.001$, which indicates that the degree of correlation between the two variables was statistically significant. As Table 6.1 also indicates, the correlation coefficients between the 2 s creep modulus and the two constituent glycosaminoglycans, chondroitin sulphate and keratan sulphate, were approximately equal and each value was only slightly less than that between the creep modulus and the total glycosaminoglycan content. It appears, therefore, that the compressive stiffness of cartilage depends to the same extent, approximately, on chondroitin sulphate and keratan sulphate.

Figure 6.11 shows the relationship between the 2 s creep modulus and the total collagen content of femoral head cartilage, from which it can be seen that the partial correlation coefficient, $r = 0.233$, was considerably less significant, $p > 0.10$, than that between the creep modulus and the glycosaminoglycan content.

The relationship between the compressive properties of cartilage and the glycosaminoglycan content was studied further by Kempson *et al.* (1972) by treating the tissue with enzymes which are known to degrade glycosaminoglycans.

The two enzymes which featured in the investigation were crystalline trypsin and purified bacterial chondroitinase. In the study of the effects of trypsin two full-thickness cylindrical specimens of cartilage were incubated for 48 h in the enzyme at 37°C and pH 7. The percentage release of glycosaminoglycan from the two specimens, measured by the uronic acid content, was 64% and 80% respectively with no detectable release of collagen in the form of soluble hydroxyproline. The compressive stiffness of the cartilage, as measured from a uniaxial compression test, was reduced by more than 50% in both specimens. Chondroitinase digestion released only 10–16% of the glycosaminoglycan from the tissue and resulted in a much smaller reduction in the compressive stiffness.

These results support the previous conclusion that the compressive stiffness of cartilage depends to a large extent on the glycosaminoglycan component of the matrix.

Results have also been obtained for the effects of the proteolytic enzymes cathepsins D and B on the mechanical properties of cartilage and these are reported in Section 4.9.

3.7. The Relationship between Compressive Stiffness and the Pathology of Cartilage

It has been suggested by Byers *et al.* (1970) that, when fibrillation of cartilage on the femoral head occurs in the region inferior to the fovea or at the articular margins it tends to be non-progressive, whereas fibrillation on the superior surface of the femoral head tends to progress to clinical osteoarthrosis. This observation raises the question: do the mechanical properties of cartilage, which appears normal to the naked eye but which is situated on a joint surface displaying areas of overt fibrillation, differ from the properties of the normal tissue on a normal joint surface?

In attempts to determine whether or not measurements of the mechanical properties of articular cartilage may be used as early indicators of the pathological condition of the tissue and whether or not such early changes are progressive, investigations have been performed to determine the relationship between the mechanical properties and the pathology of cartilage.

Hirsch (1944) used histological techniques to examine areas of patellar cartilage which had previously been subjected to indentation tests. It was found that, not only was fibrillated cartilage softer than normal, but also that a considerable loss of metachromatic staining by toluidine blue occurred in the matrix. Hirsch also showed that some areas, which appeared to be normal to the naked eye, displayed a lack of metachromatic staining in the superficial zone and that such areas were less stiff than normal. It appeared, therefore, that indentation measurements could reveal physical changes in the cartilage which were not evident to the naked eye. However, Hirsch did not perform a systematic study of the topographical variation of these changes.

Sokoloff (1966), using indentation tests and histological studies, also showed that fibrillated cartilage was considerably softer than the normal tissue and that Alcian-blue-reactive material was depleted in the matrix of the fibrillated tissue.

A systematic study of the relationship between the topographical variation of resistance to indentation and the pathology of the articular cartilage on the human femoral head was performed by Kempson *et al.* (1971).

The methods employed and the calculation of the resistance to indentation in the form of the 2 s creep modulus have already been described in this Chapter.

Before the indentation tests were performed, each femoral head was graded according to the severity of any areas of cartilage degeneration which were visible to the naked eye. The grading system used was a modified form of that developed by Byers *et al.* (1970) for the femoral head, which relies upon the naked-eye appearance of the cartilage surface. Using this system a femoral head which appeared normal to the naked eye was characterized by the letter N. Femoral heads on which the most severe degeneration appeared as only a slight roughening of the surface or as a matt appearance of the normally glossy surface, were designated as grade 1. Femoral heads on which the cartilage was visibly fibrillated with partial-thickness loss were classified as grade 2. Grade 3 femoral heads were those on which the most severe degeneration appeared as ulceration of the cartilage with full-thickness tissue loss, and those femoral heads which were taken from patients suffering from clinical osteoarthrosis were classified as grade 4.

The layered maps of Figures 6.8 and 6.9 showing the topographical variation of creep modulus over sixteen femoral heads (described in Section 3.5) also show the grade number for each femoral head and the location of the areas of cartilage degeneration. It can be seen in Figures 6.8 and 6.9 that, as the grade number of the femoral heads increases so the creep modulus values for the stiffest cartilage decreases. This is shown clearly in the two sets of layered maps by a gradual disappearance of the areas shaded black, which represents the maximum range of creep modulus, as the grade numbers of the femoral heads increases. In other words, the more severe the cartilage degeneration on a femoral head the softer was the apparently normal tissue.

This result is displayed in another way in the histograms of Figures 6.12 and 6.13. As the grade number of the femoral heads

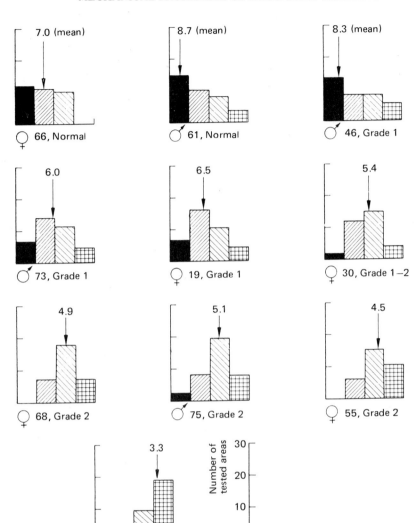

Figure 6.12 Histograms of the 2 s creep modulus, corresponding to the layered maps of Figure 6.8, which show the number of tested points which fell within each range of creep modulus and the mean creep modulus value for each femoral head. (Kempson *et al.* 1971.)

increases, so the number of indented areas falling within the upper creep modulus range decreases and there is a gradual shift towards the lower range of creep modulus values. The mean value of the creep modulus for all the areas indented on each femoral head also decreases as the grade number increases.

Figures 6.14 and 6.15 show the layered maps and histograms which were obtained by the same authors for grades 3 and 4 femoral heads which were excised from patients suffering from clinically diagnosed osteoarthrosis. These Figures clearly show

361

that the softening process illustrated for lower grade femoral heads is progressive, until, on the osteoarthrotic femoral heads, most of the cartilage displays creep modulus values which fall within the lowest range. In other words, the cartilage which is normal or nearly normal to the naked eye on an osteoarthrotic femoral head is in fact considerably softer than the normal tissue.

More recent work by Freeman, Kempson and Swanson (1973) has suggested that abnormally soft cartilage of normal naked-eye appearance as described above, was in fact histologically fibrillated to a limited extent. The method used for determining these areas of minimal surface fibrillation was that described by Meachim (1972) in which Indian ink was applied to the cartilage surface using a soft brush. The femoral head was then washed gently with physiological saline and any residual ink staining revealed areas of surface disruption which were not detectable to the naked eye on the untreated surface.

To conform with the earlier study of Kempson et al. (1971) reported above, in which only untreated femoral heads were

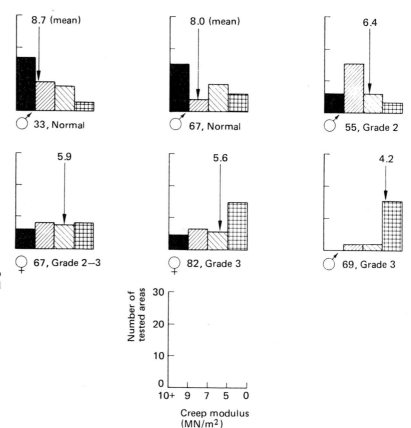

Figure 6.13 Histograms of the 2 s creep modulus, corresponding to the layered maps of Figure 6.9.

362

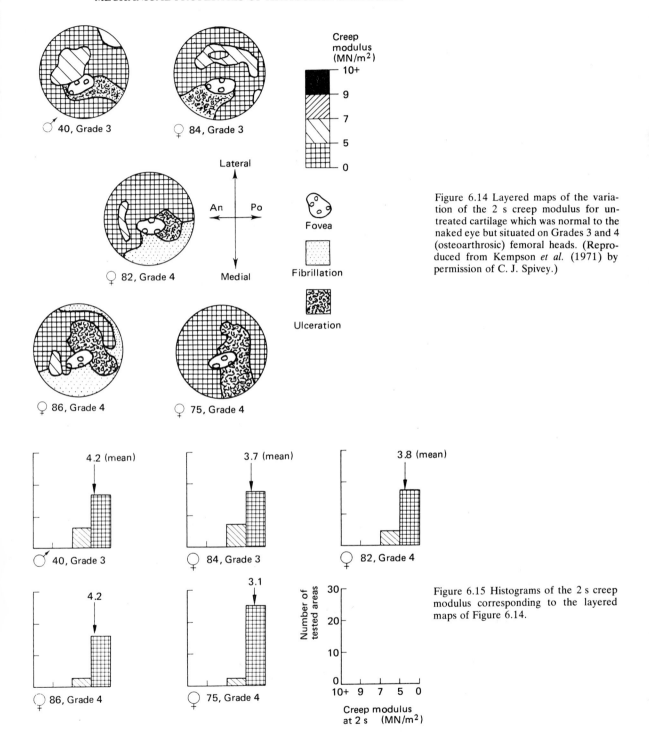

Figure 6.14 Layered maps of the variation of the 2 s creep modulus for untreated cartilage which was normal to the naked eye but situated on Grades 3 and 4 (osteoarthrosic) femoral heads. (Reproduced from Kempson *et al.* (1971) by permission of C. J. Spivey.)

Figure 6.15 Histograms of the 2 s creep modulus corresponding to the layered maps of Figure 6.14.

graded according to their naked-eye appearance, approximately 30 areas were indented on each of ten femoral heads using the plane-ended cylindrical indenter as described in Section 3.1. Each area selected for testing was graded according to the degree of residual Indian ink staining when viewed in a stereomicroscope at a magnification of ×10. Four classifications of the surface appearance were formulated: an area which displayed no residual ink staining was classified as normal; a glossy surface with slight ink fleck marks was said to display surface flecking; a surface of matt texture with moderate ink staining was classified as mildly fibrillated; and a grossly fibrillated surface with intense staining was classified as severely fibrillated.

After the mechanical tests were completed the fixed negative charge density of all the tested areas of cartilage was measured (see Chapter 4).

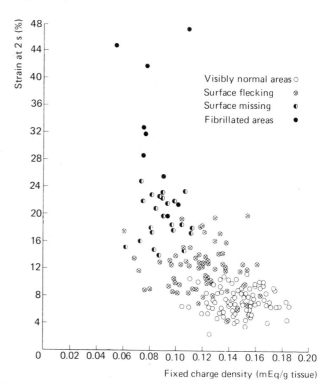

Figure 6.16 Percentage compressive strain at 2 s under a plane-ended, cylindrical indenter, 3.18 mm diameter, force = 22.2 N (5 lbf) (stress = 2.76 MN/m²; 400 lbf/in²) versus the fixed negative charge density of the cartilage. (Freeman *et al.* 1973.)

The results are presented in Figure 6.16 as the strain at 2 s (depth of indentation ÷ cartilage thickness) plotted against fixed negative charge density which in turn measures the glycosamino-glycan content (Chapter 4, Section 2.3.2). It can be seen that there was an inverse relationship between the two variables; the higher the fixed charge density the lower was the strain and, therefore, the greater was the stiffness of the cartilage. This result confirmed the observations of Kempson et al. (1971), described in Section 3.6, in which it was demonstrated that the stiffness of cartilage, expressed in the form of the 2 s creep modulus, increased as the total glycosaminoglycan content of the tissue increased.

In the results displayed in Figure 6.16 the strains in all the normal areas of cartilage were less than 11% of the tissue thickness, whereas the strains in the mildly and severely fibrillated areas were greater than 14% of the tissue thickness. There was apparently no overlap between the two ranges. A similar clear demarcation was evident in the ranges of fixed negative charge density of the normal and fibrillated cartilage; the minimum negative charge density of the normal tissue was 0.11 mEq/g of tissue whereas the maximum negative charge density of all the fibrillated areas was less than 0.11 mEq/g. Areas of cartilage in which the surface was glossy but flecked by residual ink staining displayed 2 s strain values and fixed negative charge densities which overlapped the ranges of both the normal and fibrillated tissue.

The topographical variation of the 2 s creep modulus for the ten femoral heads was similar to that described in Section 3.5.

3.8. The Relationship between the Compressive Properties of Cartilage and Fluid Transport

The matrix of adult articular cartilage usually contains 70–80% water. Most of this water can be expressed from the matrix mechanically although the resistance to flow is high, mainly because of the low permeability of cartilage (see Chapter 4, Section 6).

The significance of water efflux and influx in determining the mechanical properties of cartilage was first suggested by Benning-hoff (1924, 1925a, b, 1939), and in more recent years it has been examined both theoretically and experimentally in several investigations.

The dependence of the indentation hardness of cartilage on the concentration of the surrounding saline solution was first demonstrated by Elmore et al. (1963). Differences in the depth of indentation when a constant force was applied to cartilage via a plane-ended indenter were observed when the cartilage was immersed in isotonic and hypertonic Hank's solution or in distilled water.

These observations can be explained, phenomenologically, by the swelling pressure which exists between the cartilage matrix and the surrounding solution. This swelling pressure influences the rate at which water can be expressed from and reimbibed by cartilage and it also influences the final amount of water in the tissue at equilibrium. Changes in the external solution, and hence in the swelling pressure, are reflected in the response of the cartilage to a given load. These phenomena are explained more fully in Chapter 4, Section 6.

The movement and composition of the interstitial fluid in cartilage was studied experimentally by Linn and Sokoloff (1965). From tests performed on human patellar cartilage the authors concluded that the flow rate of interstitial fluid through the colloid matrix of cartilage was governed by several factors: namely, the cross-sectional area available for fluid flow, the permeability of the cartilage in the directions both parallel to and perpendicular to the articular surface, the swelling pressure of the matrix and finally the viscosity of the interstitial fluid.

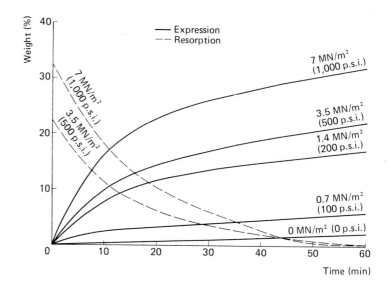

Figure 6.17 The relationship between the percentage weight of water expressed from and imbibed by cartilage vs time for increasing nominal compressive stresses. (Linn and Sokoloff 1965.)

Figure 6.17 shows experimental curves for both the weight of water expressed from cartilage versus time for given applied pressures, and for the rate of imbibition of water when the pressure was removed. It can be seen that the rate of both water efflux and influx decreases with increasing time in a manner which is similar to the rate of decrease of indentation and recovery in cartilage. It is clear, therefore, that the time-dependent response of cartilage to an applied force is influenced strongly by the movement of the interstitial fluid. It can also be seen in Figure 6.17 that the water flow did not display an initial step-response when the load was applied or removed, which contrasted with the rapid elastic response of cartilage to the application or removal of an indenting force. The authors attempted to explain this difference by the observation that, in the fluid transport study, the cylindrical cartilage specimens were restricted on all but the superior boundary and therefore radial expansion of the specimen was prevented. In the indentation study, however, the cartilage was tested *in situ* on the joint surface which allowed some radial expansion and contraction.

A recent study by Freeman, Swanson and Manley (1975) has shown that when the complete human hip joint is subjected, *in vitro*, to a periodic load from zero to three times body weight at a frequency of 0.33 Hz, the deformation of the cartilage within one complete load cycle was effectively elastic and almost reversible. However, a small amount of residual creep did occur per cycle and the effect of this was cumulative when the load was applied for several hundreds of cycles. As in the indentation tests, the rate of creep decreased with increasing time and tended towards an equilibrium value.

The relationship between the compressive properties and the permeability of cartilage was investigated experimentally by Read, Kempson and Maroudas (1970, unpublished data). Indentation tests were first performed on selected areas of the human femoral head and the 2 s creep modulus was calculated for each area using the technique described in Section 3.4.1. The cartilage was then allowed to recover in Ringer's solution at 37°C and pH7, after which the tested areas were excised and sliced, parallel to the articular surface, into serial layers each $200\,\mu$m thick. The permeability coefficient for each layer was then determined from measurements of the rate of flow of normal Ringer's solution through the cartilage under a pressure gradient of one atmosphere gauge pressure (Maroudas *et al.* 1968). The reciprocal of the permeability coefficient for the full cartilage thickness was then calculated from the expression:

$$\frac{1}{k} = \frac{1}{H}\int_0^H \frac{1}{k_h} \cdot dh \tag{18}$$

where $\quad k$ = permeability coefficient for the full thickness of cartilage,

$\quad\quad H$ = thickness of the cartilage,

$\quad\quad k_h$ = permeability coefficient of a $200\,\mu$m layer at a depth, h, below the articular surface,

$\quad\quad h$ = depth of the layer below the surface.

Figure 6.18 shows the relationship obtained between the 2 s creep modulus and the permeability coefficient for 32 areas of cartilage. It can be seen that the greater the permeability of the cartilage the lower was the compressive stiffness. The results were fitted by the best straight line according to the least squares analysis and the correlation coefficient was calculated to be $r = -0.772$ with a level of significance $p < 0.001$. Since Maroudas, Muir and Wingham (1969) have shown that the permeability of cartilage is inversely proportional to the glycosaminoglycan content, the results shown in Figure 6.18 indicate that the 2 s creep modulus of cartilage is proportional to the glycosaminoglycan content, which is consistent with the conclusions described in Section 3.6.

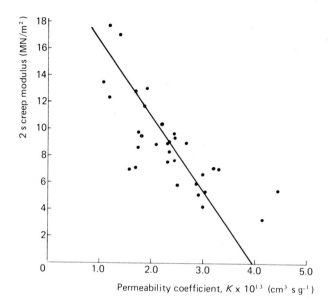

Figure 6.18 Creep modulus at 2 s versus permeability coefficient for cartilage on the human femoral head. (Author's material.)

In summary, it can be stated that the response of cartilage to a given load environment depends on the properties of both the 'solid' and liquid phases of the matrix, and the relationships between them.

3.9. The Relationship between the Compressive Properties of Cartilage and Age

To date no recorded investigation has shown any significant relationship between the compressive stiffness of cartilage and age.

3.10 Summary

When a compressive force is applied perpendicularly to the articular surface, cartilage displays a response pattern which is characteristic of materials which possess both elastic and viscous elements. The response may be regarded as the superposition of

368

two effects: namely, the elastic response of the 'solid' phase and the creep response of the fluid phase.

(a) When cartilage is dynamically loaded by a force which varies periodically, then within one complete load cycle the deformation is effectively elastic and reversible. However, there does appear to be a small net efflux of fluid from the matrix which is cumulative over many load cycles, thereby superimposing a creep deformation on the elastic response. With increasing time the rate of creep decreases and the total deformation tends towards an equilibrium value. When the disturbing force is removed the cartilage recovers to its original thickness provided that it is immersed in physiological saline solution.

(b) When cartilage is suddenly loaded with a constant, static force, a very rapid elastic and reversible deformation occurs which is followed continuously by a creep response. The rate of creep decreases with increasing time and the deformation tends towards an equilibrium value which is usually reached within 2–3 h after the force is applied. Under a static load the elastic deformation usually constitutes approximately 25% of the final equilibrium deformation. Recovery from the deformed state to the original thickness also occurs as the result of a rapid elastic recovery followed by a time-dependent phase.

(c) The final equilibrium deformation of cartilage depends on several factors: namely, the magnitude of the applied force, the permeability of the tissue, the elastic and time-dependent properties of the 'solid' elements of the matrix, the transport of fluid and the osmotic and Donnan swelling pressures of the matrix.

(d) The Young's modulus, creep modulus, shear modulus and the bulk creep compliance have all been measured for articular cartilage from axial compression tests, indentation tests, torsion tests and from dilatation tests. Typical values* which have been reported are:

* See Section 2.2 for conversion factors from SI units.

YOUNG'S MODULUS: (E)

McCutchen (1962)—bovine leg joint cartilage—uniaxial compression between porous plattens.

$E = 0.58$ MN/m^2 for water-soaked cartilage
$E = 0.32$ MN/m^2 for cartilage in physiological saline

Both of the above values were measured from the first 0.28 mm of compression.

$E = 11.1$ MN/m^2 for saline-soaked cartilage, measured immediately after the load was applied.

Sokoloff (1966)—human patellar cartilage, plane-ended indenter, physiological saline

$E = 2.28$ MN/m^2

Kempson (1975, unpublished data)—human femoral head cartilage—uniaxial compression, non-porous plattens, physiological saline

$8.4 \ \text{MN/m}^2 \leqslant E \leqslant 15.3 \ \text{MN/m}^2$ measured at 0.2 s after load application

Hayes and Mockros (1971)—For normal human articular cartilage from torsional shear and uniaxial confined compression creep tests
$E = 11.63 \ \text{MN/m}^2$

Hori and Mockros (1976)—For normal human articular cartilage from short-term torsional shear and confined compression tests
$5.57 \ \text{MN/m}^2 \leqslant E \leqslant 10.22 \ \text{MN/m}^2$ for normal cartilage
$1.37 \ \text{MN/m}^2 \leqslant E \leqslant 9.33 \ \text{MN/m}^2$ for degenerate cartilage

Johnson et al. *(1975)*—uniaxial compression

$12 \ \text{MN/m}^2 \leqslant E \leqslant 45 \ \text{MN/m}^2$ measured at 0.6 strain for a dynamic load applied at a frequency between 0.8 and 2.5 Hz

CREEP MODULUS (C)

Kempson and colleagues (Kempson 1970; Kempson, Freeman and Swanson 1971; Kempson et al. 1971)—human femoral head cartilage—indentation tests using plane and hemispherical indenters—physiological saline

$1.9 \ \text{MN/m}^2 \leqslant C \leqslant 14.4 \ \text{MN/m}^2$ measured at 2 s after load application

SHEAR MODULUS (G)

Hayes (1970) and Hayes et al. *(1972)*

$G = 4.1 \ \text{MN/m}^2$ for healthy cartilage
$G = 0.58 \ \text{MN/m}^2$ for degenerate cartilage

Hori and Mockros (1976)—For normal human articular cartilage from short-term torsional shear tests

$1.66 \ \text{MN/m}^2 \leqslant G \leqslant 3.47 \ \text{MN/m}^2$ for normal cartilage
$0.46 \ \text{MN/m}^2 \leqslant G \leqslant 3.29 \ \text{MN/m}^2$ for degenerate cartilage

BULK CREEP COMPLIANCE (B)
Hayes (1970)
$0.012 \ \text{m}^2/\text{MN} \leqslant B \leqslant 0.044 \ \text{m}^2/\text{MN}$ for healthy cartilage
$0.12 \ \text{m}^2/\text{MN} \leqslant B \leqslant 0.6 \ \text{m}^2/\text{MN}$ for degenerate cartilage

BULK DILATATION MODULUS (K)

Hori and Mockros (1976)—For normal human articular cartilage from short-term uniaxial confined compression tests

$24.9 \text{ MN/m}^2 \leqslant K \leqslant 71.4 \text{ MN/m}^2$ for normal cartilage
$9.46 \text{ MN/m}^2 \leqslant K \leqslant 167.3 \text{ MN/m}^2$ for degenerate cartilage

(e) The resistance of cartilage to indentation, expressed in the form of the creep modulus at 2 s after load application (Kempson, Freeman and Swanson 1971), has been shown to vary systematically with position on the human femoral head (Kempson *et al.* 1971). The stiffest cartilage extends in a band, resembling the shape of the cartilaginous area on the acetabulum, from the anterior aspect to the posterior aspect of the femoral head via the superior surface. The softest cartilage was found to be located in the region of the femoral head inferior to the fovea and at the articular margins, especially the margin of the fovea.

(f) It was also found that the magnitude of the 2 s creep modulus of untreated cartilage which was normal to the naked eye was related to the severity of areas of cartilage degeneration on the remainder of the femoral head; the more severe the areas of degeneration the softer was the visually normal cartilage. (More recent work has suggested that the Indian ink technique developed by Meachim (1972) is more sensitive in detecting early cartilage degeneration than is the naked-eye appearance of the untreated articular surface and therefore it is likely that some areas of cartilage which were previously classified as normal were in fact minimally fibrillated.)

(g) Chemical analysis of areas of cartilage which had previously been subjected to indentation tests showed that the resistance of cartilage to indentation depends to a significant extent on the glycosaminoglycan content of the tissue and to a lesser extent on the collagen content.

(h) No significant correlation has yet been found between the compressive properties of cartilage and age.

4. STATIC MECHANICAL PROPERTIES OF CARTILAGE IN TENSION

The mechanism by which tensile stresses can be generated in the matrix of cartilage was described in Chapter 5. In this Section the response of cartilage to applied tensile stresses is discussed.

4.1. Experimental Studies of the Tensile Properties of Cartilage in the Direction Parallel to the Articular Surface

Apart from the work of Pauwels (1959), the earlier studies concerning the mechanical significance of the superficial collagen fibres did not involve either experimental measurements of the tensile properties of cartilage or theoretical analysis of the tensile stresses which are likely to occur as the result of compression and movement in joints. However, more recently, tension tests have been performed on cartilage by Ranu (1967), Kempson et al. (1968, 1972) and Woo, Akeson and Jemmott (1976).

Ranu attempted to measure the tensile properties of full-thickness specimens of cartilage from the femoral heads of dogs in the direction parallel to the articular surface. Unfortunately, Ranu did not state whether the specimens were tested in a particular direction relative to the superficial collagen fibres. By rapidly applying tensile forces of increasing magnitude and plotting the resulting creep curve for cartilage under each load, Ranu was able to determine the Young's modulus in tension for the instantaneous response, for the equilibrium response and for the creep response of cartilage. The following values were obtained:

$E = 1.2 \text{ MN/m}^2 \ (174 \text{ lbf/in}^2)$ for the instantaneous response
$E = 1.25 \text{ MN/m}^2 \ (181 \text{ lbf/in}^2)$ for the equilibrium response
$E = 0.7 \text{ MN/m}^2 \ (102 \text{ lbf/in}^2)$ for the creep response

The tension tests of Kempson et al. (1968, 1972) were performed on human cartilage taken mainly from the femoral condyles of the knee joints.

The prick pattern which was characteristic of the femoral condyles, as shown in Figure 6.19, was first determined in a representative number of knees, using the method developed by Hultkrantz (1898). The reproducible pattern so obtained was used as a guide for excising cartilage specimens in which the long axis was either parallel to or perpendicular to the assumed predominant direction of the collagen fibres in the superficial zone.

Four rectangular, full-thickness, blocks of cartilage were excised from the femoral condyles of each knee joint. These areas were selected so that from each condyle one specimen was aligned parallel to the prick pattern and the other perpendicular to it.

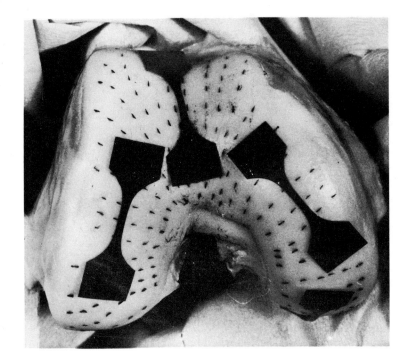

Figure 6.19 Cleavage line pattern in the superficial zone of cartilage on the femoral condyles of the human knee joint. The plastic overlays show the shape, size and position of the tension specimens which were tested either parallel to or perpendicular to the cleavage pattern. (Kempson 1972.)

Pricks were not made in the areas from which the specimens were to be excised as these could have affected the mechanical response of the tissue. Each full-thickness block of cartilage was then sliced into serial layers, 200 μm in thickness, including the superficial layer in which the articular surface was intact. Finally a specially prepared die cutter was used to cut dumb-bell-shaped tension specimens from each layer. Figure 6.19 shows plastic overlays, of the same size and shape as the final tension specimens, placed on the condylar surfaces. The orientation of the central parallel-sided gauge length to the prick pattern can be clearly seen.

Each specimen was gripped at the enlarged ends and subjected to a continuously increasing tensile force, in the direction of the central gauge length, at a rate of extension of 5.0 mm/min. A continuous record of the load versus specimen extension was made and measurements of the extension of the central gauge length were also taken at predetermined values of the tensile force. From these data and measurements of the initial cross-sectional area and gauge length of the specimen, graphs of nominal tensile stress versus tensile strain were plotted for each specimen up to, and including, fracture.

4.2. Variation of Tensile Properties with Depth below the Articular Surface

That tensile stresses parallel to the articular surface may be generated within the matrix of cartilage has been demonstrated in Chapter 5. The response of cartilage to such stresses clearly depends on the tensile properties of the tissue at all levels from the articular surface to the subchondral bone interface. Figures 6.20 and 6.21 show the variation in tensile properties with increasing depth below the articular surface. Figure 6.20 shows the results for specimens from one area in which the axis of the gauge length was parallel to the cleavage pattern in the superficial zone. Figure 6.21 shows the corresponding results for an area which was tested perpendicularly to the cleavage pattern. The results show that the tensile stiffness parallel to the articular surface, measured by the gradient to the stress/strain curve, decreases with depth from the articular surface, irrespective of the orientation of the specimens to the superficial cleavage pattern. The pattern of variation was slightly different between the two orientations since the stiffness tended to decrease gradually and continuously with increasing depth in the parallel-orientated specimen, but in many areas which

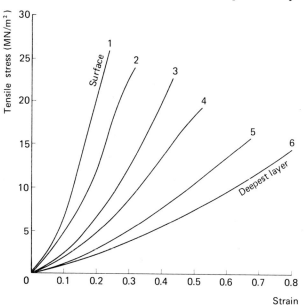

Figure 6.20 Tensile stress/strain curves for each layer of an area of cartilage which was tested in the direction parallel to the superficial cleavage pattern. Each test was taken to fracture. The specimens were immersed in Ringer's solution at pH 7. (Kempson 1972.)

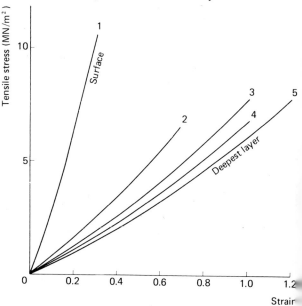

Figure 6.21 Tensile stress/strain curves for all the layers of an area of cartilage which was tested in the direction perpendicular to the superficial cleavage pattern. (Kempson 1972.)

were orientated perpendicularly to the cleavage pattern there was a sudden and relatively large decrease in stiffness from the surface to the second layer, followed by a more gradual decrease with further increasing depth from the articular surface.

It is also evident from Figures 6.20 and 6.21 that the tensile strength (fracture stress) of the superficial layer was usually greater than that of the subjacent layers and that the tensile strength tended to decrease with increasing depth. This result is illustrated in Figure 6.22 for two young normal specimens.

In a few areas of cartilage the strength of the superficial layer was less than that of the second layer and it was considered that such superficial layers were probably minimally fibrillated.

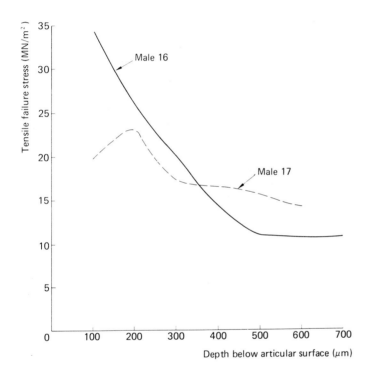

Figure 6.22 The variation of tensile fracture stress with depth below the articular surface. The results of two femoral condyles are shown; males aged 16 and 17 y. (Kempson 1972.)

Woo *et al.* (1976) also examined the relationship between the tensile properties of cartilage, in planes parallel to the articular surface, and the depth of the specimen below the surface. Using similar methods to those of Kempson *et al.* (1968, 1972), Woo confirmed that the tensile stiffness of cartilage decreased with increasing depth from the articular surface.

4.3. Variation of Tensile Properties with Orientation to the Cleavage Line Pattern of the Superficial Zone

Figure 6.23 shows typical tensile stress/strain curves for the superficial zone of two areas of cartilage from each of two knee joints (Kempson 1972). The specimens were orientated both parallel to and perpendicular to the cleavage pattern. It can be seen that the specimens which were orientated in the direction parallel to the cleavage pattern were both stiffer and stronger than those which were perpendicular to it. This result is consistent with the interpretation that the cleavage pattern indicates the predominant alignment of the collagen fibres in the superficial zone.

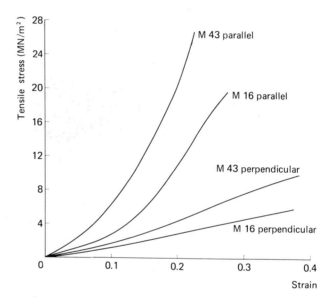

Figure 6.23 Tensile stress/strain curves showing the anisotropic property of the superficial zone of cartilage. Specimens are compared when tested parallel to and perpendicular to the superficial cleavage pattern. The results of two femoral condyles are shown; males aged 16 and 43 y. (Kempson 1972.)

Woo *et al.* (1976) also examined the relationship between the tensile stiffness of cartilage and the orientation of the specimen with respect to the superficial cleavage pattern. Measurements of the true cross-sectional area of the specimens were taken throughout the tests and the results were recorded as graphs of true stress (load ÷ true cross-sectional area) versus strain. It was found that the stiffness of specimens which were aligned and tested in the direction of the cleavage pattern tended to be only slightly greater than that of specimens which were perpendicular to the cleavage pattern. Values of maximum stiffness were recorded for specimens which were aligned and tested at 45°C to the superficial cleavage pattern.

The same authors also demonstrated that the tensile stiffness of cartilage increased as the applied strain rate increased.

It should be noted that the validity of using the true cross-sectional area of a cartilage tension specimen to calculate the true stress rests on two fundamental assumptions: namely, that the entire cross-section carries the tensile force uniformly and that, if a volume decrease occurs in the specimen, then that decrease is the same at all levels through the cartilage thickness. These assumptions may be questioned on the following grounds. First, the loss of water, and hence loss of volume, is not constant throughout the depth of cartilage as shown by the results given in Section 5. Secondly, it appears likely that most of the tensile force is transmitted through the collagen fibres rather than the water phase of the matrix. Therefore, even though the cross-sectional area of a tension specimen may decrease considerably through water efflux, the stress in the collagen fibres may not increase in proportion to that decrease in area; rather the stress in the collagen fibres increases in proportion to the decrease in their own cross-sectional area, which has not been measured.

4.4. Variation of Tensile Properties with Age

Reports in the literature have clearly shown that many connective tissues display changes in their mechanical properties with advancing age. These changes are usually associated with age-related alterations in the collagen fibre network. Since articular cartilage also possesses a large number of collagen fibres within its matrix it is possible that it might also display age-related changes in its mechanical properties and particularly in its tensile properties. Such changes, were they to occur *in vivo*, could influence the ability of cartilage to withstand normal physiological stresses.

Kempson (1975a, and 1975 unpublished data) has examined the tensile properties of cartilage, in planes parallel to the articular surface, from the femoral condyles of human knee joints within the age range of 8–91 years. Dumb-bell-shaped tension specimens, somewhat smaller than those used previously (Kempson *et al.* 1968, 1972), were prepared from the superficial layer and from the fourth layer (800 μm below the articular surface) of areas of cartilage which were orientated in the direction parallel to the superficial cleavage pattern. The areas were selected from pre-determined sites on the condyles: namely, the patellar articulation region and from the anterior, central and posterior regions of both the medial and lateral condyles.

Before excising the specimens the pathological condition of the articular surface was determined using the Indian ink technique developed by Meachim (1972). Only areas which were either normal or which displayed minimal residual ink staining were tested.

The distance of each specimen from the closest area of overt fibrillation was measured in order to determine whether the proximity of such an area affected the tensile properties of the normal areas of cartilage. The results of this part of the study are reported in Section 4.6.

The experimental procedure was identical to that described in Section 4.2, and the relationships between tensile stiffness and fracture strength and age were examined.

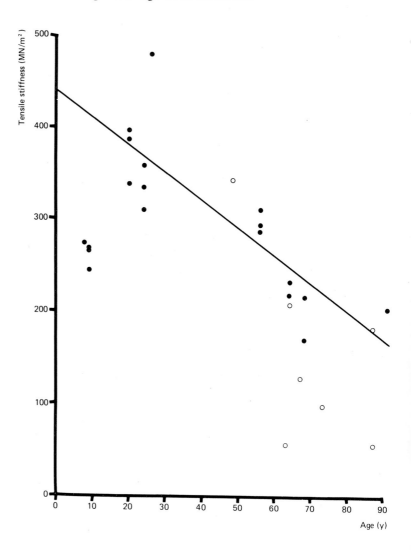

Figure 6.24 The relationship between the tensile stiffness of lateral femoral condylar cartilage, measured near to fracture, and the age of the joint from which the specimen was taken. Normal specimens which were either more than 1 cm from an area of overt fibrillation or situated on a normal joint surface are represented by ●, and normal specimens which were less than 1 cm from an area of overt fibrillation are represented by ○. All specimens were taken from the superficial zone and they were tested in the direction parallel to the cleavage pattern. The rate of extension was 5.0 mm/min. The best straight line was fitted to the points by a least squares analysis.

Figures 6.24 and 6.25 show the relationship between tensile stiffness and age for the superficial layers and the fourth layers respectively of all the areas which were tested on the lateral

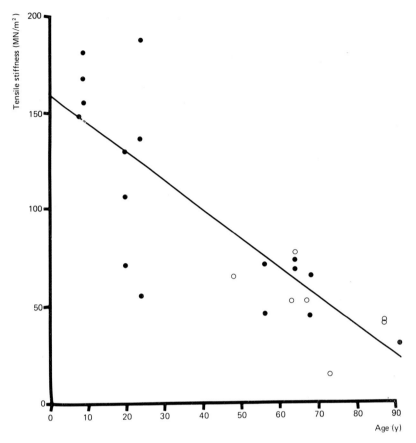

Figure 6.25 The relationship between tensile stiffness and age for specimens taken from the fourth layers (800 μm below the articular surface) of the same areas as those which are represented in Figure 6.24.

femoral condyle. Figures 6.26 and 6.27 show the corresponding relationship between fracture strength and age. The experimental points representing normal specimens which were situated either more than 1 cm from an area of overt fibrillation or on a completely normal joint surface were fitted by the best straight line according to the least squares analysis. As the results show, there was a marked decrease in both tensile stiffness and fracture strength with increasing age, both in the superficial zone of the cartilage and in the fourth layer specimens. The results for the medial femoral condyles also showed similar reductions in stiffness and strength with increasing age. One .significant difference emerged between the superficial and fourth layer specimens in respect of those specimens which were excised from joints in the first decade of life. Whereas the fourth layer specimens showed a continuous decrease in stiffness and strength from the first decade onwards, specimens from the superficial layer showed lower values of both stiffness and strength in the first decade compared to those

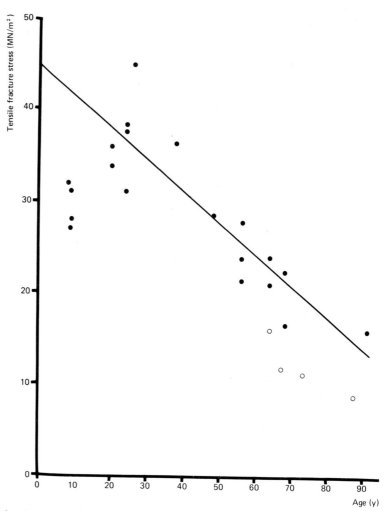

Figure 6.26 The relationship between the tensile fracture stress and age for the same superficial-layer specimens as those which are represented in Figure 6.24.

in the second decade, but thereafter both properties decreased with age. Whether this observation indicates a slower rate of maturation of the collagen fibres in the superficial zone compared to those of the deeper regions is not yet known; neither is the reason for the decrease in tensile stiffness and strength with age. However, it is suggested in Section 4.7 that it is likely that such changes are related to the collagen fibre mesh.

Table 6.2 shows the equations for the best straight lines fitted to the experimental results for all the areas which were tested. Coefficients of correlation are also shown together with the statistical level of significance of the correlation. It can be seen that in most cases the level of significance p was better than 1%, indicating a significant relationship between the tensile properties and age.

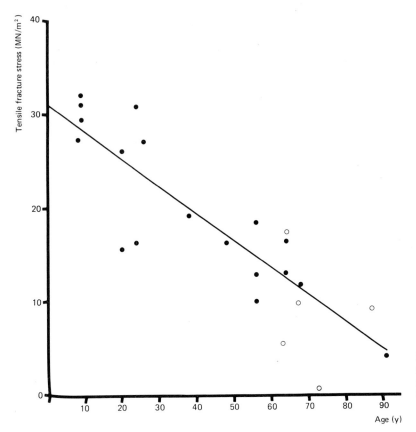

Figure 6.27 The relationship between the tensile fracture stress and age for the same fourth-layer specimens which are represented in Figure 6.25.

Table 6.2 The relationships between tensile stiffness and fracture strength vs age. Equations to the best straight lines are shown together with the correlation coefficients and their levels of significance. (Kempson 1975, unpublished data)

Femoral condyle	Zone	Equation of tensile stiffness (E) vs age in years (t)	Correlation coefficient (r)	Statistical significance (p)	Equation of tensile fracture stress vs age	Correlation coefficient	Statistical significance
Lateral	Superficial	$E = 440 - 3t$	-0.83	<0.01	$\sigma = 46.3 - 0.38t$	-0.89	<0.01
Lateral	Fourth layer	$E = 160 - 1.6t$	-0.80	<0.01	$\sigma = 30.9 - 0.29t$	-0.91	<0.01
Medial	Superficial	$E = 538 - 5.3t$	-0.92	<0.01	$\sigma = 45 - 0.42t$	-0.93	<0.01
Medial	Fourth layer	$E = 210 - 2.3t$	-0.91	<0.01	$\sigma = 35.3 - 0.34t$	-0.87	<0.01

Weightman (1975) has also reported a similar decrease in tensile strength with age from the results of dynamic fatigue tests performed on specimens of human articular cartilage, similar to those used by Kempson, from the femoral head of the hip joint (see Section 6).

4.5. The Relationship between the Tensile Properties of Normal Cartilage and the Pathological Appearance of the Joint Surface

As was stated in the preceding Section, Kempson (1975a) also examined the influence of the proximity of an area of overt cartilage fibrillation on the remaining areas of normal cartilage on the same joint surface. Specimens in which any part of the gauge length was greater than 1 cm from an area of overt fibrillation were considered to be normal and remote from degeneration, whilst specimens in which any part of the gauge length was less than 1 cm from an area of overt fibrillation were considered to be adjacent to degeneration. The state of the articular surface was determined using the Indian ink technique of Meachim (1972) and only normal areas of cartilage were tested.

The results relating to the specimens which were adjacent to overt fibrillation are also included in Figures 6.24 to 6.27.

It is evident from these Figures that the close proximity of an area of overt cartilage fibrillation does not invariably reduce the tensile properties of the adjacent, normal tissue. However, it is equally clear that the tensile strength and stiffness of some apparently normal areas which are adjacent to degenerate tissue were considerably lower than corresponding normal specimens which were within the same age range but which were remote from any area of overt degeneration or situated on normal joint surfaces.

At this stage it is not clear why some areas of cartilage are affected by the proximity of areas of degeneration whilst others are not, and research is continuing into this observation.

4.6. The Topographical Variation of the Tensile Properties of Cartilage

In Section 3.5 it was shown that the resistance to indentation of untreated, visually normal cartilage, expressed as the 2 s creep modulus, varies systematically over the human femoral head. The results obtained by Kempson (1975a, and 1975 unpublished data), which were described in Sections 4.5 and 4.6, allow the topographical variation of the tensile properties over the human femoral condyles to be examined.

Inspection of the equations given in Table 6.2 indicates that young cartilage from both zones of the medial femoral condyle is stiffer, in tension, than corresponding tissue from the lateral femoral condyle. The gradients of the lines suggest, however, that the rate of decrease of tensile stiffness is greater in the medial condylar cartilage than it is in cartilage from the lateral femoral condyle.

Thus, with advancing age the stiffness of cartilage on the medial femoral condyle. The gradients of the lines suggest, however, that condyle and indeed in middle-aged and elderly individuals it might be expected that the medial condylar cartilage would be less stiff than that of the lateral condyle.

In contrast to the stiffness results, it is evident from Tables 6.2 that the tensile fracture strength of the cartilage from both condyles is approximately equal at all ages.

A more detailed analysis of the results given in Table 6.2, to consider the different regions of the femoral condyles which were examined, revealed that the stiffness of the mid-condylar region of the medial condyle in particular, was greater than that of the lateral condyle in young joints and that the rate of decrease with age was also greater. Other results do not indicate any significant regional differences in the tensile properties of femoral condylar cartilage although more results are presently being obtained to enable firm conclusions to be drawn.

4.7. The Relationship between the Tensile Properties and the Collagen Fibre Content and Orientation

Previous investigations have shown that the resistance of cartilage to indentation, in the form of the 2 s creep modulus, depends to a large extent on the proteoglycan content and to a much smaller extent on the collagen content of the matrix. A similar investigation was performed by Kempson et al. (1972) to determine the relationship between the tensile properties of cartilage from the femoral condyles of the knee and joint and the matrix components.

In a fibre-reinforced material, such as articular cartilage, the tensile stiffness and strength of the composite material depend on several factors, two of which are the fraction of the material which is occupied by the fibres and the geometrical arrangement of the fibres.

The effect of the orientation of the collagen fibres on the tensile properties of cartilage has been discussed in Section 4.4.

The dependence of the tensile stiffness of cartilage on the collagen fibre content was examined in specimens of cartilage which were excised from the superficial zone of the femoral condyles of the knee joint and which were orientated in the direction parallel to the cleavage pattern. The results are shown in Figure 6.28. It can be seen that a significant positive correlation was found between the tensile stiffness and collagen content of cartilage specimens which appeared to be normal to the naked eye. It can also be seen in Figure 6.28 that specimens which were adjacent to areas of overt fibrillation, whilst possessing a collagen content within the normal range, were less stiff than specimens which were either remote from areas of degeneration or situated on normal joint surfaces.

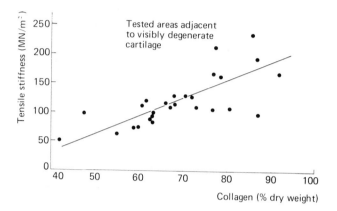

Figure 6.28 The relationship between the tensile stiffness, measured near to fracture, and the collagen fibre content for femoral condylar cartilage. All specimens were taken from the superficial zone and tested in the direction parallel to the cleavage pattern. (Kempson *et al.* 1972.)

Table 6.3 shows the correlation coefficients for the relationships between tensile stiffness and fracture stress and the glycosaminoglycan and collagen contents for specimens from all the zones of cartilage which were orientated both parallel to and perpendicular to the superficial cleavage pattern. The results emphasize that the tensile fracture strength of superficial zone specimens, which were orientated parallel to the cleavage pattern, depended to a statistically significant extent on the collagen content. Corresponding results for superficial zone specimens which were orientated perpendicularly to the cleavage pattern were not so significant. With increasing depth from the articular surface, specimens which were orientated parallel to the superficial cleavage pattern still showed a more significant correlation between stiffness and strength and the collagen content than did specimens which were perpendicular to the cleavage pattern. This result suggests that the collagen fibre organization in the deeper zones is not completely random and that the anisotropy is related to the predominant alignment of the collagen fibres in the superficial zone. This observation has also been made by Clarke (1971) and by Cameron *et al.* (1975), as was pointed out in Section 3.5. Cameron's observations also suggested that the anisotropy was related to the motion vectors between the femoral head and acetabulum in the hip joint.

The results shown in Figure 6.28 and Table 6.3 reveal that the tensile properties of visually normal cartilage depend to a significant extent on the collagen fibre content of the matrix in addition to the alignment of the fibres.

4.8. The Relationship between the Tensile Properties of Cartilage and the Proteoglycan Content

Columns 6–9 in Table 6.3 show the partial correlation coefficients for the relationships between the tensile stiffness at fracture and the fracture strength of visually normal cartilage and the proteoglycan content of the matrix, as recorded by Kempson *et al.* (1972). It can be seen that in all cases the correlations were not statistically significant.

To investigate the influence of proteoglycans on the tensile stiffness of cartilage in greater detail, Kempson *et al.* (1972) treated tension specimens with crystalline trypsin and bacterial chondroitinase to degrade the proteoglycan of the matrix.

Table 6.3 Partial correlation coefficients for the tensile stiffness and fracture stress versus collagen and total glycosaminoglycan (GAG) contents for articular cartilage of human femoral condyles. Arrows indicate parallel ↑ and perpendicular → orientations of the specimens to the predominant collagen fibre direction of the superfical layer

Layer number from the surface (each layer 200 μm thick)	Stiffness vs collagen (GAG constant)		Fracture stress vs collagen (GAG constant)		Stiffness vs GAG (collagen constant)		Fracture stress vs GAG (collagen constant)	
	↑	→	↑	→	↑	→	↑	→
Surface layer	0.691***	0.606*	0.598**	0.598*	−0.102	−0.458	−0.189	−0.073
Layer 2	0.817**	0.483	0.729*	0.368	0.061	0.096	0.349	0.132
Layer 3	0.706**	0.406	0.459	0.297	−0.088	0.020	0.056	0.164
Layer 4	0.246	0.036	0.202	−0.098	−0.058	−0.388	−0.018	−0.462
Layer 5	0.269	0.382	0.060	0.308	−0.335	−0.092	−0.398	−0.285
Layer 6	0.446	0.450	0.351	0.551	0.124	−0.169	0.221	0.055

Significance of correlation coefficients ***: $p < 0.001$. **: $p < 0.01$. *: $p < 0.05$.

No asterisk indicates that the correlation was not statistically significant.

In one series of tests, specimens from the lateral femoral condyle of the knee joint were initially subjected to a non-destructive tension test in Ringer's solution at pH 7. The same specimens were then allowed to recover in fresh Ringer's solution for at least 30 min, after which they were incubated in bacterial chondroitinase for 4 h at 37°C. After this treatment the specimens were retested in tension. The procedure was then repeated and after a further incubation period of 20 h in fresh chondroitinase the specimens were again retested. Finally both the incubation media (which had been stored in sealed containers at −20°C) and the cartilage specimens were analysed for their uronic acid content. The proportion of the total tissue uronic acid which had been released in each incubation period was then determined.

Similar tests were performed with cartilage from the medial femoral condyles which was incubated in trypsin for periods of 24 and 48 h. The amount of uronic acid which was released from each specimen is shown in Table 6.4.

Table 6.4 Percentage glycosaminoglycan released, measured as uronic acid, from tension specimens of human femoral condylar cartilage by the action of (a) trypsin and (b) bacterial chondroitinase

(a) Trypsin (medial condyle)

Layer number from the surface (each layer 200 μm thick)	Orientation of specimen to surface cleavage pattern	Percentage of the tissue uronic acid released after the following periods:	
		24 hr	48 h
Surface layer	Parallel	65.7	90.3
Layer 4	Parallel	86.4	94.5
Surface layer	Perpendicular	39.7	71.8
Layer 4	Perpendicular	72.0	88.6

(b) Chondroitinase (lateral condyle)

Layer number from the surface (each layer 200 μm thick)	Orientation of specimen to surface cleavage pattern	Percentage of the tissue uronic acid released after the following periods:	
		4 h	24 h
Surface layer	Parallel	32.6	68.7
Layer 4	Parallel	45.2	80.3
Surface layer	Perpendicular	24.1	74.8
Layer 4	Perpendicular	40.8	74.8

Figures 6.29 and 6.30 show the effects of trypsin and chondroitinase, respectively, on the tensile stress/strain curves of femoral condylar cartilage. The results show that the effect of degrading and releasing increasing amounts of proteoglycan from cartilage *in vitro* was to increase the strain at low values of stress (i.e. to decrease the stiffness). This effect was most pronounced in specimens from the deep zone and more significant in specimens which were orientated perpendicular to the superficial cleavage pattern than those which were parallel to it. At higher values of stress the tensile stiffness, as measured by the gradient to the stress/strain curve, was not significantly affected.

Figure 6.29 The effect of trypsin on the tensile properties of specimens of cartilage from the medial femoral condyle of a male aged 69, orientated (a) parallel and (b) perpendicular to the surface cleavage pattern; (c) is a detail from (a) drawn to the same scale as (b). (The curves shown in (a) and (b) are drawn to different scales because the final non-destructive load had to be estimated for each specimen before the first test. Previous results had shown that higher loads could be endured by parallel than by perpendicularly orientated layers and hence the scales in (a) and (b) are different.)

(a) Parallel to surface cleavage pattern. (b) Perpendicular to surface cleavage pattern. (c) Parallel to surface cleavage pattern.

Surface layer ● and layer 4 ▲ before treatment with enzyme, ◑ and ◮ after incubation with enzyme for 24 h, and ○ and △ after incubation for 48 h.

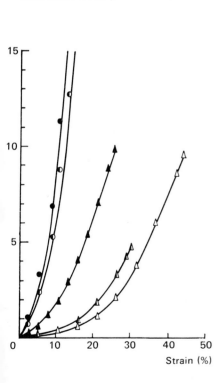

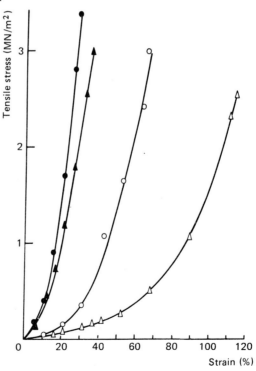

(b)

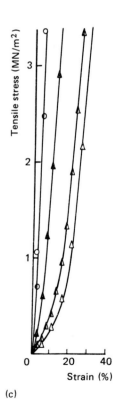

(c)

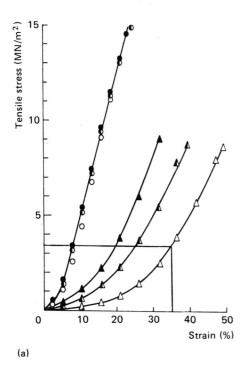

(a)

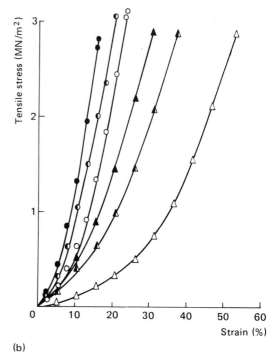

(b)

Figure 6.30 The effect of chondroitinase on the tensile properties of specimens of cartilage from the lateral femoral condyle of a male aged 69 orientated (a) parallel and (b) perpendicular to the surface cleavage pattern; (c) is a detail of (a) drawn to the same scale as (b). (The curves shown in (a) and (b) are drawn to different scales for the same reason as explained in the legend to Figure 6.29.)

(a) Parallel to surface cleavage pattern. (b) Perpendicular to surface cleavage pattern. (c) Parallel to surface cleavage pattern.

Surface layer ● and layer 4 ▲ before treatment with enzyme, ◑ and ▲ after incubation with enzyme for 4 h, and ○ and △ after incubation for 24 h.

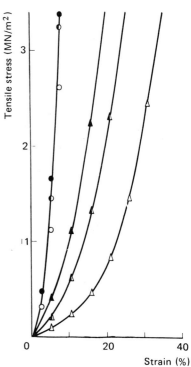

(c)

It is now suggested that the initial section of the stress/strain curve reflects the realignment of the collagen fibre mesh under the applied force. Proteoglycans influence this initial response because they occupy a domain which the collagen fibres seek to occupy and because they exist in the form of a viscous gel which offers resistance to reorganization of the collagen fibres. Removal of a significant proportion of the proteoglycans would reduce this resistance and thereby reduce the apparent tensile stiffness and allow a greater degree of tensile strain in the initial portion of the stress/strain curve. On this view, it is not surprising that the effect of proteoglycan release was greater in the deeper zones of cartilage, where the collagen fibres form an essentially random mesh, than in the superficial zone where the collagen fibres are already aligned either parallel to or perpendicular to the direction of the applied tensile force.

It seems reasonable to think that the tensile stiffness of cartilage at higher values of stress reflects the mechanical properties of the collagen fibres themselves rather than the properties of the mesh. On this view, it was to be expected that proteoglycan release would have little effect on the stiffness at higher stresses since neither of the two enzymes had any significant effect on the collagen fibres. This expectation was confirmed in the results.

4.9. The Effects of Proteolytic Enzymes on the Mechanical Properties of Cartilage

The effects upon the compressive and tensile properties of articular cartilage of proteoglycan and collagen degradation by proteolytic enzymes which have either been identified in cartilage or which could have access to the tissue have been investigated by Kempson (1975b) and Kempson et al. (1976).

The effects of three enzymes were studied in the preliminary investigation: namely, cathepsins D and B, both of which have been identified in cartilage, and purified clostridial collagenase which, although it is not present in synovial joints, is thought to possess an action similar to mammalian synovial collagenase. The action of cathepsin D is specific to proteoglycans whilst the action of purified clostridial collagenase is specific to collagen. By using these enzymes it was intended to examine further the dependence of the mechanical properties of cartilage on the proteoglycan and collagen components of the matrix with special reference to pathological situations (such as the rheumatoid inflammatory process) in life.

The effects on the uniaxial compressive properties of cartilage of the degradation and release of proteoglycan are presented in Table 6.5. It can be seen that both cathepsin D and cathepsin B released much of the proteoglycan from adult human articular

Table 6.5 The effects of cathepsins D and B on the percentage glycosaminoglycan loss, the percentage hydroxyproline released and the elastic strain at 0.2 s and the 1 and 2 min creep strains of cartilage from the femoral head of the hip joint and from the femoral condyles of the knee joint. Applied uniaxial compressive stress = 0.35 MN/m². The cartilage was tested in MES-buffered saline at pH 6; the incubation period was 100 h at 37°C

Joint and enzyme	Location of specimen on joint surface	Experimental or control	Percentage increase in compressive strain after 100 h incubation			Percentage release of proteoglycan after 100 h incubation	Percentage release of collagen after 100 h incubation
			Initial elastic strain (0.2 s)	Creep strain (1 min)	Creep strain (2 min)		
Femoral head, male 50 years, cathepsin D	Superior surface	Experimental	57	167	182	20	0.3
		Control	9	10	12	6	0.5
	Inferior to fovea	Experimental	55	429	359	35	0.5
		Control	4	49	60	9	0.4
	Perifoveal margin	Experimental	61	257	247	44	0.3
		Control	44	34	41	14	0.3
Femoral condyles, male 50 years, cathepsin D	Middle of lateral condyle	Experimental	54	472	405	99	
		Control	18	69	75	48	
	Front of lateral condyle	Experimental	92	392	356	98	
		Control	6	52	51	43	Less than 1%
	Middle of medial condyle	Experimental	57	230	203	79	
		Control	33	44	51	39	
	Rear of medial condyle	Experimental	20	170	160	60	
		Control	13	35	39	35	
Femoral head male 57 years, cathepsin B	Superior surface	Experimental	9	163	210	64	Pooled result for experimental specimens 4%
		Control	9	6	7	31	
	Inferior to fovea	Experimental	52	180	170	88	
		Control	13	33	39	48	
	Perifoveal margin	Experimental	—	38	37	88	Pooled result for control specimens 0.3%
		Control	8	9	7	41	

Table 6.6 The effect of cathepsin D on the tensile fracture stress of cartilage from the femoral condyles of the knee joint and from the femoral head of the hip joint. Specimens were tested in MES-buffered saline at pH 6 at a rate of extension of 5 mm/min. The total incubation period was 100 h at 37°C

Joint	Condyle	Orientation to surface cleavage pattern	Distance of specimen from articular surface (×200μm)	Fracture stress (MN/m²)			Proteoglycan release after 100 h (%)			Collagen release after 100 h (%)		
				(A) Experimental: After 100 h incubation in cathepsin D	(B) Control: after 100 h incubation in MES-buffered saline	(C) Control: after 100 h incubation in MES-buffered saline and pepstatin (1 μg/ml)	(A)	(B)	(C)	(A)	(B)	(C)
Femoral condyles, male 21 years	Lateral	Parallel	Surface	34	27	35	95	44	29	1.3	*	*
		Parallel	4	22	22	25	98	43	38	1.1	*	*
		Perpendicular	Surface	29	27	28	88	40	—	1.1	*	*
		Perpendicular	4	15	15	18	96	49	34	1.1	*	*
	Medial	Parallel	Surface	29	27	28	88	46	27	1.2	*	*
		Parallel	4	22	21	21	91	45	42	1.5	*	*
		Perpendicular	Surface	15	16	20	93	38	30	1.2	*	*
		Perpendicular	4	14	15	16	93	37	37	1.0	*	*
Femoral condyles, male 65 years	Lateral	Parallel	Surface	18	20		93	44	—	0.4	0.3	—
		Parallel	4	11	11		—	44	—	—	0.5	—
		Perpendicular	Surface	7	10		90	43	—	0.5	0.3	—
		Perpendicular	4	7	5		95	54	—	0.3	0.5	—
	Medial	Parallel	Surface	22	24		92	45	—	0.8	0.3	—
		Parallel	4	—	—	—	—	—	—	—	—	—
		Perpendicular	Surface	8	9		93	50	—	0.5	0.4	—
		Perpendicular	4	7	7		92	47	—	0.6	0.6	—
Femoral head, female 72 years	Posterior surface	Parallel	Surface	22	26	20	85	36	30	0.9	*	*
		Parallel	4	2	—	3.7	90	—	—	1.3	*	*
	Superior surface	Perpendicular	Surface	9.7	—	7.3	81	44	28	0.6	*	*
		Perpendicular	4	2.8	—	1.9	86	—	33	2.9	*	*
	Anterior surface	Parallel	Surface	20	29	18	81	37	36	1.0	*	*
		Parallel	4	9.4	5.9	9.5	94	55	40	1.3	*	*
	Inferior to fovea	Perpendicular	Surface	7.2	4.3	—	91	59	36	1.2	*	*
		Perpendicular	4	6.3	8.3	10.6	96	65	43	1.3	*	*

* Negligible

Table 6.7 The effect of purified clostridial collagenase on the tensile fracture stress of cartilage from the femoral condyles of one knee joint. Femoral condyles, male 62 y, extension rate = 5 mm/min. Specimens were tested in Tris-HCl-buffered saline at pH 7.8 and the total incubation period was 24 h at 37°C

Femoral condyle of knee joint (male 62 years)	Orientation to surface collagen alignment	Distance of specimen below articular surface (× 200 μm)	Tensile fracture stress (MN/m²)		Percentage proteoglycan release after 24 h		Percentage collagen release as soluble hydroxyproline after 24 h	
			Experimental (after 24 h incubation in collagenase)	Control (after 24 h incubation in Tris-HCl/saline)	Experimental	Control	Experimental	Control
Lateral	Parallel	Surface	4	22	50	37	10	0.6
	Parallel	4	0.5	16	—	23	—	1.3
	Perpendicular	Surface	2	6	35	28	5	1.0
	Perpendicular	4	2	8	39	61	8	2
Medial	Parallel	Surface	1	21	45	33	7	2
	Parallel	4	0.25	24	36	25	7	nil
	Perpendicular	Surface	0.5	11	55	24	22	nil
	Perpendicular	4	3	6	63	23	28	0.9

cartilage *in vitro* after 100 h incubation at 37°C and pH 6. In contrast, cathepsin D released less than 1% of the collagen as soluble hydroxyproline whereas cathepsin B released approximately 4% of the collagen. This latter result supported previous work which showed that cathepsin B was capable of degrading native insoluble collagen fibres from bovine tendon to a limited extent whereas cathepsin D was not (Burleigh, Barrett and Lazarus 1974). It can also be seen from Table 6.5 that the release of proteoglycan from the immediately adjacent control specimens, which were incubated in MES (2-N-morpholino ethane sulphonic acid)–NaOH buffer under identical conditions of time, temperature and pH, was considerably less than that of the experimental specimens.

Three values of the compressive strain were recorded for each specimen: namely, the elastic strain at 0.2 s after application of the load and the creep strains at 1 min and 2 min after application of the load. These latter values were obtained by subtracting the elastic strain from the total strains at 1 min and 2 min respectively. As Table 6.5 shows, the effect of proteoglycan release was to increase the three values of compressive strain considerably. The increase in the creep strains was somewhat greater than the increase in the elastic strain. This result supported the findings of previous investigations (described in Section 3.6) in which it was shown that the resistance of cartilage to indentation, in the form of the 2 s creep modulus, depended to a large extent on the proteoglycan content of the matrix. In contrast to the results obtained for specimens which were treated with the enzyme, the adjacent control areas showed only small increases in the compressive strains.

The effect of proteoglycan degradation and release on the tensile stiffness of cartilage was similar to that observed when cartilage was treated with trypsin and chondroitinase. These results were discussed in Section 4.8. Table 6.6 shows the effect of proteoglycan degradation by cathepsin D on the tensile fracture strength of cartilage from the femoral condyles of the knee joint and from the femoral head of the hip joint. Comparison of the values of fracture strength for the specimens which were incubated for 100 h in cathepsin D at 37°C and pH 6 with the corresponding values for the immediately adjacent control specimens, shows that proteoglycan degradation had little effect on the fracture strength of cartilage.

In contrast, Table 6.7 shows the effect of collagen degradation by purified clostridial collagenase on the tensile fracture strength of cartilage. It can be seen that a considerable reduction in strength occurred after only 24 h incubation in collagenase at 37°C and pH 7.8. After this period the specimens did not appear to be fibrillated or fragmented. A significant reduction in tensile stiffness was also recorded at all levels of stress after 24 h incubation in collagenase. These results emphasize the importance of the collagen fibres in determining the tensile properties of cartilage and they support the observations which were described in Section 4.8.

4.10. Summary

Articular cartilage displays the following characteristics when loaded in tension in planes parallel to the articular surface.

(a) The tensile stiffness and fracture strength are both strongly related to the extent to which the collagen fibres are orientated parallel to the direction of tension. They are also related to the collagen content of the matrix. Specimens taken from the superficial zone of the femoral condyles of the human knee joint, in which the predominant orientation of the collagen fibres was parallel to the direction of tension, were found to be both stiffer and stronger than specimens from the same zone in which the fibres were predominantly perpendicular to the direction of tension.

The tensile stiffness of cartilage decreases considerably with increasing depth from the articular surface.

The tensile fracture strength also tends to decrease with depth although in some cases the second layer has been found to be stronger than the superficial zone, possibly due to minimal fibrillation in the latter.

In the deeper zones of cartilage the anisotropy becomes less marked but superior tensile properties in the direction parallel to the superficial cleavage pattern can still be detected. This suggests that a fibre organization with directional properties is superimposed on the apparently random fibre mesh. This observation has also been made by Clarke (1971) and Cameron et al. (1975).

(b) The tensile stiffness of cartilage from the superficial zone, when tested in the direction parallel to the cleavage pattern, lies mainly within the range 150–500 MN/m^2 (21 750–72 500 lbf/in^2) and it decreases with increasing age. The corresponding range for specimens from the fourth layers (800 μm below the articular surface) is from 0 to 200 MN/m^2 (0–29 000 lbf/in^2) and again the stiffness decreases with increasing age.

(c) The tensile fracture strength of cartilage from the superficial zone, when tested in the direction parallel to the cleavage pattern, lies mainly between 10 and 40 MN/m^2 (1450–5800 lbf/in^2). The corresponding range for specimens from the fourth layers is between 0 and 30 MN/m^2 (0 and 4350 lbf/in^2). There is a decrease in fracture strength with increasing age.

(d) Cartilage specimens from the superficial layer of the femoral condyles of knee joints in the first decade of age display tensile stiffness and fracture strength values which are lower than those of the second decade. Specimens from the fourth layers of the same areas have higher values of stiffness and strength in the first decade when compared to the values for specimens from the second and subsequent decades.

The reason for this observation is not known, but it is possible that the collagen fibre mesh of the superficial zone is slower to mature than that of the deeper zones of cartilage.

(e) The close proximity of an area of overt fibrillation to a specimen of normal naked-eye appearance has a variable effect on the tensile properties; in some cases both the stiffness and strength are reduced whilst in others they are not. The explanation of these results is not clear.

(f) Statistical correlations between the tensile properties of cartilage and the proteoglycan and collagen content in the matrix show that both the stiffness at fracture and the tensile fracture strength are strongly dependent on the collagen content and, to a much smaller extent, on the proteoglycan content.

(g) Treatment of cartilage with trypsin, chondroitinase or the endogenous proteolytic enzymes cathepsins D and B, to degrade specifically the proteoglycan in the matrix, causes the tensile stiffness at low values of stress to be considerably reduced. This effect is most marked in specimens from the deeper zone of cartilage and in specimens which are aligned perpendicularly to the superficial cleavage pattern. The effect is very small in specimens from the superficial zone tissue which are aligned parallel to the cleavage pattern. In contrast, the stiffness at higher values of stress is not significantly reduced.

The tensile fracture strength of cartilage is not reduced by any of the enzymes mentioned above.

(h) Treatment of cartilage with purified clostridial collagenase causes the tensile stiffness at all levels of stress to be reduced, irrespective of the zone from which the specimens are excised or the orientation with respect to the superficial cleavage pattern.

The tensile fracture strength is also considerably reduced by the action of clostridial collagenase.

5. POISSON'S RATIO FOR CARTILAGE

Poisson's ratio for a material is the ratio between the strain in a direction which is perpendicular to the direction of the applied stress and the strain in the direction parallel to the applied stress. It is a property of a given material which may vary under different conditions.

If a uniform compressive stress is applied in the x direction to a cuboid of side lengths x, y and z, the resulting strain in these directions will be e_x, e_y and e_z. By definition

$$e_x = \frac{\delta x}{x}$$

where x = original dimension of the cuboid in the x direction,
δx = incremental change in x under the applied stress.

y, z, δy and δz are defined similarly.

Poisson's ratio in the y and z direction is given by the following expressions

$$v_y = \frac{e_y}{e_x} \text{ or } v_z = \frac{e_z}{e_x}$$

Usually, for a homogeneous and isotropic material, $v_y = v_z = v$.
The new volume, V, of the cuboid will be given by the expression

$$V_1 = x \cdot y \cdot z \, (1 - e_x)(1 + ve_x)^2 \qquad (19)$$

If, as is the case in most metals, in the elastic range e_x is sufficiently small for higher order terms $(e_x)^2$, $(e_x)^3$, etc. to be ignored, then certain conclusions can be drawn from manipulating equation (19). For example:

Since $x \cdot y \cdot z = V_0$, the original volume, equation (19) can be rewritten in the form

$$V_0 - V_1 = e_x \, (1 - 2v) \qquad (20)$$

Therefore a decrease in volume occurs if $v < 0.5$
the volume remains constant if $\qquad v = 0.5$
and an increase in volume occurs if $\qquad v > 0.5$

Therefore since the volume of cartilage clearly does not increase when loaded in compression, $v < 0.5$.

The corresponding equation when a cuboid of material is loaded in tension is

$$V_1 = x \cdot y \cdot z \, (1 + e_x)(1 - ve_x)^2 \qquad (21)$$

With the same assumptions as before (i.e. small strains) equation (21) can be written in the form:

$$V_1 - V_0 = e_x \, (1 - 2v) \qquad (22)$$

from which it can be seen that

an increase in volume occurs if $\qquad v < 0.5$
the volume remains constant if $\qquad v = 0.5$
and a decrease in volume occurs if $v > 0.5$

Since, during a tension test, the volume of cartilage tends to decrease due to fluid efflux, $v \geqslant 0.5$.

In articular cartilage it may not be valid to assume that the strains are sufficiently small to ignore second order terms and above. Certainly in experimental tests on isolated specimens of cartilage the mechanical strains may be very large. In this case, second order terms and above cannot be ignored and the following expressions should be used to determine Poisson's ratio.

Constant volume extension

$$V_1 = V_0$$

therefore
$$(1 + e_x)(1 - v \cdot e_x)^2 = 1$$

which gives
$$v = \left[1 - \sqrt{\frac{1}{(1 + e_x)}} \right] \div e_x \qquad (23)$$

When calculating Poisson's ratio for cartilage it is important to realize that some 70% of the volume of the tissue is occupied by water, most of which can be expressed under load. Therefore the volume of the tissue can decrease during a mechanical test. If, for example, the volume of the tissue decreases by 50% during a test procedure then the following expression may be used to calculate Poisson's ratio.

Half volume loss in extension

$$V_1 = \tfrac{1}{2}V_0$$

therefore
$$(1 + e_x)(1 - v \cdot e_x)^2 = \tfrac{1}{2}$$

which gives
$$v = \left[1 - \sqrt{\frac{1}{2(1 + e_x)}} \right] \div e_x \qquad (24)$$

In this case, if $e_x = 0.2$ for example, then $v = 1.77$. It can be seen, therefore, that the conditions of large strains and volume loss which may occur in experimental tests on cartilage do not prevent Poisson's ratio from taking values greater than unity.

To date, four investigations have been reported in which Poisson's ratio for cartilage has been determined.

Ranu (1967) subjected full-thickness, rectangular specimens of cartilage from the femoral heads of dogs to tensile loads and measured Poisson's ratio in the direction perpendicular to the articular surface at equilibrium. It was found that Poisson's ratio ranged between 0.4 and 0.6 approximately and that it was dependent on the magnitude of the strain in the direction of the applied tension.

Hayes (1970) calculated Poisson's ratio for cartilage from the following expression:

$$v(t) = \frac{3J(t) - 2B(t)}{2[3J(t) + B(t)]} \qquad (25)$$

in which $J(t)$ = creep compliance in shear, given by

$$J(t) = J_0 + \sum_{i=1}^{m} J_i[1 - \exp(-\gamma_i \cdot t)]$$

and $B(t)$ = bulk creep compliance, given by

$$B(t) = B_0 + \sum_{i=1}^{N} B_i[1 - \exp(-\beta_i \cdot t)]$$

Both $J(t)$ and $B(t)$ were determined experimentally. Poisson's ratio was found to decrease with time after application of the load with a range between 0.3 and 0.46 approximately. Instantaneous values of Poisson's ratio for tibial condylar cartilage ranged between 0.40 and 0.45.

Woo *et al.* (1976) determined values of Poisson's ratio from tension tests on cartilage and found it to range between 0.3 and 0.9.

Kempson (1970, unpublished data) also measured the Poisson's ratio for human femoral condylar cartilage from tension tests on specimens (200 μm in thickness) taken from all levels through the thickness of the tissue in the directions both parallel to and perpendicular to the superficial cleavage pattern. Using a photographic technique, measurements of the three strain components were made at predetermined intervals of the applied load. It proved technically difficult to measure accurately changes in the thickness of the specimens; however, such changes as were measured indicated that the value of Poisson's ratio was similar to that measured from changes in the width of the specimen. For this reason only, values obtained from changes in the width of the

Table 6.8 Poisson's ratio for human femoral condylar cartilage measured from tension tests in planes parallel to the articular surface (a) at an applied tensile force of 0.5N and (b) at a force just below that at fracture

Orientation of specimen to cleavage lines	Layer number from the surface (each layer 200 μm thick)	Poisson's ratio		
		As measured	As calculated at constant volume	As calculated at half volume loss
(a) Parallel	1	4.22	0.50	6.90
Parallel	7	1.00	0.48	3.17
Perpendicular	1	0.47	0.46	2.12
Perpendicular	7	0.42	0.46	3.35
(b) Parallel	1	3.30	0.45	2.55
Parallel	7	0.79	0.39	0.93
Perpendicular	1	0.40	0.33	0.61
Perpendicular	7	0.96	0.37	0.89

specimen are listed in Table 6.8, which shows values of Poisson's ratio measured at both the low applied tensile force of 0.5 N (0.11 lbf) and at fracture. It can be seen that the maximum values for Poisson's ratio were recorded for specimens from the superficial layer of cartilage when tested in the direction parallel to the cleavage pattern. The value at fracture was less than that recorded at an applied load of only 0.5 N (0.11 lbf). Other values of the Poisson's ratio recorded for superficial layer specimens which were orientated and tested perpendicularly to the cleavage pattern, and for specimens from the deeper layers of the tissue, ranged between 0.40 and 1.0, which is consistent with the range of values reported in the previous investigations.

Also shown in Table 6.8 are the values of Poisson's ratio for constant volume extension and for 50% volume loss as calculated from equations (23) and (24) respectively. It can be seen that the measured values fall between the two calculated values, thereby indicating that some volume decrease occurred during the tension tests.

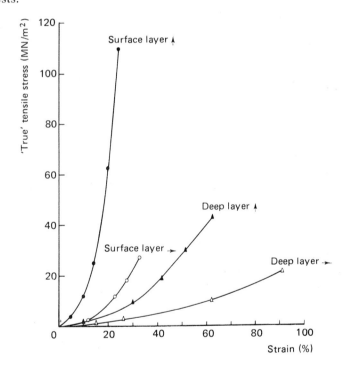

Figure 6.31 Curves of 'true' tensile stress/strain for femoral condylar cartilage. The 'true' stress was obtained by dividing the applied force by the corresponding cross-sectional area. Specimen: male 23 y, medial femoral condyle.

From measurements of Poisson's ratio the cross-sectional area of the specimens was calculated at predetermined values of the applied load and from these data 'true' stress (load ÷ actual cross-sectional area) versus strain curves were plotted. Figure 6.31 shows examples of these curves, from which it can be seen that the tensile stiffness decreased with depth and that specimens from the superficial layer were stiffer in the direction parallel to the cleavage pattern than those in the direction perpendicular to the cleavage pattern. These results were similar to those obtained by Woo *et al.* (1975) and they are consistent with the results obtained by Kempson *et al.* (1968, 1972) from curves of nominal stress (load ÷ original cross-sectional area) versus strain curves.

6. THE TENSILE FATIGUE OF CARTILAGE

To date the only published data on the tensile fatigue of articular cartilage are those of Weightman (1976a, b). The first of these two papers reported the results of tensile fatigue tests on isolated specimens of cartilage, cut from the superficial layer of more than 30 post-mortem human femoral heads. Three dumb-bell-shaped tensile specimens, aligned parallel to the predominant collagen fibre orientation and approximately 200 μm thick, were cut from each femoral head using the technique developed by Kempson *et al.* (1968) (see Section 4.1). Each of these specimens was subjected to cyclic tensile stress in the specially designed apparatus shown in Figure 6.32 until fracture occurred. The load cycle was such that the specimens were loaded for 1 s every 20 s, with the loaded phase being essentially a square wave with a rise time of approximately 0.1 s. Different specimens were subjected to different stresses, and the results were plotted on a graph of stress magnitude versus number of cycles to fracture. The results are shown in Figure 6.33, in which each datum point represents one tensile fatigue specimen. Data points from specimens cut from the same femoral head are joined to show individual fatigue curves. A considerable number of specimens either failed on the first application of load or had not failed after 10^5 cycles. These undefined data points are not shown.

Two main conclusions were drawn from these results: first, that cartilage exhibits a typical fatigue behaviour (i.e. the individual curves show that, as the magnitude of the applied cyclic stress decreases, an increasing number of load cycles is required to produce fracture); and secondly, that the fatigue resistance (or fatigue strength) of cartilage varies considerably from one femoral head to another.

The second of these two findings was unexpected since all of the specimens had been prepared from cartilage which, on the basis of Indian ink examination of the surface and proteoglycan analysis of full depth plugs, appeared to be normal. In order to investigate possible reasons for the variation in fatigue resistance the curves were analysed in the following way. It was assumed that the individual S-$\log_{10} N$ fatigue curves were straight lines, and the least mean square fit straight lines were calculated for the cartilage from each femoral head for which there were two or three data points. Each of these straight lines passed through a point given by the mean stress ($\bar{S}$) and the mean $\log_{10} N$ ($\overline{\log_{10}N}$) of the relevant data points. The mean value of the slope of all these straight lines was then calculated and found to be -1.83. Since the slopes of the individual fatigue curves were liable to large errors (because the stress on each specimen could be calculated to only $\pm 5\%$), it was then further assumed that the 'true' individual fatigue curves all had a slope of -1.83. By replotting the fatigue curves, each with a slope of -1.83 and each passing through its original ($\bar{S}$, $\log_{10}N$) points, a series of parallel S-$\log_{10}N$ curves was obtained, such that the intercept with the stress axis gave a quantitative measure of fatigue resistance. Since the intercept also represents the fracture stress of the cartilage (i.e. the stress to produce fracture on a single application) it was termed the 'projected' fracture stress.

Figure 6.32 Schematic diagram of tensile fatigue apparatus.

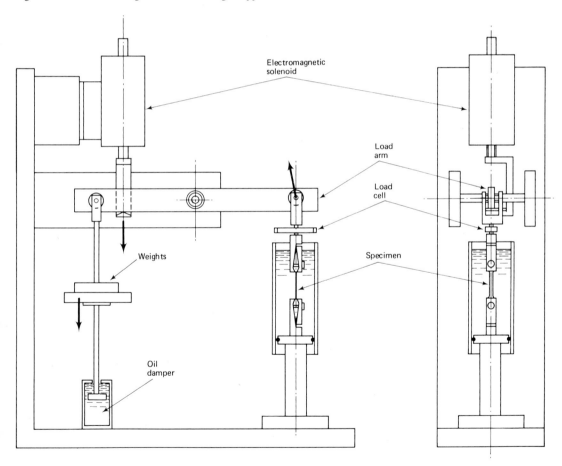

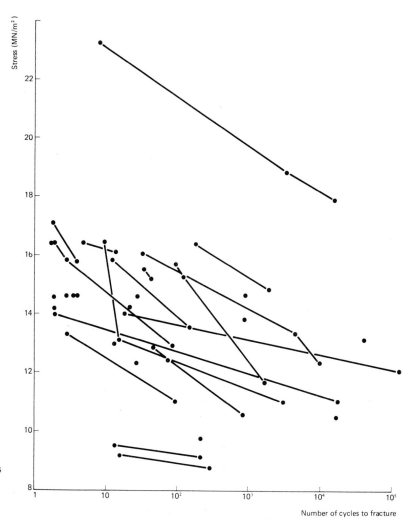

Figure 6.33 Tensile fatigue results (Weightman 1976a).

Having quantified fatigue resistance in this way, possible relationships between fatigue resistance and (a) the collagen content of the specimens, (b) the proteoglycan content of adjacent full depth plugs, and (c) the age of the cadavers from which the femoral heads were removed, were studied. No statistically significant correlations were obtained between fatigue resistance (projected fracture stress) and either collagen content or proteoglycan content (i.e. p values were greater than 0.1). Thus the observed variations in fatigue resistance could not be explained by the variations in collagen content (from 17 to 27% of wet weight) or by the variations in proteoglycan content. However, as Figure 6.34 shows, there was a marked decrease in fatigue resistance with

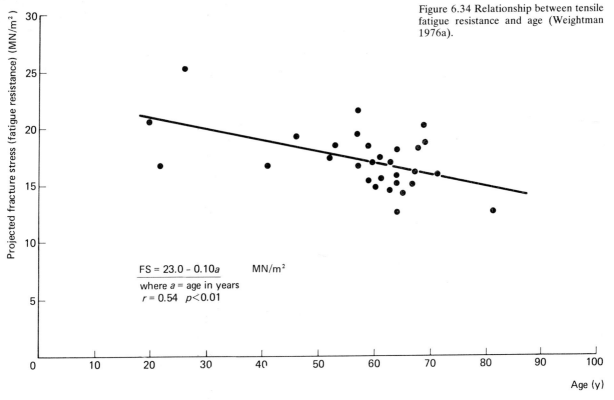

Figure 6.34 Relationship between tensile fatigue resistance and age (Weightman 1976a).

$$FS = 23.0 - 0.10a \qquad MN/m^2$$

where a = age in years
$r = 0.54 \quad p < 0.01$

age which was statistically significant ($p < 0.01$). The equation of the best fit straight line (least mean squares) relating fracture stress (FS) (i.e. fatigue resistance) and age was

$$FS = 23 - 0.1a \qquad MN/m^2$$

where a = age in years.

In an effort to estimate the possible physiological relevance of these results, the above age relationship was combined with the basic fatigue data to produce a single equation:

$$S = 23 - 0.1a - 1.83 \log_{10} N$$

where S = stress in MN/m^2,
$\qquad a$ = age in years,
$\qquad N$ = number of cycles to failure,

describing the fatigue behaviour of the superficial layer of femoral head cartilage. This equation was then used to extrapolate the experimental data to possible physiological stress levels. Figure 6.35 shows the effect of both age and stress magnitude on the number of load cycles required to produce cartilage fracture as predicted by the above equation. The drastic effect of age on the

Figure 6.35 Relationship between tensile fatigue life and age at different stress levels (Weightman 1976a).

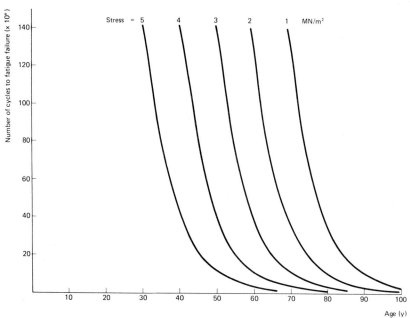

predicted number of cycles to fracture at each stress level is immediately apparent. For example, at a stress of 5 MN/m² (725 lbf/in²) 30-year-old cartilage has a predicted fatigue life of 140×10^6 cycles whereas 50-year-old cartilage has a predicted fatigue life of only 10×10^6 cycles. If 10^6 cycles is taken to represent one year's normal activity, 30-year-old cartilage might be expected to fracture after a further 140 years whereas 50-year-old cartilage might fracture after a further 10 years.

Two tentative conclusions were drawn from this analysis. Between 30 and 50 years of age a hip joint will be subjected to approximately 20×10^6 load cycles *in vivo*. Since this is significantly less than the reduction in predicted fatigue life of cartilage at physiologically likely stress levels (from 140×10^6 to 10×10^6 cycles at 5 MN/m² (725 lbf/in²) and an even greater reduction at lower stress levels), the decrease in fatigue resistance with age is apparently not due to a continuing fatigue process. Secondly, since 5 MN/m² (725 lbf/in²) is not an inconceivable *in vivo* tensile stress level, extrapolation of the experimental results suggests that the fatigue resistance of cartilage might decrease with age to such an extent that fatigue fracture of the material could occur in life.

Weightman (1976b) reported the results of a second series of nine tensile fatigue tests in which more accurate individual fatigue curves were obtained by testing a larger number of specimens from

404

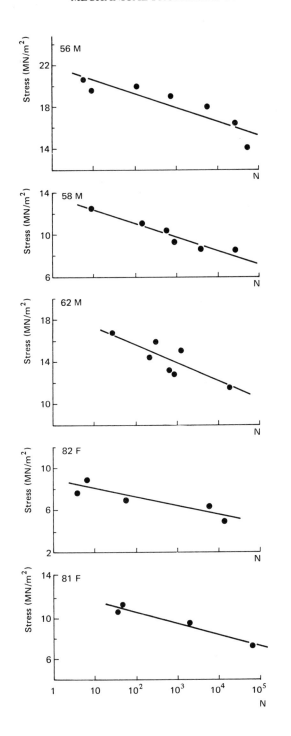

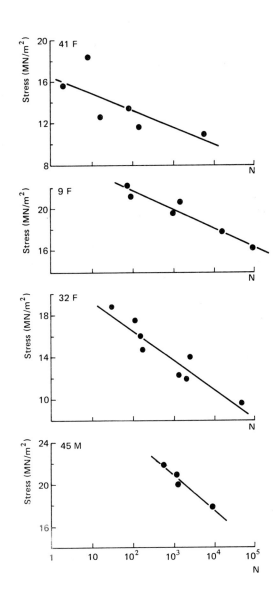

Figure 6.36 Individual tensile fatigue curves. N, number of cycles. (Weightman 1976b.)

each femoral head. Figure 6.36 shows these results. The numbers and letters on each fatigue curve indicate the age and sex of the specimens.

These results supported the assumption made in the first series of tests that the individual S-$\log_{10}N$ fatigue curves are straight lines. Although there was some variation in the slope of these curves, the mean value of the second series was in close agreement with that from the first series. For these reasons the results were analysed (i.e. the fatigue resistance was quantified) in the same way.

Figure 6.37 shows the combined results of fatigue resistance (projected fracture stress) versus age from the first and second series of tests (Weightman 1976b). The additional data from the second series of tests (shown by the open circles in Figure 6.37) improved the statistical significance of the fatigue resistance/age relationship; i.e. the correlation coefficient was 0.63 (compared with 0.54) and the significance level was 1 in 1000 (compared with 1 in 100).

The best fit straight line of the combined data had a slope of -0.13 compared with -0.10 for the first series alone, indicating that the decrease in fatigue resistance with age is more rapid than the original results had suggested.

Figure 6.37 Relationship between tensile fatigue resistance and age (Weightman 1976b).

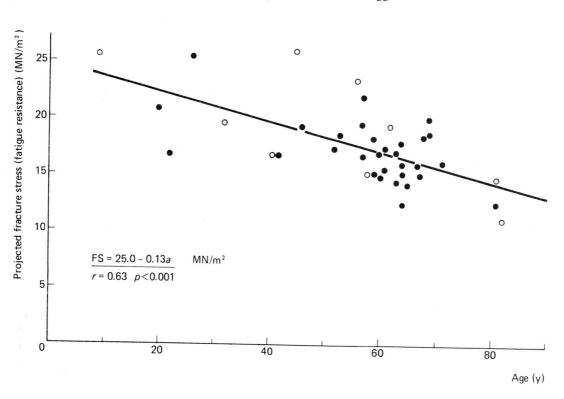

An interesting result was obtained when the fatigue resistance versus age data were divided by sex. As Figure 6.38 shows, there was much less scatter in the female data than in the male data (i.e. a higher coefficient of correlation and a greater statistical significance for the female data. Thus at any given age there appears

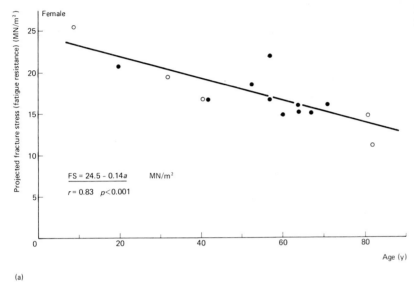

(a)

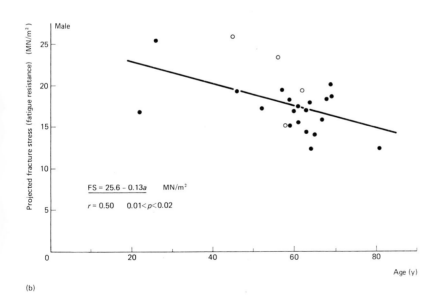

(b)

Figure 6.38 Relationship between tensile fatigue resistance and age (Weightman 1976b): (a) female; (b) male.

to be a wider variation in fatigue resistance in men than in women. The speculation was advanced that if cartilage fatigue is pathologically important, this finding might be related to the higher incidence of osteoarthrosis in women than in men.

7. THE COMPRESSIVE FATIGUE OF CARTILAGE

A number of workers have studied the effect of cyclically applied compressive stress on articular cartilage.

Radin and Paul (1971) investigated the effect of repeated impact loads on the wear of cartilage. When bovine metacarpophalangeal joints were oscillated in an arthrotripsometer for 500 h (1 200 000 cycles), under a constant load of 4.45 kN (645 lbf/in^2) with veronate buffer as lubricant, there were no visible signs of cartilage wear. In contrast, when the steady load was reduced to 2.225 kN (323 lbf/in^2) and an additional impulsive load of 2.225 kN (323 lbf/in^2) was applied during a 2 s pause in each cycle, surface roughening was produced in a centrally located area of the cartilage after 48 000 cycles and this progressed to bone exposure after 192 000 cycles. The most likely explanation of these results is that fatigue failure in cartilage, produced by repeated impulsive loading, led to an accelerated wear rate when sliding under steady load.

Simon, Radin, Paul and Rose (1972) subjected the knee joints of young adult guinea-pigs to cyclic impaction on a specially designed vibration table. The table produced an impaction force of approximately the weight of the animals 25 times per second and each joint was loaded daily for 15 min (i.e. 22 500 impacts per day). Groups of animals were sacrificed at daily intervals from 3 to 7 days and then weekly to 3 weeks. Histological studies of the cartilage with safranin O showed mild proteoglycan loss on day 5 (i.e. after approximately 100 000 impacts), progressing to severe proteoglycan loss and fibrillation by week 3.

Radin, Parker, Pugh, Steinberg, Paul and Rose (1973) subjected the knee joints of mature white New Zealand rabbits to daily 1 h periods of impulsive loading (equivalent to body weight) at a rate of 1 impact per second (i.e. 3600 impacts per day). Pairs of animals were sacrificed at 2-day intervals up to 30 days and at 36 days. Using safranin O, surface proteoglycan loss was detected at day 20 (i.e. after 72 000 impacts), deep proteoglycan loss at day 28 (100 000 impacts), and gross cartilage changes at day 30.

In both of the above series of experiments data were presented to show that the stiffness of the subchondral bone in the tested joints increased before proteoglycan loss was detected in the cartilage. In the light of this finding, cartilage destruction was attributed to increased stresses experienced by the tissue as a result of a preceding decrease in the shock-absorbing capacity of the subchondral bone. Although this is clearly one interpretation of the data, an alternative interpretation is that the observed cartilage and bone changes represent the independent response of each tissue to cyclic loading.

Weightman, Freeman and Swanson (1973) reported the results of one experiment in which surface damage had been produced in post-mortem femoral head cartilage (from a 47-year-old female) after the application, via a hemispherical Perspex indenter, of 90 000 compressure load cycles at a nominal stress of 2 MN/m² (290 lbf/in²). Figure 6.39 shows the damage produced after the

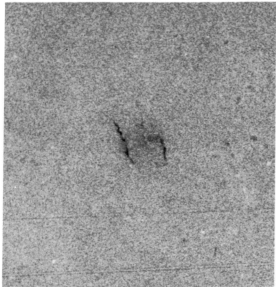

Figure 6.39 Surface splits produced by compressive fatigue (Weightman *et al.* 1973).
    Specimen: femoral head cartilage from a 47-year-old female.
    Nominal stress: 2.0 MN/m² (285 lbf/in²).
    No. of cycles: 90 × 10³.

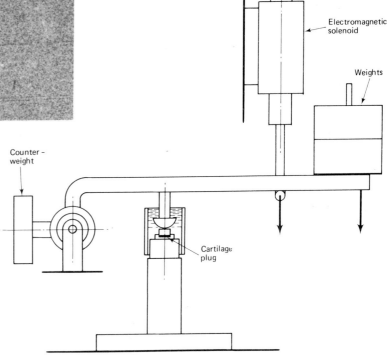

Figure 6.40 Schematic diagram of compressive fatigue apparatus; 3.18 mm diameter hemispherical Perspex indenters.
    Nominal stress: 3.78 MN/m² (550 lbf/in²).

409

cartilage surface had been washed with Indian ink. The two splits were thought to resemble certain types of osteoarthrosic fibrillation in that they were parallel to the predominant surface collagen fibre orientation as shown by pin pricking. Fixed charge density measurements showed (a) that the cartilage had a proteoglycan content typical of normal cartilage before the test, and (b) that surface splitting had occurred in the absence of proteoglycan loss from the tested region.

Continuation of this work (Weightman, unpublished), with the apparatus shown in Figure 6.40 has produced surface splitting in 5 of the 15 specimens tested to date. Further examples of the splitting produced are shown in Figures 6.41 and 6.42. Although

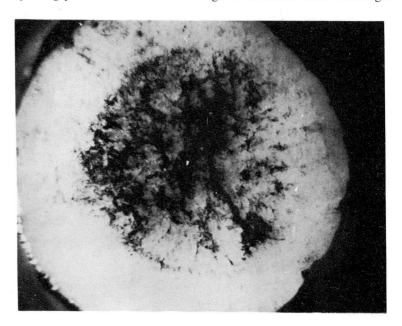

Figure 6.41 Surface splits produced by compressive fatigue.

Specimen: femoral head cartilage from a 55-year-old female; 6 mm diameter plug.

Nominal stress: 3.78 MN/m^2 (550 lbf/in^2).

Number of cycles: 500×10^3.

Note: splits produced by pin pricking (not shown) ran in a N–S direction.

the number of specimens so far tested is too small for definite conclusions to be drawn, it is perhaps worth noting, in view of the wider variation in the tensile fatigue strength of cartilage in men than in women (reported in Section 6), that surface splitting has been produced in 4 of the 5 specimens obtained from female cadavers, but in only 1 of the 8 specimens obtained from male cadavers (2 specimens, which did not develop splits, were of unrecorded sex).

Johnson, Dowson and Wright (1976) subjected 5.5 mm diameter plugs of post-mortem human cartilage, cut from femoral condyles, to a repetitive compressive stress of 5.6 MN/m^2 (812 lbf/in^2) using a flat metal platen. Surface splits visible to the naked eye were produced in 3 of the 11 tested specimens. The age and number of cycles to splitting of these specimens were: 26 years, 3600 cycles; 54 years, 7200 cycles; and 22 years, 20 000 cycles. Unfortunately, the sex of the cadavers from which the specimens were obtained were not reported.

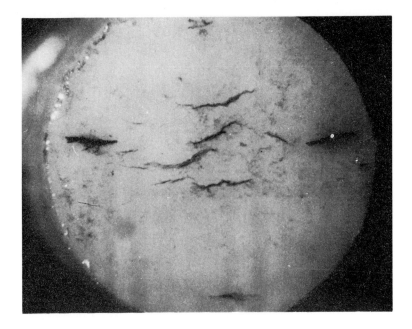

Figure 6.42 Surface splits produced by compressive fatigue.

Specimen: femoral head cartilage from a 55-year-old male; 6 mm diameter plug.

Nominal stress: 3.78 MN/m² (550 lbf/in²).

Number of cycles: 420×10^5.

Note: splits at N, S, E and W were produced by pin pricking.

In summary, cyclic compressive loading has been shown to produce (a) the destruction of cartilage when bovine metacarpophalangeal joints are run in a joint simulator, (b) cartilage degeneration in the knee joints of living animals, and (c) surface defects similar to early osteoarthrosic changes in some postmortem human cartilage.

REFERENCES

Bär E. (1926) Elasticitätsprufungen der Gelenkknorpel. *Arch. Entwicklungsmech. Organ.* **108,** 739.

Benninghoff A. (1924) Experimentelle untersuchungen über den Einfluss verschiedenartiger mechanischer Beanspruchung auf den Knorpel. *Verh. anat. Ges. (Jena)* **33,** 194.

Benninghoff A. (1925a) Die modellierenden und former haltenden Faktoren de Knorpelreliefs. *Z. Anat. Entwickl.-Gesch.* **76,** 43.

Benninghoff A. (1925b) Form und Bau der Gelenkknorpel in ihren Beziehungen zu Funktion. II: Der Aufbau des Gelenkknorpel in seinen Beziehungen zu Funktion. *Z. Zellforsch.* **2,** 783.

Benninghoff A. (1939) *Lehrbuch der Anatomie des Menschen,* Vol. 1. Lehmann, Munich.

Burleigh M. C., Barrett A.J.and Lazarus G. S. (1974) Cathepsin B1: a lysosomal enzyme that degrades native collagen. *Biochem. J.* **137,** 387.

Byers P. D., Contempomi C. A. and Farkas T. A. (1970) Postmortem study of the hip joint. *Ann. rheum. Dis.* **29,** 15.

Cameron, H. U., Pillar, R. M. and MacNab, I. (1975) The microhardness of articular cartilage. *Clin. Orthop.* **108,** 275.

Clarke, I. C. (1971) Articular cartilage: a review and scanning electron microscope study. *J. Bone Jt Surg.* **53B,** 732.

Coletti J. M., Akeson W. H. and Woo S. L. Y. (1972) A comparison of the physical behavior of normal articular cartilage and the arthroplasty surface. *J. Bone Jt Surg.* **54A,** 147.

Contini R., Gage H. and Drillis R. (1965) Human gait characteristics. *Biomechanics and Related Bioengineering Topics.* Ed. by R. M. Kenedi, p. 413. Pergamon Press, Oxford.

Elmore S. M., Sokoloff L., Norris G. and Carmeci P. (1963) Nature of imperfect elasticity of articular cartilage. *J. appl. Physiol.* **18,** 393.

Fantuzzo D. G. and Graziatti G. (1967) A mathematical model for articular cartilage. *Digest of the Seventh International Conference on Medical and Biological Engineering.* Stockholm.

Fick R. (1904–1911) *Handbuch der Anatomie und Mechanik der Gelenke,* Vols I–III. Fischer, Jena.

Freeman M. A. R., Kempson G. E. and Swanson S. A. V. (1973) Variations in the physico-chemical and mechanical properties of human articular cartilage. 2: Mechanical properties. *Perspectives in Biomedical Engineering,* Ed. by R. M. Kenedi, pp. 157–161. Macmillan, London.

Freeman M. A. R., Swanson S. A. V. and Manley P. T. (1975) Stress-lowering function of articular cartilage. *Med. Biol. Engg* **13,** 245.

Göcke E. (1927) Elastizitätsstudien am jungen und alten Gelenkknorpel. *Verh. dt. orthop. Ges.* p. 130.

Graham J. D. and Walker T. W. (1973) Motion in the hip: the relationship of split patterns to surface velocities. *Perspectives in Biomedical Engineering,* Ed. by R. M. Kenedi, pp. 161–165. Macmillan, London.

Greenwald A. S. (1970) The Transmission of Forces through Animal Joints. DPhil. Thesis, University of Oxford.

Hayes W. C. (1970) Mechanics of Human Articular Cartilage. PhD Thesis, Northwestern University, USA.

Hayes W. C. and Mockros L. F. (1971) Viscoelastic properties of human articular cartilage. *J. appl. Physiol.* **3,** 562.

Hayes W. C., Keer L. M., Herrmann G. and Mockros L. F. (1972) A mathematical analysis for indentation tests of articular cartilage. *J. Biomechanics* **5,** 541.

Hertz H. R. (1881) On the contacts of elastic solids. *J. reine angew. Math.* **92,** 156.

Hertz H. R. (1895) 'Gesammelte Werke' 1, p.155.

Hertz H. R. (1896) *Miscellaneous Papers,* p. 146. Macmillan, London.

Hirsch C. (1944) A contribution to the pathogenesis of chondromalacia of the patella. *Acta chir. scand.* **90,** Suppl. **83,** 9.

Hori R. Y. and Mockros L. F. (1976) Indentation tests of human articular cartilage. *J. Biomechanics* **9,** 259.

Hultkrantz J. W. (1898) Über die Spaltrichtungen der Gelenkknorpel. *Verh. anat. Ges. (Kiel).*

Johnson G. R., Dowson D. and Wright V. (1975) A new approach to the determination of the elastic modulus of articular cartilage. In Conference on Articular Cartilage. *Ann. rheum. Dis.* **34,** Suppl. 2, 116.

Johnson G. R., Dowson D. and Wright V. (1976) The fracture of articular cartilage under impact loading. Third Leeds-Lyon Symposium on Tribology.

Kempson G. E. (1970) Mechanical Properties of Human Articular Cartilage. PhD Thesis, University of London.

Kempson G. E. (1972) The tensile properties of articular cartilage and their relevance to the development of osteoarthrosis. *Orthopaedic Surgery and Traumatology,* pp. 44–58. Proceedings of the 12th International Society of Orthopaedic Surgery and Traumatology, Tel Aviv. Excerpta Medica, Amsterdam.

Kempson G. E. (1975a) Mechanical properties of articular cartilage and their relationship to matrix degradation and age. *Ann. rheum. Dis.* **34**, Suppl. **2**, 111.

Kempson G. E. (1975b) The effects of proteoglycan and collagen degradation on the mechanical properties of adult human articular cartilage. *Dynamics of Connective Tissue Macromolecules.* Ed. by P. M. C. Burleigh and A. R. Poole, pp. 277–305. North-Holland/American Elsevier, Amsterdam.

Kempson G. E., Freeman M. A. R. and Swanson S. A. V. (1968) Tensile properties of articular cartilage. *Nature (Lond.)* **220**, 1127.

Kempson G. E., Freeman M. A. R. and Swanson S. A. V. (1971) The determination of a creep modulus for articular cartilage from indentation tests on the human femoral head. *J. Biomechanics.* **4**, 239.

Kempson G. E., Muir H., Freeman M. A. R. and Swanson S. A. V. (1970) Correlations between the compressive stiffness and chemical constituents of human articular cartilage. *Biochim. biophys. Acta* **215**, 70.

Kempson G. E., Spivey C. J., Swanson S. A. V. and Freeman M. A. R. (1971) Patterns of cartilage stiffness on normal and degenerate human femoral heads. *J. Biomechanics* **4**, 597.

Kempson G. E., Muir H., Pollard C. and Tuke M. (1972) The tensile properties of the cartilage of human femoral condyles related to the content of collagen and glycosaminoglycans. *Biochim. biophys. Acta* **297**, 456.

Kempson G. E., Tuke M. A., Dingle J. T., Barrett A. J. and Horsfield P. H. (1976). The effects of proteolytic enzymes on the mechanical properties of adult human articular cartilage. *Biochim. biophys. Acta* **428**, 741.

Lebedev N. N. and Ufliand I. A. (1958) Axisymmetric contact problem for an elastic layer. *J. appl. Math. Mech. (PMM)* **22**, 442.

Linn F. C. and Sokoloff L. (1965) Movement and composition of interstitial fluid of cartilage. *Arthritis Rheum.* **8**, 481.

Maroudas A., Muir H. and Wingham J. (1969) Correlation of fixed negative charge with glycosaminoglycan content of human articular cartilage. *Biochim. biophys. Acta* **177**, 492.

Maroudas A., Bullough P. G., Swanson S. A. V. and Freeman M. A. R. (1968). The permeability of articular cartilage. *J. Bone Jt Surg.* **50B**, 166.

McCutchen C. W. (1962) The frictional properties of animal joints. *Wear* **5**, 1.

Meachim G. (1972). Light microscopy of Indian ink preparations of fibrillated cartilage. *Ann. rheum. Dis.* **31**, 457.

Murray M. P., Gore D. R. and Clarkson B. H. (1971) Walking patterns of patients with unilateral hip pain due to osteo-arthritis and avascular necrosis. *J. Bone Jt Surg.* **53A**, 259.

Paul J. P. (1965) Bio-engineering studies of the forces transmitted by joints. II: Engineering analysis. *Biomechanics and Related Bio-engineering Topics.* Ed. by R. M. Kenedi, p. 369. Pergamon Press, Oxford.

Pauwels F. (1959) Structure of the tangential fibrous layer of the articular cartilage in the scapular glenoid cavity as an example of an unsubstantiated strain field. *Z. Anat. Entwickl.-Gesch.* **121**, 188.

Radin E. L. and Paul I. L. (1971) Response of joints to impact loading. I. *Arthritis Rheum.* **14**, 356.

Radin E. L., Parker H. G., Pugh J. W., Steinberg R. S., Paul I. L. and Rose R. M. (1973) Response of joints to impact loading. III. *J. Biomechanics* **6**, 51.

Ranu H. S. (1967) *Rheological Behaviour of Articular Cartilage under Tensile Loads.* MSc Dissertation, University of Surrey, p. 26.

Rydell N. (1965) Forces in the hip-joint. II: Intra-vital measurements. *Biomechanics and Related Bio-engineering Topics.* Ed. by R. M. Kenedi, p. 351. Pergamon Press, Oxford.

Schäde H. (1912) Die Elastizitäts funktion des Bindegewebes und die intravitale Messung ihren Störingen. *Z. exp. Path. Ther.* **11**, 369.

Simon S. R., Radin E. L., Paul I. L. and Rose R. M. (1972) The response of joints to impact loading II. *J. Biomechanics* **5**, 267.

Simon W. H. (1971) Scale effects in animal joints. II: Thickness and elasticity in the deformability of articular cartilage. *Arthritis Rheum.* **14**, 493.

Sokoloff L. (1966) Elasticity of ageing cartilage. *Fed. Proc.* **25**, 1089.

Waters N. E. (1965a) The indentation of thin rubber sheets by spherical indenters. *Brit. J. appl. Physics* **16**, 557.

Waters N. E. (1965b) The indentation of thin rubber sheets by cylindrical indenters. *Brit. J. appl. Physics* **16**, 1387.

Weightman B. O. (1975). In-vitro fatigue testing of articular cartilage. *Ann. rheum. Dis.* **34**, Suppl. 2, 108.

Weightman B. (1976a) Tensile fatigue of human articular cartilage. *J. Biomechanics* **9**, 193.

Weightman B. (1976b) Variations in the tensile fatigue

resistance of human articular cartilage. Proceedings of the 22nd Annual Orthopedic Research Society Meeting, New Orleans, Jan. 28–30, 1976.

Weightman B., Freeman M. A. R. and Swanson S. A. V. (1973) Fatigue of articular cartilage. *Nature (Lond.)* **224,** 303.

Woo S. L. Y., Akeson W. H. and Jemmott G. (1976). A precision method of measuring the tensile properties of articular cartilage. Proceedings of the 22nd Annual Orthopedic Research Society Meeting, New Orleans, Jan. 28–30, 1976.

7. Friction, Wear and Lubrication

S. A. V. Swanson

1. INTRODUCTION

Common experience shows that a healthy synovial joint permits pain-free relative movements of the body segments connected by it, under a wide range of loads and at a wide range of speeds, all accompanied by remarkably low frictional forces and by very little wear of the cartilage surfaces. Thus the mechanics of load carriage and lubrication are an important part of the physiology of synovial joints, and must be supposed to depend in part on the properties of articular cartilage described in other Chapters, and in part on the properties of synovial fluid.

Load carriage (i.e. the transmission of forces through the cartilage itself) was discussed in Chapters 5 and 6; this Chapter is concerned with lubrication (i.e. the interaction between one layer of cartilage and the opposing layer or the fluid, if any, separating them).

Relative motion between two surfaces in contact is characterized by frictional forces and wear of one surface or both. In general engineering, the purpose of a lubricant may be to reduce friction, to protect against wear, or both; and in a synovial joint one can enquire into the means by which friction is made low, the means by which wear is limited, or both. The difficulty immediately arises that, whereas frictional forces can be measured at an instant, wear must be measured over a period of time, which raises the range of problems associated with either the use of animals for tests *in vivo* or the relevance to living tissue of long-term tests *in vitro*. Thus statements about friction in joints can usually be based on experimental observations, but statements about wear rarely can. When dealing with present knowledge of the phenomena of friction and wear, it is therefore convenient to discuss the two phenomena separately; but when possible explanations for the phenomena are discussed, it is more natural to consider them together.

Thus a series of questions such as the following may be posed about healthy synovial joints.

(a) What is the order of magnitude of the frictional forces?

(b) What is the nature of the frictional forces?

(c) Does the magnitude of the frictional forces depend on the presence of synovial fluid?

(d) What is the rate of wear?

(e) What is the mode of action of synovial fluid?

(f) To what extent do the properties of articular cartilage affect frictional forces or the rate of wear?

If the above questions can be answered in respect of healthy joints, two further questions will arise in respect of the early stages of joint degeneration.

(g) What effect may the softening and fibrillation of cartilage have on friction and wear in the joint?

(h) Does a partial or complete failure of lubrication cause fibrillation?

2. THE MAGNITUDE OF THE FRICTIONAL FORCES

2.1. Engineering Background

2.1.1. Coefficient of Friction. If a flat surface on one solid body is pressed against a flat surface on a second solid body, the presence of friction means that a certain force must be applied parallel to the flat surface in order to make one body move relative to the other. With many materials in the absence of deliberate lubrication, the limiting value of the frictional force to be overcome is found to obey a set of empirical laws. One of these is that the limiting value of the tangential force is, for a given pair of surfaces, a constant fraction of the normal force pressing the two surfaces together; this fraction is called the coefficient of friction for that pair of surfaces. Another of the laws is that the total frictional force to be overcome depends only on the total normal force, and not on the area over which it is distributed. This means that, as long as the unidirectional sliding of flat surfaces is considered, experiments on any size of rubbing surface should give the same result for the coefficient of friction.

When curved surfaces are considered the picture is less simple. For example, a spherical ball can be pressed into a matching hemispherical cup by means of a vertical force, and it will then be found that a certain minimum turning moment must be applied to the ball to make it rotate in any direction relative to the cup. The vertical force is transmitted from the ball to the cup as a large number of forces acting on small elements of the contact surface and therefore inclined at various angles to the vertical. Each of these small elements will contribute a frictional force when movement is started or attempted, and the turning moment which must be applied from outside is that which is needed to balance the sum of the moments of all these elemental frictional forces. Thus the relationship between the applied vertical force and the limiting frictional moment depends on the distribution of pressure over the contact area and on the extent of this area, as well as on the coefficient of friction for the two materials concerned. Conversely, if it is wished to derive a value for a coefficient of friction from experiments on bearings having curved surfaces, the calculations cannot be performed without a knowledge of, or assumptions about, the distribution of pressure. The degree of incongruity of the surfaces is relevant here. If, for example, the cup of a ball-and-socket joint is slightly larger in radius than is the ball, most of the force will be transmitted through a small area of contact on, or close to, the load axis, and the frictional situation is similar to that when two flat surfaces are pressed together. If, however, the ball has the larger radius, most of the force will be transmitted through an 'equatorial' region; large pressures will be exerted there and the frictional forces will be correspondingly high, and for a given vertical force acting on the whole joint an appreciably higher frictional moment will be developed than when the cup has the larger radius.

The above implies that the frictional forces are exerted by the surface of one body on the corresponding surface of the other, i.e. that no fluid film is present between the surfaces. If a fluid film is present, the frictional forces will in general be lower, and may have characteristics considerably different from those of the forces exerted between dry surfaces (these matters are considered below, in Section 3.1); but it is still possible to talk of a coefficient of friction, even though it is a property of the surfaces and the fluid together, and it may vary with load, relative velocity and the contact area.

2.1.2. Methods of Measuring Frictional Forces. The simplest possible method consists of pressing a block against a fixed surface with a measured force normal to the contact surfaces, and then measuring the force in the direction of motion needed to cause relative motion. If a repeated reciprocating motion is applied, and the forces are measured continuously, the effects, if any, of varying normal loads, of times under load or of progressive wear of the surfaces, can be observed. This method can be adapted to the rotational motion of bearings.

A different method (Stanton 1923) uses the fact that frictional forces cause a decay in the amplitude of the oscillations of a freely vibrating system. One of the simplest vibrating systems is a pendulum oscillating in the atmosphere, pivoted to a fixed frame. The combined effects of air resistance and whatever friction is

417

present in the pivot will produce observable changes in the amplitude of free vibrations of the pendulum, so that by recording the oscillations over a sufficient number of cycles and performing the necessary calculations (allowing, if necessary, for the effects of air resistance) the frictional forces in the pivot may be found.

2.1.3. Typical Values of Coefficients of Friction. Table 7.1 gives values, obtained by various methods related to those outlined above, for the coefficients of friction in various systems. Some of the systems are fluid-lubricated, and in them the frictional forces depend strongly on the properties of the fluid; others, though dry, contain significantly deformable solid surfaces, and in them the frictional forces may be expected to depend on the load; but the purpose of this Table is simply to show the range of orders of magnitude which are found in engineering systems, against which synovial joints can be considered.

Table 7.1. Typical values of coefficients of friction. (All these values are approximate: some are no more than orders of magnitude. More detailed figures, with the effects of various conditions, are given by Bowden and Tabor (1954).)

System	Coefficient of friction
Rubber tyre on dry road	1
Brake lining material against cast iron	0.4
Smooth metallic surfaces, specially cleaned and degassed	100
Steel shaft and bronze bush, oiled	0.2
Nylon against steel	0.3
PTFE against PTFE	0.07
Hydrodynamically lubricated bearing with oil	0.05
Hydrostatic air bearing	0.0005
Ball bearing	0.001

2.2. Level of Frictional Forces in Synovial Joints

2.2.1. Experiments on Entire Joints. Jones (1934) measured the static coefficient of friction. Stanton pendulums were used by Charnley (1959), Barnett and Cobbold (1962) and Little, Freeman and Swanson (1969). Unsworth, Dowson and Wright (1975) used a different type of pendulum in which the frictional turning moment was measured directly instead of being calculated from the observed decay of free oscillations. Linn (1967, 1968) developed and used a device called an arthrotripsometer, in which frictional forces can be measured while the load is varied rapidly and the joint positively moved in a cyclic fashion.

Typical values obtained by these workers are shown in Table 7.2. All the tests concerned were performed on cadaveric joints with synovial fluid present and all the workers except Jones had taken steps to exclude forces exerted by capsules or ligaments, which might act together with frictional forces and thereby give a misleading indication of the magnitude of the frictional forces.

Table 7.2. Coefficients of friction measured in entire synovial joints

Source	Joint	Coefficient of friction
Jones (1934)	Horse stifle	0.02
Charnley (1959)	Human ankle	0.014, 0.024
Barnett and Cobbold (1962)	Dog ankle	0.018–0.03
Linn (1968)	Dog ankle	0.0044
Little et al. (1969)	Human hip	0.003–0.015
Unsworth et al. (1975)	Human hip	0.02–0.042

Any attempt to perform experiments on a living joint in the body would face the problem that ligaments would exert forces probably greater than the frictional forces in the joint itself; and muscles, even with the subject anaesthetized, exert elastic and viscous forces. Thus measurements of 'joint stiffness' are not in fact measurements of joint friction, and nothing is known of any possible differences between the frictional characteristics of living and dead joints.

2.2.2. Experiments on Small Specimens. Experiments on entire joints have the obvious advantage that the constraints on the cartilage and the synovial fluid are preserved in as nearly as possible the same state as *in vivo*. One disadvantage is that, unless the joint surfaces are nearly flat, mechanical considerations arising from the shape of the loaded areas can make it difficult to calculate a coefficient of friction for the surfaces concerned. This disadvantage is avoided by the use of specimens small enough to be effectively flat, which can be rubbed against an opposing surface, but this method brings other disadvantages. One is that flat pieces of cartilage are necessarily restricted to dimensions of a few millimetres, particularly if, as is desirable, the subchondral bone is left in place, and therefore a length of relative movement comparable to that in living joints can be obtained only by rubbing a small piece of cartilage against a longer piece of some other material. Another disadvantage is that the flow of fluid in such a system, with the shorter flow path from the centre of the loaded area to its edges, may differ from that in an intact joint.

Table 7.3 gives coefficients of friction measured by various workers. All the results shown were obtained with synovial fluid as the lubricant.

Table 7.3. Coefficients of friction measured on small pieces of cartilage

Source	Bearing materials	Coefficient of friction
McCutchen (1966)	Articular cartilage on bone, against glass	0.008–0.1
Dowson et al. (1968)	Articular cartilage on bone, against glass, rubber or plastic	0.15–0.8
Walker et al. (1970)	Articular cartilage on bone, against glass	0.0014–0.07

2.3. Discussion

Comparison of the results in Tables 7.1 and 7.2 shows that the friction in synovial joints is low by engineering standards. The difficulties mentioned above in calculating the coefficient of friction from measurements made on curved surfaces may explain some of the differences between the results given in Table 7.2. Even the highest figures in that Table are, however, low compared with most of those in Table 7.1, particularly when it is remembered that the results in Table 7.2 were obtained at a range of rubbing speeds down to and including zero. The only engineering systems which can maintain such low coefficients at a range of speeds are hydrostatically pressurized sytems, in which the lubricant (oil or air) is continuously forced into the bearing by an external pump at a rate sufficient to maintain a fluid film in spite of the inevitable leakage at the edges of the loaded region, and systems with rolling rather than sliding elements, such as ball or roller bearings. Most engineering systems which function without a continuous fluid film tend to possess higher friction when starting from rest than when running. Plastics such as polytetrafluorethylene (PTFE) are free from this 'stick-slip' tendency, but their thermal conductivities are low, and the local temperature increases which accompany frictional forces can be greater than in materials which are better thermal conductors. This restricts their ability to maintain low frictional forces after repeated reversals of movement under stresses comparable to those sustained by articular cartilage in life.

Thus, considering not only the coefficient of friction but also the range of conditions in which it can be maintained, synovial joints can be seen to perform well by comparison with other systems at present known to engineers.

Two of the three sets of results in Table 7.3 are consistent with those in Table 7.2. That one set of results obtained on small specimens of cartilage should be significantly higher than those measured on entire joints is not in itself surprising in view of the factors considered above, but no explanation can be offered for the difference of up to two orders of magnitude between the results given by Dowson, Longfield, Walker and Wright (1968) and by Walker, Unsworth, Dowson, Sikorski and Wright (1970), all of which were obtained using the same apparatus.

3. THE NATURE OF THE FRICTIONAL FORCES

3.1. Engineering Background

3.1.1. Coulomb or Boundary Friction. The simple system of a dry block on a flat surface would possess frictional characteristics depending on the natures of the two solid surfaces in contact. Their roughnesses are obviously relevant, and so is the degree of contamination or cleanliness of the surfaces. Ordinary metallic surfaces in air, for example, are always oxidized to some extent, and usually have some water or other substances adsorbed or otherwise present. Such surface impurities restrict the frictional forces, and therefore, as shown in Table 7.1, effective cleaning of the surfaces results in higher frictional forces. If, instead of the surfaces being cleaned, they are deliberately 'contaminated' with a substance chosen for its ability to be adsorbed by the surfaces and to remain adsorbed at a range of loads and rubbing speeds, whilst having a molecular structure offering little resistance to relative motion of the two adsorbed layers, boundary lubrication is said to exist.

Both dry and boundary-lubricated surfaces exert frictional forces which obey (approximately) certain empirical 'laws', the most important of which are that the frictional force which must be overcome in order to start movement is proportional to the force normal to the surfaces (the constant of proportionality being the coefficient of friction), and classically is taken as being independent of both the area of contact and the rubbing speed, below a certain (low) value of the latter.

3.1.2. Viscous Friction. If the solid surfaces are completely separated by an unbroken film of fluid, the frictional forces depend on the properties of the fluid. If the film is thick enough to prevent contact between asperities on the surfaces, but not so thick, in relation to its viscosity and other factors, as to permit turbulent motion of fluid within the film, the frictional force to be overcome results from the shearing of the fluid and depends on the viscosity of the fluid. The frictional force is directly proportional to the relative speed of the two surfaces and to the wetted area, and inversely proportional to the film thickness. The film thickness in general depends on the normal force (larger forces will tend to produce thinner films) and in this indirect way the frictional force depends on the normal force.

3.1.3. Methods of Observation.

Clearly, experiments could be performed in which frictional forces were measured whilst two surfaces were rubbed together at a range of loads and speeds, but an easier form of experiment is provided by the differing effects of the two kinds of frictional forces on an otherwise freely vibrating system. As mentioned above, a Stanton pendulum enables the friction at the pivot bearing to be calculated from the decay of the pendulum's oscillations, but it is possible to go further. Some straightforward applied mathematics shows that the presence of boundary friction, independent of speed and load, will result in a linear decay of the amplitude of the pendulum's oscillations, whilst viscous friction will cause the amplitude to decay exponentially. Similar effects are produced in other vibrating systems. 'Viscous friction' in this context refers to an idealized system in which the friction varies directly and only with the speed. This is not always so.

This simple difference between boundary and viscous friction can be obscured if a system is lubricated with a fluid whose viscosity varies with the rate of shear to which it is subjected instead of a Newtonian fluid, i.e. one having a viscosity independent of shear rate. If the viscosity is lower at high rates of shear, the viscous force in a given film, instead of varying linearly with the instantaneous velocity, will be more nearly constant. If a bearing containing such a fluid is incorporated in a Stanton pendulum or other oscillating system, the behaviour of the system will tend to approach that associated with boundary friction. Synovial fluid is known to have a viscosity which varies with shear rate; the implications are considered below in Section 6.5.

3.2. Observations on Joints

Jones (1936) used a Stanton pendulum to measure the friction in a cadaveric human proximal interphalangeal finger joint. He concluded that both boundary and fluid film lubrication were present, the latter able to persist even under loads sufficient to crush the bone in the joint.

Charnley (1959) found that the decay of his pendulum's oscillations was linear, which suggested boundary rather than fluid friction. In comparing his results with those of Jones, Charnley pointed out that the capsule and ligaments, which were intact in the specimen used by Jones, would have exerted forces which, added to the frictional forces between the cartilage surfaces, could have simulated the effect of fluid friction.

Barnett and Cobbold (1962), by removing the skin, tendons and ligaments in stages, were able to show that the frictional force between the cartilage surfaces was independent of the amplitude and hence of the speed of the oscillations (a characteristic of boundary friction).

The three sets of experiments just mentioned have as a common restriction the fact that the natural frequency of any one pendulum can be varied only within narrow limits, and that the full physiological range of rubbing speeds was therefore not used. Faber, Williamson and Feldman (1967) overcame this by using, instead of a pendulum, a spring-loaded vibrating device having a rabbit's knee as the frictional element. The frequency could be adjusted to give maximum rubbing speeds between the cartilage surfaces of from 40 to 100 mm/s. The decay of oscillations was neither purely linear nor purely exponential, and the results were analysed to yield a boundary frictional force and a viscous force, each each of which varied with the load on the joint.

The experiments of Little et al. (1969), referred to in Section 2.2.1, used a pendulum which was allowed to oscillate freely, having a cadaveric human hip as its pivot, at about 1 cycle/s.* This frequency of oscillation was within the range encountered in normal walking, although, as with any pendulum experiment, the range of rubbing speeds was limited and the highest rubbing speeds attained during a walking cycle were not reached. At each of three constant loads of 156, 556 and 956 N (35, 125 and 215 lbf) the decay of oscillations was always linear or nearly so, leading to the conclusion that the dominant frictional forces were boundary in nature.

Linn (1968) concluded from his experiments using his arthrotripsometer that both boundary and fluid film lubrication were present.

Unsworth et al. (1975) used a pendulum experiment which had been specially designed to permit the measurement of frictional moments (and hence, by calculation, frictional forces) from the instant of applying load. Since the frictional moments were measured directly instead of being calculated from the observed decay of oscillations, as by Little et al., information was available, in principle, about the variation of friction within cycles; but such information is not presented by the authors. From their observa-

* A conversion table for the Système International (SI) units is given on p. 545.

tion that the frictional forces increased gradually over a few cycles following the application of load, these authors concluded that fluid film lubrication was present, the increase in friction being caused by the reduction in film thickness as the loaded surfaces approached each other by squeezing out the film. The speed of oscillation was about the same as in the experiments of Little *et al.*

3.3. Summary

Since the experiments which set out to explore wider ranges of speeds (Faber *et al.* 1967; Linn 1967) have produced observations suggesting the simultaneous presence of boundary and fluid film lubrication at higher speeds, this must be accepted, although none of the published work so far cited makes it possible to state what proportion of the total friction force is provided by which mechanism in a representative human joint (e.g. the hip) at physiological ranges of load and speed.

At low speeds, one set of experiments has suggested boundary lubrication and one other fluid film lubrication with a varying film thickness. Further comment on these possibilities will be made when the mode of action of synovial fluid is discussed in Section 6, below.

4. THE EFFECT ON THE FRICTIONAL FORCES OF THE PRESENCE OF SYNOVIAL FLUID

4.1. Experiments on Entire Joints

Some of the experimenters whose work is referred to above have performed tests in which the synovial fluid was replaced by some other fluid, usually a saline solution, or was simply removed. The results of such tests are given in Table 7.4, from which it can be seen that the replacement of synovial fluid with saline solutions has always led to some increase in friction, although the highest values quoted in Table 7.4 from tests with saline solutions are still lower than some other values obtained with synovial fluid (Table 7.2).

The exact significance of such tests must always be obscure, because it is not possible to perform a test on a joint in which synovial fluid has never been present; thus if any constituent of the synovial fluid were adsorbed onto the cartilage surfaces, mere removal of the bulk fluid and its replacement with another fluid might not suffice to remove the effect of the former presence of synovial fluid. A surface treatment which could be guaranteed to remove all traces of adsorbed substances, without otherwise

Table 7.4. Coefficients of friction measured in synovial joints with or without synovial fluid.

Source	Joint	Load (N)	Fluid	Coefficient of friction
Linn (1968)	Dog ankle	178	Bovine synovial	0.0044
	Dog ankle	178	Buffered saline	0.0099
Linn and Radin (1968)	Dog ankle	178	Bovine synovial	(0.001) 0.0035–0.0052
	Dog ankle	178	Veronate buffer	(0.005) 0.0052–0.0103
Little et al. (1969)	Human hip	935	Own synovial	0.003–0.015
	Human hip	935	Ringer's	0.009–0.022
Radin, Paul and Pollock (1970)	Bovine MTP	980	Bovine synovial	0.006
	Bovine MTP	980	Veronate buffer	0.011
	Bovine MTP	3000	Bovine synovial	0.008
	Bovine MTP	3000	Veronate buffer	0.009
	Bovine MTP	5000	Bovine synovial	0.010
	Bovine MTP	5000	Veronate buffer	0.010
Unsworth et al. (1975)	Human hip	134	Own synovial	0.03–0.04
	Human hip	134	'Dry'	0.10–0.13
	Human hip	800	Own synovial	0.025
	Human hip	800	'Dry'	0.025–0.055
	Human hip	1500	Own synovial	0.025–0.03
	Human hip	1500	'Dry'	0.025–0.05

Where single values are quoted, these have been taken from the authors' reports of single values obtained in one set of tests; ranges of values have been taken from observations made in a number of tests involving several specimens. The single values quoted in parentheses from Linn and Radin are taken from one graph apparently based on one set of tests; they are hardly typical of the other results in the same paper.

affecting the cartilage surfaces, has not yet been discovered. Little et al. (1969), after removing the synovial fluid, wiped the cartilage surfaces three times with fresh tissues soaked in Ringer's solution, in an attempt to remove any adsorbed substances, but even then although the increase in the coefficient of friction was fairly consistent from one joint to another, there can be no certainty that the state of the joints was as if no synovial fluid had ever been present. Unsworth et al. (1975) also wiped the cartilage surfaces dry, but tested the joint in that state, without adding any liquid. They observed that the joint surfaces were nevertheless wet after loads had been applied during the tests.

A summary such as that contained in Table 7.4 cannot convey details of all aspects of the different testing techniques used, and fully detailed comparisons of the various results should therefore be made not on the basis of this Table but from a study of the original publications. All but Unsworth *et al.* reported essentially long-term experiments (Radin *et al.* (1970) ran their tests until a steady value was reached, which was about two hours), and the noticeably higher values reported by Unsworth *et al.* were recorded at shorter times after the application of load; these authors, in calculating coefficients of friction, made assumptions different from those made by Little *et al.* The loads applied in the various tests have been quoted in Table 7.4 to enable some comparisons to be made between different results, but since contact areas are not usually stated, the information is of limited use; Radin *et al.* did state that the contact area of their specimens was about 600 mm^2, and this gives an average contact stress at their highest load of about $8 \times 10^6 \, \text{N/m}^2$ (1160 lbf/in^2). In a typical human hip joint subjected to a force of three times body weight in level walking, the average contact stress would be about $1.5 \times 10^6 \, \text{N/m}^2$ (c. 220 lbf/in^2); thus these experiments covered the high end of the physiological range. In contrast, the experiments of Little *et al.* and those of Unsworth *et al.*, using loads corresponding to about 1.4 and 2.0 times body weight respectively, covered the low end of the physiological range. It is therefore interesting to note that within the range of loads employed by Unsworth *et al.* the difference between the friction with synovial fluid present and that with the joint 'dry' diminished considerably with increasing load (because the friction with the joint 'dry' fell as load increased), so that at higher loads the difference was barely significant.

4.2. Experiments on Small Specimens

McCutchen (1962, 1967) rubbed a small specimen of cartilage, attached to the subchondral bone, against glass. When the lubricant was synovial fluid the coefficient of friction varied from 0.008 on the application of load to 0.7 after 26 min under load; when water was used the coefficient of friction was from 0.02 to 0.2.

This test suffers from the same limitation as those mentioned above on entire joints, in that any specimen of articular cartilage must once have been wetted by synovial fluid. A similar experiment (McCutchen 1966), using a rubber-on-glass bearing, was free from this limitation, and also showed the friction to be lower with synovial fluid than with 0.9% saline.

4.3. Conclusion

The natural and obvious assumption has been made for a long time (e.g. Hunter 1743) that synovial fluid exists partly for the purpose of lubricating synovial joints. The results quoted above show, within their limitations, that saline solution can maintain frictional forces in joints at nearly the same low values as synovial fluid, but, as discussed above, it is never possible in a synovial joint to ensure that the saline is receiving no assistance from substances left behind on the cartilage surfaces by synovial fluid. Therefore it must be concluded that the low level of frictional forces in synovial joints depends, at least in part, on the presence of synovial fluid, although perhaps not to so great an extent as has sometimes been supposed.

5. WEAR OF ARTICULAR CARTILAGE

5.1. Engineering Background

5.1.1. Adhesive wear. When two surfaces are rubbed together under load, asperities on the two surfaces may adhere, and relative sliding movement will then be possible only if the adhesions are sheared. Unless the shearing takes place exactly along the surface of the original adhesion, material will have been removed from one surface or the other, and this is the phenomenon of adhesive wear. Clearly the severity of the wear depends on the strength of the adhesions in relation to those of the adjacent materials. A small change in the balance of these strengths may have little effect on the magnitude of the frictional (shearing) force but, by changing the plane of shearing, a large proportional effect on the volume of wear; thus frictional forces and wear rate are not necessarily correlated.

5.1.2. Abrasive Wear. Asperities on one surface may remove particles from the other surface in the manner of a cutting tool. Additionally, particles removed from one surface by adhesive wear may become detached from the surface to which they temporarily adhered, and may then remove material from one or both surfaces. The latter mechanism is sometimes called 'three-body abrasive wear' and the former 'two-body abrasive wear'.

5.1.3. Fatigue Wear. Cyclic variations in load, or cyclic movements of a bearing under constant load, impose cyclically varying stresses on elements of the material. Such cyclically varying stresses may cause fatigue fractures at, or close to, the surface, thereby making it more likely that particles will become detached.

5.2. Wear in Life in Normal Conditions

It is obvious that the rate of wear in healthy joints under normal conditions of use is extremely low, because otherwise ulceration after two or three decades of use would be normal, which it is not. Any discussion of wear (or of fatigue or any other process which essentially occurs over substantial periods of time) is likely to be unrealistic when concerned with a self-renewing material. It is an observed fact that the effective rate of wear is extremely low, but this could result from the replacement at a suitable rate of material which did wear at a significant rate. If this were so, debris from the cartilage must be released into the synovial fluid and would presumably be disposed of by some biological process; but if this were happening continuously, some debris would be expected to be present in transit in synovial fluid. As far as the present writer is aware, material quantities of such debris have never been described.

5.3. Wear in Life in Mechanically Severe Conditions

5.3.1. Observations. A few experiments have been reported in which certain joints of living animals were subjected to combinations of loads and movement more severe than would occur in normal use.

Simon, Radin, Paul and Rose (1972) subjected the knee joints of guinea-pigs to repeated impact loading, but no motion was allowed and this therefore cannot be regarded as a wear test (cartilage degeneration was observed over a three-week period, and this result is considered in Chapter 6). Similar experiments, but using rabbits, were reported by Radin, Parker, Pugh, Steinberg, Paul and Rose (1973).

Seireg and Gerath (1975) reported tests in which rats' knee joints were held in 90° of flexion while a constant compressive force of about 1.5, 3 and 6 times body weight was applied along the axis of the tibia. The distal end of the leg was held in a fixed clamp, and the proximal tibia was pulled forwards, through a pad on the posterior aspect of the leg, at 25 cycles/s. From the authors' description, it appears that a small sliding movement, exploiting the laxity of the flexed knee, was imposed, rather than any movement which would occur in normal use. One knee in each of nine rats was tested thus, the other knee being used as a control. Tests were conducted for 2 or 3 h per day for 14 days, after which the animals were killed and the cartilage (from which bone the authors do not say) was examined histologically and by scanning electron microscopy. Cartilage from the loaded joint was rougher than that from the unloaded joint, and displayed surface pits and tears. Debris in the synovial fluid was apparently not sought.

5.3.2. Discussion. This one set of results sheds no light on the mechanism by which the observed changes were brought about; they may or may not have been consequences of wear.

5.4. Wear in Life with Synovial Fluid Modified

5.4.1. Observations. Key (1933) injected the knees of adult rabbits with various fluids; three injections each of 1–2 cm^3 were given per week, the total number ranging from eight to twenty-eight. The fluids were: distilled water, NaCl at 0.85% and at 10%, N/50 HCl in 0.85% NaCl, and N/50 NaOH in 0.85% NaCl. The animals were killed from 1 to 85 days after the last injection, and the joints excised and examined. All fluids gave substantially the same results as far as the cartilage was concerned: fibrillation, erosion, eburnation and marginal thickening.

Bentley, Kreutner and Ferguson (1975) treated one knee of each of 70 mature rabbits by excising the synovium from the medial and lateral compartments and from the suprapatellar pouch and the infrapatellar fat pad, whilst leaving the posterior capsule and the menisci undisturbed. The animals were left free in their cages until they were killed after from 4 to 110 days. No abnormality was detected in the cartilage of the 20 animals killed after 4, 25 and 50 days (with the exception of one specimen in one animal killed at 25 days); at 85 and 110 days some specimens were showing superficial matrix depletion and some showed fibrillation. The period between 85 and 110 days was when the synovium was regenerating.

5.4.2. Discussion. Both experiments show that gross interference with synovial fluid led to fibrillation, but neither experiment is easy to interpret. Leaving aside the acid and alkali employed by Key, his finding that repeated massive dilution of synovial fluid with water or salt solution of approximately physiological strength was associated with cartilage damage is compatible with the view that the fibrillation resulted from wear which occurred because the protective action of synovial fluid was impaired. To substantiate this, information would be needed about the dilution of the synovial fluid during the periods between injections. The results of Bentley *et al.* are compatible with the same view, but the interpretation of these tests is complicated by the presumed presence of other fluids, notably blood, in contact with the cartilage surfaces for part of the experimental period.

5.5. Wear in vitro

5.5.1. Observations. Jones (1934) reported that an equine stifle joint, washed with normal saline and dried, emitted steam and debris after being subjected to cyclic movement for 4 h under a load of 496 N (50 kgf).

Barnett (1956) performed experiments on exised rabbit ankle joints, one of each pair being injected with hyaluronidase and the other with water or buffer solution. Immobilization for 36 h produced no abnormality in either joint. Repeated dorsi- or plantar flexion under no load produced definite attrition in the hyaluronidase-treated joint after 48 h, but not after shorter periods. The same movement but under a constant or an intermittent compressive load gave some wear in both joints, but more in that treated with hyaluronidase.

Radin and Paul (1971) tested the sagittal halves of bovine metatarsophalangeal joints in an arthrotripsometer adapted so that impulsive loads could be applied during the test. A constant load of 4450 N (454 kgf) (about two-thirds of the load which caused crushing of the cancellous bone of the joints) gave no obvious changes in the cartilage after 1.2×10^6 cycles of oscillation. In tests using the same conditions except that the steady load was 2225 N (226 kgf) and an additional impulsive load of 2225 N (226 kgf) was applied during a 2-second pause in each cycle, gross damage occurred: within 24 000 cycles peripheral fissures appeared; after 48 000 cycles the central area of cartilage began to roughen; after 72 000 cycles the second layer became exposed; and at 192 000 cycles the bone was exposed. In all these tests veronate buffer solution was used instead of synovial fluid, because earlier tests (quoted in Table 7.4) had shown that at the loads in question the friction-reducing property of synovial fluid (unfortunately referred to by the authors as its 'lubricating advantage') was negligible.

W. H. Simon (1971) reported tests in which articular cartilage from human patellae and canine femoral heads was abraded by a rotary file run backwards. The depth of penetration was measured, and the debris was collected and weighed. Synovial fluid gave lower wear rates than saline solution; the difference was eliminated by predigesting the synovial fluid with trypsin but not by predigesting with hyaluronidase.

5.5.2. Discussion. The results of Radin and Paul can be distinguished from the others because the cartilage damage resulted from the application of an impulsive load while the joint was stationary. The obvious explanation is that the addition of a stress cycle led to fatigue failure in the cartilage which in turn led to breakdown of the cartilage when sliding under steady load. It therefore seems unlikely that abrasive or adhesive wear was the mechanism, but fatigue wear could have been: whether the phenomenon should be classed as one of fatigue or one of wear is as much a question of semantics as of physical fact.

The results of Jones, of Barnett and of Simon, taken together, show that cartilage lubricated by saline solution wears at a greater rate than when synovial fluid is present.

6. THE MODE OF ACTION OF SYNOVIAL FLUID

6.1. Engineering Background

6.1.1. Boundary Lubrication. This has been described above, in Section 3.1.1, but is mentioned again here for continuity. To demonstrate its presence, one should ideally show (a) that an identifiable surface layer can be adsorbed, and (b) that the frictional forces obey the appropriate laws (proportionality to normal force, independence of contact area and rubbing speed).

6.1.2. Hydrostatic Lubrication. This also has been described above. Unless the film were unusually thick or the speed unusually high in relation to the viscosity of the fluid, the frictional forces would be expected to be those due to the shearing of the fluid, and would therefore, in a given bearing, be proportional to the relative speed of the two components and to the viscosity of the fluid, provided that the fluid supply was such as to maintain the film thickness constant. To show that a bearing is lubricated hydrostatically, it is necessary also to show how the necessary pressure is supplied.

6.1.3. Squeeze-film Lubrication. If two solid surfaces are forced together with a fluid film between them, fluid will tend to flow out of the film, the thickness of which will therefore tend to decrease with increasing time under load, unless (as in hydrostatic lubrication) the supply of fluid under pressure is maintained from some source outside the loaded film. If the fluid is sufficiently viscous and the load is applied intermittently, the fluid film may persist for a time long enough to be useful, and, if expressed fluid remains close to the edges of the loaded region, it may be re-imbibed when the load is removed. Such a system is said to be lubricated by a squeeze-film, and this is clearly one possible mode to be considered in respect of synovial joints.

6.1.4. Hydrodynamic Lubrication. In some engineering systems a wedge-shaped film of fluid can be maintained between two sliding surfaces by the action of hydrodynamic forces in the fluid itself.

This action, which was first described mathematically by Reynolds (1886), depends upon (a) the fact that one surface is sliding relative to the other, and (b) the existence of either a fixed taper in the bearing clearance or some freedom of relative alignment of the two surfaces, allowing a wedge-shaped gap to be formed (a common example is provided by the crankshaft bearings of car engines, which possess small radial clearances and are free to move so that these clearances are eccentrically distributed, thus forming a film of varying thickness). Thus this mode could not operate in synovial joints at rest, but it must be considered as a possibility for joints in motion. The frictional forces obey laws which are less simple than those of the simple shearing of a viscous fluid, as in hydrostatic or squeeze-film lubrication; in particular, there is a limiting speed below which (for given conditions) the lubrication régime cannot be maintained.

6.1.5. Elastohydrodynamic Lubrication. In the hydrodynamic mode just mentioned, considerable pressures exist in the loaded region of the fluid film, and therefore are applied to the solid surfaces in that region. If the resulting deformations of the surfaces are not negligible in comparison with the general shape of the bearing surfaces and the film thickness, the régime is said to be elastohydrodynamic.

6.1.6. Desirable Measurements. In attempting to discover by what means a given bearing was lubricated, one could measure the frictional forces and their dependence on load, time and speed, which would show whether boundary or fluid film lubrication was present, and in the latter event would give some indication of how the film was maintained (e.g. if the friction was high below a certain speed at a given load, and lower above that speed, this would suggest that hydrodynamic or elastohydrodynamic lubrication was present).

To go further, one would need information about the properties of the fluid and of the bearing surfaces. The viscosity of the fluid and its dependence, if any, on shear rate, temperature and pressure would be relevant. Concerning the bearing surfaces, one would wish to know their stiffness and their roughness. Thermal conductivities and coefficients of thermal expansion would be relevant in some contexts but need hardly be considered here.

In some types of bearing, the thickness of the fluid film can be measured (e.g. by electrical methods when, as is usual, the resistivity of the fluid differs from that of the solid components of the bearing).

Some obvious difficulties arise when the attempt is made to investigate synovial joints in the manner just outlined. The measurements of frictional forces can be and have been made. Several workers have measured the viscosity of synovial fluid, but it has been found to depend on the shear rate (i.e. the relative velocity of the two surfaces forming the boundaries of the fluid film, divided by the perpendicular distance between them), and in a real joint the shear rate is not known exactly because the film thickness is not known. The obstacles to a measurement of the film thickness in an intact joint, in life, under a physiological load, hardly need to be enumerated and have so far proved insuperable. Similar difficulties attend the measurement of the surface roughness in the same conditions; the possible errors in such measurements as have been made will be considered below.

6.2. Surface Roughness of Articular Cartilage (see also Chapter 1, Section 2.6)

Ideally, a full investigation of the lubrication régime would include a knowledge of the surface roughness of living human articular cartilage, *in situ*, under physiological loads applied through an opposing cartilage surface with synovial fluid in place. For obvious reasons this is not available, but observations which approach the ideal in different ways have been made in several centres. A full review of this work has been given by Gardner (1972); here it will be considered briefly from the point of view of its relevance to lubrication. The following main possible sources of error can be identified.

Measurements made under no load will tend to give high values for the roughness, because any application of pressure must tend to reduce the heights of the asperities by unpredictable amounts.

Measurements made on post-mortem material involve the possibility of errors due to the death and subsequent collapse of chondrocytes near the surface.

Measurements made using an electron microscope have so far usually involved the dehydration of the specimen, with the obvious possibility of distortion.

Measurements made on cast replicas are open to possible errors due to the effect of water on the curing of the resin (Clarke 1971a).

Using transmission electron microscopy, Davies, Barnett, Cochrane and Palfrey (1962) found that the surface of rabbit articular cartilage was 'remarkably smooth'. Most, if not all, observations made with the scanning electron microscope, whether on cartilage itself (e.g. Walker, Dowson, Longfield and Wright 1968) or on cast replicas (e.g. Dowson, Longfield, Walker and Wright 1968) show some surface irregularities. Clarke (1971b) showed that the collapse of the surface layer into lacunae which are no longer filled by living chondrocytes can produce surface depressions about $20-40\ \mu$m in diameter and $1-6\ \mu$m in total depth. In cross-section, these surface contours appear similar to those observed by Walker *et al.* (1968) and ascribed by them to bundles of collagen fibres running along the surface. Since the possibility of some chondrocytes dying during the life of the cartilage is real, some of these depressions may exist in life. Clarke (1971a) speculated that swelling and flattening of chondrocytes in life might produce respectively hillocks on, and depressions in, the articular surface.

Gardner and colleagues (e.g. Gardner and Woodward 1969; Gardner and McGillivray 1971; Gardner 1972; Longmore and Gardner 1975) have arrived at a classification of surface contours in four groups:

Primary: the major anatomical shape of the joint surface;

Secondary: a series of undulations of about 0.4–0.5 mm wavelength or diameter;

Tertiary: a series of undulations of about 20–30 μm diameter and, as measured by interference microscopy, 1.2–2.6 μm in height;

Quaternary: irregular undulations 0.130–0.275 μm deep and 1–4 μm in diameter, observed more frequently with increased age of the specimen.

Gardner and colleagues made what appears to have been the first attempt to observe directly (instead of by means of replicas) the surface contours under load, both by compressing one cartilage surface against glass and by rapid freezing under load of the two cartilage surfaces of a rat's knee. These observations showed that the tertiary undulations were visible under load (of unspecified magnitude), but that the secondary series were not visible. The depth under load of the tertiary undulations was not stated.

Obviously the ideal body of information mentioned at the beginning of this section does not yet exist, but it seems probable that under load the surface of cartilage has on it undulations related to the superficial chondrocytes, of about 20–30 μm diameter and perhaps a few microns deep. The persistence under load of the undulations of about 0.4 mm wavelength cannot be excluded on the basis of present knowledge.

6.3. Estimates of Film Thickness

For the reasons mentioned above, no direct measurements exist, and possible values must therefore be inferred from other information.

In unloaded joints, incongruities between the adjacent surfaces can cause gaps of up to a few hundred microns, and this is therefore a possible maximum order of magnitude of film thickness at the instant before load is applied. At the other extreme, the molecule of hyaluronate–protein is estimated (Ogston and Stanier

1951) to have an effective size of about $0.5 \, \mu m$, but this is the diameter of the approximately spherical shape which it assumes when unconstrained, in relatively large volumes of liquid. If the molecule were straightened and laid on the surface of cartilage, the minimum thickness of a monomolecular layer would be of the same order of magnitude as the thickness of the core of the molecule, i.e. about 1 nm. Adsorption of the molecule onto a surface would tend to straighten the core, because the protein groups which are supposed to form the attachment points are distributed along the length of the molecule. The application of pressure would also tend to flatten the molecule from its approximately spherical shape. Ogston and Stanier (1953), compressing synovial fluid between glass surfaces, obtained films 20–50 nm thick at pressures in the range 10^6–$10^7 \, N/m^2$ (c. 150–1500 lbf/in^2). Roberts (1971), compressing normal synovial fluid between rubber and glass, obtained equilibrium film thicknesses (after 3–6 h under pressure) of about 15 nm at a pressure of $5 \times 10^4 \, N/m^2$ (7.2 lbf/in^2). This pressure is very low by physiological standards. At even lower pressures the films were thicker (and fluid from different joints gave different thicknesses), and there was an apparent tendency towards a constant thickness at the upper end of the pressure range. Thus these results may be compatible with the slightly greater thicknesses measured by Ogston and Stanier at much higher pressures. All these results show that synovial fluid under a physiological pressure can be squeezed into a film the thickness of which is about one-tenth of the diameter of the free molecule of hyaluronate–protein. It therefore seems reasonable to suppose that this thickness (i.e. of the order of hundredths of microns) represents that attainable under load in a joint. Calculations made by Tanner (1966) and Fein (1967), which will be referred to in more detail below, lead to film thicknesses of the order of tenths of microns up to a few microns, whereas the work of Maroudas (1969) suggested an equilibrium film thickness of about 22 nm.

The greater of these thicknesses are of the same order of magnitude as the depths of the surface depressions about 20–$30 \, \mu m$ in diameter observed under no load by Clarke and by Gardner. Thus, unless both these smaller depressions and the larger ones observed under no load by Gardner and McGillivray are all completely flattened under load, there is a possibility that under load the film thickness is of the same order of magnitude as the surface depressions. If this is so, the film thickness within the loaded region must vary, by factors of about two to one if the calculated film thicknesses are relevant, or by factors of ten or even a hundred to one if the film thicknesses measured between solid surfaces are relevant. Such variations would have implications for the lubrication régime, but there is always the restriction that the surface contours in life under load are unknown.

6.4. Properties of Synovial Fluid

6.4.1. General. Synovial fluid is well known to be a dialysate of blood plasma with the addition of a hyaluronate–protein complex of large molecular weight (c. 10^6 according to Ogston and Stanier 1950) and size (an effective molecular domain of c. $0.5\,\mu$m, according to Ogston and Stanier 1951). Whether the protein is an integral part of a hyaluronate–protein complex or is more loosely attached is apparently open to question (Silpananta, Dunstone and Ogston 1968; Radin, Swann and Weisser 1970). Various properties of synovial fluid have been described by Davies (1967), Ogston and Stanier (1950, 1951, 1953), Ropes, Robertson, Rossmeisl, Peabody and Bauer (1947) and Sundblad (1953), and will not be dealt with here.

6.4.2. Viscosity. Synovial fluid is visibly more viscous than water, but simple measurements of its viscosity show the viscosity to be inversely related to the rate of shear. This means that true measurements can be made only with a viscometer which imposes a uniform rate of shear throughout the volume of the sample being tested. A cone-and-plate viscometer does this, and in the commercially available form of the Weissenberg Rheogoniometer has been used by several workers. Many of the published results have been obtained with bovine fluid, and more recent workers have used human fluid. A composite graph, made by the present author from published results, is shown in Figure 7.1. The results reproduced there relate to joints said to be 'normal' or 'healthy', but these terms are almost incapable of being precisely defined. Gross departures from normality can, of course, be identified. De Keizer (1976), whose results for normal fluid showed negligible scatter, found that fluid from knees with meniscus lesions, arthrotic changes or synovitis was nearly always significantly less viscous. The observations of Cooke on fluid from osteoarthrotic joints, shown in Figure 7.1, confirm this. Jebens and Monk-Jones (1959) gave the results of measurements on fluids removed from human knees in three categories: 91 normal, 63 traumatized and 45 ostcoarthrosic. Their measurements were made with a capillary viscometer which could not apply a uniform rate of shear, but a controlled rate of flow was used in all tests (which with a Newtonian fluid would have imposed an average rate of shear of about 13 s^{-1}), so that the results from the three groups could reasonably be compared. The viscosity of normal fluid decreased with increasing age according to the equation

$$\eta = 1.26 - 0.011\,A$$

where η = viscosity in Ns/m^2 (1 Ns/m^2 = 10 poise)
and A = age in years in the range 8–80.

The coefficient of correlation was 0.71. Fluids from abnormal knees were less viscous, typically by a factor of 10, and the viscosity of fluid from osteoarthrosic knees depended more on the severity of the arthrosis than on the patient's age.

Because these results were obtained with a non-uniform shear rate, they cannot be compared directly with those represented in Figure 7.1, but the range of viscosities (c. 0.4–1.2 Ns/m^2) obtained by Jebens and Monk-Jones lies above the curves of Figure 7.1 when the shear rate is about 10 s^{-1}. This is consistent with the evidence of the other results in Figure 7.1, that human synovial fluid is more viscous than bovine.

Figure 7.1 Variation of viscosity of synovial fluid with rate of shear (log–log plot). 1: King (1966), fluid from bovine knee. 2: Davies (1967), fluid from bovine tibiotarsal joint. 3: Davies (1967), fluid from bovine radiocarpal joint. 4: King (1966), fluid from bovine ankle. 5: Vos and Theyse (1969), mean values for fluids from several normal human joints. 6: de Keizer (1976), mean values for fluids from four human knees. 7: Cooke (1974), fluid from normal human knee, 27 year-old-male. 8: Cooke (1974), fluid from normal human knees, 43- and 48-year-old males, pooled. 9: Cooke (1974), fluid from osteoarthrotic human knees (range of results from four samples).

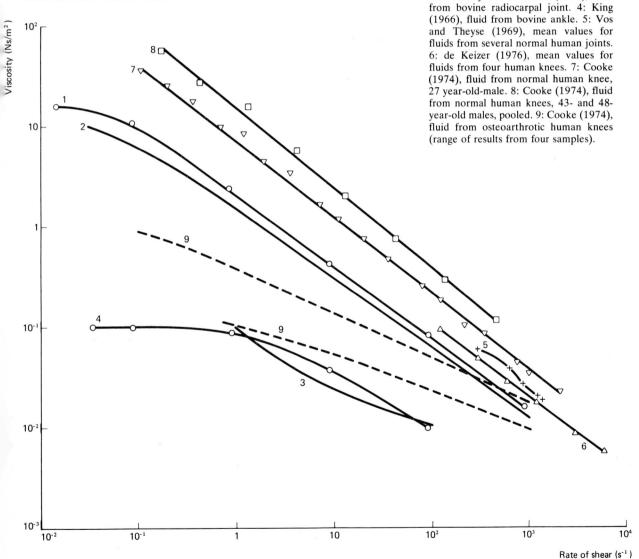

Synovial fluid, in common with other liquids whose viscosities vary with shear rate, displays when sheared a pressure perpendicular to the shearing planes. Some authors (e.g. Davies 1967) have speculated that this pressure could be relevant to the lubrication of joints. The highest values reported for this pressure (known as normal stress) are peak values of 2 N/m^2 (c. 0.0003 lbf/in^2) at a shear rate of 1000 s^{-1} for a specimen of fluid from a bovine radiocarpal joint (Davies 1967) and 20 kN/m^2 (c. 2.9 lbf/in^2) at 9000 s^{-1} for fluid from a bovine knee (King 1966). De Keizer (1976) recorded a normal stress varying up to about 1.5 kN/m^2 (c. 0.2 lbf/in^2) at a shear rate of 6000 s^{-1} with fluid from healthy human knees. The average stress acting on a human femoral head under a load of five times body weight is very approximately 2 MN/m^2 (290 lbf/in^2) which is 100–1000 times higher than the normal stress measured in synovial fluid. The normal stress increases with increasing shear rate according to a power law; if this law is extrapolated beyond present observations, it suggests that the normal stress would become significant at a shear rate of about 10^7 s^{-1}. If, as discussed below in Section 6.11, the effective lubricant in joints is a concentrate of synovial fluid, the normal stress in this concentrate might be relevant.

6.5. Measured Frictional Forces and the Viscosity of Synovial Fluid

6.5.1. Calculation of Viscosity from Frictional Measurements.
The measurements discussed in Section 3 all led to the conclusion that in those synovial joints tested the frictional forces were partly boundary and partly fluid in nature. The coefficients of friction listed in Table 7.2 were calculated assuming that all the friction was boundary. It is equally possible to treat the experimental observations as if viscous forces alone acted, and thereby to obtain an order of magnitude for the viscosity of synovial fluid which would be required to account for these forces. Such a calculation will now be presented, using the observations from which the results of Little *et al.* (1969) were calculated.

Figure 7.2 shows diagrammatically the pendulum concerned and Figure 7.3 the bearing surfaces. Let

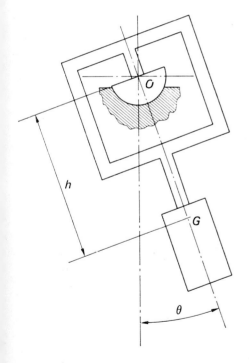

Figure 7.2 Diagrammatic view of pendulum used for measuring friction in a cadaveric human hip.

m be the mass of the pendulum,
h be the distance of its centre of gravity (G) from the pivot O,
k_0 be the radius of gyration about O,
R be the radius of the spherical bearing,
t be the film thickness (assumed uniform),
η be the viscosity of the fluid (assumed uniform and constant),
φ be the semi-angle subtended at O by an annular element,

$\delta\psi$ be the angle subtended at O in plan view by a small sector of an annular element at angle ψ as shown,

$\dot{\gamma}$ be the rate of shear (velocity gradient) in the film,

φ_1, φ_2 be the values of φ at the limits of the contact region,

θ be the angular displacement of the pendulum from the vertical, and

M_F be the frictional moment exerted on the pendulum by the bearing.

Taking moments about O, trigonometry gives the component of M_F exerted by a sector of an annular element to be

$$n\dot{\gamma}\ R^3 \sin\varphi\ (\cos^2\varphi+\sin^2\varphi\ \cos^2\psi)^{\frac{1}{2}}\ \delta\psi\delta\varphi.$$

Further trigonometry gives

$$\dot{\gamma} = R\ (\cos^2\varphi + \sin^2\varphi\ \cos^2\psi)^{\frac{1}{2}}\ \dot{\theta}/t.$$

Substituting for $\dot{\gamma}$ and integrating with respect to ψ, the component δM_F exerted by the annular element becomes

$$\delta M_F = \eta R^4(\dot{\theta}/t)\sin\varphi\ (2\pi\cos^2\varphi + \pi\sin^2\varphi)\ \delta\varphi,$$

so $\qquad M_F = -\pi\eta R^4(\dot{\theta}/t)\displaystyle\int_{\varphi_1}^{\varphi_2}(1 + \cos^2\varphi)\ \mathrm{d}\ (\cos\varphi).$

Experimentally, the mean values of φ_1 and φ_2 found by using engineer's blue on several hips were 30° and 65°.

Then $\qquad M_F = \pi\eta R^4(\dot{\theta}/t)\displaystyle\int_{65}^{30}(1+\cos^2\varphi)\ \mathrm{d}\ (\cos\varphi)$

which gives

$$M_F = 2.0\ R^4\dot{\theta}\eta/t.$$

Then the equation of motion of the pendulum is, taking moments about O,

i.e. $\qquad -mgh\theta-2R^4\dot{\theta}\eta/t = mk_\delta^2\ \ddot{\theta},$

i.e. $\qquad \ddot{\theta} + 2\dfrac{R^4}{mk_\delta^2}\left(\dfrac{\eta}{t}\right)\dot{\theta} + \dfrac{gh}{k_\delta^2}\ \theta = 0.$

Comparing this with the standard equation for a system with viscous damping,

$$\ddot{\theta} + 2(c/c_0)\omega\dot{\theta} + \omega^2\theta = 0,$$

where ω = undamped natural circular frequency,

c = actual damping coefficient, and

c_0 = critical damping coefficient,

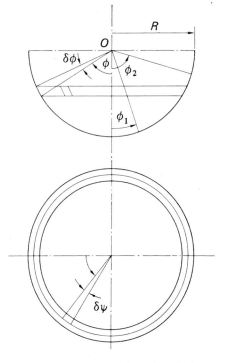

Figure 7.3 Elevation (upper) and plan (lower) views of bearing surface in the hip used as the pivot of the pendulum.

439

it follows that

$$\frac{c}{c_0} = \frac{R^4}{k_\theta m (gh)^{\frac{1}{2}}} \left(\frac{\eta}{t}\right).$$

(c/c_0) is calculable from the decay of oscillations, thus:

$$2\pi(c/c_0)\,[1 - (c/c_0)^2]^{-\frac{1}{2}} = (1/n)\,\ln\,(\theta_i/\theta_{i+n}).$$

R, h and m are measurable, and k_0 can be simply calculated from the measured natural frequency of the pendulum. Thus (η/t) can be obtained numerically. Table 7.5 shows values of (η/t) calculated for two of the hips tested by Little *et al.* (1969), each at two loads, one at the lower end of the physiological range and one a little below the middle of the physiological range.

The viscosity and film thickness cannot be separately found from this calculation. It is possible, however, to eliminate the film thickness because the rate of shear $(\dot\gamma)$ depends on it. An exact calculation is not possible because $\dot\gamma$ varies from point to point in the hip at any instant, but the variation is within a range of about two to one for the geometry considered in these calculations.

At any instant when the angular velocity of the pendulum is $\dot\theta$,

$$\dot\gamma_{max} = R\dot\theta/t$$

or
$$\dot\gamma_{max}t = R\dot\theta.$$

The maximum values of $\dot\theta$ are known from the experimental observations, and thus the content of Table 7.5 may be extended by combining the values of (η/t) with those of $\dot\gamma t$ to give values of $\eta\dot\gamma$; the figures are given in the last column of Table 7.5.

Calculations from tests on several other hip joints all lead to the same result: a product $\eta\dot\gamma$, of the order of 10^4 N/m^2 (10^5 poise/s). Since the order of magnitude of the frictional forces in the tests on which these calculations are based is the same as that of those in the other series summarized in Table 7.2, it seems certain that corresponding calculations from these other observations would produce similar results.

6.5.2. Comparison of Measured and Calculated Viscosities.

The obtaining of a value for $\eta\dot\gamma$ implies that a graph of $\log\eta$ against $\log\dot\gamma$ would be a straight line with a gradient of -1. Taking $\eta\dot\gamma$ as 10^4 N/m^2 (a representative value in Table 7.5), η would be 10 Ns/m^2 when $\dot\gamma$ was 1000 s^{-1}. Inspection of Figure 7.1 shows that the viscosities calculated as above are, at any value of $\dot\gamma$, about 100–1000 times higher than the viscosities measured on synovial fluid.

Viscosities have not been measured at shear rates much above 10^3 s^{-1}, whereas the highest physiological shear rates may be as high as 10^5 or even 10^7 s^{-1}, depending on the film thickness; the calculated and experimental lines in Figure 7.1 may converge in the unexplored region. With this restriction, it can be concluded that, if at lower shear rates the lubrication were provided entirely by a fluid film, this film would have to be much more viscous than synovial fluid in bulk. Thus the possibility (referred to in Section 3.1.3) that a non-Newtonian fluid film might simulate the characteristics of boundary friction cannot be examined by reference to the viscosity of synovial fluid as so far measured.

6.5.3. Experimental Reductions in Viscosity. McCutchen (1966), using his rubber-on-glass bearing, tested the effect of filtering synovial fluid. Fluid was filtered through pores of three sizes: 0.22, 0.45 and 0.65 μm, and the residue resuspended in a volume of 0.9% NaCl equal to that of the original solution. The filtrate and the resuspended residue were tested in turn. With the 0.45 μm filter, the frictional performances of the filtrate and of the residue were indistinguishable, suggesting that the particles responsible for the distinctive lubricating ability of synovial fluid have a range of sizes of which 0.45 μm is approximately the median. With the smaller (0.22 μm) filter, the residue gave lower friction than the filtrate, whereas with the larger (0.65 μm) filter the filtrate gave lower friction than the residue. These results suggest that the range 0.22–0.65 μm covered the sizes of a large proportion of the

Table 7.5. Values of the factor (viscosity/film thickness) and the product (viscosity $\times$ shear rate) calculated from observations made by Little *et al.* (1969)

Test	Natural frequency (Hz)	Load on hip (N) [lbf]	Time under load (min)	No. of cycles 'n' used in calculation	$\dfrac{c}{c_0}$	$\dfrac{\eta}{t}$ (N/m³)	Max θ (rad/s)	$\eta\dot{\gamma}$ (N/m²)
5.12.68	0.86	156	0	12	0.0216	3.02×10^5	0.56	4.4×10^3
		[35]	2	16	0.0115	1.61×10^5	1.13	4.7×10^3
			15	12	0.0293	4.10×10^5	0.79	8.3×10^3
	0.97	956	0	20	0.0165	1.95×10^6	0.42	2.1×10^4
		[215]	2	10	0.0140	1.65×10^6	0.54	2.3×10^4
29.1.69	0.847	156	0	8	0.0474	6.64×10^5	0.73	1.2×10^4
		[35]	2	10	0.0290	4.06×10^5	1.02	1.0×10^4
			5	8	0.0312	4.36×10^5	0.80	8.4×10^3
			15	8	0.0481	6.73×10^5	0.84	1.4×10^4
			25	5	0.0329	4.60×10^5	0.84	9.4×10^3
	0.961	956	0	8	0.0044	4.52×10^5	0.84	9.1×10^3
		[215]	2	10	0.0065	6.57×10^5	0.79	1.3×10^4
			8	10	0.0121	1.23×10^6	0.60	1.8×10^4
			20	10	0.0185	1.88×10^6	0.64	2.9×10^4

particles concerned with lubrication. Other experiments by McCutchen (1966) involved synovial fluid which had been digested by hyaluronidase so that it was watery, and then filtered through a 0.1 μm filter. The original fluid, the digested fluid and the resuspended residue all gave similar coefficients of friction, and the filtrate gave slightly higher values. Although these frictional tests were not accompanied by viscosity measurements, there can be no doubt that the viscosity had been considerably reduced by the digestion, and it must be concluded that the lubrication of a rubber-on-glass bearing by synovial fluid does not depend strongly on either the size of the hyaluronate–protein molecule or the viscosity of the fluid.

Similar results were produced by Wilkins (1968).

Linn (1968), testing dog's ankle joints lubricated with bovine synovial fluid, found that fluid which had been passed through filters having pore sizes of 0.01–0.30 μm lacked lubricating ability, and fluid passed through a 0.5 μm filter reduced friction to a limited extent. Depolymerization of synovial fluid with hyaluronidase, sufficient to reduce its viscosity from 0.0052 Ns/m^2 almost to that of the buffered saline (0.0012 Ns/m^2 compared with 0.00096 Ns/m^2) had little effect on the coefficient of friction. A solution of hyaluronic acid obtained from bovine vitreous humour had a lubricating ability little different from that of the saline solution, although its viscosity, at 0.1 Ns/m^2, was about 20 times higher than that of the synovial fluid and about 100 times higher than that of the saline. These viscosities were measured in a modified Ostwald viscometer at low velocity, and would therefore maximize the differences between the various fluids, since synovial fluid is less viscous at higher shear rates.

Walker and co-workers (1970), in the tests referred to above in Section 2.2.2, used in turn three grades of synovial fluid described as 'tacky', 'normal' and 'watery' between cartilage and glass, the cartilage being in the form of full-thickness specimens of 0.13 cm^2 contact area attached to the subchondral bone, stuck to a specimen holder and reciprocated sinusoidally with a maximum speed of 30 mm/s. The 'tacky' fluid gave frictional forces lower, and the 'watery' fluid higher, than the 'normal' fluid, all on 'normal' cartilage.

Some of the results just quoted are more quantitative than others, but those obtained with entire joints show, first, that the viscosity of synovial fluid has little effect on the frictional forces in joints, and secondly, that a solution of higher viscosity, containing hyaluronic acid instead of the hyaluronate–protein complex naturally present in synovial fluid, is a less effective lubricant than is synovial fluid itself.

6.6. The Possibility of Boundary Lubrication

6.6.1. Variations of Friction with Speed, Load and Time. Table 7.6 summarizes results, which have been mentioned above in Sections 3.2 and 3.3, relating frictional forces to rubbing speeds. As mentioned above, Unsworth *et al.* measured frictional forces directly instead of calculating them from the decay of oscillations, and thus obtained values in individual cycles. Their results certainly support their conclusion that a fluid film of varying thickness was present, and it is possible that the earlier experiments of others in fact displayed this phenomenon but could not distinguish it from boundary lubrication. All the speed ranges quoted go down to zero because in oscillatory experiments such as these speed is necessarily zero at the instants of reversal. The highest rubbing speed in the human hip during normal walking was estimated by Paul (1967) to be about 80 mm/s.

Table 7.6. Rubbing speeds and type of frictional force (based on frictional experiments on entire joints)

Source	Joint	Rubbing speeds at cartilage surfaces (mm/s)	Type of frictional force
Charnley (1959)	Human ankle	0–c. 7	Boundary
Barnett and Cobbold (1962)	Dog's ankle	not available	Boundary
Faber *et al.* (1967)	Rabbit's knee	0–100	Boundary+fluid
Linn (1968)	Dog's ankle	0–52	Boundary+fluid
Little *et al.* (1969)	Human hip	0–25	Mainly boundary
Unsworth *et al.* (1975)	Human hip	0–7	Mainly fluid

All those workers who have investigated the effects of varying loads have found that the coefficient of friction (not merely the frictional forces) varied with load. Dowson *et al.* (1968), by rubbing small specimens of cartilage, attached to bone, against glass, found a considerable drop in the coefficient of friction, from about 0.9 at a nominal stress of 0.3 MN/m² (50 lbf/in²) to about 0.12 at a physiological stress of 2.8 MN/m² (400 lbf/in²); at a higher nominal stress of 6.9 MN/m² (1000 lbf/in²) the value had fallen only to about 0.1. These values were those reached after several minutes under load. Radin, Paul and Pollock (1970), testing the sagittal halves of bovine metatarsophalangeal joints in an arthrotripsometer, found the coefficient of friction (measured after 2 h under load) to increase from 0.006 at a nominal stress of

443

1.6 MN/m^2 to 0.011 at 8.0 MN/m^2. Over roughly the upper half of the range of loads used, the coefficient of friction with veronate buffer was practically the same as with synovial fluid, and with either lubricant the same values were maintained for up to 12 h of continuous oscillation under load.

Unsworth *et al.* (1975), testing human hips in their pendulum, found small reductions in friction with increasing load in the range 134–1480 N (29–337 lbf); but the results reported are from experiments using two hips, one tested with static loads and the other with suddenly applied loads.

It is difficult to draw firm conclusions from the variation of friction with load, particularly since the three sets of results are not in agreement. One possible conclusion is that the effective area of contact depends on the load, but further experiments would be needed to separate this from the other possible variables.

Similarly, most workers who have looked at the effect of time under load have found that the coefficient of friction increases with increasing time from the application of load, but at a decreasing rate, so that it tends to a constant value after about 30 min under load. This could be ascribed to the expulsion of fluid from the film in the loaded region between the cartilage surfaces, to progressive changes in the effective contact area consequent on the viscoelastic deformation of the cartilage, or to a continuous increase in the concentration of the fluid in the loaded region, in accordance with the process discussed in Section 6.11 below.

From all the above it must be concluded that, at least in some circumstances, the frictional forces are such as would result from the presence of a boundary lubricant.

6.6.2. Adsorption of Substances from Synovial Fluid.

McCutchen (1962) found that when small specimens of cartilage were pressed against glass the coefficient of friction was lower with synovial fluid than with water. When this type of experiment was repeated (McCutchen 1966) with a rubber-on-glass bearing, which had the advantage that new surfaces could be used, free of synovial fluid, several minutes of running with synovial fluid in place were needed before the coefficient of friction became lower than that obtained with 0.9% NaCl. McCutchen suggested that this time was that during which the active constituent of synovial fluid was being adsorbed onto the surface of the rubber.

Wilkins (1968) used the same type of rubber-on-glass bearing as McCutchen, and examined the effect on the coefficient of friction of digesting the synovial fluid. Mild digestion (10 min in specified conditions) with hyaluronidase produced no increase in friction, but digestion for 43 h in the same conditions with hyaluronidase increased the coefficient of friction from 0.01 to 0.15. Digestion with trypsin instead of with hyaluronidase gave a value of 0.2.

Hyaluronidase is thought (Ogston and Stanier 1953) to break the molecule of hyaluronic acid into smaller molecules, whilst trypsin is thought to destroy the protein component of the molecule. Thus these tests showed the friction-reducing ability of the mucin in synovial fluid to depend on the presence of the protein component, and Wilkins suggested that the protein acted by serving as the anchor or as a link to some small undiscovered anchoring group. The *in vitro* wear tests of W. H. Simon (1971) led to the parallel observation that the wear-protecting ability of synovial fluid was impaired by digestion with trypsin but not by digestion with hyaluronidase.

Linn and Radin (1968) used the arthrotripsometer described by Linn (1967) to investigate the effects of various treatments of synovial fluid on the friction in cadaveric dogs' ankle joints. Some of their results confirmed those obtained by Wilkins (1968) on a rubber-on-glass bearing, in that hyaluronidase reduced the viscosity of synovial fluid without changing the coefficient of friction, whilst trypsin increased the coefficient of friction significantly whilst not reducing the viscosity. In another test, a coefficient of friction of 0.005 obtained with synovial fluid was increased by the addition of heparin; from 20 to 300 USP units of heparin per cm^3 the increase of friction was linear to a value of about 0.007 at the higher concentration. It was thought that the heparin might either react with the lubricant or block its attachment sites on the cartilage. Human synovial fluids from rheumatic or traumatized knees had higher viscosities than the bovine fluids normally used, and lubricated better than they did.

Radin, Swann and Weisser (1970), using bovine metatarsophalangeal joints in the same apparatus, treated bovine synovial fluid by a purely physical method (centrifuging) so as to remove either the hyaluronate or the protein; test lubricants were then made up to contain neither hyaluronate nor protein, hyaluronate only, or protein only. The lubricant containing protein and no hyaluronate gave almost the same coefficients of friction in three joints as did the original synovial fluid; the lubricants containing no protein, with or without hyaluronate, gave the same friction as the veronate buffer. Further results of the same kind were reported by Swann, Radin, Nazimiec, Weisser, Curran and Lewinnek (1974). These results obviously support the implication of previous studies, namely that only the protein of the hyaluronate–protein complex in synovial fluid is relevant to the lubrication of cartilage surfaces. In contrast, preliminary results of work at Leeds (O'Kelly and Dowson 1976, personal communication), in which synovial fluid was digested either with hyaluronidase or with trypsin, show no significant differences in friction, as measured using human hip joints in the pendulum used by Unsworth *et al.* (1975), between the three types of fluid: untreated, digested with hyaluronidase, digested with trypsin.

Maroudas (1969), using electrophoretic methods, found that the hyaluronate–protein molecule as present in synovial fluid was adsorbed onto particles of cartilage, but so was pure hyaluronic acid (Chapter 4, Section 7.2). Her experiments did not enable measurements to be made in times shorter than several minutes, so any difference in rates of adsorption cound not be detected. These experiments were performed on small particles of cartilage produced by grinding (at low temperature) 100 μm thick specimens of articular cartilage; thus any peculiarity in behaviour of the surface layer would be lost.

6.6.3. Conclusion. The combined evidence leads to the conclusion that the hyaluronate–protein molecule is adsorbed onto the surface of articular cartilage, and that the adsorbed layer, of unknown thickness, acts as a boundary lubricant, in which activity the viscosity of the synovial fluid is irrelevant. In the hyaluronate–protein complex, the protein, not the hyaluronate, may be the lubricant.

6.7. The Possibility of Hydrostatic Lubrication

Assuming that in some circumstances the frictional forces are partly those exerted by the shearing of a fluid film, the means of providing and maintaining such a film must be considered, and hydrostatic lubrication is one possibility. Obviously there is no provision in or around joints for the supply of fluid at the necessary pressure from outside the joint, and therefore the normal engineering method of externally pressurized hydrostatic lubrication need not be considered. The possibility of self-pressurization has, however, been introduced (Lewis and McCutchen 1959, McCutchen 1959, 1962, 1967, 1969). The experiments leading to this concept were performed by rubbing articular cartilage, in place on the end of a bone, against glass. When this was done, the coefficient of friction rose from about 0.008 on the application of load to 0.1 after 26 min under load. Removal of the load for 1 s produced a small, temporary reduction in friction, while removal of the load for 10 s gave a larger reduction which was reversed more slowly. When the impermeable layer at the cartilage–bone junction had been removed, the rate of increase of the coefficient was greatly increased. These results led McCutchen to conclude that fluid, squeezed out of the cartilage as this was compressed by the load on the bearing, was maintaining the film between the glass and the cartilage by replacing the fluid which leaked away at the edges. This method of maintaining a fluid film was described by McCutchen first as a 'weeping bearing' and later as a 'self-pressurized hydrostatic bearing'.

There is no doubt that, as shown by some of the subsidiary experiments of McCutchen and the observation by Unsworth *et al.* (1975) that cartilage surfaces which were wiped dry before a test under load were wet at the end of the test, liquid is expressed from cartilage by the application of pressure. The latter observation implies no more than that liquid is expressed somewhere, not necessarily in the most highly loaded area. Since healthy cartilage is impermeable to hyaluronate, any liquid expressed must be, not synovial fluid, but a saline solution, which would dilute and reduce the viscosity of the synovial fluid in the loaded region, unless the outward flow of liquid detached protein or other substances adsorbed on the cartilage surface. The calculation presented in Section 6.5 showed that the measured viscosities of synovial fluid are too low, by orders of magnitude, to account for the observed frictional forces. This fact does not show that weeping lubrication is completely impossible, but it does mean that, if weeping lubrication does provide that part of the total frictional force which arises from fluid friction, this must be a very small proportion of the total frictional force.

6.8. The Possiblity of Squeeze-film Lubrication

Fein (1967) calculated that the known compliance of articular cartilage and the measured viscosities of synovial fluid would enable a squeeze-film to persist for physiologically useful times: a Young's modulus of 10^7 N/m^2 (1450 lbf/in^2) and a viscosity of 0.01Ns/m^2 gave, for a postulated human hip joint under a load of 300 N (67.5 lbf), a film thickness of 3.5 μm after 1 s under load and 0.058 μm after 1 h. Fein remarked that the trapping of synovial fluid films between joint surfaces would account for their low friction even after long periods under static loading, and calculated from Archard and Kirk's (1963) equation that the squeeze-film could be replenished hydrodynamically when relative movement of the cartilage surfaces took place.

One obvious limitation in this calculation is that it ignores the permeability of the cartilage to water and small solutes and the time-dependence of the deformation of cartilage. The effect of permeability in a squeeze-film bearing would usually be to increase the rate of leakage and thereby to reduce the time for which the bearing could support load, but in this instance the effect would be to allow water and small solutes to leak away from the loaded region while leaving the hyaluronate and protein present. Thus the effect may be less serious than it would be if the lubricating fluid were simpler. The question of the concentration of synovial fluid in the loaded region has been considered by Maroudas (1967) and will be referred to below.

The one test reported by Unsworth *et al.* (1975) in which the

447

friction increased over the first few cycles after the sudden application of load, compared with the absence of any such increase when the load had been applied for a long time or when synovial fluid was not present, strongly suggests the action of a squeeze-film.

6.9. The Possibility of Hydrodynamic Lubrication

The first to suggest this was MacConaill (1932) who, before any of the experimental results mentioned above had been obtained, postulated that the incongruities present between the surfaces of most joints would assist the formation of fluid films by the classical hydrodynamic method. He also (MacConaill 1932, 1950, 1960) suggested that the menisci in the knee joint could perform this function, the differences of curvature between the tibial and femoral condyles themselves being too large for the formation of wedge-shaped fluid films.

Charnley (1959) pointed out that in most joints the surface incongruities relied upon by MacConaill (and observed when the joint components are separated and unloaded) would be removed by normal physiological loads. Whilst Charnley used this as an argument against hydrodynamic lubrication, it could have been an argument in favour of elastohydrodynamic lubrication. Tanner (1959), a collaborator with Charnley, produced a simple calculation to show that at any probable shear rate the viscosity of synovial fluid (which decreases with increasing shear rate) would be too low to permit the building up of a hydrodynamic film.

Dintenfass (1963) also found that the equations for hydrodynamic lubrication could not be satisfied by any credible combination of film thickness and viscosity.

6.10. The Possibility of Elastohydrodynamic Lubrication

Dintenfass (1963) suggested that elastohydrodynamic lubrication was possible. Tanner (1966) showed that the equation of Archard and Kirk (1963) for elastohydrodynamic lubrication could be satisfied by using the best available values for the viscosity of the fluid, the Young's modulus of the cartilage, the load on the human hip joint, the difference of curvatures of the acetabular and femoral surfaces, and the rubbing speed. The equation gave a film thickness of $0.1\ \mu\text{m}$ and a coefficient of friction of 0.003, which might be increased in life by the presence of some boundary friction between asperities.

6.11. Concentration of Synovial Fluid

The calculations by Dintenfass, by Fein and by Tanner, referred to above, all ignore the possible effects of the permeability of articular cartilage.

Ogston and Stanier (1953) remarked that the size of the hyaluronic acid molecule would cause it to be trapped between cartilage surfaces under load, instead of passing into the cartilage matrix with the water and small solutes. Maroudas (1967) applied this observation to joint lubrication by performing experiments and calculations which showed that, as two initially unloaded cartilages are forced together under load, the resistance to sideways flow of fluid from the loaded area will increase until it becomes comparable to that of the path through the cartilage matrix which is, however, available only to the water and small solutes. Thus the latter will flow from the loaded region more readily than the hyaluronic acid–protein, the concentration of which in the loaded region will therefore rise, to a level limited by osmotic considerations. Maroudas (1969) predicted that such a gel, with a concentration of hyaluronic acid–protein and free protein many times that in synovial fluid, should stabilize at a film thickness of about 22 nm after a few seconds under a physiological load. Thus, if the rheology of any fluid is relevant to the lubrication of synovial joints, it should be the rheology of such a gel and not that of normal synovial fluid. This topic is discussed further in Chapter 4, Section 7.1.

Dowson *et al.* (1968) described experiments in which cartilage attached to bone was reciprocated under controlled loads against a flat surface of glass (or rubber or plastic). The frictional force could be measured continuously and hence its variations with load and with time under load could be followed. The maximum sliding speed was 25 mm/s. Tests in which the horizontal frictional force was measured under constant vertical load showed that the frictional shear stress increased with increasing time under load, which the authors attributed to the wringing out of fluid from the film. If during the wringing-out process the vertical load was removed, the frictional force was initially lower when the load was replaced than it had been just before the removal of the load. The time from the re-application of the load to the instant when the frictional force returned to the value which it had had just before the load was removed was called the 'squeeze-film time'. This time had a value of nearly 1 min when unloading and reloading took place 1.5 min after the initial loading, and a value of just under 2 min at 30 min after the initial loading. From these squeeze-film times, and assuming a minimum separation of the surfaces under load of 0.25 μm (said to correspond to the combined thickness of two flattened molecules of hyaluronic acid–protein), Dowson and

449

co-workers were able to calculate the average viscosity of the fluid during the squeeze-film process. The result was about 2 Ms/m² (20 poise, P), which is towards the top of the range of the published results on which Figure 7.1 is based, and certainly higher than the values measured at realistic shear rates. It was therefore concluded that 'a very thick substance' had formed on the cartilage surface during the squeezing process.

Dowson, Unsworth and Wright (1970), assuming a linear variation of viscosity with hyaluronic acid–protein concentration and that flow through the cartilage was negligible compared with that outwards within the fluid film, calculated the variations of squeeze-film thickness with time for three geometrical shapes representing joint configurations. An initial film thickness of 10 μm was assumed, and the time taken for this to fall to 1 μm (said to be the smallest realistic value) was calculated, and was between 32 and 126 times greater than the time calculated assuming no increase in viscosity.

Accepting the possibility that synovial fluid becomes concentrated in loaded regions, the question arises: how is this done? The work of Ogston and Stanier (1953) and of Maroudas (1969) shows that after several seconds under load, filtration by flow of water and small solutes through the cartilage would suffice. Maroudas found that no hyaluronic acid was retained on filters having a pore size of 0.8 μm or larger, and this result is consistent with those of McCutchen (1966) and Wilkins (1968) mentioned above in Section 6.5.3. Swann et al. (1974) found that the residue obtained by filtering bovine synovial fluid through 0.22 μm pores and resuspending gave substantially the same friction with articular cartilage as did synovial fluid itself. These results all suggest that, if concentration is effected by sideways flow of the synovial fluid through the gap between the cartilage surfaces, this cannot happen until the gap has become appreciably narrower than 1 μm. Dowson et al. (1970) assumed that concentration took place by flow through gaps of 1 μm or more, but no evidence was quoted for the assumption.

Dowson et al. (1970) assumed also that this process was assisted by the trapping of pools of synovial fluid in depressions in the cartilage surfaces. There is little doubt that this could happen, and scanning electron micrographs by Walker et al. (1970) show aggregates of something which could well be hyaluronate–protein. Whether pools would be trapped between two undulating surfaces which were moving relative to each other seems more doubtful; as the opposing undulations passed each other, adjacent pools would be in communication, and it seems likely that the overall effect would be mainly that resulting from the general approach and flattening of the two cartilage surfaces.

As Higginson and Norman (1974) pointed out, the two concentration mechanisms (flow through the cartilage and flow through the gap) could exist together; more information about the detailed events in joints under load is needed before statements about the exact mechansim can be made with confidence.

6.12. Conclusion

The results of frictional measurements in entire joints point to the operation of boundary lubrication by adsorbed hyaluronate–protein, perhaps combined with fluid film lubrication by a fluid having a viscosity orders of magnitude higher than that of synovial fluid. Separate experiments have shown that hyaluronate–protein can be adsorbed by articular cartilage, and that independently of the adsorption process (though, if anything, assisted by it) filtration of synovial fluid by cartilage can produce a concentrate on the cartilage surface in the loaded region. That this concentrate can be produced in times as short as that in which the load on a joint can rise from a low value to a high physiological value (of the order of 0.01 s or less) has not been shown experimentally.

The work of Radin, Swann and Weisser (1970) and of Swann *et al.* (1974), showing that protein alone is responsible for the friction-reducing ability of synovial fluid, does not invalidate these conclusions, because the hyaluronate–protein which is present in synovial fluid is as well able to reduce friction as is protein alone; but this work does make the hyaluronate component (or the hyaluronate–protein complex, if a separate protein is involved) appear redundant.

The fewer results from wear tests are compatible with the above; synovial fluid protects cartilage against wear better than does saline solution, and this property of synovial fluid is not strongly dependent on its viscosity but is impaired by tryptic digestion which interferes with the protein part of the hyaluronate–protein complex.

Considering the friction-reducing and the wear-protecting properties of synovial fluid together, a credible but incompletely proven concept emerges: the distinctive constituent of synovial fluid, hyaluronate–protein, exists primarily to protect the cartilage surfaces against wear. Remembering that the matrix of cartilage is an hydrated proteoglycan gel and that the effective lubricant provided by synovial fluid, according to the observations discussed in Section 6.11, is another hydrated gel of similar general characteristics, it is not surprising that the friction of cartilage on cartilage lubricated by water should be only slightly higher than when lubricated by synovial fluid. The provision of a readily movable and replaceable intermediate layer of hyaluronate–protein gel might, however, reduce considerably the wear of the cartilage surfaces.

One question remains: if the protein rather than the hyaluronate is the constituent of synovial fluid principally responsible for the lubrication of articular cartilage (and it is noted above that experimental results relating to this point are not all consistent), what is the function of the hyaluronate? Before the friction-reducing properties of the protein moiety were known, the demonstrated irrelevance of the viscosity of bulk synovial fluid had led McCutchen (1969) to speculate that this viscosity was relevant to the lubrication of the contacts between the synovial membrane and other intra-articular structures. The lubrication of synovial membrane (strictly outside the scope of this Chapter) has been further investigated by Radin, Paul, Swann and Schottstaedt (1971), Swann *et al.* (1974) and Cooke, Dowson and Wright (1976), and it is perhaps here that hyaluronate has a physiological role to play. If so, the lubrication of the 'bearing' between synovial membrane and cartilage may be similar to that between, for example, the visceral and parietal surfaces of the pleural, pericardial and peritoneal surfaces but dissimilar from that between cartilage and cartilage.

7. POSSIBLE LUBRICATING PROPERTIES OF ARTICULAR CARTILAGE

7.1. Ploughing

This is strictly the reverse of a lubricating property, but can best be considered here. When any two deformable surfaces are pressed together under load, work is done in deforming the loaded regions. When the load is removed, even if the deformation is fully reversed, the work done will usually be incompletely recovered. With a material such as ball-bearing steel, the net loss of energy is extremely small, but is responsible for part of the extremely low losses in ball bearings. With a more deformable and viscoelastic material such as cartilage, the losses are likely to be higher. Even if the load on a joint is constant, the act of moving the joint under load means that some regions of the cartilage are alternately loaded and unloaded, and the loss of energy in these regions is manifested as a frictional resistance, often known as a 'ploughing frictional force'. Linn (1967) discussed the contribution made by this type of force to the total resistance to movement in the joints tested by him. By comparing his measurements of frictional moments with those of cartilage compression, he deduced the significance of the ploughing component after varying times under load, but all such deductions are limited by the fact that a simple measurement of total frictional force cannot distinguish between friction in the strict sense of the word and losses due to ploughing.

Where a region is cyclically loaded and unloaded, the dissipation of energy in deforming the material is likely to be greater than where the stresses are substantially constant, because the cyclic deformations are greater. This state of affairs is attained under a reciprocating edge, and it seems likely that the local contribution to the energy dissipation and hence, in principle, to the apparent friction, will be greater under such an edge than that from similar areas elsewhere, if of course the stresses are similar.

7.2. Boundary Lubrication

7.2.1. Proteoglycans. Assuming that in healthy cartilage the superficial collagen fibres are coated with proteoglycans, it seems likely that these proteoglycans could act as boundary lubricants even in the absence of hyaluronate–protein. This could presumably be achieved if the molecular structure provided relatively long and flexible chains such as those formed when metallic soaps are produced on metallic surfaces lubricated by fatty acids. It is suggested above, in Section 6.12, that the lubricating effect of synovial fluid is to protect these cartilage proteoglycans against wear.

7.2.2. Fat. Articular cartilage is known to contain fat, extracellularly as well as intracellularly; Stockwell (1967) estimated the total fat content to be about 1–2% of the wet mass, and more detailed but compatible analyses were reported by Bonner, Jonsson, Malanos and Bryant (1975). Little *et al.* (1969), in the experiments already referred to, made further measurements of the friction in human hip joints in which the cartilage surfaces of the femoral head and acetabulum were thoroughly washed with Ringer's solution (in an attempt to remove substances adsorbed from the synovial fluid), re-wetted with synovial fluid, washed again with Ringer's solution and then soaked in chloroform–methanol (with the intention of removing extracellular fat) followed by Ringer's solution, and finally re-wetted with synovial fluid. Any interference with the cartilage surfaces resulted in an increase in the friction, which was only partly reversed when synovial fluid was put back; treatment with chloroform–methanol produced the biggest increase in the coefficient of friction (to 0.016–0.024 compared with 0.005–0.012 in the intact joint, all these values being those obtained after 4 min under 956 N load). Parallel tests showed that the chloroform–methanol had removed the extracellular fat near the cartilage surface, as shown by Sudan black and Sudan III stains, whilst leaving the compressive stiffness and permeability unchanged. It is possible, therefore, that the fat was contributing to the lubrication of the joints, at least in the absence of synovial fluid, by acting as a boundary lubricant. Alternatively, the chloroform–methanol may have interfered with the sites at which hyaluronate–protein was adsorbed onto the surface (Stockwell 1969, personal communication). This possibility would account for the limited reduction of the friction when synovial fluid was replaced, but would explain the higher friction when the hips were lubricated with Ringer's solution after the chloroform–methanol treatment only if it is assumed that the preceding washing and wiping with Ringer's solution had left some hyaluronate–protein adsorbed. Thus one interpretation of these results is that the natural lubrication depends on an adsorbed layer of hyaluronate–protein, the bonding of which depends at least in part upon the fat in the cartilage matrix, and which was partly removed by rubbing and by immersion in Ringer's solution and further removed by treatment with chloroform–methanol. Alternatively, both hyaluronate–protein and fat may act as boundary lubricants. The fact that all the records obtained in this series of tests showed an almost entirely linear decay of the oscillations is consistent with both interpretations.

8. DEGENERATION OF CARTILAGE

8.1. Do Softening and Fibrillation of Cartilage Affect the Lubrication of the Joint?

Degeneration of cartilage is characterized by softening and fibrillation (Chapter 6, Section 3.7, and Chapter 9, Section 4).

It seems obvious that one function of articular cartilage is to distribute the load transmitted through a joint over an area large enough for the stresses in both the cartilage and the bone to be safe. If the cortices of the participating bone ends were perfectly congruous and smooth, this function of cartilage would be unnecessary. Given that the bone surfaces are incongruous and incompletely smooth, it seems clear that an optimum stiffness of the combined cartilage layer exists: if the cartilage were of zero stiffness, or as stiff as the bone itself, the stress concentrations would be the same as if the cartilage were absent. There seems little room for doubt that severe softening or the absence of articular cartilage leads to increased stresses in the underlying bone, but whether slight softening does so or not depends on whether the 'normal' stiffness is equal to or greater than the optimum (Chapter 5, Section 2.4.1). This is not known, and strictly this consideration is relevant to the degeneration of joints but not to lubrication. The lubrication of joints would be affected (for the better) by an increase in the area of contact of the articular surfaces of the two layers of cartilage. Such an increase could occur microscopically by the more nearly complete flattening of asperities, or macroscopically by the increased congruity of the two cartilage surfaces. Softening of cartilage must tend to give this increase in contact area, but the tendency would be merely theoretical if the stiffness of healthy cartilage were such as to give either the largest possible contact area or even an area large enough to make possible a stable lubrication régime. Both microscopically and macroscopically, the experimental information about cartilage surface contours under load is, for the reasons discussed above, inadequate to enable any definite statements to be made about this.

Fibrillation can be dealt with more certainly than softening. Fibrillation must impair the inherent slipperiness of the surface, may impede adsorption (if the adsorption sites are characteristic of the original superficial layer), and may make less certain the filtration of hyaluronate–protein and the consequent formation of a gel. The surface contours of fibrillated cartilage under no load are much rougher than those of normal cartilage, and this would make more difficult the maintenance of a film of lubricant; but, again, the contours under physiological loads are not known, and because fibrillated cartilage is softer than normal the surfaces may be congruent under load. If this is so, and if adsorption sites are still available in fibrillated cartilage, it is possible to imagine that boundary lubrication is as effective with fibrillated cartilage as with normal. Thus, whilst there is no reason to suppose that fibrillation would assist lubrication, it may or may not impair it seriously.

The experimental evidence is not conclusive. Walker *et al.* (1970) found that small specimens of 'soft' cartilage, attached to bone and tested against glass, gave higher friction than did 'normal' cartilage, but they did not say whether the 'softer' cartilage was also fibrillated, and, as remarked above, the relevance of tests on small detached specimens to the state of affairs in entire joints is questionable. In the tests of Little *et al.* (1969) the coefficients of friction in hip joints showing some fibrillation were not significantly different from those in visually normal joints (Table 7.7).

In this connection it may be noted that the series of results so far published include too few specimens to enable anything to be stated about the relationship between age (in the absence of fibrillation) and friction.

Turning from friction to wear, the only relevant results are those produced by W. H. Simon (1971) using a backward-turning rotary abrader. He found that fibrillated human patellar cartilage was abraded significantly more rapidly than intact cartilage when both were lubricated with synovial fluid and when both were lubricated with saline solution; on fibrillated cartilage synovial fluid reduced the abrasion rate less, compared with saline solution, than on normal cartilage. In contrast, normal cartilage from which the surface had previously been shaved wore at about the same rate as normal cartilage not so treated. That fibrillated cartilage is abraded more readily than normal cartilage, and that synovial fluid protects the fibrillated surface less effectively than it does the intact surface, is hardly surprising.

Table 7.7. Coefficients of friction in human hips showing different degrees of cartilage damage. (Values shown were obtained, using the methods of Little *et al.* (1969), a few seconds after the application of a load of 956 N (215 lbf).)

State of cartilage	Number of hips	Coefficient of friction	
		Range	Mean
Normal	5	0.003–0.009	0.006
Minimal fibrillation	8	0.003–0.010	0.006
Severe fibrillation, some with ulceration	6	0.003–0.010	0.006
All	19	0.003–0.010	0.006

8.2. Is the Fibrillation of Cartilage Caused by a Failure of Lubrication?

In principle, a failure of lubrication might be expected to initiate degeneration of articular cartilage, much as a failure of lubrication initiates the destruction of metallic bearing surfaces. In metallic bearings, lubrication failures are commonly caused, in fluid film lubrication, by an inadequate supply or quality of fluid in relation to the surface roughnesses, speed, etc., or in boundary lubrication by a failure of the adsorbed layer.

The experimental evidence so far available and reviewed above does not help much in answering the question. For reasons discussed above, wear tests on synovial joints are more difficult than friction measurements, and it seems likely that with cartilage, as with other materials, friction and wear are not necessarily correlated. A further difficulty is that to establish whether or not lubrication failure caused fibrillation one would need to show increased wear rates not in fibrillated but in prospectively fibrillated cartilage.

Turning to the theoretical possibility of a lubrication failure, it is difficult to identify any change in the earlier stages of degeneration which could precipitate such a failure. Certainly plenty of fluid is present, and even if the increased dilution of the fluid, observed in late osteoarthrosis, is present also in the earliest stage, the experimental evidence reviewed above shows that the effect on friction is little affected by the dilution or viscosity of synovial fluid. Linn and Radin (1968) found that rheumatoid human synovial fluid gave about the same level of friction in canine ankle joints as did apparently normal bovine synovial fluid. If the dominant lubrication is boundary, it is conceivable that this could be impaired by a failure of prospectively fibrillated cartilage to adsorb hyaluronate–protein, but for this there is no evidence. Even if that were so, the formation of a gel would not be impaired.

Thus there exists at present no experimental evidence which certainly shows that a failure of lubrication is or is not a causative factor in the first stages of cartilage degeneration, and some theoretical grounds exist for supposing it not to be.

REFERENCES

Archard J. K. and Kirk M. T. (1963) Influence of elastic modulus properties on the lubrication of point contacts. *Proc. Instn Mech. Engrs Conv. Lub. Wear*, p. 181. Institution of Mechanical Engineers, London.

Barnett C. H. (1956) Wear and tear in joints. An experimental study. *J. Bone Jt Surg.* **38B**, 567.

Barnett C. H. and Cobbold A. F. (1962) Lubrication within living joints. *J. Bone Jt Surg.* **44B**, 662.

Bentley G., Kreutner A. and Ferguson A. B. (1975) Synovial regeneration and articular cartilage changes after synovectomy in normal and steroid-treated rabbits. *J. Bone Jt Surg.* **57B**, 454.

Bonner W. M., Jonsson H., Malanos C. and Bryant M. (1975) Changes in the lipids of human articular cartilage with age. *Arthritis Rheum.* **18**, 461.

Bowden F. P. and Tabor D. (1954) *The Friction and Lubrication of Solids*, 2nd edn. Oxford University Press, London.

Charnley J. (1959) The lubrication of animal joints. *Proc. Symp. Biomechs*, p. 12. Institution of Mechanical Engineers, London.

Clarke I. C. (1971a) Human articular surface contours and related surface depression frequency studies. *Ann. rheum. Dis.* **30**, 15.

Clarke I. C. (1971b) Surface characteristics of human articular cartilage: a scanning electron microscope study. *J. Anat. (Lond.)* **108**, 23.

Cooke, A. F. (1974) A Study of the Rheological Characteristics of some Fluids and Tissues in Synovial Joint Lubrication. PhD thesis, University of Leeds.

Cooke A. F., Dowson D. and Wright V. (1976) Lubrication of synovial membrane. *Ann. rheum. Dis.* **35**, 56.

Davies D. V. (1967) Properties of synovial fluid. *Proc. Instn mech. Engrs* **181** (3J), 25.

Davies D. V., Barnett C. H., Cochrane W. and Palfrey A. J. (1962) Electron microscopy of articular cartilage in the young adult rabbit. *Ann. rheum. Dis.* **21**, 11.

Dintenfass L. (1963) Lubrication in synovial joints: a theoretical analysis: a rheological approach to the problems of joint movements and joint lubrication. *J. Bone Jt Surg.* **45A**, 1241.

Dowson D., Longfield M. D., Walker P. S. and Wright V. (1968) An investigation of the friction and lubrication in human joints. *Proc. Instn mech. Engrs* **182** (3N), 68.

Dowson D., Unsworth A. and Wright V. (1970) Analysis of 'boosted lubrication' in human joints. *J. Mech. Engg Sci.* **12**, 364.

Faber J. J., Williamson G. R. and Feldman N. T. (1967) Lubrication of joints. *J. appl. Physiol.* **22**, 793.

Fein R. S. (1967) Are synovial joints squeeze-film lubricated? *Proc. Instn mech. Engrs* **181** (3J), 125.

Gardner D. L. (1972) The influence of microscopic technology on knowledge of cartilage surface structure. *Ann. rheum. Dis.* **31**, 235.

Gardner D. L. and McGillivray D. C. (1971) Living articular cartilage is not smooth. *Ann. rheum. Dis.* **30**, 3.

Gardner D. L. and Woodward D. H. (1969) Scanning electron microscopy and replica studies of articular surfaces of guinea-pig synovial joints. *Ann. rheum. Dis.* **28**, 379.

Higginson G. R. and Norman R. (1974) A model investigation of squeeze-film lubrication in animal joints. *Phys. Med. Biology* **19**, 785.

Hunter W. (1743) Of the structure and diseases of articulating cartilages. *Phil. Trans. R. Soc.* **42**, 514.

Jebens E. H. and Monk-Jones M. E. (1959) On the viscosity and pH of synovial fluid and the pH of blood. *J. Bone Jt Surg.* **41B**, 388.

Jones E. S. (1934) Joint lubrication. *Lancet* i, 1426.

Jones E. S. (1936) Joint lubrication. *Lancet* i, 1043.

de Keizer G. (1976) Over Synoviale Vloeistof, Gewrichtssmering en Arthrosis Deformans. MD Thesis, State University of Utrecht.

Key J. A. (1933) The production of chronic arthritis by the injection of weak acids, alkalis, distilled water, and salt solution into joints. *J. Bone Jt Surg.* **15**, 67.

King R. G. (1966) A rheological measurement of three synovial fluids. *Rheologica Acta* **5**, 41.

Lewis P. R. and McCutchen C. W. (1959) Experimental evidence for weeping lubrication in mammalian joints. *Nature (Lond.)* **184**, 1285.

Linn F. C. (1967) Lubrication of animal joints. I: The arthrotripsometer. *J. Bone Jt Surg.* **49A**, 1079.

Linn F. C. (1968) Lubrication of animal joints. II: The mechanism. *J. Biomechanics* **1**, 193.

Linn F. C. and Radin E. L. (1968) Lubrication of animal joints. III: The effect of certain chemical alterations of the cartilage and lubricant. *Arthritis Rheum.* **11**, 674.

Little T., Freeman M. A. R. and Swanson S. A. V. (1969) Experiments on friction in the human hip joint. *Lubrication and Wear in Joints*, Ed. by V. Wright, p. 110. Sector, London.

Longmore R. B. and Gardner D. L. (1975) Development with age of human articular cartilage surface structure. A survey by interference microscopy of the lateral femoral condyle. *Ann. Rheum. Dis.* **34**, 26.

MacConaill M. A. (1932) The function of intra-articular fibrocartilages with special reference to the knee and inferior radio-ulnar joints. *J. Anat. (Lond.)* **66**, 210.

MacConaill M. A. (1950) The movements of bones and joints. 3: The synovial fluid and its assistants. *J. Bone Jt Surg.* **32B**, 244.

MacConaill M. A. (1960) Lubrication of mammalian joints. *Nature (Lond.)* **185**, 920.

McCutchen C. W. (1959) Mechanism of animal joints. Sponge-hydrostatic and weeping bearings. *Nature (Lond.)* **184**, 1284.

McCutchen C. W. (1962) The frictional properties of animal joints. *Wear* **5**, 1.

McCutchen C. W. (1966) Boundary lubrication by synovial fluid: demonstration and possible osmotic explanation. *Fed. Proc.* **25**, 1061.

McCutchen C. W. (1967) Physiological lubrication. *Proc. Instn mech. Engrs* **181** (3J), 55.

McCutchen C. W. (1969) Why did nature make synovial fluid slimy? *Clin. Orthop.* **64**, 18.

Maroudas A. (1967) Hyaluronic acid films. *Proc. Instn mech. Engrs* **181** (3J), 122.

Maroudas A. (1969) Studies on the formation of hyaluronic acid films. *Lubrication and Wear in Joints,* Ed. by V. Wright, p. 124. Sector, London.

Ogston A. G. and Stanier J. E. (1950) On the state of hyaluronic acid in synovial fluid. *Biochem. J.* **46**, 364.

Ogston A. G. and Stanier J. E. (1951) The dimensions of the particle of the hyaluronic acid complex in synovial fluid. *Biochem. J.* **49**, 585.

Ogston A. G. and Stanier J. E. (1953) The physiological function of hyaluronic acid in synovial fluids: viscous, elastic and lubricant properties. *J. Physiol. (Lond.)* **119**, 244.

Paul J. P. (1967) Forces transmitted by joints in the human body. *Proc. Instn mech. Engrs* **181** (3J), 8.

Radin E. L. and Paul I. L. (1971) Response of joints to impact loading. I: In vitro wear. *Arthritis Rheum.* **14**, 356.

Radin E. L., Paul I. L. and Pollock D. (1970) Animal joint behaviour under excessive loading. *Nature (Lond.)* **226**, 554.

Radin E. L., Swann D. A. and Weisser P. A. (1970) Separation of a hyaluronate-free lubricating fraction from synovial fluid. *Nature (Lond.)* **228**, 377.

Radin E. L., Paul I. L., Swann D. A. and Schottstaedt E. S. (1971) Lubrication of synovial membrane. *Ann. rheum. Dis.* **30**, 322.

Radin E. L., Parker H. G., Pugh J. W., Steinberg R. S., Paul I. L. and Rose R. M. (1973) Response of joints to impact loading. III: Relationship between trabecular microfractures and cartilage degeneration. *J. Biomechanics* **6**, 51.

Reynolds O. (1886) On the theory of lubrication and its application to Mr Beauchamp Tower's experiments, including an experimental determination of the viscosity of olive oil. *Phil. Trans. R. Soc.* **177**, 157.

Roberts A. D. (1971) The role of electrical repulsive forces in synovial fluid. *Nature (Lond.)* **231**, 434.

Ropes M. W., Robertson W., Rossmeisl E. C., Peabody R. B. and Bauer W. (1947) Synovial fluid mucin. *Acta med. scand.* Suppl. **196**, 700.

Seireg A. and Gerath M. (1975) An in vivo investigation of wear in animal joints. *J. Biomechanics* **8**, 169.

Silpananta P., Dunstone J. R. and Ogston A. G. (1968) Fractionation of a hyaluronic acid preparation in a density gradient. *Biochem. J.* **109**, 43.

Simon S. R., Radin E. L., Paul I. L. and Rose R. M. (1972) The response of joints to impact loading. II: In vivo behaviour of subchondral bone. *J. Biomechanics* **5**, 267.

Simon W. H. (1971) Wear properties of articular cartilage in vitro. *J. Biomechanics* **4**, 379.

Stanton T. E. (1923) Boundary lubrication in engineering practice. *Engineer* **135**, 678.

Stockwell R. A. (1967) Lipid content of human costal and articular cartilage. *Ann. rheum. Dis.* **26**, 481.

Sundblad L. (1953) Studies on hyaluronic acid in synovial fluids. *Acta Soc. Med. upsalien.* **58**, 113.

Swann D. A., Radin E. L., Nazimiec M., Weisser P. A., Curran N. and Lewinnek G. (1974) Role of hyaluronic acid in joint lubrication. *Ann. rheum. Dis.* **33**, 318.

Tanner R. L. (1959) Calculation of the shear rate in the hip joint lubricant. *Proc. Symp. Biomechs,* p. 21. Institution of Mechanical Engineers, London.

Tanner R. L. (1966) An alternative mechanism for the lubrication of synovial joints. *Phys. Med. Biology* **11**, 119.

Unsworth A., Dowson D. and Wright V. (1975) Some new evidence on human joint lubrication. *Ann. rheum. Dis.* **34**, 277.

Vos R. and Theyse F. (1969) Lubricating properties of synovial fluid in human and animal joints. *Lubrication and Wear in Joints.* Ed. by V. Wright, p. 29. Sector, London.

Walker P. S., Dowson D., Longfield M. D. and Wright V. (1968) Boosted lubrication in synovial joints by fluid entrapment and enrichment. *Ann. rheum. Dis.* **27,** 512.

Walker P. S., Unsworth A., Dowson D., Sikorski J. and Wright V. (1970) Mode of aggregation of hyaluronic acid protein complex on the surface of articular cartilage. *Ann. rheum. Dis.* **29,** 591.

Wilkins J. F. (1968) Proteolytic destruction of synovial boundary lubrication. *Nature (Lond.)* **219,** 1050.

8. Nutrition and Metabolism

B. McKibbin and A. Maroudas

1. INTRODUCTION

Four separate but related subjects are discussed or referred to in this Chapter: the source of nutrients for cartilage as a tissue; the transport mechanisms which affect the movement of nutrients within the matrix; the metabolic activities of the chondrocyte; and finally the nutritional and metabolic changes associated with fibrillation.

2. THE SOURCE OF NUTRIENTS FOR CARTILAGE AS A TISSUE

The fact that articular cartilage contains no blood-vessels was first recognized by William Hunter (1743) as a result of his vascular injection studies, thus raising for the first time the question of how nutrients gain access to this tissue.

There are clearly only two possibilities, for since articular cartilage is a thin layer of avascular tissue, nutrients must enter either from its deep aspect which is adjacent to vascular bone or from its superficial surface which is bathed in synovial fluid.

Evidence has been produced to support a belief in both these routes but unfortunately it is to some extent contradictory, so that a long-standing controversy exists as to the relative importance of each.

2.1. Nutrition by the Subchondral Route

This, perhaps the most obvious route, was the first to be considered historically. Although Hunter was unable to demonstrate vessels passing from the bone into the cartilage substance, he appears to have regarded this to be a result of the limitations of his technique, believing that smaller calibre vessels were present but that 'the blood vessels are so small that they do not admit the red globules of the blood'. This view was supported in general by Toynbee (1841) although he did point out that there appeared to be a barrier to these vessels in the form of the dense bone of the subchondral plate. Toynbee suggested a process of avascular diffusion to account for the passage of fluid across this zone.

Trueta and Harrison (1953), using injection techniques, have described in detail the vascular anatomy of the bone/cartilage interface in the femoral head of the adult human. They found that the precapillary vessels arising in the marrow pass through canals in the subchondral bone plate and form single broad capillary loops at the deep surface of the calcified cartilage. Although these observations disposed of the subchondral bone plate as a barrier, Hunter's expectation of vascular channels in the cartilage was not realized. Thus it is again necessary to postulate a diffusion process between the terminal capillary loops and the substance of the cartilage.

Objections have been raised to this diffusional route on the grounds that there is a further barrier to fluid and solute transfer provided by the dense calcification which is invariably present in the basal zone of normal adult cartilage. Collins (1949) believed this barrier to be absolute, basing his conviction on general biological grounds. He pointed out that whenever cartilage and vascular bone lie in 'stable' contact, whether in a joint, an intervertebral disc or a rib, a calcified zone is invariably present, and that its absence, with direct contact between blood-vessels and cartilage, implies that the interface is temporary, 'unstable' and often pathological. Thus Collins believed that this unbroken zone exists for the very purpose of preventing metabolic exchange and preserving stability.

While it is true that vascular channels have never been seen to cross the calcified zone, not all workers are prepared to accept that the zone is continuous. Holmdahl and Ingelmark (1950) described direct connections between the medullary cavity and the cartilage and referred to an earlier description of these by Peterson (1930). However, their choice of 10-month-old rabbits as study material casts doubt on the relevance of their findings to adult human cartilage. The joint cartilage of an immature animal is fundamentally different from that of its adult counterpart for not only does it serve as a load-bearing gliding surface but it also provides new cartilage for the growth of the epiphyseal nucleus. The anatomy of the bone/cartilage interface is quite different from the adult state: active endochondral ossification is in progress, there is direct contact between blood-vessels and cartilage, and, since this is a temporary and changing condition, in accordance with Collins' (1949) dictum the controversial zone of calcified cartilage is not present. This distinction is of the greatest importance and failure to appreciate it is responsible for much of the apparent conflict in the experimental evidence concerned with cartilage nutrition. Conclusions as to the possibility of subchondral nutrition based upon work using immature animals are not necessarily relevant to the adult. In the specific instance of the rabbit, for example, Greenwald and Haynes (1969) (in contrast to Holmdahl and Ingelmark) were unable to detect any communication between bone and cartilage when they were careful to ensure that the animals studied were completely mature.

A further source of confusion has been identified by Greenwald and Hayes (1969), who pointed out that not only is there a difference in the vascular arrangements in the subchondral region between mature and immature rabbits but also between mature rabbits and humans. Like Trueta and Harrison (1953), they found that in the normal adult femoral head, vascular channels may be seen in contact with the undersurface of the calcified zone of cartilage in a way not seen in rabbits (Figure 8.1). Furthermore,

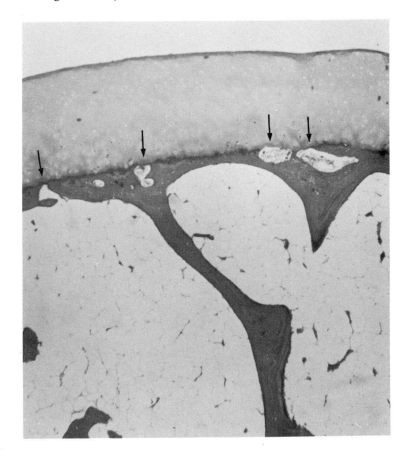

Figure 8.1 The plantar area of the first metatarsal head which, unlike most other phalangeal joints, has subchondral vascular channels (arrowed).

Decalcified paraffin section H & E ×100.

(Reproduced from Greenwald and Haynes (1975) by kind permission of the authors.)

Haynes and Woods (1975) have subsequently pointed out that even in the human these vessels are confined to some of the large joints while in other situations, such as the interphalangeal joints, the arrangements are more comparable with those in the rabbit (Figure 8.2). There are obvious dangers therefore in drawing general conclusions from the study of a particular joint.

Nevertheless, although vessels may be seen in contact with the

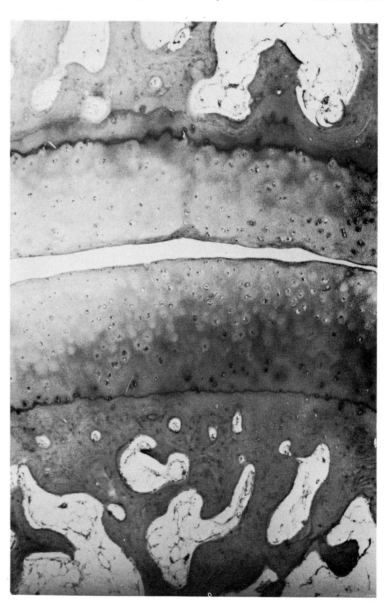

Figure 8.2 Interphalangeal joint. There are no subchondral vascular channels or breaks in the calcified line.

Decalcified paraffin section H & E ×200.

(Reproduced from Greenwald and Haynes (1975) by kind permission of the authors.)

calcified cartilage, there is as yet no evidence that they ever penetrate beyond it except in diseased states. If such vessels contribute to the nutrition of the cartilage then they must do so by diffusion through the calcified zone either because it is more permeable than has formerly been supposed or because it contains specific defects.

Mital and Millington (1970) using the stereoscan electron microscope claim to have demonstrated such channels and these are illustrated in Figure 8.3. They observed that as these channels passed from the spongy bone through the subchondral plate into the basal layers of the cartilage they became progressively smaller and could not be traced beyond the junction of the basal and mid-zone of the femoral cartilage, and were even shorter on the acetabular side of the joint. These defects therefore show a degree of penetration greater than can be demonstrated by vascular injection studies, suggesting that they are non-vascular prolongations of the more proximal channels which carry the vessels themselves. Such pathways could obviously conduct the solutes which have diffused from terminal capillary loops into the cartilage substance but the possibility must be borne in mind that they could exist for some alternative purpose.

One of the weaknesses inherent in all arguments based on morphological studies is the uncertain relationship between form and function: although a particular anatomical arrangement may strongly suggest a certain function, it can never of itself afford proof. Since we are concerned with a physiological process which can, by definition, be studied only in the living, it is important to supplement the anatomical observations by experiments which seek to demonstrate directly the passage of fluid and solute from bone into cartilage, preferably during life.

A number of workers using animal preparations have shown that injections of identifiable solutes into the subchondral bone can result in their subsequent appearance in the overlying cartilage. Solutes and suspensions which have been used include silver nitrate (Ishido 1923), rice grains (Ingelmark and Saaf 1948) and carmine and gelatine.

Several objections can be laid against these experiments, many of which were performed *in vitro*, employing high injection pressures and marker substances which were not inert. Supporters of the subchondral route therefore usually cite the more physiological experiments of Ekholm (1951, 1955). Ekholm performed subchondral infusions in living rabbits using a radioisotope marker and subsequent autoradiography to identify the solute, and was able to demonstrate the penetration of the cartilage by the isotope. Similar results were obtained by Brodin (1955) using a fluorescent solute.

Although the conditions under which these experiments were performed were as physiological as possible, the relevance of the

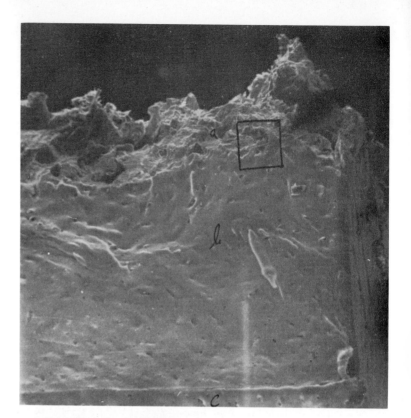

Figure 8.3 (a) Scanning electron micro-graph of the osseocartilaginous junction. A = bone; B = fracture surface of cartil-age; C = peeled cartilage. Channels pass through the subchondral plate into the cartilage ×55.
(b) Scanning electron micrograph show-ing a detail of channel outlined in (a) ×650.
(Reproduced from Mital and Milling-ton (1970) by kind permission of the authors.)

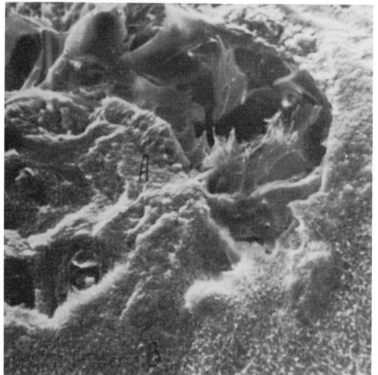

(b)

conclusions to adult man must again be questioned because of the use of immature animal material. Brodin's (1955) rabbits were clearly stated to be immature and, while Ekholm did not specify the age of his animals, the published illustrations suggest that at least some of them were still growing. Because of this uncertainty his experiments were repeated by Hodge and McKibbin (1969) using two groups of animals, the one definitely immature and the other equally certainly mature. Ekholm's findings were confirmed in the immature group, but no penetration into the mature cartilage could be demonstrated. Ekholm's evidence must therefore be set aside when the nutrition of adult cartilage is being considered. Honner and Thompson (1971) studied the uptake of intravenously injected ^{35}S (as sulphate) by the articular cartilage of mature and immature rabbits. In both groups of animals, some joints were dislocated prior to injection of ^{35}S. Isotope was absent from dislocated joints in mature animals, from which Honner and Thompson concluded that sulphate had reached the immature cartilage by both the synovial and osseous routes but that only the synovial route was available in the mature animals.

Attempts have been made to demonstrate fluid and solute transfer from subchondral bone using human material but the studies have necessarily been carried out *in vitro*, and again the results appear at first sight to be contradictory.

Maroudas, Bullough, Swanson and Freeman (1968), using a diffusion chamber, found no measurable transfer of solutes such as methylene blue or glucose across the zone of calcification in adult human cartilage, whereas when immature cartilage was used, considerable transfer occurred within the same time interval. Greenwald and Haynes (1969), on the other hand, using a fluorescent marker in the adult femoral head, were able to show some penetration into the cartilage after prolonged exposure. Penetration appeared to be related to the anatomical defects in the calcified zone described above. In this experiment, exposure for several hours was required before penetration so that it is possible that commencing autolysis had weakened the calcified barrier.

However, more recently, Haynes and Woods (1975) have carried out a more physiological version of these experiments which appear to confirm the findings. Freshly amputated human lower limbs were perfused with 20% pyronin for 1 or 2 min and the fluorescent dye was subsequently sought in the cartilage of the knee and other joints. It was found that in the femoral condyles and patella, and in the first metatarsophalangeal joint, dye had accumulated in the basal zone of the cartilage as well as in its superficial aspect. Furthermore, the infiltration from the subchondral region appeared to be in relation to the subchondral vessels referred to earlier (Figure 8.4). Of great significance was the finding that in those joints where such vessels cannot be identified, such as the interphalangeal joints, no infiltration in the basal zone

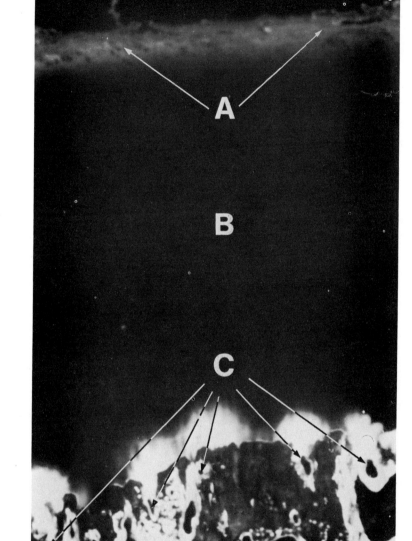

Figure 8.4 Femoral condyle after 1 min perfusion of the limb with 20% pyronin. The superficial zone of cartilage (A) is uniformly fluorescent. There is no fluorescence in the mid-zone (B) but in the basal cartilage there is intense fluorescence which is greatest adjacent to the subchondral vessels (C).

Frozen section   u.v. light   ×100.

(Reproduced from Greenwald and Haynes (1975) by kind permission of the authors.)

was seen (Figure 8.5). This suggests that the subchondral vessels are indeed capable of supplying solutes to the cartilage. However, because of the limited number of these vessels per unit area of the bone/cartilage interface, the fraction of nutrients which penetrate via the subchondral route is considered to be negligible compared with that via the synovial surface.

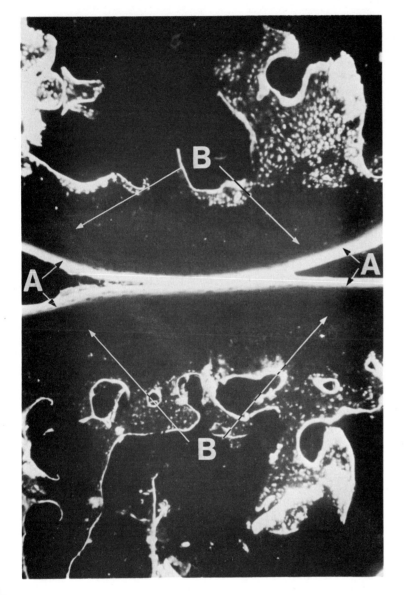

Figure 8.5 Interphalangeal joint after 1 min perfusion of the limb with 20% pyronin. The superficial zones of both articular cartilages are intensely fluorescent (A) as are the bone surfaces and osteocyte lacunae. Note that there is no fluorescence in the basal zones (B).

Frozen section u.v. light ×100.

(Reproduced from Greenwald and Haynes (1975) by kind permission of the authors.)

However, even if it is conceded that fluid and solute passage is possible through the calcified zone, it remains to be determined whether or not this makes a contribution to the well-being of the cartilage. In the absence of measurable transfer by this route, the only way that this can be done is to study the effects of its withdrawal.

Infarction of subchondral bone is seen in a number of pathological states in man, and in such conditions it may be presumed that any nutrition of the overlying cartilage will be prevented. There seems no doubt that in these circumstances the cartilage often survives, apparently intact, for prolonged periods, but whether its nutritional state is entirely normal in these circumstances is less certain.

McKibbin and Holdsworth (1969) produced subchondral infarction experimentally for a number of weeks in adult sheep while preserving normal joint function but were unable to produce any changes in the overlying cartilage. Although this result contrasted sharply with the effects of similar experiments in immature animals, the period of study was very short and better examples of this type of study are to be found in naturally occurring human pathological material.

Catto (1965b) studied the cartilage changes in the avascular femoral head following femoral neck fracture and found that in general the cartilage thickness was well preserved months and even years after infarction. However, in 25 out of 109 cases there were fewer chondrocytes than would have been expected simply from the age of the patient, and in 1 case where the head had been dead for over two years there was complete loss of the chondrocytes. It is difficult to say whether these changes resulted from the withdrawal of a source of partial nutrition or whether the cartilage had been affected by an accompanying loss of function in the joint, or by structural changes in the underlying bone.

2.2. Nutrition by the Synovial Fluid

The suggestion that synovial fluid might contribute to the nutrition of articular cartilage appears to have originated with Leidy (1849), who was able to show that the surface of cartilage was capable of imbibing fluid. He considered, however, that this mechanism could support only the most superficial layers.

The observations that loose bodies in joints often contain apparently healthy cartilage was made by Virchow in 1863, lending support to this suggestion; but at the same time, he put forward his concept of the *vita minima* with its implication that, although this process might be sufficient to keep the cartilage from undergoing necrosis, it did not follow that it would be sufficient to fulfil all the needs of normally functioning orthotopic articular cartilage. Strangeways (1920) provided evidence that actual growth of entirely loose bodies could occur, suggesting more than a *vita minima*, and Ito (1924) confirmed Strangeways' observations by producing experimental loose bodies and observing their growth. Bywaters (1937), using measurements of *in vitro* glycolysis and oxygen consumption, calculated that synovial fluid could be expected to support all but the deepest layers of the cartilage.

In contrast to the uncertainty surrounding the physiological evidence for fluid and solute transfer via the subchondral route, there has been no difficulty in demonstrating solute transfer into cartilage by diffusion from its synovial surface both *in vivo* and *in vitro*; this has now been recorded many times using a variety of marker substances including ^{3}H-labelled cytidine (Mankin 1963), methylene blue, glucose and alizarin red (Maroudas *et al.* 1968), and ^{35}S-labelled sulphate (Hodge and McKibbin 1969; Honner and Thompson 1971).

The effect of withdrawing synovial fluid also provides a striking contrast with the parallel situation with regard to subchondral nutrition in that it leads to a very rapid deterioration of the cartilage. This is well seen in clinical practice following amputations through joints when the cartilage rapidly degenerates and eventually disappears altogether (Fisher 1922), and indeed there appear to be no circumstances where cartilage can survive unless it is in contact with synovial fluid. Woods, Greenwald and Haynes (1970) have pointed to an apparent exception to this in rheumatoid arthritis where live cartilage can be seen although separated from synovial fluid by the pannus characteristic of the disease. This is scarcely a fair comparison, however, since it is very doubtful if the cartilage is healthy under these circumstances: indeed, it is in the process of destruction and removal. There is also little doubt that such cartilage is freely invaded by subchondral vessels since this is one of the 'unstable states' referred to by Collins (1949).

However, although it appears that normal articular cartilage cannot survive in the absence of contact with synovial fluid, it cannot be assumed that this is necessarily the result of a failure in the supply of essential nutrients. There is some evidence that the synovial fluid has a specific protective role in relation to cartilage and it may be upon this that its dependence lies. Sengupta (1974) has shown that free transplants of articular cartilage undergo necrosis more rapidly when they are transplanted to an extrasynovial site than when they lie as loose bodies in a joint, suggesting that ordinary tissue fluid is not an adequate substitute for synovial fluid. Ogston and Phelps (1961) showed that hyaluronate, one of the constituents of synovial fluid, can effectively resist the diffusion of other macromolecules into solutions containing hyaluronic acid, and Sweet and Solomon (1971) have suggested that the loss of ground substance from normal articular cartilage *in vivo* may be retarded by the presence of hyaluronate in synovial fluid. This is obviously a phenomenon which must be taken into consideration when the role of synovial fluid is being assessed. Maroudas *et al.* (1968) have emphasized the importance of joint movement in the provision of nutrition via the synovial route. If the fluid in contact with the cartilage surface is stagnant, it becomes depleted with respect to nutrients so that the diffusion path increases in length as nutrients diffuse from adjacent parts of the synovial cavity. In contrast, if the synovial fluid is made to circulate as a result of joint movement, a maximal concentration of nutrients is always maintained on the cartilage surface (see Section 3.1).

2.3. Summary of the Evidence

The evidence in favour of the two proposed routes of nutrition can be conveniently grouped under three headings: morphological (where function is inferred from structure); physiological (when the direct demonstration of solute transfer is attempted); and pathological (in which the effects of withdrawal of the supposed route are studied).

In the case of synovial nutrition the evidence appears to be overwhelming on all three counts: there is no apparent anatomical barrier to prevent it; solutes can easily be made to pass from the joint into the cartilage; and cartilage apparently cannot survive in the absence of synovial fluid. It may be concluded that synovial fluid certainly makes a significant contribution to the nutrition of articular cartilage.

The evidence in support of the subchondral route, on the other hand, is more difficult to assess, largely because there appear to be differences between different species and even between different joints in the same species. Nevertheless, it does seem that in most animal joints and in some of the smaller human articulations the route can be excluded on all three counts. Thus there is an anatomical barrier in the form of an intact zone of basal calcification, it has not proved possible to demonstrate the passage of fluid and solutes under physiological conditions, and the cartilage appears to survive substantially intact for very long periods even when the underlying bone is infarcted. All of this is in marked contrast to the situation with regard to synovial nutrition, forcing us to conclude that in these circumstances the cartilage is entirely dependent on synovial nutrition, *faute de mieux*.

However, one of the most fascinating aspects of the problem lies in the exceptions which exist to this general rule, particularly since they apply to man. They have an obvious historical significance in that they have been responsible for confusion and apparent conflict of evidence in the past but, in addition, their existence inevitably prompts speculation as to the reason for this distinction.

All immature joint cartilage receives a significant additional contribution from the subchondral route and reasons for this, based on developmental considerations, have been suggested elsewhere (McKibbin, 1974). In the case of adult cartilage, on the other hand, the exceptions appear to be confined to a few of the larger human joints including the hip, knee and first metatarsophalangeal joint. Two questions immediately arise: first, given that there is a pathway between bone and cartilage in these particular joints, to what extent is this responsible for the total nutrition of the cartilage; and secondly, why should it exist at all in these special circumstances.

Direct measurement of the inflow by the two routes is not possible at present but some indication of the relative contributions may be obtained from the perfusion experiments of Haynes and Woods (1975). They found that the intensity of the dye fluorescence was actually greater in the basal zone of the cartilage than in the superficial parts (see Figure 8.5), suggesting that the latter route was of the greatest importance. However, it must be remembered that circumstances of this experiment were far from physiological and, in particular, normal joint movement was not possible. Since there are reasons for thinking that joint movement almost certainly facilitates the penetration via synovial fluid but would not help penetration from the bone, synovial nutrition is seen at a relative disadvantage in an immobile joint. Moreover, the dye they used—pyronin—is a cationic dye which accumulates preferentially in zones of high glycosaminoglycan content such as the basal zone whilst it has little affinity for the superficial zone where the GAG concentration is low. The degree of fluorescence thus gives an indication of the affinity of a given zone for the dye rather than its distance from the source of supply.

Perhaps a better estimate is provided by Catto's (1965b) study of the chondrocyte population in avascular human heads since, by a fortunate coincidence, this is one of the joints in which subchondral channels have been demonstrated. The fact that there was a small but nevertheless perceptible diminution in the number of these cells suggests that the contribution from the bone is also small but probably essential.

In the present state of our knowledge one can only speculate as to the reasons for this exceptional behaviour. One obvious possibility is that, since only the largest human joints possess the anatomical features by which nutrition could be supplied by the subchondral route and since in these joints the synovial route may be incapable of providing an adequate supply of oxygen to deep chondrocytes because of the thickness of the cartilage (see Section 3.1), the defects in the calcified zone exist to oxygenate deep chondrocytes. However, if this were so, one might expect this mechanism to operate in all the joints of still larger animals but so far there is no evidence of this. In fact, in some admittedly limited observations on the femoral head of the cow, Haynes and Woods (1975) were unable to find evidence of subchondral channels. Furthermore, the thicker the cartilage, the lower the cell density (Chapter 2, Section 4) and hence the lower the rate of consumption of nutrients (including oxygen) per unit volume of tissue. This means that even if the synovial surface were the sole source of supply, the concentration of nutrients in the basal layers of the larger joints may not be too different from that in the smaller joints. This is obviously a field in which further work is required.

A further interesting feature of these exceptional joints is that they are prone to osteoarthrosis. This applies particularly to the first metatarsophalangeal joint which lies in this group while the interphalangeal joints which do not share its propensity for degenerative change show no evidence of subchondral nutrition. However, while it is interesting to draw attention to this association, in the present state of our knowledge it is probably unwise to speculate further.

Finally, one rather more prosaic and unexciting explanation of the phenomenon may be that we are simply observing the end of the maturation process. The subjects studied by Haynes and Woods were all young adults and it is possible that, with further maturation, this subchondral route could dissappear. The situation has a parallel in the rabbit where the full constitution of the calcified cartilage layer often occurs later than the closure of the epiphysis. This question can only be answered by an extension of their studies to other age groups.

At present therefore one must conclude that limited subchondral nutrition is an established fact in certain of the larger human joints, perhaps being responsible for the supply of oxygen to deep chondrocytes (see Section 3.1). In smaller human joints it seems certain that subchondral nutrition does not occur.

3. NUTRIENT TRANSPORT WITHIN THE MATRIX

A priori, nutrients might be transferred within the matrix of cartilage by one or more of three mechanisms: simple diffusion; active transfer by the chondrocytes; and a pumping action produced by alternate compression and relaxation of the matrix.

3.1. Principles Underlying Transport of Solutes by Diffusion

Although the rate of movement of solutes within cartilage itself is dependent only on their diffusion coefficients within the tissue, the actual rate of penetration of solutes from synovial fluid or other external media into cartilage is also a function of the distribution coefficient (see Chapter 4, Section 4). Table 4.3 (Chapter 4) summarizes the data for both the partition and the diffusion coefficients of various solutes.

Since the distribution coefficient is several times higher for cations than it is for anions, the rate of exchange of cations between synovial fluid and cartilage is much more rapid than that of anions. Since the rate of penetration of an electrolyte (e.g. Na_2SO_4) into cartilage is controlled by the penetration of the slower of the two ions (i.e. the anion), the transport of an electrolyte into cartilage is usually slower than that of an uncharged solute of similar size.

For illustration, the rates of transport of glucose and the sulphate ion into cartilage may be compared. Although the diffusivity of glucose is lower than that of sulphate (2.5 as compared with 3.0 cm²/s at 37°C), the sulphate ion is partially excluded from cartilage because of the Donnan equilibrium, its molar distribution coefficient being of the order of 0.3–0.4 for the femoral head (Maroudas and Evans 1974) as compared with a value of 0.7 for glucose. Accordingly, the rate of transport of the sulphate ion from synovial fluid into cartilage will be approximately equal to 60% of that for glucose.

It should also be noted that whilst in the case of small uncharged solutes the glycosaminoglycan content has no effect on the rate of transport, the penetration of electrolytes is dependent on fixed charge density. Thus the transport properties of an electrolyte will vary from joint to joint and within any one joint.

Although differences exist between non-ionic and ionic solutes, and the transport of the latter is somewhat dependent on fixed charge density, it can be said on the whole that substances of low molecular weight are able to diffuse fairly rapidly into and out of cartilage under all physiological conditions. On the other hand, the passage of larger molecules (of the size of serum albumin, for instance) is very restricted and critically dependent on the glycosaminoglycan content (see Chapter 4, Section 3.3). Thus, there could be conditions under which the utilization of large solutes by the chondrocytes (in some regulatory processes, for instance) might actually be controlled by their rate of diffusion. However, since little is known of such processes and since most common nutrients are of small molecular weight, the transport of large solutes will not be considered in this Section.

3.1.1. Balance between Cellular Requirements for Solutes and the Rate of Diffusion through the Matrix.

If the cellular requirements for a given solute are known (a subject discussed in Chapter 2, Section 3.1), it is possible to calculate whether transport by diffusion from the synovial cavity is sufficiently fast to satisfy these requirements throughout the depth of cartilage. This possibility may be illustrated by reference to glucose, the sulphate ion and oxygen. If it is assumed that the rate at which glucose is consumed by the cells is independent of the glucose concentration in the matrix, the concentration of glucose in the cartilage will decrease with the distance from the articular surface, in a manner dependent on the cell distribution profile, reaching zero at a depth where the rate of diffusion from the surface is exactly balanced by the rate of consumption by the cells. The glycolysis rate is assumed to be the same for all the cells.

Using these assumptions and Fick's law of diffusion, an expression may be derived relating the maximum depth of penetration of glucose into the cartilage to the cell density profile (Maroudas

1979). Using the cell density profile determined by Stockwell for human femoral condyles (Chapter 2) and the glycolysis rate per cell as measured by Bywaters (1937) ($q = 1.0 \times 10^{-11}$ mmol mm^{-3} h^{-1}), the maximum depth of penetration for glucose may be calculated to be 5.8 mm. Since the actual depth of cartilage on the femoral condyles seldom exceeds 2.5 mm, diffusion from the synovial cavity is more than adequate for chondrocyte nutrition, the margin of safety being over 100%. (A previous estimate of 3.0 mm for the maximum depth of penetration (Maroudas *et al.* 1968) was made before accurate data on cell density profiles had been published.) If, instead of using Bywaters' value for the glycolysis rate, the highest value found in the literature were to be taken (namely that obtained by Rosenthal, Bowie and Wagoner (1941): $q = 5.0 \times 10^{-11}$ mmol mm^{-3} h^{-1}), the maximum depth of penetration would be 3.6 mm, i.e. still in excess of the actual depth.

With respect to the sulphate ion, its concentration in synovial fluid, its partition coefficients and its rate of incorporation into the glycosaminoglycans of the matrix are all known (Maroudas and Evans 1974; Maroudas 1975; see also Chapter 4, Section 3). If a similar calculation is made for the maximum depth of penetration, it is found that an even greater margin of safety exists (more than 200%), i.e. that cartilage cells up to a total depth of about 8–10 mm could be supplied with sulphate from the synovial cavity. This implies that for cartilage of the thickness found in man (2–3 mm) there is only a small drop in the concentration of inorganic sulphate with distance from the articular surface. Such small differences in concentration are not likely to affect the rate of glycosaminoglycan synthesis (Maroudas and Evans 1974).

Finally, it is of interest to consider oxygen since this presents a somewhat different case. The reported oxygen tensions for synovial fluid are 20–100 mmHg, corresponding to oxygen concentrations of $3–10 \times 10^{-8}$ mol/cm^3; oxygen consumption for bovine cartilage has been given by Rosenthal *et al.* (1947) as 16×10^{-19} mol O_2 s^{-1}. If the mean cell density for human femoral condyle cartilage is taken as being equal to 15×10^6 cells/cm^3 (Chapter 2) and the diffusion coefficient of oxygen in cartilage as equal to 40% of its value in free solution (i.e. 1.3×10^{-5} cm^2/s), the depth at which the oxygen concentration becomes zero works out to be 1.83–3.0 mm. This would imply that cells in the deep zone of cartilage are exposed to very low, if not zero, oxygen tensions. Since the actual oxygen consumption as well as both the glycolysis rate and the sulphate incorporation have been reported to depend on oxygen tension, variations in the latter with depth may play an important part in the control of synthetic processes of the chondrocytes in different zones of cartilage.

As more data become available on the requirements of chondrocytes for different substances, it will be possible to determine to what extent these requirements are likely to be satisfied by simple diffusion. At present it appears that a nutritionally adequate supply of small molecular weight solutes can be ensured by diffusion from the synovial cavity but that the supply of oxygen to deep chondrocytes may be limited.

The supply of high molecular weight solutes will be very low indeed, as they are severely excluded by the matrix proteoglycans.

3.2. Active Transfer by Chondrocytes

Active transfer of nutrients by chondrocytes implies, since the cells are apparently not in cytoplasmic contact, that some or all cells are capable of extracting nutrients from the matrix on their synovial side and of secreting these nutrients into the matrix on their osseous side. The effect of such a mechanism, if it exists, would be to promote the diffusion of nutrients through the intercellular matrix by increasing the concentration gradients between cells. Although the relatively high cellularity of the superficial zone, and the fact that the cells in it have an unusual discoid shape, might conceivably be related to a nutritional function possessed by these cells, such a mechanism seems unlikely on general biological grounds and no direct experimental evidence exists in support of it. Brower, Akahoshi and Orlic (1962) have, however, reported that the penetration of articular cartilage by dye in the experimental animal occurs rapidly while the animal is alive, but very much more slowly one hour after somatic death. They argued that this implies the existence of a vital process of dye transfer. Against this conclusion it can be argued, first, that chondrocytes are still alive one hour after somatic death so that the change in dye penetration reported by Brower and co-workers seems unlikely to have been due to the cessation of cellular activity in cartilage. Secondly, the findings of Brower and his co-workers in the living animal are explicable solely in terms of passive diffusion (Maroudas *et al.* 1968), whereas their findings after death are difficult to explain on any basis and have not proved to be repeatable.

Two more recent experiments lead to the conclusion that solute transport through the matrix of cartilage obeys the same laws *in vivo* as *in vitro*; i.e. that it is unaffected by cellular activity (except by removing metabolites from the matrix by which cellular activity will alter the relevant concentration gradients).

In the first of these experiments (Maroudas and Evans 1974) the partition and diffusion coefficients of the sulphate ion were determined *in vitro* on fresh cartilage slices within 2–6 hours of their removal either at operation or at post-mortem. The cartilage slices were then frozen. When the slices were thawed several days later and the permeability experiments repeated, both the diffusion and the partition coefficients were found to be unchanged.

Since chondrocytes are known to remain viable for at least 24 hours after death (Collins and Meachim 1961), but are destroyed by freezing and thawing, the above results show that transport processes are not affected to any measurable degree by the presence of living cells.

In the second set of experiments (Maroudas 1975, 1978) radioactively labelled sulphate was injected into rabbits which were sacrificed at different time intervals after the tracer injection. Their joints were rapidly excised and the cartilage was analysed for the radioactivity due to free (^{35}S) sulphate. Blood samples were taken at the same time and also analysed for free plasma (^{35}S) sulphate. Since rabbit cartilage is very thin (usually about 0.5 mm), calculations based on the diffusion coefficient obtained *in vitro* predict that, for the sulphate ion, equilibrium should exist between cartilage and plasma (provided synovial fluid is in equilibrium with the latter) very soon after the tracer injection. This in fact was found to be the case since the ratio N_1/N_0 (where N_1 = radioactivity due to ^{35}S in cartilage and N_0 = radioactivity due to ^{35}S in the plasma) corresponded closely to the value of the partition coefficient of the sulphate ion determined for rabbit cartilage *in vitro*.

Similar results were obtained after the intravenous injection of (^{35}S) sulphate and (^{3}H) methylglucose into dogs, equilibrium being observed between plasma, synovial fluid and cartilage (Maroudas 1975; also Maroudas and Holm, in preparation).

3.3. A Pump

The fact that fluid is expressed from the matrix of cartilage when the tissue is compressed, and subsequently reimbibed when the compressive force is released, has led to the suggestion that intermittent compression of the cartilage during life might 'pump' fluid through the matrix and thus contribute to the nutrition of the chondrocyte (Hildebrand 1896; Müller 1929). The source of such intermittent compression has generally been considered to be the variations in loading of the cartilage surface produced by the movement upon it of the other component of the joint (Ingelmark and Saaf 1948; Ekholm 1955).

Despite the wide currency of this belief, direct experimental confirmation is lacking and Maroudas *et al.* (1968) were unable to show that mechanical indentation of cartilage increased the penetration of the cartilage by methylene blue any more than would have been expected from simple diffusion.

Most of the support for the idea has been derived indirectly from the fact that anything which interferes with the normal movement of one joint component on the other, such as immobilization (Fisher 1922; Salter and McNeil 1965; Sood 1971) or

478

dislocation (Fisher 1922; Konig 1923; Bennett and Bauer 1937), leads to regressive changes in the cartilage, it being assumed that such changes have a nutritional basis. Conversely, exercise has been shown experimentally to increase the penetration of cartilage by solutes in synovial fluid (Ingelmark and Saaf 1948; Ekholm 1955; Maroudas *et al.* 1968), and it has also been claimed that the total fluid content of cartilage is increased by exercise in both animals and man, as shown by an increase in thickness of the cartilage (Ingelmark and Ekholm 1948) and swelling of the chondrocytes (Ekholm and Norback 1952). These latter findings are somewhat surprising since it is very difficult to get cartilage to swell significantly *in vitro*: even a tenfold reduction in the electrolyte osmotic pressure produces a volumetric increase of only 1–2% (Maroudas 1976).

Nevertheless, there seems no doubt that exercise does result in an increased penetration of the cartilage but it does not necessarily follow that this is the result of the hypothetical pump action.

In considering the possibility that intermittent compression may affect solute transport in cartilage, a distinction must be drawn between (a) the transport of low molecular weight solutes within the matrix, (b) the transport of high molecular weight solutes within the matrix and (c) the transport of all solutes to the cartilage surface by the agitation (stirring) of the synovial fluid which in life must be caused by the movements accompanying intermittent compression.

3.3.1. The Role of a Pump in the Transport of Low Molecular Weight Solutes. Since the cartilage/bone interface is practically impermeable to water flow, when cartilage is placed under load, flow of fluid will take place in a radial direction towards the unloaded region. An expression for radial flow through cartilage which can approximately be applied to describe the above situation was given by McCutchen (1962) in the following form:

$$q = \frac{\mathrm{d}h}{\mathrm{d}t} = \frac{8WK_T h}{\pi R^4} \tag{1}$$

where h = cartilage thickness,

$\frac{\mathrm{d}h}{\mathrm{d}t}$ = rate at which cartilage is losing water and hence deforming,

q = fluid velocity,

W = applied load,

K_T = tangential permeability,

R = mean radius of the cartilage area under load = 22 mm (2.2 cm) for the hip (Day, Swanson and Freeman 1975).

The mean value of the load in the hip during the walking cycle can be taken as 200 kg (Paul 1965).

The mean permeability for the hip is about 2×10^{-16} m^3 s kg^{-1} (2×10^{-14} cm^3 s g^{-1}) (Chapter 4, Section 6).

Insertion of these values into equation (1) gives for dh/dt a value of 8×10^{-9} mm/s (8×10^{-7} cm/s). If the compression and the relaxation periods are taken (for the purpose of the calculation) to be approximately of the same duration, the overall rate of imbibition of fluid (which in life can be assumed to be solute-rich) will be given by:

$$\frac{q}{2} = 4 \times 10^{-9} \text{ m}^3/\text{s per m}^2 \text{ of surface}$$

For a solute such as glucose, with a concentration in the fluid (C_o) of 1 gram per litre the total quantity of solute transferred into cartilage per square metre of surface per second will be

$$\frac{q}{2} \times C_o = 4 \times 10^{-9} \text{ kg}$$

However, some glucose will also be lost from the cartilage with the expelled fluid. If a linear concentration gradient of glucose in the cartilage is assumed, decreasing in the deep zone to approximately half its surface value, then the expelled fluid will have a mean glucose content corresponding to $0.75 \, C_o$.

Using the above figures, the net amount of glucose gained by cartilage through fluid flow works out to be 1×10^{-9} kg m^{-2} s^{-1} (1×10^{-10} g s^{-1} cm^{-2}). In actual fact this must be an overestimate because (a) the amount of fluid lost per cycle is not completely recovered (Freeman, Swanson and Manley 1975) and (b) the permeability of the superficial and middle zones of cartilage is higher than that of deep cartilage (Maroudas et al. 1968); thus more fluid will be lost from the former than from the latter and more glucose will be lost with it.

The amount of glucose transferred into cartilage by diffusion alone is given by

$$J_s = \bar{D}\frac{d\bar{C}}{dx} \tag{2}$$

where J_s = flux of solute molecules,
$\bar{D}$ = solute diffusivity.

For glucose, $\bar{D}$ at 37°C = 2.6×10^{-10} m^2/s (2.6×10^{-6} cm^2/s). Assuming the same concentration gradient as above:

$$J_{s \text{ (diff)}} = 2.6 \times 10^{-6} \times \frac{10^{-3}}{0.4}$$

$$= 6.5 \times 10^{-8} \text{ kg m}^{-2}$$
$$(6.5 \times 10^{-9} \text{ g s}^{-1} \text{ cm}^{-2})$$

It is obvious from the above values that the physiological pumping action due to cyclic loading of cartilage is far less effective, even at peak physiological loads, in supplying small solutes (such as common nutrients) to the cells than simple diffusion.

Recent experiments in which the penetration of radioactively labelled potassium iodide was studied in matched plugs of cartilage—one of which was subject to cyclic loading whilst one was left immersed in a stirred solution—have shown no difference in the rate of ^{125}I uptake by the two plugs (Maroudas and Tomlinson, in preparation), thus confirming the above conclusions.

It can thus be concluded that, as far as small solutes are concerned, the diffusion process is the controlling mechanism for the supply of nutrients to cartilage.

3.3.2. The Role of a Pump in the Transport of High Molecular Weight Solutes. The diffusivities of larger solutes (such as serum albumin) are considerably lower than those of small solutes (such as glucose) (see Chapter 4, Section 4). Thus the contribution made by fluid transfer (i.e. by a 'pump') to their transport may well be significantly greater than that made to the transport of small solutes. Indeed, preliminary experiments (Maroudas and Tomlinson 1977, unpublished) suggest that this is so.

4. THE METABOLIC ACTIVITIES OF THE CHONDROCYTE

This subject is discussed in Chapter 2, Section 3, Chapter 3 and Chapter 4, Section 5. It will not be recapitulated here.

5. NUTRITIONAL AND METABOLIC CHANGES ASSOCIATED WITH FIBRILLATION

5.1. The Source of Nutrients

The analysis in Section 2 has been based on the supposition that the cartilage concerned has been 'normal' and unaffected by any disease process. This distinction does not pose any particular difficulties in most animal experiments, but where human material has been used there is more need for caution. The problem of ageing changes in human cartilage is discussed in Chapter 9, including the difficulty of distinguishing between physiological and truly pathological changes. However, in the present context it is sufficient to recall that these changes do exist and to recognize that if such cartilage is used for experimental purposes, it does not necessarily follow that the conclusions will be valid for intact (i.e. non-fibrillated) cartilage.

These precautions are of course even more important when the cartilage is involved in frank disease. In these circumstances, two problems need to be considered: first, whether or not the nutritional mechanism is altered in diseased states; and secondly, whether such alterations are themselves the result of the disease or, alternatively, play a part in its causation. As before, the two main routes of nutrition are considered separately.

5.1.1. Nutrition by the Synovial Route. In osteoarthrosis the surface of the degenerated cartilage remains freely accessible to the synovial fluid, but in inflammatory conditions where a layer of pannus covers the articular surface the possibility must be considered that this could be acting as an anatomical barrier, as suggested by Woods *et al.* (1970). Certainly in these circumstances the cartilage is usually unhealthy; however, this may not necessarily be the result of interference with nutrition but could reflect the effect of enzymal or other direct action of the pannus.

The importance of joint movement and contact with the opposite joint surface has already been mentioned in relation to synovial nutrition. This idea has been elaborated by Bullough, Goodfellow and O'Connor (1973), who have proposed an ingenious theory in which they suggest that the facilitation of this type of nutrition gradually declines with the years to the ultimate prejudice of the cartilage. Central to their hypothesis is the concept that an essential 'design feature' of the joints of young animals is a small degree of incongruity between the surfaces, which feature enhances the 'wetting' of the cartilage surface by synovial fluid during joint movement. With increasing age this incongruity tends to diminish, resulting eventually in a near-perfect match of the two surfaces. Under these circumstances 'wetting' is less effective, nutrition is impaired and the cartilage suffers. Unfortunately, the support for this interesting idea is so far entirely circumstantial and its confirmation must await the direct demonstration of a relationship between the degree of incongruity and the nutritional status of the cartilage. Even then, the link between cause and effect will have to be carefully assessed.

5.1.2. Nutrition by the Subchondral Route. Whatever may be the extent of the normal barrier to the diffusion of nutrients in the subchondral region, there is little doubt that it is significantly compromised in degenerative and chronic inflammatory disease. Trueta (1968) has described the process whereby, in osteoarthrosis, the gradual advance of vessels into the calcified zone may be seen, especially in relation to osteophyte formation. The resumption of endochondral ossification which is often seen in these circumstances also implies that the normal barrier to the entry of blood vessels in adult cartilage is absent. The nutritional significance of these changes is, however, far from clear. It is very tempting to suggest that as a result of mechanical interference with synovial nutrition the cartilage is deprived of nutrients and its subsequent invasion by blood vessels is an attempt to compensate for this. However, it must be remembered that the direct penetration of cartilage by vessels is not its normal mode of nutrition and it is possible that these invading vessels have nothing to do with nutrition but are concerned mainly in the formation of osteophytes. In fact, an admittedly limited study by Greenwald and Hayes (1969) of osteoarthrosic cartilage suggested that the number of defects in the subchondral barrier which are a normal feature of the human femoral head are actually decreased in this condition. This finding immediately prompts the alternative hypothesis that the changes in the cartilage are produced by the disappearance of these channels, cutting off an important route of supplementary nutrition. It is obvious, however, from the observations of Catto (1965a, b) in avascular necrosis of the femoral head that the changes which could be attributed to such a mechanism are very slight. When a femoral head which has been completely infarcted revascularizes before any collapse has taken place, the cartilage shows only a slight although definite increase in fibrillation and some decrease in the number of chondrocytes. This presumably represents the effect of total withdrawal of subchondral nutrition. If, on the other hand, segmental collapse has occurred resulting in disorganization of the joint, the cartilage becomes rapidly osteoarthrosic with vascular invasion of the cartilage and osteophyte formation. It is likely that in these circumstances synovial nutrition has also been interfered with and that this may explain the breakdown of the resistance of the cartilage to vascular invasion. If so, it follows that if nutritional failure plays any part in the degeneration of cartilage, it is a breakdown in the synovial route which is of the greatest importance.

Similar considerations apply to arthropathy in chronic inflammatory disease. Here also direct vascular invasions of the cartilage can be seen (Woods *et al.* 1970) but in these circumstances it seems even more likely that this is a response to cartilage which has been directly damaged rather than to a deprivation of nutrition occasioned by the masking action of the pannus.

5.2. Nutrient Transport within the Matrix

In Section 3 it was concluded that diffusion from the synovial surface was the process chiefly responsible for the transport of small molecular weight solutes within the matrix of cartilage, and that large molecular weight solutes might be transported in part by bulk fluid transfer (i.e. by a 'pump').

It has been demonstrated in Chapter 4 that the diffusion of small, uncharged solutes such as glucose, glycine, proline, oxygen or water varies relatively little with the chemical composition of the matrix although it does show a slight increase with increase in the water content. Since fibrillated cartilage has a higher water content than intact tissue, the diffusion of the above solutes will be slightly enhanced. This has been confirmed experimentally in the case of tritiated water diffusing through fibrillated cartilage from osteoarthrosic femoral heads (Maroudas and Venn 1977).

Much larger differences are observed between fibrillated and normal specimens in the case of solutes of large molecular weight or of electrolytes because the degree of their penetration into cartilage is very sensitive to changes in the proteoglycan concentration. Since fibrillation is associated with swelling as well as proteoglycan loss, the effective proteoglycan concentration per wet weight of tissue is usually significantly lower. This leads to a considerable increase in the permeability to electrolytes (Chapter 4) and large molecules (Snowden and Maroudas 1976).

The chondrocytes will become more accessible to solutes of large molecular weight, a change whose effect cannot be predicted. It seems, for example, that proteoglycan depletion might expose the chondrocyte to antigens and antibodies from which they are normally protected—a phenomenon which might be relevant to the pathogenesis of rheumatoid arthritis.

It may therefore be concluded that fibrillation will not of itself have an adverse effect upon nutrient transfer; if anything, the reverse is the case. It remains to consider the possibility that a defect in nutrient transfer causes fibrillation. From what was said in Section 3.1, the most likely causal sequence in this context would be a failure of oxygenation of deep chondrocytes leading to deep matrix defects. Although deep horizontal clefts are seen in the matrix of fibrillated cartilage (Chapter 9, Section 3.3) and some deep chondrocytes undergo necrosis, the former could well be caused by shear (Chapter 9, Section 5.5) whilst the latter is only seen as part of a more widespread cell necrosis. Furthermore, the fact that the changes in the matrix in fibrillated cartilage affect the surface whilst reactive cluster formation and increased proteoglycan synthesis are particularly in evidence in the deep zone (Chapter 9, Section 2.3.3), is hard to reconcile with this hypothetical mechanism.

On balance, therefore, it seems fair to conclude that fibrillation neither causes nor is caused by a disturbance of nutrient transport in the matrix.

5.3. Metabolic Changes

These are discussed in Chapter 2, Section 8, in Chapter 4, Section 5, and in Chapter 9, Section 2.2.12.

REFERENCES

Bennett G. and Bauer W. (1937) Joint changes resulting from patellar displacement and their relation to degenerative hip disease. *J. Bone Jt Surg.* **19,** 667.

Brodin H. (1955) Paths of nutrition in articular cartilage and intervertebral discs. *Acta orthop. scand.* **24,** 177.

Brower T. D., Akahoshi Y. and Orlic Patricia (1962) The diffusion of dyes through articular cartilage in vivo. *J. Bone Jt Surg.* **44A,** 456.

Bullough P., Goodfellow J. and O'Connor J. (1973) The relationship between degenerative changes and load-bearing in the human hip. *J. Bone Jt Surg.* **55B,** 746.

Bywaters E. G. L. (1937) The metabolism of joint tissues. *J. Path. Bact.* **44,** 247.

Catto M. (1965a) A histological study of avascular necrosis of the femoral head after trans-cervical fracture. *J. Bone Jt Surg.* **47B,** 749.

Catto M. (1965b) The histological appearances of late segmental collapse of the femoral head after trans-cervical fracture. *J. Bone Jt Surgery,* **47B,** 777.

Collins D. H. (1949) *The Pathology of Spinal and Articular Diseases.* Edward Arnold, London.

Collins D. H. and Meachim G. (1961) Sulphate ($^{35}SO_4$) uptake by chondrocytes in relation to histological changes in osteoarthritic human cartilage. *Ann. rheum. Dis.* **19,** 318.

Day W. H., Swanson S. A. V. and Freeman M. A. R. (1975) Contact pressures in the loaded cadaver hip. *J. Bone Jt Surg.* **57B,** 302.

Ekholm R. (1951) Articular cartilage nutrition. *Acta anat.* Suppl. 15.

Ekholm R. (1955) Nutrition of articular cartilage. *Acta anat.* **24,** 177.

Ekholm R. and Norback B. (1952) On the relation between articular changes and function. *Acta orthop. scand.* **81,** 881.

Fisher A. G. T. (1922) A contribution to the pathology and aetiology of osteoarthritis. *Brit. J. Surg.* **10,** 52.

Freeman M. A. R., Swanson S. A. V. and Manley P. (1975) Stress lowering function of articular cartilage. *Med. Biol. Engg* **13,** 245.

Greenwald A. J. and Haynes D. W. (1969) A pathway for nutrients from the medullary cavity to the articular cartilage of the femoral head. *J. Bone Jt Surg.* **51B,** 747.

Ham A. W. and Leeson T. S. (1961) *Histology*, p. 298. Pitman Medical, London.

Hamerman D., Rosenberg L. C. and Schubert M. (1970) Diarthrodial joints revisited. *J. Bone Jt Surg.* **52A,** 725.

Haynes D. W. and Woods C. G. (1975) Nutritional pathways for adult human articular cartilage. *Orthopaedics* **8,** 1.

Hildebrand O. (1896) *Dt. Z. Chir.* **42,** 292. Cited by Ekholm R. (1951).

Hodge J. and McKibbin B. (1969) The nutrition of mature and immature joint cartilage in rabbits. *J. Bone Jt Surg.* **51B,** 140.

Holmdahl P. E. and Ingelmark B. E. (1950) The contact between the articular cartilage and the medullary cavities of bone. *Acta orthop. scand.* **20,** 1156.

Honner R. and Thompson R. C. (1971) The nutritional pathways of articular cartilage. *J. Bone Jt Surg.* **53A,** 742.

Hunter W. (1743) On the structure and diseases of articulating cartilages. *Phil. Trans.* **42,** 514.

Ingelmark B. E. and Ekholm R. (1948) A study on variations in the thickness of articular cartilage in association with rest and periodic load. *Upsala Läk-för Förh.* **53,** 61.

Ingelmark B. E. and Saaf J. (1948) Uber die Ernahrung des Gelenkknorpels. *Acta orthop. scand.* **17,** 303.

Ishido B. (1923) Gelenkuntersuchungen. *Virchows Arch.* **244,** 424.

Ito L. K. (1924) The nutrition of articular cartilage and its method of repair. *Brit. J. Surg.* **12,** 31.

Konig F. (1923) Uber reaktive Vorgange am Knorpel nach verschiedenen Schadigungen. *Arch. klin. Chir.* **124,** 1.

Leidy J. (1849) On the intimate structure and histology of articular cartilage. *Amer. J. Med. Sci.* **17,** 277.

McCutchen C. W. (1962) The frictional properties of animal joints. *Wear* **5,** 1.

McKibbin B. (1974) In *Normal and Osteoarthrotic Articular Cartilage,* Ed. by S. Y. Ali, M. W. Elves and D. H. Leaback. Institute of Orthopaedics, London.

McKibbin B. and Holdsworth F. W. (1966) The nutrition of immature joint cartilage in the lamb. *J. Bone Jt Surg.* **48B,** 793.

McKibbin B. and Holdsworth F. W. (1969) The nutrition of articular cartilage. *Sonderdruck aus Orthopadischer Gemeinschaftskongres Bucherei des Orthopaden,* Band 4. Ferdinand Enke Verlag, Stuttgart.

Mankin H. J. (1963) Localisation of tritiated cytidine in articular cartilage of immature and adult rabbits, after intra-articular injection. *J. Lab. Invest.* **12,** 543.

Maroudas A. (1975) Glycosaminoglycan turn-over in articular cartilage. *Phil. Trans. R. Soc. Lond.* B **271,** 293.

Maroudas A. (1976) Transport of solutes in cartilage. *J. Anat. (Lond.)* **122,** 113.

Maroudas A. (1977) Physical chemistry of articular cartilage. *Synovial Fluid and Joints,* Ed. by L. Sokoloff. Academic Press, New York.

Maroudas A. (1979) Physico-chemical basis of turn-over studies. *Proceedings of Workshop on Models of Osteoarthrosis,* Ed. by G. Nuki. Pitman Medical, Tunbridge Wells, in press.

Maroudas A. and Evans H. (1974) Sulphate diffusion and incorporation into human articular cartilage. *Biochim. biophys. Acta* **338,** 265.

Maroudas A. and Venn M. F. (1977) Chemical composition and swelling of normal and osteoarthrotic femoral head cartilage. II: Swelling. *Ann. rheum. Dis.* **36,** 399.

Maroudas A., Bullough P., Swanson S. A. V. and Freeman M. A. R. (1968) The permeability of articular cartilage. *J Bone Jt Surg.* **50B,** 166.

Mital M. A. and Millington P. F. (1970) Osseous pathway of nutrition to articular cartilage of the human femoral head. *Lancet* **i,** 842.

Muller W. (1929) *Biologie der Gelenke.* Leipzig. Cited by Ekholm R. (1951).

Ogston A. G. and Phelps C. F. (1961) The partition of solutes between buffer solutions and solutions containing hyaluronic acid. *Biochem. J.* **78,** 827.

Paul J. P. (1965) Bioengineering studies of the forces transmitted by joints. II: Engineering analysis. *Biomechanics and Related Bio-engineering Topics,* Ed. by R. M. Kenedi. Pergamon Press, Oxford.

Peterson H. (1930) Die Organs Des Skeletsytems. *Handbuch der mikrosk. Anat. des Menschen,* by W. von Mollendorff. Cited by Holmdahl P. E. and Ingelmark B. E. (1950).

Rosenthal O., Bowie M. A. and Wagoner G. (1941) Studies on the metabolism of articular cartilage. *J. cell. comp. Physiol.* **17,** 221.

Salter R. B. and McNeil R. (1965) Pathological changes in articular cartilage secondary to persistent joint deformity. *J. Bone Jt Surg.* **47B,** 185.

Sengupta S. (1974) The fate of transplants of articular cartilage in the rabbit. *J Bone Jt Surg.* **56B,** 167.

Snowden J. McK. and Maroudas A. (1976) The distribution of serum albumin in human normal and degenerate articular cartilage. *Biochim. biophys. Acta* **428,** 726.

Sood S. C. (1971) A study of the effects of experimental immobilisation on rabbit articular cartilage. *J. Anat. (Lond.)* **108,** 497.

Strangeways T. S. P. (1920) The nutrition of articular cartilage. *Brit. med. J.* **1,** 661.

Sweet M. B. E. and Solomon L. (1971) Gelatin as an experimental model for hyaluronate. *J Bone Jt Surg.* **53B,** 514.

Toynbee J. (1841) The non-vascularity of certain animal tissues. *Phil. Trans.* **131,** 159.

Trueta J. (1968) *Studies of the Development and Decay of the Human Frame.* William Heinemann, London.

Trueta J. and Harrison M. H. M. (1953) Osteoarthritis of the hip: a study of the nature and evolution of the disease. *J Bone Jt Surg.* **35B,** 442.

Virchow R. (1863) *Die Krankhaften Geswulate,* I. Berlin. Cited by Ekholm R. (1951).

Woods C. G., Greenwald A. J. and Haynes D. W. (1970) Subchondral vascularity in the human femoral head. *Ann. rheum. Dis.* **29,** 138.

9. Ageing and Degeneration

M. A. R. Freeman and G. Meachim

1. INTRODUCTION

In this Chapter the relationship between ageing, cartilage fibrillation and osteoarthrosis are considered in the light of the observations recorded in previous Chapters, and the nature and pathogenesis of the changes which develop in fibrillated cartilage are discussed. Although it is probable that fibrillation often occurs as an age-related change of no clinical significance, it is widely believed that it also represents the initial lesion in idiopathic ('primary') osteoarthroisis. In this Chapter, the view, necessarily to some extent hypothetical, is advanced that fibrillation can result from an age-related loss of strength in the fibre network of the cartilage matrix, probably combined with locally increased contact stresses, and that in certain instances it may lead to bone exposure and to clinically manifest osteoarthrosis.

2. THE CHANGES IN CARTILAGE ASSOCIATED WITH AGE-ING AND FIBRILLATION

Before considering the influence of age on human articular cartilage, four comments are pertinent.

First, the findings in articular cartilage in relation to age differ from those in costal cartilage (McElligott and Collins 1960; Linn and Sokoloff 1965) and in intervertebral discs (Sokoloff, Snell and Stewart 1967). Thus it is important to ensure that observations on 'cartilage' refer to articular cartilage.

Second, changes occurring in articular cartilage during ageing in adult life must be distinguished from the maturation changes which occur in joints during skeletal development. Here it should be noted that the cartilage of immature joints is fundamentally different from that in adults, since it serves a dual purpose: much of the immature cartilage is temporary, and is replaced by bone during epiphyseal development; only the region nearest the syno-

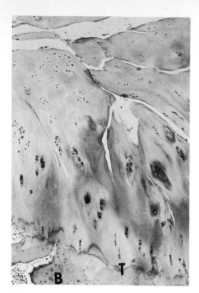

Figure 9.1 Deep splitting of uncalcified cartilage, of fibrillation type, on the zenith of an osteoarthrosic femoral head. T: uncalcified/calcified cartilage junction; B: subchondral bone.

H & E ×42.

Figure 9.2 Thinned uncalcified cartilage with a virtually smooth synovial interface. Note the cell necrosis (loss of nuclear staining) beneath the interface. Zenith of an osteoarthrosic femoral head. T: uncalcified/calcified cartilage junction; B: subchondral bone.

H & E ×46.

vial cavity remains unossified and becomes the permanent articular cartilage of the adult. McKibbin and Holdsworth (1967) comment that conventional nomenclature takes no account of this dual nature of the immature cartilage, as it is referred to variously as 'articular', 'joint' or 'epiphyseal'.

Third, the articular cartilage in adults often develops localized areas of structural disintegration. These degenerative lesions are usually due to the process termed 'fibrillation' (Chapter 1, Section 9). Their development is accompanied, or perhaps preceded, by local changes in the morphology and physicochemical properties of the affected tissue. Results obtained from cartilage samples showing fibrillation must therefore be analysed separately when studying the effects of ageing as such, and results obtained from cartilage adjacent to fibrillated sites must be interpreted with caution.

Finally, a comment is necessary here concerning the interpretation of metabolic and other studies of human osteoarthrosic femoral heads. Two types of non-osseous surface tissue are often present on the articular surface of such specimens: exposed old cartilage (Figures 9.1, 9.2 and 9.3), and new tissue of granulation, intermediate, fibrous or cartilaginous texture (Figures 9.4 and 9.5). It is important that data from these two types of tissue be analysed separately. Only samples consisting entirely of exposed

Figure 9.3 Horizontal cleft at the level of the junction (T) between uncalcified cartilage and its calcified zone. Note also the fine, vertical split from the synovial interface down to the horizontal cleft. Zenith of an osteoarthrosic femoral head.

H & E ×38.

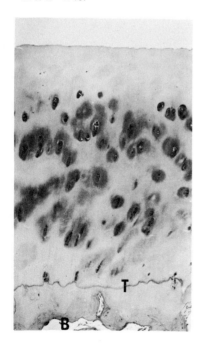

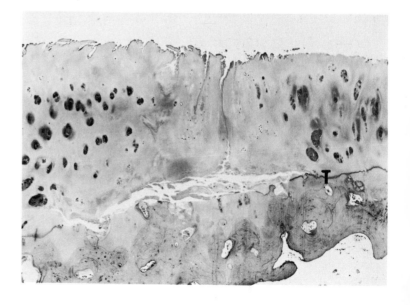

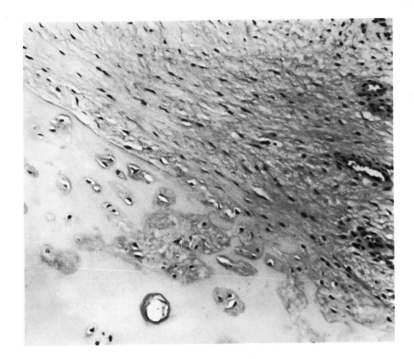

Figure 9.4 Histological section of tissue at the articular surface of an osteoarthrosic femoral head. New non-osseous tissue (top and right) invading the superficial aspect of old cartilage matrix. ×150.

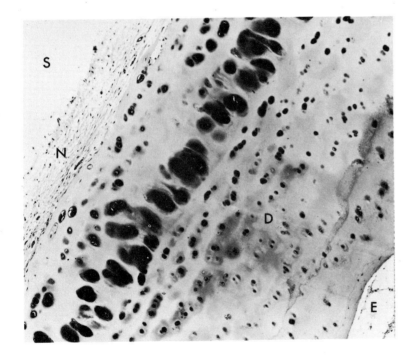

Figure 9.5 Histological section of the articular surface of an osteoarthrosic femoral head. A thin layer of new fibrous tissue (N) of para-articular origin is seen at the surface. D: cartilage; E: underlying bone and marrow spaces; S: synovial cavity. ×60.

old cartilage (Figures 9.1, 9.2 and 9.3) are directly relevant to the investigation of the metabolic changes in cartilage fibrillation, since the new tissue has been shown histologically to be due to repair processes of a sort in which the new tissue is extrinsic in origin (Meachim and Osborne 1970; Meachim and Roberts 1971).

2.1. The Terminology used to describe Fibrillation

Fibrillation (Figure 9.1) is a structural abnormality of cartilage characterized by splitting and fraying of the tissue, the details of which are described in Section 2.3. Before discussing the morbid anatomy of fibrillation and its correlates, consideration must be given here to the terminology. At present this is confused because some observers have restricted the description 'fibrillated' to lesions which are macroscopically apparent *en face* on unstained surfaces, while others have also used the term to describe changes of a less obvious nature, as shown by Indian ink staining or by light microscopy.

The ease with which fibrillation can be detected in a sample of cartilage will be influenced by the degree of change present and by the method used to examine the specimen. Severe change is readily apparent to the naked eye on macroscopic examination of unstained surfaces. In contrast, the demonstration of minimal changes may require examination of ink-stained surfaces, or of histological sections with the light microscope; moreover, it is possible that these mild histological changes are themselves a development from ultrastructural disruptions, at and below the cartilage surface, which can only be detected by transmission electron microscopy (Meachim and Roy 1969). The methods used to detect fibrillation, the relationships between the terms used to describe the findings, and the nature of some associated changes are set out in Table 9.1.

It will be apparent that, when discussing minimal amounts of this structural change, the distinction between 'fibrillated' and 'non-fibrillated' cartilage is to some extent arbitrary. In the opening Chapters of this book, 'fibrillation' was defined as a state in which the articular surface no longer appears structurally intact (Figure 9.6) when examined by the light microscope in histological sections (i.e. paraffin section 5–7 μm thick examined at magnification up to × 150, or, for some investigations, araldite-embedded sections 1 μm thick). In the account which follows the terms 'histologically fibrillated' (Figure 9.6) and 'histologically intact' refer to cartilage samples classified according to this definition, which correlates well with results from Indian ink staining (Table 9.1).

When a joint shows fibrillation, the abnormality is usually not distributed uniformly across the whole joint surface: fibrillated

Figure 9.6 Histological section, cut vertical to a 'macroscopically intact' articular surface. The plane of section was at right angles to elongated linear 'fractures' of the sort shown in Figure 9.18 and demonstrates 'histological fibrillation'. Note the thin strands of tissue at the surface (right and extreme left). The exact nature of the elongated cleft (centre) is uncertain: it may represent 'fibre separation' or the undermined edge of a 'surface fracture'.
Transmitted light   ×150.

and non-fibrillated areas can both be present, and in fibrillated areas the severity of the change often varies from place to place. This topographical variation can be observed on macroscopic examination of the joint, and is sometimes apparent even within a histological section taken from a small area of the joint surface. Thus it is important to specify whether a given change associated with fibrillation occurs only in cartilage that is itself fibrillated, or in a sheet of cartilage, some but not all of which is fibrillated.

It is difficult to relate, with absolute accuracy, the mechanical and chemical properties of cartilage to the presence or absence of fibrillation at the microscopical level in the tested specimen (as distinct from in the joint as a whole), since it is rarely practicable to examine histologically specimens that have been tested mechanically or chemically. Therefore workers studying the mechanical and chemical properties of cartilage have usually examined, with the naked eye, the appearances of the unstained surface in order to decide whether or not fibrillation is present. This method of classification has recently been improved by painting the surface with Indian ink and examining it *en face* with the naked eye or under low magnification. Mechanical studies are often carried out on blocks of tissue having a moderately large surface area (of the order of 0.06 cm^2), part of which may be fibrillated and part intact, giving rise to further difficulties of classification. For these reasons it is not possible to give the precise mechanical and chemical correlates of the changes which can be observed histologically as cartilage fibrillates, but a reasonable approximation is given in Table 9.1 and is described elsewhere in this Section.

Table 9.1 The terms used to describe the appearance of articular cartilage when examined in various ways and some correlated chemical and mechanical properties

Method of examination									
Naked eye	Naked eye	Light microscopy	Light microscopy	Transmission electron microscopy	Fixed charge density* (proteoglycan content)	Water content	Collagen content*	Compression stiffness	Tensile strength and stiffness
Orientation									
En face	*En face*	*En face*	Vertical section	Vertical section					
Staining									
None	Indian ink	Indian ink	Conventional	Conventional					
Magnification									
× 1	× 1	× 10 to 150	× 150	× 20 000 to 50 000					
'Macroscopically intact'	'Intact'	'Intact'	'Histologically intact'	'Intact'	'Normal'	'Normal'	Unchanged	'Normal'	'Normal'
				'Ultra-structural disruptions'			Decreased (because water content rises)		
	'Surface flecking'	'Minimal fibrillation'	'Histologically fibrillated'	'Fibrillated'	Progressively decreased	Increased		Values overlap the normal and reduced ranges	Variably reduced
'Fibrillated'	'Mild fibrillation'	'Overt fibrillation'						Progressively reduced	
	'Severe fibrillation'							untestable	untestable
'Ulcerated' ± new tissue (i.e. a full-thickness loss of old cartilage)					not applicable				
Old cartilage covered by new tissue									

* Expressed per wet weight of tissue

Table 9.2 Types of cartilage lesions

Non-destructive or Potentially destructive	*Cartilage not thinned* Regressive changes Minimal fibrillation (various *en face* patterns) 'Ravines' Overt fibrillation Tiny splits at uncalcified/calcified interface
Destructive	*Cartilage thinned* *Overt fibrillation with deep splitting ('splitting') *Horizontal splitting at uncalcified/calcified interface ('gouging') *Smoother-surfaced destructive thinning ('grinding') Localized rounded or elongated defect *Full-thickness loss of uncalcified cartilage* *Area of exposed calcified cartilage and/or bone *Loss of bony height beneath exposed bone* * Abrasive wear of exposed bone with necrosis of superficial osteocytes * Small segment of non-septic bone necrosis ? Bony collapse from microfractures in viable bone deep to surface * Subarticular bone 'cysts' large enough to suggest possibility of 'collapse'
Reparative	Re-covering of an exposed bone surface by new non-osseous layer (± destructive changes in new non-osseous surface tissue)
Peripheral remodelling	Covering of cartilage surface by new non-osseous tissue ('pannus') Replacement of old cartilage by new non-osseous tissue Intracartilaginous ossification (can lead to 'expansile remodelling') Peripheral bony outgrowths ('osteophytic lipping')
Remodelling of cartilage base	Active ossification at chondro-osseous junction Duplication of tidemark ? Thickening of calcified zone
Other lesions	Modulation of chondrocytes to 'fibroblasts', for example

Articular cartilage lesions in the Liverpool population. For most, but not all, of the lesions listed, examples have been encountered both in specimens of synovial joints from random necropsies and in surgical excision specimens from patients with clinical osteoarthrosis. The frequency of some of the lesions listed differed between the two groups of specimens. The asterisks (*) indicate lesions which, taking the series as a whole, have been encountered at topographical sites of 'progressive' (i.e. osteoarthrosic) destructive change on femoral heads. The histology of this change at its early, preclinical stage is not known.

2.2. Observations on Histologically Intact Tissue

2.2.1. Cellularity. Ageing has no significant effect on the overall cellularity of samples of adult human articular cartilage from the knee or shoulder, but only provided that the surface of the cartilage sample is microscopically intact (Chapter 2, Section 4.3). In the case of the cartilage on the head of the humerus, this observation may still be true if the superficial layer (zone 1) and the deeper uncalcified layers (zones 2 and 3) are considered separately (Meachim and Collins 1962). However, in the case of the cartilage on the femoral condyles, an age-correlated decrease in cellularity in the superficial layer does occur; it is balanced by a slight increase in cellularity in the deeper tissue (Stockwell 1967a). Vignon (1976, personal communication) reports an age-related decrease in both the superficial layer and the overall cellularity of the femoral head.

2.2.2. Thickness. Ageing has no effect on the thickness of the uncalcified matrix of the cartilage on the head of the humerus (Meachim 1971) or on the zenith of the femoral head (Vignon 1976, personal communication).

2.2.3. Surface Contour. Longmore and Gardner (1975) have shown that both the depth and the diameter of the 'tertiary hollows' of the cartilage surface increase during skeletal maturation, and suggest that this increase with age perhaps continues after maturation is complete. They also note that microscopic irregular surface ridges ('quaternary irregularities'), as seen *en face* by reflected light interference microscopy of the lateral femoral condyle, become more frequent with age. These 'quaternary irregularities' may be the equivalent of the age-related phenomenon described in Chapter 1 as 'minimal fibrillation' (Table 9.1), since on transmission light microscopy at $\times 150$ the latter shows 'undercut' ridging in association with splitting, fraying and other irregularities of the surface contour (Meachim 1972b, Figures 14–19); this phenomenon can start to develop before the age of 20 years (see Chapter 1, Sections 2.6 and 8).

2.2.4. Chemical Composition. When one discusses the percentage composition of cartilage, it is important to state clearly whether it is based on dry or wet weight of tissue. From the physiological point of view, it is the ratio of various constituents to water which is the important parameter (Chapter 4, Section 2.2.1).

Although previous workers found no change in the water content with age (Chapter 1, Section 3), more recent data indicate that there is a steady decrease (Chapter 4, Section 2.2.1).

The variations in the collagen content are small: on a dry basis it decreases somewhat due to an increase in the total content of acid glycosaminoglycans and non-collagenous protein, whilst on a wet basis it remains approximately constant (Chapter 4, Section 2.1).

2.2.5. Matrix Fibres. As noted above, the total amount of collagen in cartilage is unaffected by ageing. This would not, of course, preclude an alteration during ageing in the morphology of the individual collagen fibres or in the fibre network. Age-correlated changes have been demonstrated in the matrix fibres of murine (Silberberg, Silberberg, Vogel and Wettstein 1961) and rabbit (Barnett, Cochrane and Palfrey 1963) articular cartilage, but it is not known whether fibre morphology alters during ageing in man nor whether ageing affects the physicochemical properties of human cartilage fibres. The effect of ageing on the amount of cross-link formation in the collagen is also unknown. Even so, the age-related changes now known to occur in the mechanical properties of cartilage indicate that the collagen fibre network does deteriorate with age.

2.2.6. Pigmentation. Adult articular cartilage frequently shows a yellowish tint, but there is no evidence that this so-called 'degenerative' pigmentation does in fact predispose to fibrillation (Chapter 1, Section 6).

2.2.7. Physicochemical Properties. There is a small but significant increase in fixed charge density with age (Chapter 4, Section 2.3.1). Although there has been no systematic experimental study of other physicochemical properties as a function of age, because of the decrease in the water content and increase in fixed charge density, differences can be anticipated (Chapter 4, Sections 3, 4 and 6). Thus the rate of transport of all types of solutes will be decreased; this effect being more pronounced for electrolytes and large molecules. Also the hydraulic permeability can be expected to decrease whilst the osmotic pressure should increase, both these factors contributing to decrease in the overall rate of fluid transport.

2.2.8. Mechanical Properties. Two age-related changes in the mechanical properties of intact articular cartilage are described in Chapter 6, Sections 4.4 and 6: (a) a fall in the static tensile stiffness and fracture strength, and (b) a massive fall in the tensile fatigue strength. Since the tensile properties of articular cartilage have been shown to be related to the collagen fibre network, these changes imply that some element in the network changes with age. The nature of this change is at present unknown but it is not due to a reduction in the total collagen present nor to the application to cartilage of an ever-increasing number of load cycles as the years go by (Chapter 6, Section 6). Theoretically, the change might consist of fragmentation of the collagen fibres themselves or of 'rupture' of the bonds between them. Since broken collagen fibres cannot at present be identified as such by morphological methods and since the nature of the bonds linking collagen fibres in cartilage is unknown, it is at present impossible to carry any further an understanding of the mechanism underlying the age-related fall in the tensile stiffness, tensile strength and tensile fatigue strength of the tissue.

No age-related change has been demonstrated in the compressive properties of intact cartilage.

2.2.9. Frictional Properties. In Chapter 7, Section 8.1, it was stated that no change in the frictional properties of intact articular cartilage and synovial fluid has been observed with advancing age. Barnett and Cobbold (1968) have, however, observed that the mobility of living human finger joints tends to decrease with age, although there is a wide scatter in the measurements obtained and some old people have finger joints as mobile as in the second decade of life. As Barnett and Cobbold (1968) point out, there are several factors which could have reduced joint mobility independently of any change in the frictional properties of the articulating surfaces: thus the results they obtained might have been due, for example, to changes in the tension within the joint capsule, or in the stiffness of the overlying skin; moreover, it is possible that cartilage ulceration may have been present in some of the older subjects, thus affecting the results.

2.2.10. Mechanical Environment. The hip joint surfaces tend to become more congruent with age (Goodfellow 1970, personal communication), a fact which may have a bearing upon nutrition via the synovial route (Chapter 8, Section 2). It is not known whether a change in congruence occurs in other joints.

2.2.11. Nutrition. Woods, Greenwald and Haynes (1970) have studied the incidence of subchondral bone plate 'defects' extending into the base of the articular cartilage of healthy femoral heads. They find that the total number of 'defects' shows no change throughout adult life; however, the proportion of 'vascularized defects' to 'total defects' shows a steady decline with increasing age. From these observations, Woods and his colleagues conclude that 'useful vascularity' decreases with age in the basal part of the cartilage. The defects they studied at the chondro-osseous junction extended either into calcified matrix only or through into the uncalcified matrix causing a break in the 'tidemark'. The possible role of these basal vascular ingrowths in the nutrition of normal cartilage is discussed in Chapter 8. From this discussion it can be concluded that such ingrowths play at most only a minor part in the total nutrition of the uncalcified part of normal cartilage, which is nourished mainly or entirely by the synovial route. Thus the ageing change observed by Woods and co-workers is unlikely to have any major effect on the total nutrition of the uncalcified cartilage.

No data are available on the effect of ageing on cartilage nutrition by the synovial route (see Chapter 8, Section 5).

2.2.12. Metabolism. A reduction in oxygen utilization with increasing age has been reported in adult bovine cartilage. This change may be more apparent than real, and be attributable to loss of superficial cells in the cartilage in the older age groups (Chapter 2, Section 3.1.2; and Section 2.2.1. of this Chapter). No other metabolic abnormalities have been reported. In particular, ageing has no appreciable effect on the mean level of sulphate uptake *in vitro* by the cells of non-fibrillated cartilage from the head of the humerus (Collins and Meachim 1961).

2.2.13. Conclusion. Observations of articular cartilage in which the surface is still histologically intact have so far revealed only one group of age-related changes of significance: the static tensile fracture strength, the static stiffness and the tensile fatigue strength all decrease. These changes all imply a change in the collagen fibre network (but not necessarily in the fibres themselves since the total amount of collagen in the tissue does not decrease with age). Although the morphology of the collagen in murine and rabbit articular cartilage changes with age, no corresponding data are available in man and at present no morphological nor chemical explanation for these mechanical changes can be given.

Other age-related changes which have been observed include an alteration in the colour of the cartilage, an alteration in the glycosaminoglycans in the deep zone (Chapter 1, Section 4.6), and an alteration in vascularity at the chondro-osseous junction, but none of these changes appears to be of any major functional importance.

A change with age has been reported in the congruence of the articular surfaces at the hip, but it is not known whether a similar change occurs in other joints.

2.3. Observation on Histologically Fibrillated Cartilage

2.3.1. Collagen Network. In so far as there are splits in fibrillated cartilage, it is obvious that the collagen network which originally crossed the split must have ruptured. It is thus certain that ruptures of the collagen fibre network occur in fibrillated cartilage.

The morphological evidence suggests that the splits occur in the direction in which the network is weakest, i.e. parallel to the predominant fibre direction (see Chapter 6, Section 4.3). Thus in fibrillation the splitting process, as seen in vertical sections of the cartilage (Figure 9.1), develops and propagates in the same alignment as that of the matrix collagen fibre network. In the superficial layer (zone 1) of intact cartilage the collagen fibres are aligned parallel to the surface (Chapter 1, Section 2.5.1), and in mild superficial fibrillation there is horizontal splitting at the cartilage surface with the formation of thin strands of tissue, broader-based tufts and small pits (Meachim, Ghadially and Collins 1965). In more severe fibrillation the 'fibre lines' are next opened in the transitional layer (zone 2). Finally, vertical splitting occurs in the deep, uncalcified layer (zone 3) where, in contrast to the superficial zone, fibre alignment is radial to the surface (Chapter 1, Section 2.5.2). In each layer successively affected by fibrillation, the splitting process tends to precede the actual destruction of tissue (Collins 1949); thus in mild superficial fibrillation the cartilage is not thinner than normal (and may even be slightly thicker) (Meachim 1971), although deep fibrillation is, of course, accompanied by tissue loss which can eventually lead to complete destruction of the affected cartilage.

Both mild and severe fibrillation can be accompanied by horizontal splitting at the uncalcified/calcified interface (Figures 9.3 and 9.7), and in severe fibrillation areas of a smoother-surfaced destructive thinning (Figure 9.2) are sometimes also present on the affected joint surface. The total quantity of collagen is unaffected by fibrillation but since the hydration of the tissue increases the amount of collagen per unit of wet weight falls.

Figure 9.7 Tiny splits at the uncalcified/calcified cartilage interface (T) in a patellar specimen from a random necropsy. ×230.

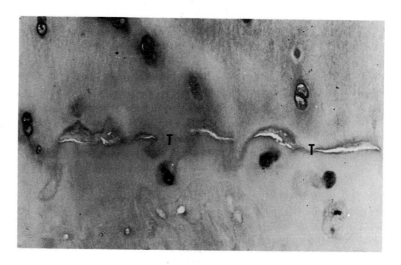

2.3.2. Matrix Glycosaminoglycans and Water. Fibrillated cartilage shows a decreased content of glycosaminoglycans in its intercellular matrix and an increase in the total amount of water in the tissue (Chapter 1, Section 9.1.2; Chapter 4, Section 2).

2.3.3. Cells and Sulphate Incorporation. (See also Chapter 2, Section 8, and Chapter 8, Section 4.) The chondrocytes in fibrillated cartilage show a variable amount of necrosis, and in the superficial layer (zone 1) the cellularity is reduced in histologically fibrillated as compared with histologically intact cartilage (Meachim and Collins 1962). A variable amount of cell necrosis can also occur in the deeper, uncalcified layers (zones 2 and 3), but at the same time multicellular rounded clusters are often formed by other, viable, chondrocytes. There is a local increase in cellularity in deeper layers containing such clusters (Meachim and Collins 1962). In many, but not all, of the clusters the cells have the ability to incorporate sulphate *in vitro*, suggesting that they are still actively synthesizing glycosaminoglycans (Collins and McElligott 1960); thus cluster formation is considered to be a 'reactive response' by the cells and not a degenerative phenomenon (Chapter 2, Section 8).

These two contrasting changes of cell necrosis and of viable, reactive cluster formation must both be taken into account when discussing the possible role of the cells in relation to the decreased content of glycosaminoglycan in the intercellular matrix (Section 5.2).

In general, it now appears that the rate of proteoglycan synthesis is below normal in severely fibrillated tissue and either normal or above normal in minimally fibrillated tissue.

2.3.4. Mechanical Properties. Fibrillated cartilage is so weak in tension that no meaningful testing can be carried out on the material.

Reference to Chapter 6, Section 3.7, shows that softening in compression is present as soon as fibrillation is detectable to the naked eye following Indian ink staining of the surface, and that it increases as the severity of fibrillation increases.

2.3.5. Lubrication. The evidence relating to the relationship between fibrillation and disturbances of lubrication is conflicting, but it suggests that no very marked increase in friction occurs when cartilage fibrillates (Chapter 7, Section 8). It is probable, however, that fibrillated cartilage wears more rapidly than normal.

2.3.6. Physicochemical Properties. The presence of clefts in severely fibrillated cartilage makes permeability and other related measurements on such tissue meaningless.

2.3.7. Calcification. It has recently been shown that cartilage from human osteoarthrosic femoral heads contains an increased number of matrix vesicles (Chapter 2) which form apatite crystals in the deeper layers and are associated with increased alkaline phosphatase activity (Ali 1977). It is not clear how early this change occurs in the osteoarthrosic process and hence to what extent it can be regarded as an initiating process: clearly the possibility arises, however, that apatite crystals could prejudice the mechanical properties of the matrix and act as abrasives if they were liberated into the joint cavity.

2.3.8. Conclusions. Cartilage fibrillation is characterized by a splitting process which, as seen in vertical sections, develops and propagates in the same alignment as that of the matrix collagen network and which must therefore involve the rupture of that part of the network which once crossed the split. In mild fibrillation, histological evidence of this process is confined to the superficial layer of the cartilage. In more severe fibrillation, the process extends into the deeper layers, and is accompanied by disintegration and thinning of the tissue; in some instances cartilage destruction eventually leads to exposure of the underlying bone.

There is no alteration in the amount of collagen within fibrillated tissue, but the amount of water increases and of proteoglycan decreases. The cells show a variable amount of necrosis, but in the deeper layers this feature is often accompanied by reactive formation of multicellular clusters by other, viable, chondrocytes which actively synthesize glycosaminoglycans. These structural changes are accompanied by softening in compression and weakness in tension.

Because the tissue is vertically fragmented, it has no measurable strength nor stiffness in tension. Its frictional properties are probably unchanged but it seems likely that the cartilage wears more rapidly than normal.

2.4. Observations on Histologically Intact Cartilage Adjacent to Areas of Fibrillation

From the standpoint of the pathogenesis of fibrillation, it would be of great interest if any of the abnormalities found in fibrillated cartilage could be demonstrated in histologically intact tissue adjacent to fibrillated sites. In so far as such tissue has been studied, the findings are listed in this Section.

2.4.1. Collagen Content. The macroscopically normal cartilage adjacent to fibrillated areas is normal with respect to its collagen content (Matthews 1953). From this it can be assumed that histologically intact cartilage adjacent to fibrillated areas is similarly normal.

2.4.2. Surface Ultrastructure. Although the total quantity of collagen in cartilage is unaffected by fibrillation (see Section 2.3.1), the collagen network may not be structurally normal. When examined with the transmission electron microscope, the surface of human articular cartilage from mature adults shows much structural variation. There is variation between specimens obtained from different individuals and often variation between different areas of the same specimen. These variations range through the following patterns as seen in ultrathin sections cut vertical or tangential to the surface (Chapter 1, Section 8):

(a) Areas of the surface which appear structurally intact even at magnification in the range of ×40 000;

(b) Areas which show ultrastructural evidence of minor 'disruptions' and separations of the collagen network in a surface which appears histologically intact when examined by light microscopy;

(c) Areas, absent in some specimens, in which transmission electron microscopy show deep clefts and frank erosion of the surface, sufficiently pronounced to be apparent as a mild histological fibrillation on light microscopy.

Meachim and Roy (1969) have speculated that the ultrastructural disruptions which can be observed in some histologically intact surfaces (pattern b, above) may fail to heal, and that they could predispose to the deep clefts and frank erosion seen on electron microscopy of histologically fibrillated areas (pattern c, above). However, it is not known whether ultrastructural disruptions are more common on surfaces immediately adjacent to histologically fibrillated sites. Thus the significance of the observations reported by Meachim and Roy (1969) is debatable. Even so, it is reasonable to assume that the 'histological' stage of fibrillation must be preceded by an 'ultrastructural' stage at which changes such as splitting and separation of the surface collagen are apparent only at the high magnifications available by the use of transmission electron microscopy.

2.4.3. Loss of Glycosaminoglycan. Light microscopy of a section of cartilage in which the surface at the actual site sectioned is still histologically intact sometimes shows evidence of glycosaminoglycan depletion. This appearance is confined to microscopic foci in the superficial layer of the matrix, is more common at some joint surfaces (such as the femoral condyle) than at others (such as the humeral head), and is accompanied by circumstantial evidence of a variable amount of chondrocyte necrosis in this zone of the tissue (Chapter 1, Section 8.1). Although the histologically intact tissue immediately adjacent to a histologically fibrillated site sometimes shows an advanced form of this change (Meachim et al. 1965), it must be emphasized that in other instances the adjacent intact cartilage shows no obvious abnormality on light microscopy (Meachim and Illman 1967; Meachim, unpublished). Thus it is by no means certain that microscopic foci of surface glycosaminoglycan depletion regularly precede fibrillation at the site concerned.

Estimations of glycosaminoglycan content using the fixed charge density method upon samples (surface area: 0.06 cm^2) of full-thickness tissue have not revealed evidence of decreased glycosaminoglycan content in cartilage in which the Indian ink stained surface is intact (Chapter 4, Section 2), thus confirming previous results using chemical analysis (Anderson, Ludowieg, Harper and Engelman 1964; Bollet and Nance 1966). These methods may be insufficiently sensitive to detect microscopic foci of glycosaminoglycan loss.

2.4.4. Mechanical Properties. Provided that fibrillation is sought by staining the surface of cartilage with Indian ink and examining it with the naked eye prior to testing, softening in compression cannot be demonstrated in non-fibrillated tissue (Chapter 6, Section 3.7).

The static tensile strength and stiffness of cartilage adjacent to areas of fibrillation are sometimes reduced, but not always (Chapter 6, Section 4.5). The tensile fatigue strength of cartilage has not yet been investigated in relation to the effect of adjacent areas of fibrillation.

2.4.5. Physicochemical Properties. The permeability of the surface layers of cartilage adjacent to histologically fibrillated areas has not been examined systematically. On the basis of such studies as have been made, however, no change would be anticipated in the absence of proteoglycan depletion or fragmentation of the surface.

2.4.6. Conclusions. The cartilage adjacent to areas of fibrillation may show disruption of the collagen network at the ultrastructural level, a reduction in the tensile strength and stiffness of the tissue, and focal proteoglycan depletion. None of these changes is invariably present and such cartilage may appear to be perfectly normal.

2.5. Cartilage Remodelling during Ageing

The term 'remodelling' can be used to describe a variety of different phenomena ranging in scale from the ultrastructural, or even molecular, level to ones which are histologically or macroscopically apparent. The following account concerns two such phenomena, both of a histological nature, which may be associated with ageing.

2.5.1. Remodelling of the Cartilage Base. At least in abnormal circumstances, structural remodelling of the cartilage base can result from an advance of active ossification buds into the calcified and deeper uncalcified layers, thus replacing the basal cartilage with bone. Similarly, an upward shift in the position of the uncalcified/calcified cartilage interface can occur, thus giving duplication of the interface 'tidemark'. The extent to which these phenomena are active in normal adult cartilage is not known. They could be concerned in slowly altering the contour of non-peripheral parts of an articular surface, and thus might play a part in the changes in hip joint congruence reported to take place with increasing age (Goodfellow, Bullough and O'Connor 1973).

2.5.2. Peripheral Remodelling. Particularly in older subjects, remodelling can occur at the perimeters of cartilage sheets and can do so in the absence of osteoarthrosis in the joint concerned. At the histological level, this remodelling is due to various inter-related phenomena in which old cartilage is covered or replaced by extrinsic new bony or non-bony tissue; osteophytic lipping can develop as one of the features seen (Table 9.2).

3. THE RELATIONSHIP BETWEEN AGEING AND FIBRIL-LATION

3.1. The Effect of Ageing upon the Incidence of Fibrillation

Heine (1926) studied the incidence of structural disintegration of cartilage in relation to age in 1002 human necropsies. Data were obtained for various synovial joints, including the knee, hip, shoulder and elbow. From these data it is possible to calculate (Collins 1949), for each age group, the percentage of persons in whom the joint showed naked-eye evidence of cartilage degeneration of various grades of severity. Heine's data show that degenerative lesions of articular cartilage become more common and more severe with increasing age, and his data also show that a wide variety of synovial joints can be affected. The influence of age upon the severity of cartilage degeneration has subsequently been confirmed in studies of the knee (Bennett, Waine and Bauer 1942), the knee and shoulder (Collins and Meachim 1961), and the elbow joint (Goodfellow and Bullough 1967). These studies have also shown that the lesions are not confined to middle-aged or elderly subjects. During early adult life superficial degenerative lesions are often demonstrable at certain sites (Heine 1926) such as the patella (Table 9.3) and the radial head (Goodfellow and Bullough 1967), and in old age the cartilage at these sites often has an area of deep 'ulceration' with bone exposure.

3.2. Topographical Distribution of Age-related Fibrillation

Although cartilage fibrillation is an age-related process, it cannot be regarded as a uniform or generalized accompaniment of ageing:

Table 9.3. Age incidence of fibrillation

Incidence and severity of fibrillation of the central part of the articular cartilage in 38 paired necropsy specimens of patella and of head of humerus, by 20-year age groups in human adults. Joints with evidence of rheumatoid disease have been excluded. The cartilages are classified according to the most severely affected central area found in each specimen on naked-eye examination supplemented by histology; the classification used ignores peripheral fibrillation sites on the cartilage, these being almost always present in adults (if Indian ink staining is used).

O: articular surface histologically intact; A: mild fibrillation only; B: deep fibrillation but no exposure of bone; C: deep fibrillation with bone exposure.

Age group (years)	No. of persons	Site of cartilage	O	A	B	C
25–44	10	Humerus	9	1	0	0
		Patella	5	5	0	0
45–64	13	Humerus	12	1	0	0
		Patella	1	6	6	0
65–84	15	Humerus	8	7	0	0
		Patella	0	0	8	7

(Data from Collins and Meachim (1961).)

the nature of the relationship varies from person to person, from joint to joint and from area to area within an affected joint.

Table 9.3 compares patellar cartilage with cartilage from the head of the humerus, in a paired series of necropsy specimens from three different adult age groups (Collins and Meachim 1961). It will be seen from this Table that adult patellar cartilage frequently shows histological evidence of fibrillation. In contrast, articular cartilage from the central part of the humeral head quite often remains intact.

Studies of sites such as the knee (Collins 1949), the elbow (Goodfellow and Bullough 1967) and the hip (Byers, Contempomi and Farkas 1970) have shown that age-related lesions of articular cartilage are not distributed uniformly throughout an affected joint. Histologically overt fibrillation, representing a frank split-ting (at the microscopic level) of the cartilage, initially affects the periphery of cartilage sheets (including the parafoveal area of the femoral head), the boundaries between articulation territories, and certain other characteristic sites such as the medial surface of the patella (Meachim 1972b) and the inferomedial segment of the femoral head (Byers, Contempomi and Farkas 1970). The hyaline cartilages of the tibial plateaux are an exception, in that their initial change is mainly, although not entirely, non-peripheral. On the menisci of the knee the brunt of the damage is at the free inner edges of the fibrocartilage. In older subjects much or all of the articular cartilage often becomes affected in certain joints such as the patellofemoral, the lumbar apophyseal and the radiohumeral. In contrast, sites such as the central part of the humeral head (Table 9.3) and the superior aspect (zenith) of the femoral head quite often remain free from 'histologically overt' damage.

In the elbow joint of young and middle-aged adults, lesions visible to the naked eye are localized to the rim of the radial head and to a corresponding area on the humeral articular surface; in old age the radiohumeral articulation quite often shows severe loss of cartilage with bone exposure, but in contrast the humeroulnar articulation usually remains free from severe destructive lesions (Goodfellow and Bullough 1967).

Thus cartilage fibrillation is initially a focal change, so that it seems likely that local factors in the mechanical environment or in the original structure of cartilage are at least partly responsible for its development. Moreover, there is evidence that the local mechanical environment and local character of the cartilage influences the actual morphology of the cartilage lesions (Meachim and Fergie 1975).

3.3. The Histological Appearance of Age-related Fibrillation and Other Lesions

The findings summarized in the preceding Sections (3.1 and 3.2) have an important implication for the terminology used in cartilage studies. Since sites with breaks in the continuity of the cartilage surface are so common in adult human synovial joints, 'normal' cartilage can be either histologically 'intact' or 'non-intact'.

A number of different lesions can be observed in adult cartilage (Table 9.2) from random necropsies. Most of them affect cartilage still exposed to the synovial cavity. Others are peripheral remodelling phenomena (Table 9.2) in which there is growth of new tissue over and into the old cartilage (Chapter 1, Section 9.2), which thus becomes separated from the synovial cavity; the cartilage may ossify to produce new bone in a plane vertical to that of the old chondro-osseous junction ('epiarticular' osteophytosis); osteophytic lipping by bony outgrowth beyond the original perimeter of the cartilage sheet can also occur.

Lesions affecting cartilage still exposed to the synovial cavity include the following.

First, most of the lesions seen in random necropsy specimens (Figure 9.8) show fraying and splitting of uncalcified cartilage segments due to cartilage fibrillation. When still in its 'minimal' stage, histological fibrillation presents a variety of appearances *en face*, suggesting that more than one mechanism of damage may be concerned in its initial pathogenesis (Meachim and Fergie 1975). Later in this Chapter, the speculation will be advanced that fatigue failure of the matrix collagen network may be one of the possible causes of cartilage fibrillation. In its mild form, fibrillation is confined to the superficial layer (zone 1) of the cartilage. In its more severe form the splitting extends into the deeper uncalcified layers (zones 2 and 3), and is then associated with thinning of the cartilage from tissue loss by disintegration (Figure 9.8). In some instances the full depth of the cartilage is lost ('ulcerated'), with exposure of the underlying bone (Figure 9.9). Fibrillated cartilage is abnormally soft ('chondromalacia').

Secondly, segments of uncalcified cartilage occasionally show a relatively smooth-surfaced destructive thinning, without the deep vertical splitting typical of severe fibrillation but sometimes having shallow indentations. This lesion can probably be attributed to abrasive wear. In joints in which movement is unidirectional, this type of wear can sometimes cause 'track markings' *en face* on the cartilage; such markings can develop in joints in either the presence or the absence of bone exposure elsewhere on the surface.

Figure 9.8 Naked-eye appearance of transverse slices of two specimens of patellae obtained from random necropsies. In the upper specimen the articular surface is 'macroscopically intact'; in the lower specimen the cartilage shows thinning as a consequence of fibrillation. a: articular cartilage; b: bone.

Figure 9.9 Patellar articular surface, viewed *en face*, from a random necropsy. There is a large area of bone exposure ('ulceration') as a consequence of cartilage fibrillation. The linear highlights represent grooving attributable to abrasive erosion into the exposed bone surface.

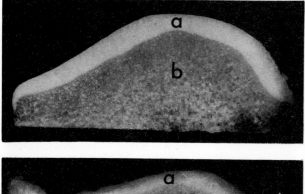

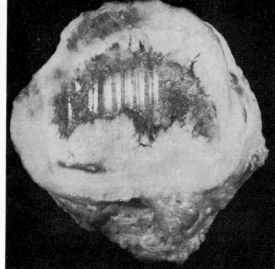

Thirdly, horizontal cleft formation is seen at the interface between the uncalcified cartilage layers and the calcified zone in some specimens (see Figure 9.7). This appearance would be consistent with 'shearing damage'. When severe, it can lead to 'gouging out' of the uncalcified cartilage segment overlying the cleft.

3.4. The Natural History of Age-related Fibrillation

Ideally the natural history of fibrillation should be observed by 'longitudinal' studies, in which the same individual is compared at different ages. Since this is not at present practicable, it is necessary to accept the limitations of 'transectional' ('transverse') studies, in which different individuals from the same general population are compared in samples taken from various ages. Care is needed that the samples for each age group are, as far as possible, representative of the population as a whole.

A survey of this nature has been made of the state of the articular surfaces in a random series of synovial joints from 350 necropsies in the city of Liverpool (Emery and Meachim 1973; Meachim and Emery 1973, 1974; Meachim 1975a, 1976). This survey confirms that, with increasing age, histologically overt fibrillation tends to spread tangentially across the cartilage surface. Spread is mainly by circumferential and radial enlargement from initially peripheral foci, but new central foci can also develop. Susceptibility to tangential spread varies according to anatomical site, and between individuals. Thus, as already mentioned, in older persons much or all of the cartilage surface often becomes affected on sites such as the patella and on the bare area (i.e. not covered by meniscus) of the lateral tibial plateau (Figure 9.10), while, in contrast, sites such as the superior aspect (zenith) of the femoral

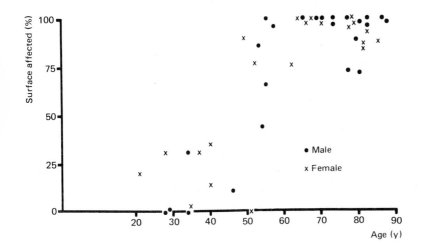

Figure 9.10 Percentage of the surface of the bare area of the left lateral tibial plateau affected by histologically overt fibrillation in a random series of 47 necropsies; note that the meniscus-covered cartilage is not included in the results. In two of the subjects, both women, there was upper tibial bone exposure, and the percentage shown for these subjects (E), is the sum obtained by adding the percentage of fibrillated cartilage to the percentage of exposed bone.

(Reproduced from Meachim (1976) by courtesy of the Editor, *Journal of Anatomy.*)

507

head quite often remain free from histologically overt fibrillation, even in the elderly.

Particularly in younger persons, many of the necropsy lesions are not apparent on naked-eye examination of unstained surfaces, are confined to the superficial layer of the cartilage, and are not associated with destructive thinning of the tissue. In some older subjects, however, destructive thinning can progress towards exposure of bone at a site where the biomechanical environment then subjects the bone to abrasive and other damage (Figure 9.9). This vertical spread of wear becomes more common with increasing age, but susceptibility to it varies between individuals and between the two sexes, as well as according to anatomical site. In necropsy specimens the incidence of bone exposure is higher at the patellofemoral than the tibiofemoral articulation, and greater at the knee than at the hip, shoulder and, especially, the ankle. The affected joints show a morphological appearance indistinguishable from that seen in surgical specimens from patients with clinical osteoarthrosis; however, the proportion of necropsy subjects who had clinical trouble from the affected joint during life is not known.

Within the limitations of a 'transectional' study, the Liverpool survey indicates that the vertical spread, downwards into the cartilage, of breaks on its surface continuity, so as to cause destructive thinning of the material, is not inevitable, and, when it occurs, not always relentless; moreover, vertical extension of wear is not uniform in terms of the time sequence of events at different sites on the same cartilage sheet (Emery and Meachim 1973). For example, minimal splitting is common on the non-malleolar surfaces of the ankle joint, but it is unusual for this component of the joint to develop a destructive thinning with increasing age (Meachim 1975). Again, histologically overt fibrillation or other damage is often found on the medial part of the medial patellar surface and on the inferomedial segment of the femoral head, but it is uncommon for either of these sites to develop bone exposure in older subjects.

Severe destructive thinning of cartilage is crucial in destroying its function as a covering material protecting bone from undesirable effects (Figure 9.9). Clinically apparent osteoarthrosis can be regarded as a failure of this protective function.

3.5. Conclusions

Lesions due to cartilage fibrillation are frequent in adults, and become more common and more severe with increasing age. At certain sites a mild superficial fibrillation is often demonstrable histologically even in young adults and is universal in the elderly.

Age-related fibrillation is initially focal in distribution, so that local factors appear to be at least partly responsible for its development. In any particular joint the areas prone to develop age-related fibrillation are fairly constant in distribution from subject to subject. With increasing age, histologically overt fibrillation tends to spread tangentially across the joint surface; susceptibility to tangential spread varies according to anatomical site and between individuals.

Vertical spread into the tissue to cause its destructive thinning and potentially to expose bone can also occur; susceptibility to this again varies according to anatomical site and between different individuals.

Age-related, non-destructive and destructive, lesions of articular cartilage present a variety of different morphological appearances. This strongly suggests that more than one mechanism can be concerned in their pathogenesis.

4. OSTEOARTHROSIS AND FIBRILLATION

Osteoarthrosis (osteoarthritis) is a disease of synovial joints. In the fully developed pathological condition (Figure 9.11) there is loss of the original articular cartilage from part or all of the joint

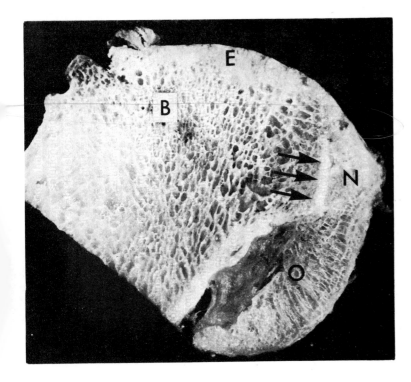

Figure 9.11 Mid-coronal slice from a surgical specimen of an osteoarthrosic femoral head. The upper aspect shows loss of the original articular cartilage with exposure and erosion (E) of the underlying bone (B); bone loss has caused flattening of the projected original curvature on this aspect of the specimen. The inferomedial aspect, in contrast, shows new bone formation (N) external to the line of the original chondro-osseous junction (arrows); the new bone is in continuity with an osteophytic downgrowth (O).

surface, with exposure of the underlying bone; in severe osteoarthrosis destructive loss of osseous tissue can also occur at the
exposed bone surface, which undergoes abrasive wear (Figure
9.11). Beneath its exposed surface, the bone shows active remodelling with thickening of trabeculae (osteosclerosis), and it often
contains radiolucent areas ('cysts') filled with non-osseous tissue
or partly liquefied material. At the periphery of the joint, growth of
new tissue is usually seen, with the development of bony outgrowths ('osteophytic lipping') external to the original joint margin (Figure 9.11), and sometimes with spread of new non-osseous
and osseous tissue over and into the periphery of the original
articular cartilage. In some osteoarthrotic femoral heads, intracartilaginous ossification can cause expansile bony remodelling of the
original inferomedial segment ('epiarticular osteophytosis'), as
distinct from mere osteophytic lipping by bony outgrowths beyond
the original perimeter of the cartilage sheet.

4.1. 'Primary' and 'Secondary' Osteoarthrosis

Osteoarthrosis is conventionally classified into primary and secondary varieties. This terminology is, in a sense, misleading. The
term 'primary' osteoarthrosis implies 'idiopathic' osteoarthrosis,
where the cause or causes are unknown. In contrast, the term
'secondary' osteoarthrosis implies that major aetiological factors
can be demonstrated.

The secondary variety arises in a joint which has already been
altered (a) by an inflammatory process such as rheumatoid
disease, (b) by a disorder such as pyrophosphate arthropathy or
ochronosis, (c) by a structural abnormality such as Perthes'
disease, dislocation, acetabular dysplasia, epiphysiolysis or articular fracture, or (d) by bone infarction. In such a joint the initial
destruction of the articular cartilage is basically attributable to the
pre-existing condition. In rheumatoid arthritis, for example, there
is a proliferation of periarticular and synovial tissue which invades,
softens and destroys articular cartilage (Mills 1970). In pyrophosphate arthropathy deposits of crystals, and in ochronosis deposits
of pigment (Laskar and Sargison 1970), accumulate in the cartilage, presumably altering its mechanical properties and thus
making it more susceptible to destruction. In osteoarthrosis secondary to a structural abnormality of the joint, cartilage destruction
can perhaps be attributed to the development of dangerously high
contact pressures (Figure 9.12); osteoarthrosis following bone
infarction can be explained on a similar basis, since collapse of
bone at the site of an infarct deforms the contour of the overlying
articular surface.

'Primary' osteoarthrosis, in contrast to the secondary variety,
develops in a joint previously free from disease or obvious

510

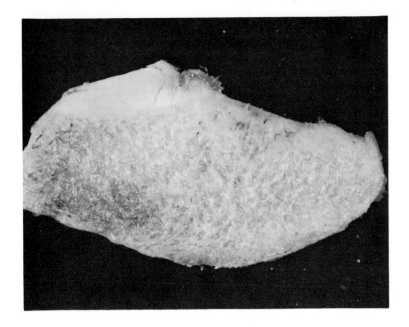

Figure 9.12 Transverse slice of a patella excised surgically because of recurrent dislocation. At the upper right the articular surface shows cartilage loss and bone exposure of osteoarthrosic type; adjacent to this area (centre) the cartilage is fibrillated. In contrast, the cartilage at the upper left is virtually intact, without any obvious thinning.

mechanical abnormality. It seems likely that there may be several different forms of 'primary' osteoarthrosis and that several aetiological agents may be responsible. For example, genetic predisposition is thought to be important in a particular type of osteoarthrosis with multiple joint involvement, termed 'primary generalized osteoarthrosis' (Kellgren 1961). However, for all forms of 'primary' osteoarthrosis the exact aetiology is unknown.

In practice, it is sometimes difficult to determine whether a particular example of osteoarthrosis is of the 'primary' or 'secondary' variety. This difficulty applies to the clinical and radiological assessment of an osteoarthrosic joint, and to the pathological examination of surgical specimens. Moreover, there is also the problem of assessing whether or not relatively minor anatomical abnormalities, acquired, for example, during adolescence (Murray and Duncan 1971), have been a major factor in the eventual development of osteoarthrosis later in life: is the osteoarthrosis in such a patient to be classified as of 'primary' or 'secondary' type?

In spite of these difficulties in interpretation, the concept that there are 'primary' and 'secondary' varieties of osteoarthrosis has an important implication: it means that in attempting to understand and prevent osteoarthrosis in the general population, attention must be paid not only to the articular cartilage, but also to the possible role of factors which might adversely affect its environment.

4.2. The Pathogenesis of 'Primary' Osteoarthrosis

Collins and others (Allison and Ghormley 1931; Bennett *et al.* 1942; Collins 1949; Harrison, Schajowicz and Trueta 1953; Lang 1934; Nichols and Richardson 1909; Trias 1967) have expressed the view that the tissue first affected in primary osteoarthrosis is the articular cartilage, and this view has now achieved widespread, but not universal, acceptance. An alternative pathogenesis to one involving a primary disturbance of articular cartilage rests upon the observation that bone haemodynamics are altered in the cancellous bone adjacent to an osteoarthrosic joint. Alterations in bone haemodynamics can be demonstrated using phlebography in joints presenting clinically with primary osteoarthrosis (Meriel, Ruffie and Fournie 1955; Brookes and Helal 1968; Hulth and Hernborg 1968; Arnold, Linderholm and Müssbichler 1972) and there is no doubt that vascular disturbances (specifically, ischaemia producing bone infarction) can produce osteoarthrosis secondary to deformation of the bone in man (Arlet and Ficat 1968); vascular disturbances have also been implicated in a rare, bizarre form of 'osteoarthrosis', termed Kashin–Beck disease, which occurs in Siberia and which is thought to be due to dietary ingestion of toxic fungal products with vasoactive products (Gardner 1965). In general support of a vascular aetiology, changes said to resemble osteoarthrosis have been produced experimentally in animals by venous obstruction (Bernstein 1933). However, in man deep venous obstruction does not appear to cause osteoarthrosis, although it may lead to structural changes in bone (Arnoldi, Linderholm and Vinnerberg 1972).

The logical weakness in the argument that 'primary' osteoarthrosis is due to a vascular disorder, is that by the time the primary osteoarthrosic process is clinically manifest, it is pathologically advanced. The alteration in bone blood flow which has been demonstrated in clinically manifest primary osteoarthrosis can be explained as a consequence of the pathological changes (Freeman 1972), and therefore it is not necessarily the case that the haemodynamic change initiated the osteoarthrosic process. To resolve this matter, vascular injection studies would have to be made upon the bones of volunteers with preclinical osteoarthrosis (i.e. with painless, radiogically normal joints in which the cartilage was not even fibrillated). Such studies are never likely to be forthcoming, partly for ethical reasons and partly because of the present impossiblity of demonstrating early cartilage abnormalities during life except by arthroscopy or surgical exploration of the joint.

The 'vascular hypothesis' discussed above suggests that the first pathological event in primary osteoarthrosis is a change in bone haemodynamics. Another different hypothesis suggests that the first abnormality is in the structure and functional properties of the osseous trabeculae. A major pathological lesion of this sort (such as bone infarction or Paget's disease) is known, for example, to precede some forms of secondary osteoarthrosis. Minor, but still pathological, lesions such as the 'tilt deformity' of the femoral head described by Murray and Duncan (1971), or an anatomical variation in the acetabulum apparently causing high contact pressures in the hip (Day, Swanson and Freeman 1975), may precede some forms of osteoarthrosis which are at present classified as 'primary' in type. Other, more subtle and less frankly pathological, bony abnormalities might also predispose to osteoarthrosis. Thus Radin and Paul (1970) have suggested that osteoarthrosis may be caused by loss of resilience of the underlying bone. Similarly, Foss and Byers (1972) have shown that osteoarthrosis of the hip may be associated with above-average skeletal bone density as assessed by radiological examination of the second metacarpal. These studies do not, of course, prove that there is a frankly pathological disturbance in bone resilience or density. But even so, this line of investigation emphasizes the need to consider articular cartilage in the context of its biological environment, particularly in terms of the functional interplay with its underlying bone in a joint destined to develop osteoarthrosis.

Since morbid anatomical studies have revealed the presence of cartilage abnormalities in the absence of frankly pathological lesions in the adjacent bone, it seems reasonable on the present evidence to accept Collins' view and to regard 'primary' osteoarthrosis as a pathological process set in train by one, or probably several, disturbance(s) in the functional properties of articular cartilage or in its physiological environment, leading to destruction of the cartilage and finally to destruction of bone. If this view is correct, the first pathological event at the macroscopic level in 'primary' osteoarthrosis is fibrillation of the cartilage (Collins 1949).

4.3. Does Age-related Fibrillation Progress to Osteoarthrosis?

Since primary osteoarthrosis occurs in older subjects, it seems *a priori* reasonable to suggest that the clinical disease represents an exaggerated or accelerated development of the age-related asymptomatic cartilage fibrillation which is encountered so frequently amongst the general population at necropsy. (This suggestion would not of course be inconsistent with the genetic predisposition known to be important in the 'primary generalized' form of the disease (Kellgren 1961).) It is therefore of interest to compare cartilage fibrillation as seen in unselected subjects at necropsy with the cartilage lesions found in patients with clinically overt primary osteoarthrosis. In the case of osteoarthrosis, this comparison will be made first for the hip, and then for other joints, and will be presented mainly in terms of the histology and distribution of the lesions. For the histological comparisons with fibrillated cartilage obtained from unselected necropsies, the data used from necropsy studies will not be restricted to findings in the joint under discussion: this approach is legitimate, since the histology of the necropsy lesions is basically the same regardless of the anatomical site examined (Collins 1949).

4.3.1. Histology of the Lesions in the Hip. There is clinical and radiological evidence that osteoarthritis of the hip is not a single entity, but is instead the common end result of a number of different pathological processes (Kellgren 1961). In keeping with this concept, femoral heads excised surgically from diseased joints vary considerably in their naked-eye and histological appearance. This variation is still found after excluding patients with rheumatoid disease or other obvious causes of secondary osteoarthrosis. In general, however, three main regions can be recognized on the femoral head in presumed primary osteoarthrosis, although it must be emphasized that all three regions are not represented in every surgical excision specimen.

(a) An inner region of variable size, consisting of exposed bone (Figure 9.13) interspersed with plugs of new non-osseous tissue. There is human (Meachim and Osborne 1970) and experimental (Meachim and Roberts 1971) evidence that the new non-osseous tissue has a potential to spread over the exposed bone, thus re-covering it by extrinsic fibrocartilaginous or fibrous surface repair. In most patients this attempt at repair of the exposed bone surface is severely counteracted or completely overwhelmed by the osteoarthrosic destructive mechanism, but, following osteotomy, surface re-covering can be at least partly achieved, until the new tissue is in turn destroyed by the osteoarthrosic process.

(b) A region adjacent to or just within the periphery of the exposed bone, and comprising a variable amount of old cartilage with a surface still exposed to the synovial cavity. In some specimens this region is absent. The exposed old cartilage shows destructive lesions; old cartilage which is still intact is sometimes also apparent.

(c) Beyond these regions, there is in many specimens a region (see Figures 9.4 and 9.5) where the articular surface is covered by a layer of new non-osseous, or osseous and non-osseous tissue, sited external to the line of the original chondro-osseous junction (see Figure 9.11). Segments of old cartilage submerged beneath this new tissue are often in continuity with exposed old cartilage on their inner aspect. In a few specimens there is evidence that the new tissue has itself been undergoing destruction, and exposure and eburnation of new bone is occasionally seen.

Thus, in primary osteoarthrosis of the hip, one, or often two, major changes are responsible for loss of cartilage from the articular surface of the femoral head. One change is destruction of old cartilage where such cartilage still has its surface exposed to the synovial cavity. The second change is a growth at the periphery of the femoral head of new tissue into and over old cartilage, which is thus separated from the synovial cavity, and partly or completely invaded and destroyed (Harrison *et al.* 1953). In terms of the histological findings, only the first of these two changes in osteoarthrosis is suitable for comparison with cartilage fibrillation as seen in necropsy material.

When this comparison is attempted, a difficulty arises because most surgical specimens are from the advanced stage of the disease. In these specimens cartilage destruction has progressed to bone exposure on or near the zenith. Thus cartilage is no longer available for examination from the crucial site where it underwent destruction prior to its full-thickness loss. It is, of couse, often still possible to examine (Meachim 1972a) the adjacent cartilage, or samples from elsewhere on the femoral head: however, it is debatable whether such cartilage manifests the fundamental changes of osteoarthrosis, or whether its histological appearances have been at least partly modified by local alterations in the mechanical environment consequent to bone exposure elsewhere in the joint; a similar comment applies to metabolic studies. Recently this histological difficulty has been partly overcome, since it has been possible to examine a small number of surgically excised femoral heads on which the zenith cartilage was undergoing osteoarthrosic destructive thinning before the advanced stage of its full-thickness loss. The affected cartilage on these specimens shows one or more of the following lesions:

(a) Deep splitting and disintegration of uncalcified cartilage, of fibrillation type (see Figure 9.1).
(b) A smoother-surfaced destructive thinning of uncalcified cartilage, without the deep splits typical of fibrillation (see Figure 9.2).
(c) Horizontal cleft formation at the calcified/uncalcified cartilage interface, of the sort that could lead to gouging out of the uncalcified segment overlying the cleft (see Figure 9.3).

These three lesions are not mutually exclusive, and sometimes more than one can occur together in the same cartilage segment. Acting singly or together, they can lead to exposure of calcified cartilage and bone at a site where the bone will then be subjected to high contact stresses and to abrasion (Figure 9.13). Similar lesions can then be observed in the old cartilage adjacent to the area of exposed bone (Meachim 1972a).

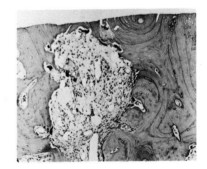

Figure 9.13 Typical histological lesion of osteoarthrosic bone exposure. Note the 'clean cut' transection of trabeculae at the synovial interface, and the empty osteocyte lacunae beneath it.
H & E ×40.

515

The studies of surgical specimens described above have the limitation that they do not directly reveal the histological features of the preclinical stage of the osteoarthrosic lesions, nor do they exclude the possibilities that the femoral lesions might have been modified by the presence of bone exposure on the opposing acetabulum. Subject to these reservations, the findings suggest that osteoarthrosic cartilage lesions, as seen in surgical specimens of femoral heads, share many histological features in common with those of the age-related fibrillation and other lesions (Section 3.3) seen in specimens from a random series of necropsies. This is not to imply that the relative frequency of the various lesions is the same in the two groups of specimens, nor that there are no other differences in detail: for example, cartilage segments showing a smooth-surfaced destructive thinning are much more common in the surgical than in the necropsy groups; again, reactive multicellular cluster formation in deeply fibrillated cartilage seems to be less frequent in the surgical specimens than would be expected from the findings in the necropsy studies.

4.3.2. The Site and Natural History of the Lesions in the Hip. In the preceding Section (4.3.1) the comment was made that osteoarthrosic cartilage lesions in surgical specimens share many features in common with age-related changes as seen in necropsy specimens. This similarity holds true provided that the comparison is restricted to the histological findings in the sample, and provided that allowance is made for the fact that the destructive process is already at an advanced, or at best an intermediate, stage in the surgical specimens. However, important differences have been reported when femoral cartilage lesions in the hip are compared in terms of their frequency, their presumed natural history, and their anatomical site (Figure 9.14) within the joint.

Byers *et al.* (1970) have classified cartilage alterations in the hip joint on the basis of the anatomical site, naked-eye appearance and radiological texture of the features seen. The study was made on specimens from a series of random necropsies; in addition, the findings were compared with those in femoral heads resected in the treatment of osteoarthrosis and of femoral neck fractures. From analysis of these data, Byers and his colleagues conclude that adult femoral heads frequently develop age-related cartilage lesions (Figure 9.14) of a type which, in Byers' view, do not have an inherent potential to progress to clinical disease and to anatomical deformity; this type of lesion is seen, for example, inferomedial to the fovea. Byers and co-workers state that these lesions of 'limited cartilage degeneration' are so frequent that it is difficult to conceive that they progress to osteoarthrosis. In contrast, a second 'progressive' type of cartilage alteration is occasionally seen in necropsy material on, for example, the zenith of the femoral head, and shows a macroscopic appearance closely similar to that found

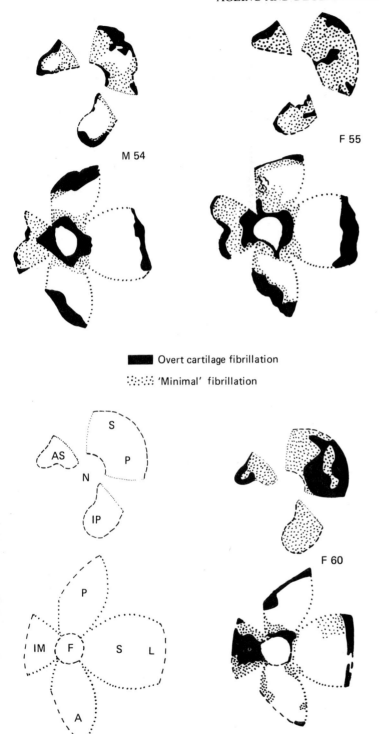

Overt cartilage fibrillation

'Minimal' fibrillation

Figure 9.14 Representative selection of drawings of left hip joints from random necropsies, showing the distribution of fibrillation. For each joint the letter and number give the sex (M, male; F, female) and age in years of the subject. The key shows the position of the fovea (F) and the inferomedial (IM), anterior (A), posterior (P) and superolateral segments (SL) of the femoral head and the position of the anterosuperior (AS), superoposterior (SP) and inferoposterior (IP) segments of the acetabular articular surface in relation to the acetabular notch (N).

(Reproduced from Meachim and Emery (1973) by courtesy of the Editor, *Journal of Anatomy*.)

in femoral heads resected during the treatment of osteoarthrosis. Byers and co-workers believe that only the 'progressive' lesions are truly osteoarthrosic in type. On the femoral head the two processes are said to be independent of one another, although independence was not established for the features seen on the acetabulum. The results suggest that osteoarthrosic cartilage changes in the hip may not simply be an exaggerated or accelerated form of the cartilage fibrillation which occurs during the 'normal ageing'. Thus the development of clinically overt osteoarthrosis in this joint may be due to an additional or separate factor. It is already known that in some patients with osteoarthrosis of the hip the disease is of 'secondary' type (Kellgren 1961), being due to rheumatoid disease, to bone infarction, or to factors such as congenital hip dislocation, acetabular dysplasia, Perthes' disease, epiphysiolysis ('slipped epiphysis') or other cause. Further studies may show that a proportion of what is at present regarded as idiopathic, 'primary' osteoarthrosis of this joint is precipitated by minor anatomical abnormalities, either inherited or acquired during childhood or adolescence (Murray and Duncan 1971; Day, Swanson and Freeman 1975).

4.3.3. The Site and Natural History of Lesions in Other Joints. Collins has reported his conclusions from his study of osteoarthrosis in a wide variety of synovial joints (Collins 1949; Collins and McElligott 1960). He noted that many of the cartilage lesions found at necropsy are mild and asymptomatic. However, he pointed out that, from a series of necropsies, it is possible to demonstrate a continuous series of changes, with superficial fibrillation of cartilage at one end of the series, and at its other end severe fibrillation of cartilage with bone exposure of the sort seen in clinical osteoarthrosis. He therefore believed that the clinical disease can develop from the cartilage fibrillation associated with ageing amongst the adult population (Heine 1926), although he qualified this conclusion by the following comment: 'Provided sufficient consideration is given to each case, it is exceptional to see advanced osteoarthritis in a joint without being able to discover some aggravating circumstance or condition' (Collins 1949, p. 103).

For the knee joint, Bennett *et al.* (1942) suggested that asymptomatic cartilage changes during 'normal ageing' can eventually lead to osteoarthrosis of the knee. Emery and Meachim have recently investigated this suggestion. In the case of the patellofemoral component of this joint, they obtained necropsy data which led to the following conclusions (Emery and Meachim 1973; Meachim and Emery 1974):

(a) Osteoarthrosic and age-related changes are not topographically independent at the patellofemoral articulation. This statement must, however, be qualified by noting that changes on the medial strip of the medial patellar surface have much less potential to progress to bone exposure than those on the central or lateral part of the patellar surface.

(b) Morphological changes caused by factors, such as recurrent dislocation (see Figure 9.12) or malalignment of the joint, which might induce patellofemoral osteoarthrosis independently of the effects of ageing, must often develop *pari passu* with the age-related changes.

(c) Osteoarthrosic patellofemoral changes are more common in older women than in older men.

(d) In some elderly Liverpool women, it would seem that ageing acting alone can eventually cause sufficient patellofemoral damage to constitute osteoarthrosis (see Figure 9.9). The numerical importance, if any, of this hypothetical cause of primary osteoarthrosis, in terms of its contribution to the total amount of clinically significant patellofemoral osteoarthrosis in the Liverpool population, is not known.

The phenomenon of age-related fibrillation at the patellar surface is also relevant to the question of the pathogenesis of the clinical condition termed 'chondromalacia patellae' (for discussion and references, see Annotation 1972).

In the case of the tibiofemoral component of the knee, again no clear-cut distinction can be made between osteoarthrosic and age-related changes (Meachim 1976). However, this observation does not in itself prove that primary tibiofemoral osteoarthrosis is due simply to ageing.

It is pertinent to note that the patellofemoral osteoarthrosis seen in some elderly Liverpool subjects at necropsy can occur independently of any tibiofemoral osteoarthrosic bone exposure; conversely, tibiofemoral osteoarthrosis can occur independently of patellofemoral bone exposure (Meachim 1976).

The incidence at necropsy of osteoarthrosic bone exposure in elderly subjects (over 70 years old). and thus arguably due to 'ageing', varies according to anatomical site. It is less common at the tibiofemoral and shoulder joints than at the patellofemoral articulation, and is rare at the ankle. The articular cartilage of normal shoulder, hip and, especially, ankle joints often gives good service for at least 70 years. Clinical osteoarthrosis of the ankle, when it does occur, is typically of the secondary sort, due to fracture, neuropathy or rheumatoid disease.

4.4. Conclusions

In some patients with osteoarthrosis the condition develops because the affected joint has already been altered by inflammation, metabolic disorder or overt mechanical deformity. In other patients osteoarthrosis is idiopathic, developing as 'primary' osteoarthrosis in what appears to have been a previously healthy joint.

The view that fibrillation of the cartilage is the initial lesion in 'primary' osteoarthrosis has achieved widespread, but not universal, acceptance.

In osteoarthrosis the histology of the destructive lesions in exposed cartilage is often similar to that of the age-related form of cartilage fibrillation, although differences are sometimes apparent in the advanced stage of the disease. In spite of this histological similarity, the cartilage destruction seen in osteoarthrosis of the hip may not simply be the result of severe age change, since on the femoral head the topographical distribution of age-related fibrillation and of the lesions of osteoarthrosis appear to differ. However, in the case of other synovial joints, it is possible that some instances of 'primary' osteoarthrosis may develop from the type of cartilage fibrillation associated with ageing: the patellofemoral joint of elderly women would seem to provide an example of this.

Thus it may be that whereas the first naked-eye change in 'primary' osteoarthrosis is always fibrillation, fibrillation does not always lead to osteoarthrosis, being often a pathologically and clinically benign accompaniment of ageing.

5. THE PATHOGENESIS OF FIBRILLATION: AN HYPOTHESIS

Present knowledge is insufficient to provide a definitve account of the pathogenesis of fibrillation. It is, however, sufficient to advance the following hypothesis to account for the fundamental mechanism, the age relationship, the topography, the natural history and the morphology of fibrillation. Since there are grounds for thinking that fibrillation is the first event visible to the naked eye in the development of osteoarthrosis, this topic is of major clinical importance.

5.1. Fragmentation of the Fibre Network

5.1.1. Network Fragmentation as a Cause of Fibrillation. It is now known that the mechanical properties of the fibre network in cartilage deteriorate with advancing age. This fact may be demonstrated by static tensile tests (Chapter 6, Section 4.4) or, more dramatically, by tensile fatigue tests (Chapter 6, Section 6). The following lines of argument suggest that this deterioration in the mechanical properties of the network is responsible for fibrillation.

(a) This mechanical change is so far the only age-related abnormality to be demonstrated in intact articular cartilage. Since fibrillation is also age-related, this suggests, but does not prove, that the two are causally connected and that fibre network deterioration precedes fibrillation.

(b) Fibrillation consists morphologically of matrix fragmentation, and this must imply the presence of multiple ruptures in the fibre network. Thus any abnormality which weakens the fibre network might reasonably be considered as a possible precursor of fibrillation.

(c) Since histologically overt fibrillation is known to spread tangentially over the articular surface, it is reasonable to seek its precursor in areas of histologically intact cartilage adjacent to areas of fibrillation. The tensile fatigue properties of such cartilage have not yet been examined, but its static tensile strength and stiffness are (variably) diminished. These abnormalities demonstrate an abnormality of the fibre network.

(d) The Indian ink stained surface (Figure 9.15) of cartilage which has been subjected to a cyclical compressive load *in vitro* displays appearances similar to the *en face* appearances of some forms of 'minimal' histological fibrillation (Chapter 6, Section 7).

(e) The total uncalcified thickness of cartilage showing histological evidence of surface fraying appears to be slightly greater than that of cartilage on which the surface is histologically intact (Meachim 1971) and its water content is increased (Chapter 4, Section 6.2.5). Since the collagen fibre network has a low elasticity, swelling can only take place if the network has first become abnormally distensible. Thus the swelling of the tissue would imply a fibre network abnormality (i.e. increased distensibility attributable to fragmentation). In keeping with this interpretation, results from transmission electron microscopy (Meachim and Roy 1969) indicate that, in man, fibrillation may be preceded by an ultrastructural state in which there is abnormally wide separation (Figure 9.16), fragmentation and disorientation of the collagen fibres of the superficial cartilage layer. It is of interest that Ficat (1975) has observed a similar ultrastructural 'oedema' in the softened cartilage from patients with chondromalacia patellae.

(f) In a canine experimental model of osteoarthrosis, the first detectable abnormality seen before fibrillation is demonstrable by Indian ink staining of the surface is once again an increase in the thickness and water content of the cartilage, accompanied by a qualitative change in proteoglycan synthesis (McDevitt and Muir 1976). The increased hydration of the tissue again implies increased distensibility of, and hence mechanical changes in, the fibre network. As in man, separation of the collagen network can be seen with the electron microscope.

(g) If age-related fibrillation in man is the result of a mechanical deterioration in the collagen network of hyaline articular cartilage,

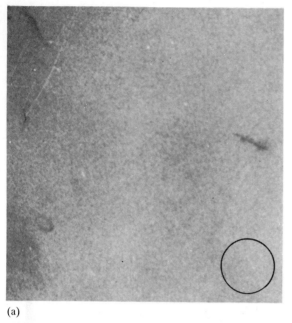

(a)

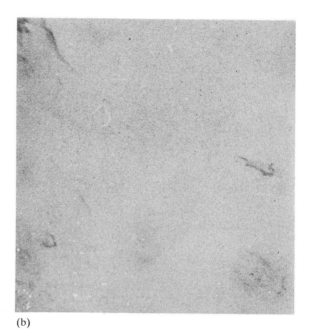

(b)

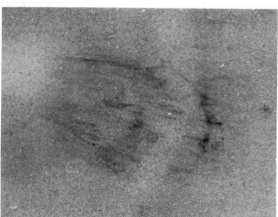

(c)

Figure 9.15 a–c (a) Part of the cartilage surface of the tibial plateaux from a 48-year-old female; stained with Indian ink and viewed at a magnification of ×8.4. It will be seen that prior to cyclical loading no surface markings were present in the area of cartilage to be fatigued. This area is encircled in (a). (b) The same area of cartilage following the application of 6×10^4 loading cycles at a nominal stress of 2 MN/m^2 (285 lbf/in^2). The area has been restained with Indian ink and is again viewed at a magnification of ×8.4. It will be seen that Indian ink now stains fissures which have developed in the surface layers of the fatigued area. (c) The fatigued area shown in (b), viewed at a magnification of ×27.

Figure 9.16 (*below*) Transmission electron micrographs of sections cut tangential to the synovial interface, showing abnormally wide separation of the surface cartilage collagen fibres (A) compared with their appearance at a nearby unaffected site (B) on the same articular surface. ×25 000.

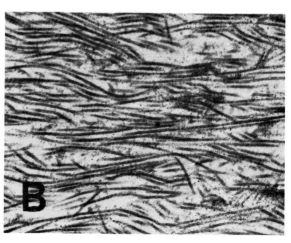

a phenomenon similar to fibrillation might be expected also to occur in other collagenous tissues to a similar mechanical environment. A recent study of the fibrocartilaginous menisci of the human knee (Meachim 1975b) has shown that these structures do in fact undergo an age-related process of fraying and splitting, several features of which are similar to those seen in fibrillation of hyaline articular cartilage.

Ways in which a mechanical deterioration in the collagen fibre network may interact with normal and abnormal mechanical stresses in the environment of hyaline articular cartilage are discussed in Sections 5.3 and 5.4.

5.1.2. The Cause of Mechanical Abnormalities in the Fibre Network. It is known that the fibre of which this network is composed is collagen, and that collagen turnover occurs very slowly, if at all, in human adult articular cartilage. Furthermore, collagenase is thought to be absent from normal cartilage, although cathepsin B, which is present, does degrade collagen to a slight extent. For these reasons it seems unlikely that a metabolically induced abnormality in the collagen fibres themselves is responsible for weakening the network. On the other hand, the very inertness of collagen suggests the possibility of its being degraded mechanically (rather then chemically), since over the course of a lifetime each fibre will experience a very large number of load cycles and hence may fatigue. Although progressive fatigue failure of the collagen fibres themselves may play a part in the age-related weakening of the fibre network, it cannot, however, be the main factor responsible, since the shortening of the endurance life in aged cartilage as compared with that in youth is too great to be accounted for by the number of load cycles borne by the fibres in the intervening years (Chapter 6, Section 6). Instead, it seems possible, even likely, that the fundamental event does not concern the individual collagen fibres as such, but instead concerns their 'linkage' together to form a fibre network.

Virtually nothing is known of the way in which individual fibres are linked to produce a network capable of resisting tension: possibly the fibres are simply interlocked physically, or perhaps some other constituent of the matrix functions as a 'glue' (Chapter 3). If the latter proves to be the case, abnormalities in the 'bonding' constituent (which might in quantitative terms be an insignificant component of the matrix) could be responsible for the loss of network strength, and might have a metabolic basis. This hypothetical metabolic change might occur without any major quantitative or qualitative abnormalities in proteoglycan profile of the kind discussed in the following Section. Alternatively, the integrity of the fibre network might be prejudiced by abnormal calcification in the matrix (see Section 2.3.7).

5.2. The Cause of a Reduced Proteoglycan Concentration

The proteoglycan content of fibrillated cartilage is reduced (see Table 9.1). Since there is a slow but active turnover of proteoglycan in cartilage, it is relevant to consider the possibility that a metabolic abnormality in cartilage might be the cause of the decrease in proteoglycan. Furthermore, the nature of the (presumably) causal relationship between fibrillation and proteoglycan decrease requires elucidation: does fibrillation cause a decrease in proteoglycan concentration, or does a decrease in proteoglycan concentration cause fibrillation? This poses the difficult question of the exact time sequence of two closely related phenomena.

Several possible metabolic factors, not mutually exclusive, have been suggested as the immediate cause of the reduction in proteoglycan content (Chapter 2, Section 8.3). First, necrosis of some of the chondrocytes is known to occur in the superficial zone, and can sometimes also be observed in the deeper uncalcified layers of fibrillated cartilage; this change might be expected to diminish the total amount of proteoglycan synthesized. Secondly, there is evidence for increased chemical degradation of proteoglycan, attributable to the activity of a lysosomal proteolytic enzyme, possibly cathepsin D, acting either extracellularly or perhaps intracellularly. Thirdly, there is the possibility that the cells may synthesize proteoglycan which is qualitatively different from that usually synthesized in adult human articular cartilage; such a change has, in fact, been demonstrated in canine experimental osteoarthrosis (McDevitt and Muir 1976) where, in response to altered mechanical stresses, mature chondrocytes synthesize proteoglycans that contain more chondroitin sulphate relative to keratan sulphate than occurs normally in adult cartilage (but, in contrast, as occurs normally in immature articular cartilage).

The possibility that a decrease in proteoglycan concentration precedes fibrillation receives support from an experimental study made by Bentley (1971), who produced fibrillation and ultimately osteoarthrosis by papain-induced proteoglycan depletion. On the other hand, fibre network fragmentation (as evidenced by a loss of tensile static and fatigue strengths) occurs in human cartilage which is not proteoglycan-depleted (Chapter 6, Sections 4.4 and 4.6). This latter observation raises the possibilities that network fragmentation eventually exposes the cells to nutritional or mechanical damage, as a consequence of which metabolic abnormalities diminish the proteoglycan content, or that fragmentation of the network 'releases' proteoglycan from the matrix, or that both mechanisms occur.

That chondrocytes may be damaged by disturbances in their mechanical environment is suggested by the fact that cartilage changes can be induced experimentally by the external application of compressive loads combined with immobilization (Salter and Field 1960; Trias 1961). Perhaps of closer relevance to the cellular changes in fibrillated cartilage is the work of Meachim (1963), who studied experimentally the tissue changes which developed *in vivo* after multiple criss-cross pattern incisions that had been made into the surface of adult rabbit articular cartilage at the patello-femoral articulation. The surgical procedure used did not involve any tearing or laceration of the tissue, nor were the incisions sufficiently deep to extend into the subchondral bone. Following this procedure, the cartilage developed focal changes which, in histological preparations, resembled those seen in naturally occurring cartilage fibrillation in man. These structural changes were accompanied by necrotic and reactive alterations in the chondrocytes: multicellular cluster formation was sometimes apparent; the intercellular matrix showed glycosaminoglycan decrease, and there were changes in the amount of sulphate fixed *in vitro* by the cartilage samples. Chrisman (1967) has subsequently demonstrated increased activity of proteolytic enzymes in cartilage damaged in this way. The observations made on this experimental model thus indicate that many of the biochemical, metabolic and cell population abnormalities seen in naturally occurring fibrillation can develop as secondary effects of physical damage to the tissue. It should be noted that 'fibrillation' produced by the method described has only a limited potential for tangential or vertical spread, and that osteoarthrosic bone changes do not result.

That the proteoglycan concentration in dead cartilage can be reduced by repeated compression has been demonstrated experimentally by Weightman (work in progress), but although this phenomenon occurs it is not regularly reproducible.

Thus it would appear that (a) both the mechanisms (i.e. altered metabolism and proteoglycan leakage) by which fibre network fragmentation might theoretically produce a decrease in proteoglycan receive some experimental support, and (b) that fibre network fragmentation can be inferred (by mechanical testing) in cartilage with a normal proteoglycan content. Hence, on balance, the present authors take the view that fibrillation is usually (if not always) initiated by fragmentation of the collagen fibre network: subsequent decrease in proteoglycan, due to leakage and cellular damage, may well soften the cartilage in and immediately adjacent to fibrillated areas, and hence be one of the factors which promote the tangential spread of network fragmentation, a topic discussed further in Section 5.4.2.

The view that fibrillation is initiated by fibre network fragmentation does not, of course, preclude the possibility that proteoglycan decrease may sometimes predispose to network fragmentation in man. To take two examples: the reduced content of proteoglycan in pathological cartilage eroded by rheumatoid pannus may make the network of such cartilage abnormally susceptible to mechanically induced damage (Jacoby and Jayson 1976); and a physiologically low content of proteoglycan may predispose to fibrillation at certain sites in non-rheumatoid, normal joints (Section 5.4.1).

5.3. Why is Fibrillation Age-related?

Any account of the genesis of fibrillation must explain the fact that the incidence of this disorder rises with age. Weightman's finding that the tensile fatigue strength of cartilage falls dramatically with age (Chapter 6, Section 6) suggests part of the explanation: presumably the tensile stresses generated in the cartilage of most if not all joints by everyday activities are insufficient to produce fragmentation of the youthful fibre network, but become progressively more able to do so as the age of the cartilage increases and its fatigue strength diminishes. This phenomenon would account for a rising inception rate for network damage, but not necessarily for a rising incidence of actual fibrillation with age.

A rising inception rate for network fragmentation will lead to an increased incidence of fibrillation only if the lesion has a poor or absent repair potential. Thus it is appropriate here to consider the capacity for repair possessed by articular cartilage. As discussed in Chapter 2, Section 7, two kinds of repair process (here referred to as 'intrinsic' and 'extrinsic') can take place in cartilage. Intrinsic repair, in so far as it exists, is dependent upon the synthesis of new matrix by the chondrocyte in an attempt to repair part-thickness splits or defects such as those in fibrillated cartilage. However, although the cells of adult articular cartilage have the ability to manufacture new matrix proteoglycans, they have only a limited capacity to form new collagen and to restore the continuity of the collagenous superficial layer after it has been disrupted (Meachim 1963). Altered proteoglycan synthesis such as occurs in fibrillated cartilage, could be viewed as an attempt to 'repair' the ground substance of the matrix, hampered by inability to mend the collagen network. Thus intrinsic repair of adult articular cartilage by cells native to the damaged tissue is exceptional, although there is evidence from experimental animals that the process can be artificially stimulated by aspirin (Chrisman, Snook and Wilson 1972) and, more effectively, by growth hormone (Chrisman 1975). Intrinsic repair is the only form of repair which might reverse early fibrillation, except in the special case of peripheral repair by extrinsic new tissue of peripheral origin. The potential for central repair by new tissue of subarticular origin becomes possible only in the later stages of cartilage destruction.

Thus the increasing incidence of fibrillation with age may be accounted for by (a) an increased inception rate of fibre network fragmentation due to a diminishing fatigue strength in the fibre network with age and (b) a virtual absence of any capacity to repair this lesion.

5.4. The Topographical Distribution and Natural History of Fibrillation

In Sections 4.3.2. and 4.3.3, attention was drawn to certain characteristic features in the topographical distribution of fibrillation: some joints are more susceptible than others, and within certain joints (for example, the hip) fibrillation in certain areas appears to be a benign accompaniment of ageing whereas elsewhere it is the precursor of osteoarthrosis. Any hypothesis advanced to explain the pathogenesis of fibrillation must account satisfactorily for this variation in its topographical distribution and natural history, and must suggest reasons why progression to osteoarthrosis occurs in some individuals but not in others.

If fibrillation is due to fibre network fragmentation, its occurrence in one location and its absence in another must be due either to differences in the nature of the mechanical environment in the area in question or else to differences, congenital or acquired, in the strength of cartilage from place to place. Unfortunately, insufficient is known of both the environment and the strength of cartilage to demonstrate with certainty the presence or absence of such differences. It is reasonable, however, to advance the following possibilities.

5.4.1. Initial Sites. There is a high inception rate of fibrillation at the periphery of cartilage sheets. This peripheral fibrillation, although histologically overt, is not always obvious to the naked eye unless the surface has been stained with Indian ink. Several factors might contribute to the high inception rate. First, although the compressive stresses applied normal to the surface in such areas are probably low, the periphery of convex surfaces are subject to the to-and-fro motion of the opposing articular edge. This might tend to damage the surface by 'ploughing', a topic discussed in Chapter 7. Furthermore, intermittent contact will produce rapid changes in the compressive stress applied to the cartilage—from zero when no contact is being made to some positive value when contact is achieved. It is possible (but unproven) that rapid stress changes of this kind, especially if combined with a ploughing effect, may be particularly liable to induce fatigue failure in the fibre network in cartilage.

Secondly, the periphery of the articular cartilage can sometimes show a surface covering of a thin layer of fibrous tissue; this is seen particularly on the patella, and can occur in the absence of rheumatoid disease. Moreover, the outer edge of true hyaline cartilage, not just on the patella but also elsewhere, may blend with other synovial tissues in the transitional zone at the joint margin. It is possible that this admixture or covering with non-hyaline tissue may predispose to fraying of the peripheral articular territory, or that for some unknown reason the periphery of the cartilage has a structurally inferior surface.

Susceptibility to histological fibrillation is not confined to the periphery of cartilage sheets. Cartilage is also susceptible at the boundaries between articulation territories and at certain other, non-peripheral, sites such as the inferomedial segment of the femoral head, and the bare (i.e. not covered by meniscus) area of the tibial plateau. An explanation put forward by Bullough, Goodfellow and O'Connor (1973) may account for susceptibility both at these more central sites and at the periphery. Bullough and colleagues suggest that insufficiently frequent cartilage-to-cartilage contact may be responsible, causing the tissue to 'degenerate'.

The 'insufficiency' of the contact in these areas has, however, a mechanical aspect. Such cartilage is subject to intermittent contact with the opposing articular surface and in this it is similar to the marginal cartilage on convex surfaces. Thus, the femoral cartilage inferomedial to the fovea is sometimes in contact with the acetabular fat pad and sometimes with the acetabular cartilage. The cartilage in the centre of the tibial plateau is in contact with the femur in extension but not in flexion, because the femoral condyle moves backwards across the tibia as the knee flexes.

Furthermore, both the peripheral cartilage and that inferomedial to the fovea on the femoral head are normally softer in compression than is the cartilage on the zenith (Chapter 6, Section 3.5). Thus, in these areas the fibre network may be less well supported by a proteoglycan gel than elsewhere and hence be more susceptible to mechanical damage. It is not known whether similar topographical variations in compression properties occur in other joint surfaces but topographical variation in tensile stiffness (a property of the fibre network itself) has been shown to occur in the femoral condyles (Chapter 6, Section 4.6).

Thus, certain areas of articular cartilage (such as those at the periphery of joints or inferomedial to the fovea) may be liable to fibrillate because (a) their mechanical environment is disadvantageous and (b) the tissue may be structurally inferior. The involvement of peripheral cartilage may also be related to its proximity to other, synovial tissues.

5.4.2. Tangential Spread. The tendency for histological fibrillation to spread tangentially across a cartilage surface with increasing age (see Figure 9.10) varies with the individual and with the anatomical site. The reason for this variation is not known, but the following factors may be concerned in local spread. Decrease in proteoglycan, due to leakage and cellular damage, may soften the cartilage immediately adjacent to fibrillated areas, thus promoting fragmentation of the nearby collagen fibre network. Tangential spread may also be induced by an increase in the stresses applied to cartilage adjacent to fibrillated areas: it seems very likely that the presence of a fibrillated area of cartilage, which, because of the softness of the cartilage, effectively represents a hole in the load-bearing surface, will result in stress increases in adjacent intact cartilage; the load originally borne by the defect is now applied as an additional load to the remainder of the surface, and lateral support is removed from the cartilage adjacent to the defect.

An observed age-related increase in the percentage of an articular surface area affected by histologically overt fibrillation is not always due solely to an enlargement of the initially affected foci; new, independent foci can also develop as the surface ages.

5.4.3. Topographical Variation in Vertical Spread. The initiation of histologically apparent cartilage wear and its tangential spread across the articular surface are so common in the adult population that such lesions must often be asymptomatic. In contrast, vertical progression of the lesions to cause destructive thinning of the tissue is a more crucial phenomenon in terms of loss of the protective function of the articular cartilage on the underlying bone. Clinical osteoarthrosis can be regarded as a failure of this protective function.

The initiation and tangential spread of histological fibrillation often implies only a superficial disintegration, without any major thinning of the cartilage. The findings presented in Section 3 suggest that the vicious cycle of collagen network disintegration and proteoglycan loss is not always relentless in its vertical progression towards bone (Figure 9.17). Thus clues to the

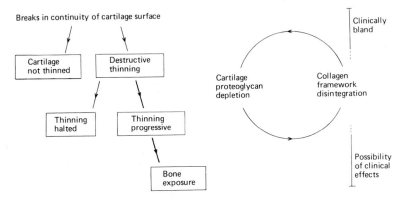

Figure 9.17 Model depicting asymptomatic cartilage damage and clinically apparent osteoarthrosis.

pathogenesis of clinically apparent, symptomatic osteoathrosis may come from studies of the factors which influence any subsequent progressive thinning of the cartilage towards bone exposure at a site where the environment then subjects the bone to crushing and abrasion (see Figure 9.16). There is a need to consider what mechanical factors in the environment and chemical factors in the tissue determine whether or not degenerate cartilage will continue to wear to the point of its functional failure as a material, and to discuss variation between individuals in this respect. The topic requires separate consideration for the hip, the knee and other joints.

In the case of the hip joint, progression to femoral head osteoarthrosic bone exposure occurs in some subjects only. When it occurs it is usually, but not invariably, sited on or near the zenith, while, in contrast, the inferomedial segment and the periphery are at first spared. The relative immunity of these latter sites to bone exposure (although not to fibrillation) might be due to an absence of high local compressive stresses or to a diminishing frequency of contact with the opposing surface as the extremes of the range of hip movement are used less frequently with advancing age. In contrast, fibrillation at the zenith of the femoral head has a lower incidence but appears to progress to full-thickness loss, bone damage, pain and stiffness (i.e. to osteoarthrosis). A possible explanation for this observation has been provided by the work of Day et al. (1975). These workers identified an anatomical feature consisting of a triangular area of fibro-, rather than hyaline, cartilage in the roof of the articular surface of some (but not all) acetabula. When present, this feature did not make contact with the femoral head in some young adult hips even at a load of three times the body weight, a finding in line with other studies of contact in the hip (Bullough et al. 1973). In elderly subjects, however, this feature always made contact with the femoral head, perhaps because of the acetabular remodelling which is said to occur with advancing age (Walmsley 1928). When contact was made with the femoral head, the resulting stresses were sometimes (but not always) very high: in 5 of 14 hips studied, the pressure in this area was more than 2.5 times greater than the average pressure in the hip as a whole. Thus had these hips been subjected to a load in life of five times the body weight, the cartilage at the zenith of the femoral head would have encountered a pressure equivalent to fifteen times the body weight if applied to the hip as a whole. Laboratory studies suggest that the repetitive application of a compressive stress of this magnitude would be sufficient to induce fibre network fatigue failure in the elderly (Chapter 6, Section 6). It seems likely that once such a stress had induced fibre network fatigue, its continued application would produce progressive damage to the cartilage and then to the bone.

Thus fibrillation at the zenith of the femoral head may occur (but be uncommon) because high pressure contact between fibrocartilage in the zenith of the acetabulum and the femoral head occurs (but is likewise uncommon). It may be progressive (a) because of the great magnitude of the applied stresses and (b) because this area of the femoral head cannot be offloaded (as can the periphery) by a symptomatically acceptable limitation of the range of movement at the hip. It is not, of course, suggested that this explanation necessarily accounts for all instances of osteoarthrosis of the hip.

It will be noticed that the hypothetical explanations presented above for the development of fibrillation, first at the periphery of the femoral head and inferomedial to the fovea (see Figure 9.14) and secondly at the zenith of the femoral head, involved a knowledge of the areas of contact in the hip, the location of the areas of the head subjected to the maximum compressive stresses, the magnitude of those stresses, and the nature of topographical variations in the mechanical properties of the cartilage covering the femoral head. It is not suprising that these variables need to be defined if a mechanical explanation for fibrillation is to be provided, for such an explanation essentially takes the form of postulating that in some areas of a sheet of cartilage the mechanical environment to which the tissue is subject is such that the strength of the tissue is inadequate. Unfortunately, there is unsufficient knowledge of one or all of these variables at every other joint in the body to extend such 'explanations' to them. Thus comparable 'explanations' for the genesis of fibrillation at the knee could take advantage only of a knowledge of the total load applied to this joint, some knowledge of the contact areas and a minimal knowledge of topographical variations in the mechanical properties of the femoral cartilage. At the metacarpophalangeal joint of the thumb no information whatsoever is available, so any 'explanation' would be so speculative as to be worthless.

Thus in view of our present ignorance of the relevant variables, 'explanations' for the progression of fibrillation must be confined to the hip. In particular, the problem of the pathogenesis of osteoarthrosis in the joints of the upper limb is unsolved, as is that of generalized primary osteoarthrosis.

5.5. The Morphological Appearances of Fibrillated Cartilage

It is of interest to compare the morphological changes which might be predicted theoretically, from a knowledge of the microanatomy and mechanical properties of cartilage, with the changes actually seen after cyclical compressive loading in the laboratory (see Figure 9.15) and in fibrillated cartilage in life.

Theoretically, a compressive stress applied normal to the surface of cartilage might be expected to produce secondary tensile stresses in the surface layers (Chapter 5). Since the surface is weaker in tension in the *en face* direction at right angles to the predominant fibre orientation than in the direction parallel to the fibre orientation (Chapter 6, Section 4.3), such stresses, if evenly distributed, would be expected to produce *en face* surface splits between the fibres, i.e. splits parallel to the artificial prick lines. Such splits are in fact seen in cartilage which has been cyclically loaded in compression in the laboratory (see Chapter 6, Figures 6.41 and 6.42). In such cartilage, however, there are also multidirectional 'crazings' which do not display any obvious relationship to the microanatomy of the surface. (They have not, as yet, been studied by *en face* microscopy at a magnification of ×150.)

These findings can be compared with those in cartilage loaded in life. The surface morphology of minimally fibrillated cartilage can be studied *en face* (Figure 9.18) by stereomicroscopy and by

Figure 9.18 Indian ink preparation, viewed *en face* in reflected light, of patellar articular surface from a random necropsy. Most of the area illustrated appeared 'macroscopically intact' and was smooth to palpation. However, the Indian ink has shown up 'minimal fibrillation', with elongated linear 'fractures' (upper left and upper centre) and some irregular fine 'cracking' (S). More overt superficial fibrillation is also demonstrated as a semiconfluent blackening (upper right and near lower right). The linear 'fractures' were parallel to the predominant orientation *en face* of the superficial collagen. ×16.

transmission light microscopy of tangential surface slices (Figure 9.19). The affected surfaces show a variety of markings *en face* when examined as Indian ink preparations at magnifications up to ×150 (Meachim and Fergie 1975). Some, but not all, of the superficial markings show orientation in the sense that they have one or more dominant *en face* alignments. The direction of this orientation can then be studied in relation to that of movement in unidirectional joints and that of elongated splits made by artificially pricking the surface with the rounded point of a pin (Figure 9.19). Such studies (Meachim and Fergie 1975) show that the *en face* orientation of the naturally occurring superficial markings is in many instances (Figure 9.19a) parallel with the predominant orientation of the surface collagen; i.e. they have the same orientation as those produced by cyclic compression *in vitro*. In some instances (Figure 9.19c), however, the orientation is parallel with the direction of movement at uniaxial joints (such as the ankle) and thus suggests abrasion. (It should be made clear that this can occur in joints showing no evidence of bone exposure.) In some instances such 'movement markings' and 'fatigue-consistent' markings can be seen together on the same cartilage surface.

Thus in minimally fibrillated cartilage (in which the primary changes are presumably most in evidence) the morphology in part resembles that seen *in vitro* after cyclic compressive loading but in part suggests that abrasion may also be concerned, a topic referred to in Section 5.6.

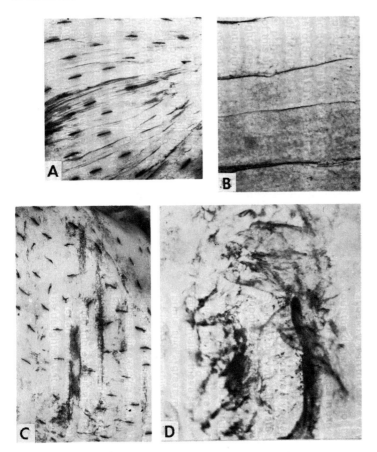

Figure 9.19 (A) Indian ink preparation of part of the patellar groove of distal femur; necropsy specimen. The fine linear markings are due to the 'parallel linear' pattern of minimal fibrillation. These natural markings are parallel to the *en face* alignment of splits made artificially into the cartilage surface (short black lines). Compact with (C) ×3.

(B) Transmission photomicrograph *en face* of 'parallel linear' pattern minimal fibrillation of the sort shown in (A) ×160.

(C) Indian ink preparation of the superior surface of a talus; necropsy specimen. The parallel markings are due to a type of minimal fibrillation which differs from that shown in (A): they run parallel to the direction of flexion–extension movement, and not to that of the artificial splits ×3.

(D) Transmission photomicrograph *en face* of part of a surface marking of the type shown in (B). ×160.

(Reproduced from Meachim, Denham, Emery and Wilkinson (1974) by courtesy of the Editor, *Journal of Anatomy*.)

In the case of segments of cartilage showing more developed damage, one or more of the following lesions, described in Sections 3.3 and 4.3.1, can occur in the affected segment: (a) overt superficial or deep fibrillation (see Figure 9.1), usually without any obvious *en face* orientation; (b) smoother-surfaced destructive thinning; and (c) horizontal cleft formation at the interface between uncalcified and calcified cartilage. All three of these appearances can be accounted for in structural and mechanical terms.

The lack of any particular *en face* orientation in deeper fibrillation conforms with the more random *en face* orientation of collagen fibres in the deeper as compared with the superficial zone of cartilage (Chapter 1, Section 2.5): the fact that *en face* split lines cannot be demonstrated in the deeper layers, as they can in the superficial, is another expression of this anatomical feature.

Smooth-surfaced destructive thinning (see Figure 9.2) suggests abrasive wear, a topic discussed in Section 5.6.

Horizontal cleft formation at the interface between the calcified and uncalcified zones (see Figures 9.3 and 9.7) suggests a shearing mechanism. In normal cartilage, vertical compression will produce a tendency for lateral expansion of the cartilage, the extent of which is normally limited by the inelastic fibre network in the matrix (Chapter 5). If the network in fibrillated cartilage is fragmented, the amount of lateral spread which the matrix itself will permit will increase (i.e. the Poisson ratio for the material will increase). The greater the lateral expansion permitted by the matrix itself, the greater will be the shear stresses between the uncalcified matrix and the virtually inelastic calcified zone. High shear stresses in soft tissue tend in general to result in cleft formation (other examples being blister formation in the skin of the hands after manual work, or the development of adventitious bursae in loose connective tissue). Thus horizontal clefts at the interface between the calcified and uncalcified zones could be explained by the development of high shear stresses, which in turn can be viewed as a consequence of fibre network fragmentation.

In the case of osteoarthrosic joints at the advanced stage of bone exposure, it seems certain that at least some of the cartilage and bone destruction is due to abrasion by exposed bone and loose fragments.

Thus, in summary, the appearance of fibrillated human cartilage in its early stages suggests the action of both fibre network fragmentation due to fatigue and abrasion. The later appearances suggest the progression of both these mechanisms (abrasion being particularly likely, indeed certain, when bone is exposed) and of shear failure in the deep zone. Fibre network fragmentation has already been considered at length; it remains now to consider the mechanism of abrasion.

5.6. The Role of Wear in the Pathogenesis of Fibrillation

Three types of wear were listed in Chapter 7, Section 5 (adhesive wear, abrasive wear and fatigue wear). In Section 5.5 of this Chapter it was noted that the morphological appearances of cartilage surfaces showing 'minimal' histological fibrillation in man are in many instances consistent with a 'fatigue wear' (being parallel to the predominant *en face* orientation of the surface collagen), but in some instances are instead indicative of abrasive or adhesive wear (being parallel to the direction of joint movement). On the basis of the scanty experimental evidence available it was concluded in Chapter 7 that synovial fluid (as compared with saline) has the property of protecting articular cartilage from wear. If, as seems very likely (see Chapter 7, Section 6.6.3), some component of synovial fluid, perhaps the protein, is adsorbed onto the cartilage surface, this action would be expected, since movement would tend to wear away the adsorbed layer rather than the cartilage.

Difficulties arise when an attempt is made to apply these observations to the problem of the genesis of fibrillation. First, the question arises: what wear mechanism is likely to be involved?

Adhesive wear seems unlikely since the coefficient of friction (which reflects the extent to which the bearing surfaces adhere) between cartilage surfaces is extremely low, and does not rise even when the tissue is fibrillated (Chapter 7, Section 8.1). Fatigue wear is essentially the mechanism proposed here to account for fibre network fragmentation especially in cartilage sheets subjected to the reciprocating action of the edge of the opposite articular surface (Section 5.4.1). Thus to say that it occurs does not postulate the action of any new destructive mechanism.

Abrasive wear remains to be considered. *In vitro,* non-fibrillated cartilage is extremely resistant, even to harsh abrasive wear produced by a rotating steel abrader (Simon 1975). *In vivo,* with soft bearing surfaces such as represented by opposing cartilage sheets, the abrasion of one surface by another is relatively unlikely. It is none the less possible, especially if the cartilage on one surface were to be much stiffer in compression than that on the other. It is known that such variations in stiffness can occur within any one surface but there are as yet no observations which permit comparisons between the stiffness of opposing cartilages. Three-body abrasion (due to the action of loose particles of normal cartilage, and particularly of crystal-containing cartilage (see Section 2.3.7) or of bone) seems *a priori* to be a more likely mechanism to wear cartilage but no studies have been made of the action of such particles *in vitro*.

These difficulties would diminish if it could be shown that the wear-protecting function of synovial fluid is sometimes lost in normal joints. Unfortunately, insufficient data are available on this question. While it is true that many studies have been made using coefficient of friction measurements to assess the 'slipperiness' of synovial fluid, this property may not be identical with the 'wear-protecting' property. Moreover, most studies have not taken sufficient account of the possible part played by particles in the synovial fluid.

Once the surface of cartilage has broken in life (i.e. once it has become fibrillated) the tissue wears more rapidly *in vitro*—even when lubricated with synovial fluid (Simon 1975)—than does normal cartilage (see Chapter 7, Section 8.1). Thus, if fibrillation were to be initiated by some other mechanism—say fibre network fragmentation due to fatigue—the damaged tissue could be expected then to wear more rapidly, perhaps because, being soft in compression and weak in tension, it could more readily be abraded both by the opposing cartilage surface and by loose fragments of cartilage. Obviously, once bone is exposed in the articular surface the abrasion of the opposite cartilage surface seems not only possible but certain: this is very probably one of the mechanisms responsible for 'smooth-surfaced thinning' and it must contribute to the formation of score marks ('track marks') in cartilage; however, it should be made clear that 'smooth-surfaced thinning' with score marks can also occur prior to bone exposure.

In summary, although abrasive wear might initiate fibrillation, especially if loose particulate debris is present in the normal joint, it seems more likely that fibrillation is initiated by fatigue (which can in a sense be viewed as a form of wear) rather than by adhesive or abrasive wear. Once cartilage has fibrillated, however, it will wear more rapidly than normal, giving rise to the combined morphological features of fatigue and abrasion described in Section 5.5. Once bone is exposed, the rapid abrasion of cartilage seems certain.

5.7. A Summary of the Concept of Fibre Network Fragmentation

It is appropriate here to review the concept of fibre network fragmentation which has been advanced in this Chapter to account for the development of fibrillation. The concept can be recapitulated by answering three questions related to this phenomenon:

(a) How may 'fragmentation' be detected?
(b) What chemical and structural abnormalities constitute 'fragmentation'?
(c) What is the cause of 'fragmentation'?

5.7.1. How may Network Fragmentation be Detected? First, since the collagen fibre network confers tensile strength and rigidity upon the tissue, 'fragmentation' may be inferred when there is a decrease in static tensile rigidity, a decrease in static tensile strength and a decrease in tensile fatigue strength (Chapter 6).

Secondly, since distension of the collagen network will limit the tendency of the proteoglycans to imbibe water, 'fragmentation' can be inferred when there is swelling of cartilage and an increase in its hydration (Chapter 4, Section 6.2.5).

Thirdly, fragmentation may be seen morphologically (at its

extreme) when the tissue as a whole is fragmented, i.e. fibrillated (see Figure 9.1). Lesser degrees of fragmentation may be inferred from increased separation between collagen fibres (see Figure 9.16) seen by the electron microscope (Section 5.1.1).

5.7.2. What Chemical and Structural Abnormalities Constitute Network Fragmentation? To date no quantitative chemical abnormalities have been found in cartilage presumed to be fragmented. A qualitative change in the glycosaminoglycan composition of the proteoglycans has been described in association with network fragmentation in dog cartilage samples in which the articular surface (i.e. synovial interface) is still 'histologically intact' (McDevitt and Muir 1976).

Theoretically, 'fragmentation' could be due to a change in the mechanical properties of individual collagen fibres (which seems unlikely since it implies an entirely new form of collagen), to rupture of individual collagen fibres, or to a 'loosening' of the bonds (whatever they may be) between individual collagen fibres. It is important here to emphasize that these 'bonds' are a structurally vital component of the 'collagen network', but that the nature of the bonding agent is unknown; it might well be, for example, a proteoglycan fraction, and thus the qualitative proteoglycan changes mentioned above might affect the mechanical properties of the fibre network.

5.7.3 What is the Cause of Network Fragmentation? Fragmentation has been produced *in vitro* by the cyclic loading of cartilage (Chapter 6, Sections 6 and 7). Such fragmentation can be regarded as fatigue-failure. A fall in the tensile strength and stiffness of the fibre network has been produced by exposing cartilage to collagenase (Chapter 6, Section 4.9). Thus both mechanical forces or enzymatic attack directed against the collagen network *in vitro* can be shown to bring about changes in its morphological and physical properties.

We believe that cartilage may be destroyed in life by a process which begins with fragmentation of the fibre network. Histological fibrillation, and thus by implication the precursor lesion here postulated of fibre network damage, is a normal feature at certain sites in adult synovial joints. It follows that hypotheses about the cause of network fragmentation which deal solely in terms of 'abnormal' factors in its pathogenesis are based on a false assumption. This, of course, is not to deny that in certain circumstances fragmentation may be initiated or potentiated by pathological alterations in a cartilage segment or its mechanical environment, as follows:

(1) Normal cartilage subjected to:
   (a) a cyclic load at abnormally high stress; or

(b) a cyclic load at abnormally high frequencies but normal stress.
(2) Normal environment but fibre network weakened by:
    (a) enzymatic attack;
    (b) congenital or metabolic abnormality; or
    (c) some unknown process associated with ageing.

5.8. Conclusions

Articular cartilage degeneration is a normal feature in adult synovial joints. The degenerative change starts in the joint as a focal process on cartilage sheets which are otherwise still intact. The lesions are often mild and not obvious to the naked eye, and thus often require techniques such as microscopy or Indian ink staining for their detection. They first develop at the periphery of cartilage sheets and on certain other characteristic sites. The reason for the high susceptibility of the periphery to mild damage is debatable. With increasing age, degeneration tends to affect an increasing proportion of the cartilage surface, including more central sites in the affected joint.

One form of degenerative lesion, not initially apparent to the naked eye, is characterized by ultrastructural evidence of fragmentation of the collagen fibre network, seen in transmission electron micrographs as abnormally wide separations between individual fibres. This lesion can develop beneath a cartilage surface which is still histologically intact, or it can be accompanied by surface changes seen on light microscopy as minute splits, irregularities and ridges at the tissue/synovial interface ('minimal fibrillation'; 'quaternary irregularities'). At this stage the cartilage can become thicker than normal.

More than one mechanism may be concerned in the initiation of this focal degeneration. It is here suggested that one cause is fatigue failure of the collagen fibre network, implying that the cartilage matrix develops structural failure from repeated applications of cyclic loading at stresses and frequencies which it was at first able to withstand without damage. In some instances there is morphological evidence that abrasive (or, just possibly, adhesive) wear at the cartilage surface is an additional or alternative factor, and the possibility that synovial fluid helps to protect against this type of wear cannot be discounted ('wear-protective' properties are not necessarily identical with those measured as 'slipperiness' in coefficient of friction studies with synovial fluid).

Because the collagen, proteoglycan and cells of articular cartilage are functionally interdependent, the exact time sequence of changes during the initiation of degeneration is difficult to analyse. The first event may not be the same in all lesions. In some, collagen network fragmentation and a qualitative change in proteoglycans both seem to occur together as inherent initial features of the degenerative process. In this context it must be remembered that some proteoglycan fraction may be a structural component of the collagen network by bonding the fibres to each other. In other lesions, a decrease in proteoglycan, due to decreased synthesis or increased enzymatic degradation by the cells, may be the first event, in turn weakening the support to the collagen network and thus predisposing it to mechanically induced damage.

Degenerative lesions, such as fibre network fragmentation initially occurring at the ultrastructural level, can lead to a 'histologically overt' fibrillation (i.e. frank splitting) of the cartilage and sometimes can develop into macroscopically obvious cartilage damage of fibrillation or other type. Such damage can in turn lead to destructive thinning of the material, from splitting and disintegration due to fibrillation, sometimes accompanied by lesions due to abrasive wear and to shearing damage. If progressive cartilage breakdown occurs, it eventually results in bone exposure and in an appearance indistinguishable from that in surgical excision specimens from osteoarthrosic joints. At this late stage, an abrasive or grinding mechanism becomes an important factor in the bone and cartilage damage at the site of the destructive lesion. Thus osteoarthrosis is characterized by cartilage thinning potentially to expose bone at a site where the bone will then be subjected to abrasive and other damage: it represents a failure of the protective function of articular cartilage. It is usually accompanied by remodelling phenomena (e.g. osteophytosis) elsewhere on the affected surface.

The time sequence of age-related degenerative changes is not uniform across the whole of a cartilage sheet. For example, in the case of the patellar surface, mild lesions, requiring histology or Indian ink staining for their detection, first appear at the periphery of the articular surface and on the medial part of the medial surface ('the odd facet'). In contrast, more severe lesions, macroscopically obvious without staining the surface, are often first apparent at one or more sites along the territory of the transverse ridge.

A distinction must be drawn between the initiation and the progression of cartilage lesions. Cartilage degeneration, particularly if 'histological' lesions are included, is so common amongst the general population that it must often be clinically bland. Progression of cartilage breakdown towards bone exposure and abrasive wear of osteoarthrosic type, with the possibility of clinically significant effects, is not inevitable and not always relentless. Whether or not it occurs is influenced by local factors in the cartilage segment concerned: for example, the magnitude of compressive loading and perhaps other, unknown, factors in the case of joints such as the fingers in primary generalized osteoarthrosis. Ageing does not in itself appear to be an important aetiological factor in osteoarthrosis, except for the patellofemoral joint in elderly women. In most instances, some additional factor is required: circumstances in which the mechanical environment of the cartilage is unfavourable, for example from an anatomical abnormality of the joint; circumstances in which the cartilage has defective fatigue- or wear-resistance as a material, for example from crystal or pigment deposition, from proteoglycan depletion or, most commonly, for unknown reasons. 'Mechanical' and 'biochemical' hypotheses for the pathogenesis of osteoarthrosis are not mutually exclusive, since this is a heterogeneous disorder with a variety of different predisposing causes.

REFERENCES

Acheson R. M., Chan Y.–K. and Clemett A. R. (1970) New Haven Survey of Joint Diseases. XII: Distribution and symptoms of osteoarthrosis in the hands with reference to handedness. *Ann. rheum. Dis.* **29**, 275.

Ali S. Y. (1977) Mineral containing matrix vesicles in human osteoarthrotic cartilage. *Proceedings of a Symposium on the Osteopathogenesis of Osteoarthrosis.*

Allison N. and Ghormley R. K. (1931) *Diagnosis in Joint Disease.* Oxford University Press, London.

Anderson C. E., Ludowieg J., Harper H. A. and Engleman E. P. (1964) The composition of the organic component of human articular cartilage. *J. Bone Jt Surg.* **46A**, 1176.

Annotation (1972) Chondromalacia patellae. *Brit. med. J.* **2**, 123.

Arlet J. and Ficat P. (1968) Diagnostic de l'ostéo-nécrose fémoro-capitale primitive au stade I (Stade pré-radiologique). *Revue Chir. orthop.* **54**, 637.

Arnoldi C. C., Linderholm H. and Müssbichler H. (1972) Venous engorgement and intra-osseous hypertension in osteoarthritis of the hip. *J. Bone Jt Surg.* **54B**, 409.

Arnoldi C. C., Linderholm H. and Vinnerberg A. (1972) Skeletal and soft tissue changes in the lower leg in patients with intracalcanean hypertension. *Acta chir. scand.* **138**, 25.

Barnett C. H. and Cobbold A. F. (1968) Effects of age upon the mobility of human finger joints. *Ann. rheum. Dis.* **27**, 175.

Barnett C. H., Cochrane W. and Palfrey A. J. (1963) Age changes in articular cartilage of rabbits. *Ann. rheum. Dis.* **22**, 389.

Bennett G. A., Waine H. and Bauer W. (1942) *Changes in the Knee Joint at Various Ages with Particular Reference to the Nature and Development of Degenerative Joint Disease.* Commonwealth Fund, New York.

Bentley G. (1971) Papain-induced degenerative arthritis of the hip in rabbits. *J. Bone Jt Surg.* **53B**, 324.

Bernstein M. A. (1933) Experimental production of arthritis by artificially produced passive congestion. *J. Bone Jt Surg.* **15**, 661.

Bollet A. J. and Nance J. L. (1966) Biochemical findings in normal and osteoarthritic articular cartilage. II: Chondroitin sulfate concentration and chain length, water and ash content. *J. clin. Invest.* **45**, 1170.

Brookes M. and Helal B. (1968) Primary osteoarthritis, venous engorgment and osteogenesis. *J. Bone Jt Surg.* **50B**, 493.

Bullough P. G., Goodfellow J. and O'Connor J. (1973) The relationship between degenerative changes and load-bearing in the human hip. *J. Bone Jt Surg.* **55B**, 746.

Byers P.D., Contempomi C. A. and Farkas T. A. (1970) A post mortem study of the hip joint. *Ann. rheum. Dis.* **29**, 15.

Chrisman O. D. (1967) *Cartilage: degeneration and repair,* Ed. by C. A. L. Bassett, p. 81. National Research Council, Washington DC.

Chrisman O. D. (1975) The effect of growth hormone on established cartilage lesions. *Clin. Orthop.* **107**, 232.

Chrisman O. D., Snook G. A. and Wilson T. C. (1972) The protective effect of aspirin against degeneration of human articular cartilage. *Clic. Orthop.* **84**, 193.

Collins D. H. (1949) *The Pathology of Articular and Spinal Diseases,* pp. 74–115 and 221. Edward Arnold, London.

Collins D. H. and McElligott T. F. (1960) Sulphate ($^{35}SO_4$) uptake by chondrocytes in relation to histological changes in osteo-arthritic human articular cartilage. *Ann. rheum. Dis.* **19**, 318.

Collins D. H. and Meachim G. (1961) Sulphate ($^{35}SO_4$) fixation by human articular cartilage compared in the knee and shoulder joints. *Ann. rheum. Dis.* **20**, 117.

Day W. H., Swanson S. A. V. and Freeman M. A. R. (1975) Contact pressures in the loaded human cadaver hip. *J. Bone Jt Surg.* **57B**, 302.

Ehrlich M. G., Mankin H. J., Jones H., Grossman A., Crispen C. and Ancona D. (1975) Biochemical confirmation of an experimental osteoarthritis model. *J. Bone Jt Surg.* **57A**, 392.

Emery I. H. and Meachim G. (1973) Surface morphology and topography of patello-femoral cartilage fibrillation in Liverpool necropsies. *J. Anat. (Lond.)* **116**, 103.

Ficat P. (1975) Contribution to the study of the initial stage of cartilage degeneration. *Ann. rheum. Dis.* **34**, Suppl., 125.

Foss M. V. L. and Byers P.D. (1972) Bone density, osteoarthrosis of the hip, and fracture of the upper end of the femur. *Ann. rheum. Dis.* **31**, 259.

Freeman M. A. R. (1972) The pathogenesis of osteoarthrosis: an hypothesis. *Modern Trends in Orthopaedics—6.* Ed. by A. Graham Apley, p. 40 Butterworths, London.

Gardner D. L. (1965) *Pathology of the Connective Tissue Diseases,* pp. 313–316. Edward Arnold, London.

Ghadially F. N. and Roy S. (1969) *Ultrastructure of Synovial Joints in Health and Disease,* pp. 85–95. Butterworths, London.

Goodfellow J. W. and Bullough P. G. (1967) The pattern of ageing of the articular cartilage of the elbow joint. *J. Bone Jt Surg.* **49B,** 175.

Harrison M. H. M., Schajowicz F. and Trueta J. (1953) Osteoarthritis of the hip: a study of the nature and evolution of the disease. *J. Bone Jt Surg.* **35B,** 598.

Heine J. (1926) Über die Arthritis deformans. *Virchows Arch.* **260,** 521.

Hulth A. and Hernborg J. (1968) Blood circulation in osteoarthritic joints. *J. Bone Jt Surg.* **50B,** 227.

Jacoby R. K. and Jayson M. I. V. (1976) Synthesis of glycosaminoglycan in adult human articular cartilage in organ culture from patients with rheumatoid arthritis. *Ann. rheum. Dis.* **35,** 32.

Kellgren J. H. (1961) Osteoarthrosis in patients and populations. *Brit. med. J.* **2,** 1.

Lang F. J. (1934) Arthritis deformans und spondylitis deformans. *Handbuch der Speziellen Pathologischen Anatomie und Histologie,* Ed. by O. Lubarsch and F. Henke. Julius Springer, Berlin.

Laskar F. H. and Sargison K. D. (1970) Ochronotic arthropathy. *J. Bone Jt Surg.* **52B,** 653.

Linn F. C. and Sokoloff L. (1965) Movement and composition of interstitial fluid of cartilage. *Arthritis Rheum.* **8,** 481.

Longmore R. B. and Gardner D. L. (1975) Development with age of human articular cartilage surface structure. *Ann. rheum. Dis.* **34,** 26.

McDevitt C. A. and Muir H. (1976) Biochemical changes in the cartilage of the knee in experimental and natural osteoarthritis in dogs. *J. Bone Jt Surg.* **58B,** 94.

McElligott T. F. and Collins D. H. (1960) Chondrocyte function of human articular and costal cartilage compared by measuring the in vitro uptake of labelled ($^{35}SO_4$) sulphate. *Ann. rheum. Dis.* **19,** 31.

McKibbin B. (1971) Immature joint cartilage and the homograft reaction. *J. Bone Jt Surg.* **53B,** 123.

McKibbin B. and Holdsworth F. W. (1967) The dual nature of epiphyseal cartilage. *J. Bone Jt Surg.* **49B,** 351.

Maroudas A. and Evans H. (1974) Sulphate diffusion and incorporation into human articular cartilage. *Biochim. biophys. Acta* **338,** 265.

Matthews B. F. (1953) Composition of articular cartilage in osteoarthritis: changes in collagen/chondroitin sulphate ratio. *Brit. med. J.* **2,** 660.

Meachim G. (1963) The effect of scarification on articular cartilage in the rabbit. *J. Bone Jt Surg.* **45B,** 150.

Meachim G. (1971) Effect of age on the thickness of adult articular cartilage at the shoulder joint. *Ann. rheum. Dis.* **30,** 43.

Meachim G. (1972a) Articular cartilage lesions in osteoarthritis of the femoral head. *J. Path.* **107,** 199.

Meachim G. (1972b) Light microscopy of Indian ink preparations of fibrillated cartilage. *Ann. rheum. Dis.* **31,** 457.

Meachim G. (1975a) Cartilage fibrillation at the ankle joint in Liverpool necropsies. *J. Anat. (Lond.)* **119,** 601.

Meachim G. (1975b) The state of knee meniscal fibrocartilage in Liverpool necropsies. *J. Path.* **119,** 167.

Meachim G. (1976) Cartilage fibrillation on the lateral tibial plateau in Liverpool necropsies. *J. Anat. (Lond.)* **121,** 97.

Meachim G. and Collins D. H. (1962) Cell counts of normal and osteo-arthritic articular cartilage in relation to the uptake of sulphate ($^{35}SO_4$) in vitro. *An. rheum. Dis.* **21,** 45.

Meachim G. and Emery I. H. (1973) Cartilage fibrillation in shoulder and hip joints in Liverpool necropsies. *J. Anat. (Lond.)* **116,** 161.

Meachim G. and Emery I. H. (1974) Quantitative aspects of patello-femoral cartilage fibrillation in Liverpool necropsies. *Ann. rheum. Dis.* **33,** 39.

Meachim G. and Fergie I. A. (1975) Morphological patterns of articular cartilage fibrillation. *J. Path. (Lond.)* **115,** 231.

Meachim G. and Illman O. (1967) Articular cartilage degeneration in hamsters and in pigs. *Z. Versuchstierk.* **9,** 33.

Meachim G. and Osborne G. V. (1970) Repair at the femoral articular surface in osteoarthritis of the hip. *J. Path.* **102,** 1.

Meachim G. and Roberts C. (1971) Repair of the joint surface from subarticular tissue in the rabbit knee. *J. Anat. (Lond.)* **109,** 317.

Meachim G. and Roy S. (1969) Surface ultrastructure of mature adult human articular cartilage. *J. Bone Jt Surg.* **51B,** 529.

Meachim G., Ghadially F. N. and Collins D. H. (1965) Regressive changes in the superficial layer of human articular cartilage. *Ann. rheum. Dis.* **24,** 23.

Meachim G., Denham D., Emery I. H. and Wilkinson P. H. (1974) Collagen alignments and artificial splits at the surface of human articular cartilage. *J. Anat. (Lond.)* **118,** 101.

Meriel P., Ruffie R. and Fournie A. (1955) La phleobographie de la hanche dans les coxathroses et des malades osteoarticulaires. *Revue Rhumat.* **22,** 238.

Mills K. (1970) Pathology of the knee joint in rheumatoid arthritis. *J. Bone Jt Surg.* **52B,** 746.

Murray R. O. and Duncan C. (1971) Athletic activity in adolescence as an aetiological factor in degenerative hip disease. *J. Bone Jt Surg.* **53B,** 406.

Nichols E. H. and Richardson F. L. (1909) Arthritis deformans. *J. med. Res.* **21,** 149.

Radin E. L. and Paul I. L. (1970) Does cartilage compliance reduce skeletal impact loads? *Arthritis Rheum.* **13,** 139.

Salter R. B. and Field P. (1960) The effects of continuous compression on living articular cartilage: an experimental investigation. *J. Bone Jt Surg.* **42A,** 31.

Silberberg R., Silberberg M., Vogel A. and Wettstein W. (1961) Ultrastructure of articular cartilage of mice of various ages. *Amer. J. Anat.* **109,** 251.

Simon W. H. (1975) Wear properties of articular cartilage. *Ann. rheum. Dis.* **34,** Suppl. 2, 117.

Sokoloff L., Snell K. C. and Stewart H. L. (1967) Degenerative joint disease in Praomys (Mastomys) natalensis. *Ann. rheum. Dis.* **26,** 146.

Stockwell R. A. (1967a) The cell density of human articular and costal cartilage. *J. Anat. (Lond.)* **101,** 753.

Stockwell R. A. (1967b) Lipid content of human costal and articular cartilage. *Ann. rheum. Dis.* **26,** 481.

Trias A. (1961) Effect of persistent pressure on the articular cartilage. An experimental study. *J. Bone Jt Surg.* **43B,** 376.

Trias A. (1967) Vascular factors. *Bull. rheumat. Dis.* **17,** 461.

Walmsley T. (1928) The articular mechanism of the diarthroses. *J. Bone Jt Surg.* **10,** 40.

Woods C. G., Greenwald A. S. and Haynes D. W. (1970) Subchondral vascularity in the human femoral head. *Ann. rheum. Dis.* **29,** 138.

Conversion Table

The system of units used throughout this book is the Système Internationale (SI), which has been adopted in the United Kingdom and in many countries in Europe. However, since SI units are not used world-wide, more conventional units are also given in the text, within parentheses.

The following notes and conversions may be useful.

Mass: the kilogram (kg), equal to 1000 grams or 2.2 pounds

Volume: cubic centimetre (cm^3) or cubic metre (m^3)

Force: the newton (N), equal to 0.102 kilograms force or 0.225 pounds force

Length: the metre (m), equal to 1000 millimetres or 39.36 inches. (Also used are the millimetre (mm; 10^{-3} m), the micron (μm; 10^{-6} m) the nanometre (nm; 10^{-9} m) and—although not strictly an SI unit—the ångstrom (Å); 10^{-11} m).)

Time: the second (s). (Also used are the minute (min) and the hour (h).)

Pressure or Stress: newtons per square metre (N/m^2) or, more usually, meganewtons per square metre (MN/m^2; $10^6\,N/m^2$) or kilonewtons per square metre (kN/m^2; $10^3\,N/m^2$). In more conventional units, pressure is expressed in atmospheres: 1 atm = $10^5\,N/m^2$.)

Frequency: the hertz (Hz), equal to 1 cycle per second

Rate of shear: seconds^{-1} (s^{-1}) (because shear is displacement/distance, dimensionless)

Viscosity: newton seconds per square metre (Ns/m^2), equal to 10 poise

Diffusion coefficient: square metre per second (m^2/s) or square centimetre per second (cm^2/s)

Hydraulic permeability: cubic metre per second per kilogram ($m^3\,s^{-1}\,kg^{-1}$)

Index